INTRODUCTION TO
SYSTEM THEORY

McGRAW-HILL SERIES IN ELECTRONICS SYSTEMS

John G. Truxal and Ronald A. Rohrer, Consulting Editors

CHUA *Introduction to Nonlinear Network Theory*
DIRECTOR AND ROHRER *Introduction to System Theory*
HUELSMAN *Theory and Design of Active RC Circuits*
MEDITCH *Stochastic Optimal Linear Estimation and Control*
MELSA AND SCHULTZ *Linear Control Systems*
RAMEY AND WHITE *Matrices and Computers in Electronic Circuit Analysis*
ROHRER *Circuit Theory: An Introduction to the State Variable Approach*
SCHULTZ AND MELSA *State Functions and Linear Control Systems*
STAGG AND EL-ABIAD *Computer Methods in Power System Analysis*
TIMOTHY AND BONA *State Space Analysis: An Introduction*

INTRODUCTION TO SYSTEMS THEORY

STEPHEN W. DIRECTOR
Department of Electrical Engineering
University of Florida, Gainesville

RONALD A. ROHRER
Department of Electrical Engineering
University of California, Berkeley

McGRAW-HILL BOOK COMPANY
New York San Francisco St. Louis Düsseldorf Johannesburg
Kuala Lumpur London Mexico Montreal New Delhi Panama
Rio de Janeiro Singapore Sydney Toronto

This book was set in Monotype Modern 8A, printed on permanent paper, and bound by The Maple Press Company. The designer was Janet Bollow; the drawings were done by AYXA Art. The editors were Charles R. Wade and Eva Marie Strock. Charles A. Goehring supervised production.

INTRODUCTION TO SYSTEM THEORY

Printed in the United States of America.

Library of Congress catalog card number: 76-147162

1234567890 MAMM 798765432

07-017014-2

DEDICATED TO THE READER

in the hope that

he can place system theory in

its proper engineering perspective

CONTENTS

PREFACE

This book is intended to be used in a first course on system theory. In writing it we tried to pay close attention to the modeling of physical situations as well as the usual mathematical manipulations.

We based the book on the notes that evolved through many courses called "System Theory" in numerous universities. Rohrer generated the original set of notes for courses taught at the University of Illinois and the State University of New York at Stony Brook, and at Berkeley he rewrote the notes. Director subsequently revised the notes while teaching two courses in this area at the University of Florida. The present book is closely aligned with this last set of notes.

Because the system theory field is so broad, we encountered the usual problem of what to omit. In all instances we tried to base our decisions on the difficulty of the material. Of course, "difficulty" is a hard concept to deal with since it varies from person to person. Hence, we worked on the assumption that most modern engineering students know some basic mathematical manipulations, but they must be motivated by physical situations. The material in virtually every chapter could be, or already is, a book unto itself. Our work is not definitive, but we hope that it is motivational.

We wish to thank all our former students whose reception of the material was the ultimate arbiter of what appears here. Ed Butler and Bruce Wooley were especially helpful in preparing detailed solutions to many of the problems.

STEPHEN DIRECTOR
RONALD ROHRER

INTRODUCTION TO SYSTEM THEORY

INTRODUCTION: THE FIRST-ORDER SYSTEM

1

System theory as presented in this book is merely the formal name for a body of mathematical concepts useful in the study of a wide variety of physical situations. Attempts to formalize the concept beyond this simple explanation would lead us far afield of our intent to present as simply as possible some basic, but widely applicable approaches to engineering analysis.

When we bring mathematics to bear on physical problems, we recognize that some approximation (modeling) is entailed. In this book we confine our attention to those physical situations which may be modeled adequately solely in terms of a finite number of interrelated algebraic and ordinary differential relations. Lumped electrical circuits and many mechanical systems fall naturally into this category. In such situations we may employ a uniform mathematical representation, the *state variable*, for system characterization.

The state-variable characterization will allow us to represent many physical systems by a set of first-order differential equations of the form

$$\dot{\mathbf{x}}(t) = \mathbf{f}(\mathbf{x}(t),\mathbf{u}(t),t)$$

and a set of algebraic equations of the form

$$\mathbf{y}(t) = \mathbf{g}(\mathbf{x}(t),\mathbf{u}(t),t)$$

in which t represents time, $\mathbf{u}(t)$ system inputs, $\mathbf{y}(t)$ system outputs, and $\mathbf{x}(t)$ state variables. Given a system with designated inputs and outputs, the first problem is to choose the state variables and to obtain the relations represented by the functions $\mathbf{f}$ and $\mathbf{g}$. The second problem is, of course, to understand thoroughly the mathematics associated with these expressions. The wide applicability of the state-variable equations in physical system modeling allows us to study such systems in terms of a uniform mathematical format.

In the sequel we shall be concerned primarily with how one goes about obtaining the state-variable equations for a given physical system, as well as their quantitative and qualitative manipulation. We begin with simple first-order systems which entail a minimum of mathematical manipulation and gradually build up the knowledge of modeling and mathematics requisite to the comprehension of systems in general. Many concepts that are introduced in this chapter (and Chap. 2) are not described in precise terms. Rather it is intended for these ideas to provide a general basis for more detailed development in later chapters.

1.1 EXAMPLES OF FIRST-ORDER SYSTEMS

Many physical systems can be described by first-order differential equations. Such systems are called *first-order systems*. These systems are not only important in their own right, but sometimes the behavior of more complicated systems are predicted on the assumption that a first-order characterization is adequate. In this chapter we will introduce a number of important concepts without getting bogged down in the mathematical details which must of necessity accompany the study of higher-order systems. The emphasis here is on the characterization of first-order systems and the qualitative properties of such a characterization.

The following examples illustrate both the familiarity and applicability of first-order systems.

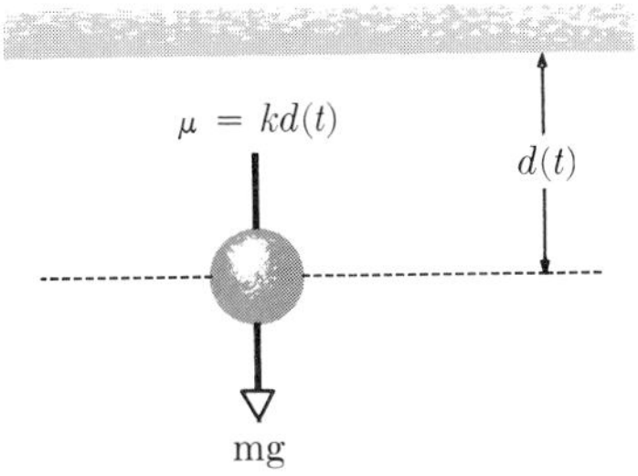

FIG. 1.1 An object of mass m falling in a viscous medium with resistance proportional to the velocity.

(1.1) Example
Consider the situation shown in Fig. 1.1. A mass m is falling in a viscous medium with resistance k proportional to velocity $x(t)$. There are two external forces on the mass, that of gravity g and that of viscosity. If d denotes the distance below some reference level, then the equation of motion is

$$m\ddot{d}(t) = mg - k\dot{d}(t)$$

Since the velocity $x(t)$ is

$$x(t) = \dot{d}(t)$$

$$\dot{x}(t) = -\frac{k}{m}x(t) + g \tag{1.2}$$

a first-order differential equation. ∎

(1.3) Example
Each of the six simple networks shown in Fig. 1.2 is made up of one linear, time-invariant resistance element, one linear, time-invariant energy-storage element, and one independent source. If the output variable is considered to be the variable conjugate to the source variable (that is, the current through an independent voltage source or the voltage across an independent current source) then the equations which characterize these networks may be written as follows:

$$\dot{x}(t) = -\frac{1}{RC}x(t) + \frac{1}{RC}\hat{v}(t)$$

and

$$i(t) = -\frac{1}{R}x(t) + \frac{1}{R}\hat{v}(t)$$

for the network of Fig. 1.2a;

$$\dot{x}(t) = -\frac{1}{C}\hat{\imath}(t)$$

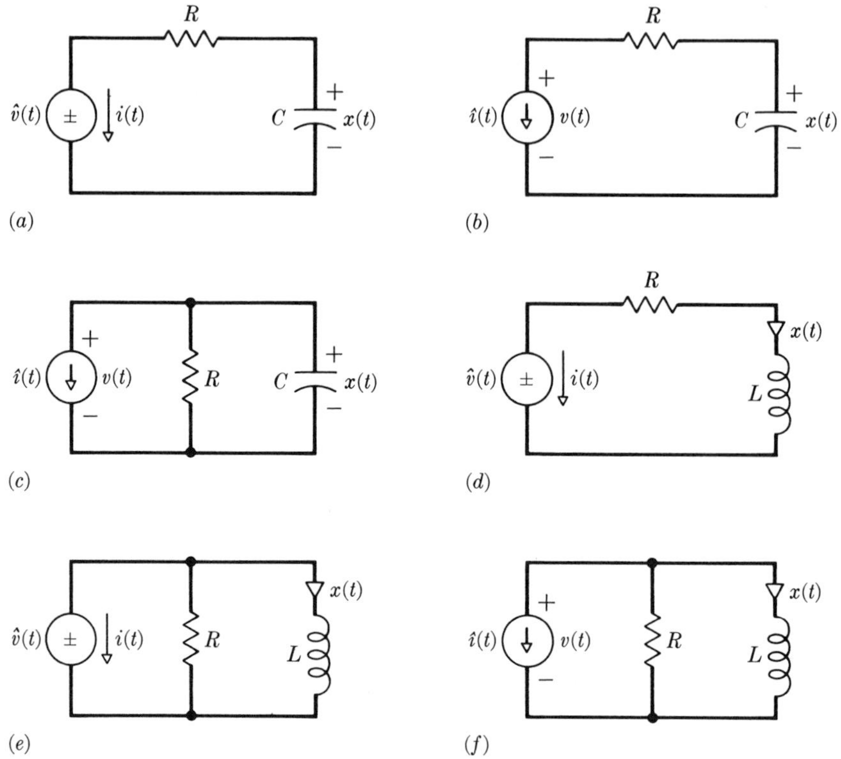

FIG. 1.2 Six simple networks each made up of one linear, time-invariant resistance element, and one linear, time-invariant, energy-storage element, and one independent source.

and

$$v(t) = x(t) - R\hat{\imath}(t)$$

for the network of Fig. 1.2*b*;

$$\dot{x}(t) = -\frac{1}{RC}x(t) - \frac{1}{C}\hat{\imath}(t)$$

and

$$v(t) = x(t)$$

for the network of Fig. 1.2*c*;

$$\dot{x}(t) = -\frac{R}{L}x(t) + \frac{1}{L}\hat{v}(t)$$

and

$$i(t) = -x(t)$$

for the network of Fig. 1.2*d*;

$$\dot{x}(t) = \frac{1}{L}\hat{v}(t)$$

and

$$i(t) = -x(t) - \frac{1}{R}\hat{v}(t)$$

for the network of Fig. 1.2*e*;

$$\dot{x}(t) = -\frac{R}{L}x(t) - \frac{R}{L}\hat{\imath}(t)$$

and

$$v(t) = -Rx(t) - R\hat{\imath}(t)$$

for the network of Fig. 1.2*f*. ▮

Observe that in every case any branch variable (any chosen output function) could be obtained as a linear combination of the variable x and the input-independent source function. We further recognize that the equations which describe these six networks, along with Eq. (1.2) which describes the mechanical system of Example 1.1, share in common a characterizing linear, *constant-coefficient* differential equation of the form

$$(1.4) \qquad \dot{x}(t) = ax(t) + bu(t)$$

where a and b are real, scalar constants, and u is the input function [$g, \hat{v}(t)$, or $\hat{\imath}(t)$ as appropriate]. Moreover, the six networks share in common a characterizing linear, constant-coefficient algebraic equation of the form

$$(1.5) \qquad y(t) = cx(t) + du(t)$$

where c and d are real, scalar constants and $y(t)$ is the output function [$i(t)$ or $v(t)$, as appropriate]. Therefore, solution of Eqs. (1.4) and (1.5) suffices to determine solutions for all the systems described above.

It is important to note that it is not only possible to characterize many simple electrical and mechanical systems by first-order differential equations, but other physical phenomena can be similarly described. For instance, processes which involve chemical reactions and the formation of mixtures are often appropriately described in first-order terms.

(1.6) Example

Suppose that a tank contains g gallons of water, that brine containing w lb of salt per gallon flows into the tank, and the resulting mixture flows out, both at a constant rate of q gallons per minute. The mixture is kept uniform by stirring. We wish to find the amount of salt present at any time $t > 0$.

Let the amount of salt at time t be denoted by $x(t)$. The increase in salt equals the income less the outgo, i.e.,

$$(1.7) \quad \dot{x}(t) = -\frac{r}{g}\, x(t) + (wr + q)$$

and since we are interested in the amount of salt present at time t,

$$(1.8) \quad y(t) = x(t)$$

Observe that expressions (1.7) and (1.8) are similar to expressions (1.4) and (1.5), respectively. ▮

The systems described above are *time invariant* as indicated by the fact that they can be characterized by *constant-coefficient* differential equations. We now present some examples of linear, time-variable first-order systems, which must be described by variable-coefficient differential equations of the form

$$(1.9) \quad \dot{x}(t) = a(t)x(t) + b(t)u(t)$$

(1.10) Example

Rockets are propelled by the momentum reaction of the exhaust of gases expelled from the tail. Since these gases arise from the reaction of the fuels carried in the rocket, the mass of the rocket is not constant, but in fact, decreases as the fuel is expended. Let the mass of the rocket in terms of its fuel at time t be denoted by $m(t)$, the speed of the rocket by $x(t)$, and the speed of the gases by $u(t)$. The only external force on the system at time t is that of gravity. The equation of motion of such a rocket in vertical motion can be written as

$$\dot{x}(t) = \frac{1}{m(t)}\, \dot{m}(t)(x(t) - u(t)) - g$$ ▮

(1.11) Example

Consider the network of Fig. 1.3. The resistance increases linearly with time, perhaps because of the movement of a potentiometer, while the inductance remains constant. If the input is the voltage $v(t)$ and the out-

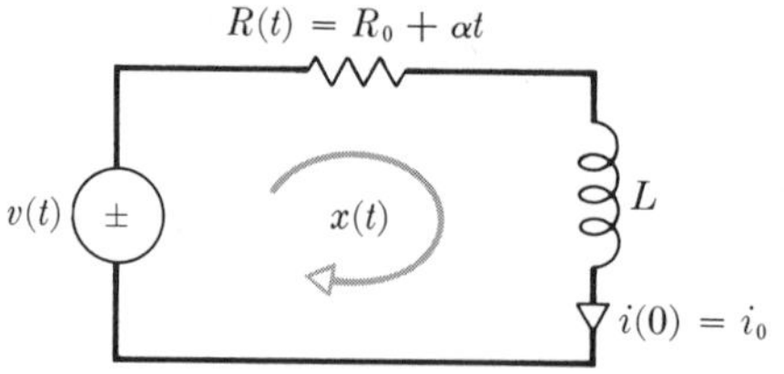

FIG. 1.3 A first-order, linear, time-variable network.

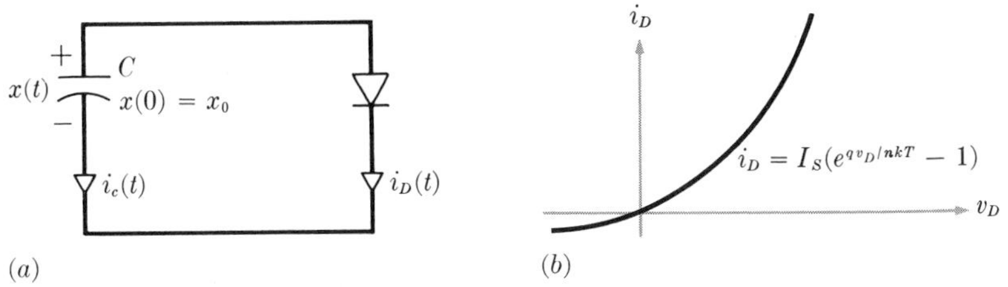

FIG. 1.4 (*a*) A simple nonlinear electrical network, and (*b*) the diode characteristic.

put is the loop current $x(t)$, the equation describing the system can be written as

$$\dot{x}(t) = -\frac{R_0 + \alpha t}{L} x(t) + \frac{1}{L} v(t)$$ ∎

Finally we present an example of a first-order nonlinear system which must be described by the most general form of a first-order differential equation

(1.12) $\dot{x}(t) = f(x(t), u(t), t)$

where $u(t)$ is some input forcing function.

(1.13) Example

The network shown in Fig. 1.4 consists of a linear capacitor characterized by

$$i_c(t) = C \frac{dx(t)}{dt}$$

in parallel with a nonlinear resistance (diode) characterized by

$$i_D = I_S \left[\exp\left(\frac{qv_D}{nkT}\right) - 1 \right]$$

From Kirchhoff's current law,

$$i_D(t) \equiv -i(t)$$

and Kirchhoff's voltage law,

$$v_D(t) \equiv x(t) + u(t)$$

we obtain

$$\dot{x}(t) = \frac{I_S}{C} \left\{ \exp\left[\frac{q(x(t) + u(t))}{nkT}\right] - 1 \right\}$$

which has the form of (1.12). ∎

The most general form of first-order differential equations so far presented has been Eq. (1.12). For a given system, one usually designates various functions of the internal variables as outputs. Therefore, at least one additional equation of the form

$$(1.14)\quad y(t) = g(x(t),u(t),t)$$

is used in conjunction with the differential equation (1.12) to describe the system. If a system has more than one input, expressions (1.12) and (1.14) are written as

$$(1.15)\quad \dot{x}(t) = f(x(t),u_1(t),u_2(t), \ldots ,u_n(t),t)$$

and

$$(1.16)\quad y(t) = g(x(t),u_1(t),u_2(t), \ldots ,u_n(t),t)$$

A given system might also have several outputs, in which case it may be described by (1.15) and the set

$$(1.17)\quad \begin{aligned} y_1(t) &= g_1(x(t),u_1(t),u_2(t), \ldots ,u_n(t),t) \\ y_2(t) &= g_2(x(t),u_1(t),u_2(t), \ldots ,u_n(t),t) \\ &\cdots\cdots\cdots\cdots\cdots \\ y_n(t) &= g_n(x(t),u_1(t),u_2(t), \ldots ,u_n(t),t) \end{aligned}$$

(1.18) Example

Consider the two input—three output system of Fig. 1.5. The equations which describe this network are

$$\begin{aligned} \dot{x}(t) &= \tfrac{4}{15}x(t) + \tfrac{1}{5}v(t) + \tfrac{4}{15}i(t) \\ y_1(t) &= \tfrac{22}{5}x(t) + \tfrac{9}{5}v(t) + \tfrac{27}{5}i(t) \\ y_2(t) &= \tfrac{4}{5}x(t) + \tfrac{1}{5}v(t) + \tfrac{19}{5}i(t) \end{aligned}$$

and

$$y_3(t) = \tfrac{4}{15}x(t) + \tfrac{1}{5}v(t) + \tfrac{4}{15}i(t)$$ ∎

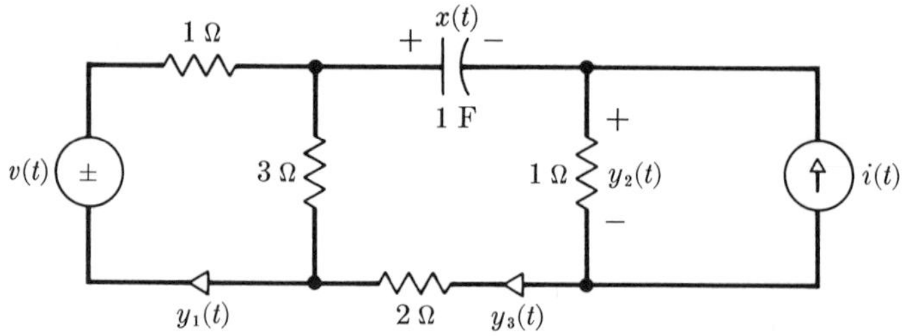

FIG. 1.5 A network having more than one input and output.

1.2 THE CONCEPT OF STATE AND PROPERTIES RELATED TO STATES

For the remainder of this chapter we limit our discussion to single input—single output systems. This restriction is solely for notational convenience, imposes no real restriction, and is easily removed. We have seen that the most general mathematical description of a first-order system is

$$(1.19a)\quad \dot{x}(t) = f(x(t),u(t),t)$$

and

$$(1.19b)\quad y(t) = g(x(t),u(t),t)$$

It is well known that the solution of a first-order differential equation such as (1.19*a*) depends on one initial condition, for example, $x(t_0) = x_0$, where t_0 is the initial time of observation. If we are not interested in the nature of the response before the initial time t_0 and the subsequent application of the input, then for a given input the output is uniquely determined by the initial condition.

(1.20) Example

The equation which describes the simple RC network of Fig. 1.6 is

$$\dot{x}(t) = -\frac{1}{RC}x(t) + u(t)$$

where $x(t)$ is the voltage across the capacitor. A solution of this equation is

$$x(t) = \exp\left[-\frac{1}{RC}(t-t_0)\right]x(t_0) + \int_{t_0}^{t}\exp\left[-\frac{1}{RC}(t-\tau)\right]u(\tau)\,d\tau$$

which can be verified by direct substitution. If the input $u(t)$ is known for all $t \geq t_0$, then $x(t)$ can be determined precisely from knowledge of $x(t_0)$, the initial capacitance voltage. ∎

From the above example, we recognize the necessity of including the initial condition in the system characterization. The value of this important quantity directly affects the subsequent behavior of the system. We may think of the initial condition as describing the status or state of the system at the initial time t_0. More formally we have the following definition.

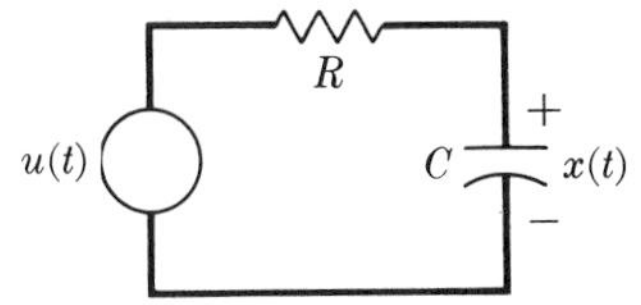

FIG. 1.6 A simple RC network used to demonstrate the concept of state.

(1.21) State
A *state* of a system at time t_0 is any amount of information, which together with any possible input function specified for $t_0 \leq t \leq t_f$, is adequate to determine uniquely the output function for $t_0 \leq t \leq t_f$ for any $t_f \geq t_0$. ▮

Often we are interested in a *canonic* representation and in such cases specify that an acceptable state be a *minimal* amount of such necessary information.

For the case of systems which can be described by first-order differential equations, an initial condition specified at t_0 can be taken to be a state of the system at time t_0. We postpone to a subsequent chapter a general discussion of what in general constitutes a state of a given system.

Note that in Example (1.20) the capacitance voltage $x(t)$ can be considered to be a state of the system for any arbitrary time t. To see this, consider time $t_1 > t_0$, then

$$x(t_1) = \exp\left[-\frac{1}{RC}(t_1 - t_0)\right]x(t_0) + \int_{t_0}^{t_1} \exp\left[-\frac{1}{RC}(t_1 - \tau)\right]u(\tau)\,d\tau$$

so that for all $t > t_1$,

$$x(t) = \exp\left[-\frac{1}{RC}(t - t_1)\right]\left\{\exp\left[-\frac{1}{RC}(t_1 - t_0)\right]x(t_0) + \int_{t_0}^{t_1} \exp\left[-\frac{1}{RC}(t_1 - \tau)\right]u(\tau)\,d\tau\right\} + \int_{t_1}^{t} \exp\left[-\frac{1}{RC}(t - \tau)\right]u(\tau)\,d\tau$$

which can be written as

$$x(t) = \exp\left[-\frac{1}{RC}(t - t_1)\right]x(t_1) + \int_{t_1}^{t} \exp\left[-\frac{1}{RC}(t - \tau)\right]u(\tau)\,d\tau$$

Since t_1 was arbitrary, let it be replaced by the variable σ so that in general

$$x(t) = \exp\left[-\frac{1}{RC}(t - \sigma)\right]x(\sigma) + \int_{\sigma}^{t} \exp\left[-\frac{1}{RC}(t - \tau)\right]u(\tau)\,d\tau$$

The knowledge of $x(\sigma)$ and $u(t)$, $t \geq \sigma$ completely determines all system behavior for $t \geq \sigma$. Therefore, $x(t)$ is a state of the system for any t.

Equations (1.19) are to be referred to as the *standard-form state equations*. Specifically, expression (1.19*a*) is the *differential-state equation* and expression (1.19*b*) is the *input-state-output equation*.

There are three special types of states which are noteworthy in that they play a major role in the practical analysis of systems: a zero state, the ground state, and an equilibrium state.

(1.22) Zero state
A *zero state* is any state θ for which

$$0 = g(\theta,0,t)$$

for all $t_0 \leq t < \infty$. ▮

In other words, a zero state is any state such that if the system starts in the zero state

$$x(t_0) = \theta$$

and if the input to the system is the zero input

$$u(t) = 0 \qquad t_0 \leq t < \infty$$

then the system output is zero,

$$y(t) = 0 \qquad t_0 \leq t < \infty$$

Note that "the" zero state need not be unique.

(1.23) Ground state
The *ground state*, if it exists, is that unique state γ toward which the system gravitates under the zero-input condition, regardless of the initial state. ▮

(1.24) Equilibrium state
An *equilibrium state* is any state η in which the system remains when subjected to the zero input

$$f(\eta,0,t) = 0$$

for any $t_0 \leq t < \infty$. ▮

(1.25) Example
These three special types of states are easily envisioned with the aid of an example of a bead sliding on a wire as shown in Fig. 1.7. Suppose that the bead is attached to the wire and there is a frictional force along the wire upon sliding. We assume that gravity is everpresent, but that gravity is augmented with an external force. The speed of the bead along

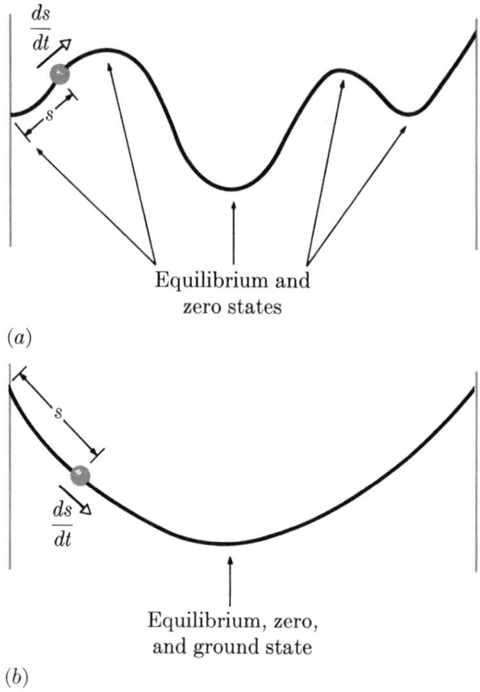

FIG. 1.7 Illustration of three special types of states: (*a*) a system with equilibrium and zero states but no ground state; (*b*) a system that settles to a unique ground state.

the wire is proportional to the component of the total force exerted on the bead which is directed along the wire:

$$\frac{ds}{dt} = \mu f$$

To describe the system mathematically, we assume that the external force on the bead (to which gravity must be added) constitutes the input function, the speed of the bead in traveling along the wire is the output function, and the position of the bead on the wire (the arc length s from the left-hand end of the wire) is the state of the system. The equilibrium states and zero states are indicated in Fig. 1.7*a*; this system has no ground state; a similar system with a ground state is illustrated in Fig. 1.7*b*. Note that the equilibrium and ground states would not coincide were we to define the output as the height above some arbitrary level. Then there would only be a zero state were the arbitrarily defined zero level to coincide with the height of one of the equilibrium states—no longer would the other equilibrium states qualify as zero states (unless they happened to coincide in level). ▮

This example has illustrated the important system-theoretic consideration that the original qualitative characterization of a system (choice of state) may affect its subsequent quantitative analysis (existence and properties of special states). We recall in similar simpler terms the problem of particle motion in a central force field: in cylindrical coordinates (angular) momentum is conserved and the problem simplifies considerably from that obtained in terms of the cartesian coordinate characterization.

1.3 LINEARITY, LINEARIZATION, AND TIME INVARIANCE

The study of linear systems is undertaken for two reasons. First, many systems behave linearly over several of their useful operating ranges, and second, detailed mathematical analysis of linear systems is possible while such analysis for more general systems may be impossible. The term "linearity" connotes some sort of proportionality between inputs and outputs. We wish to define this concept precisely. To this end we introduce some preliminary notions.

If the input to a system is zero and the response is nonzero, then this response is due solely to the initial state (or initial stored energy) and is called the *zero-input response.* Note that if the system started in the zero state, the zero-input response would be zero. Similarly we define the *zero-state response* as the system response due to an arbitrary input when the initial state is the zero state. We now introduce the following useful definitions.

(1.26) Zero-state linearity

A system is said to be *zero-state linear* if the following two conditions are satisfied.

(1) *Homogeneity:* If y is the zero-state response to an arbitrary input u, then cy is the zero-state response to the input cu, where c is an arbitrary constant.

(2) *Additivity:* If y_1 is the zero-state response to the arbitrary input u_1 and y_2 is the zero-state response to the arbitrary input u_2, then $y_1 + y_2$ is the zero-state response to the input $u_1 + u_2$. ▌

(1.27) Zero-input linearity

A system is said to be *zero-input linear* if the following two conditions are satisfied.

(1) *Homogeneity:* If the zero-input response to an arbitrary initial state x_0 is y_0, then the zero-input response to the initial state cx_0 is cy_0.

(2) *Additivity:* If y_1 is the zero-input response to an arbitrary initial state

x_1 and y_2 is the zero-input response to an arbitrary initial state x_2, then $y_1 + y_2$ is the zero-input response to the initial state $x_1 + x_2$. ∎

We illustrate the above definitions with several examples.

(1.28) Example
Consider a system for which the zero-state response is given by the relation

$$y(t) = \int_{t_0}^{t} e^{-(t-\tau)} u(\tau)\, d\tau \qquad t \geq t_0$$

where u is a real-valued function of time. Clearly this system is homogeneous, since if the response to u is y, then the response to cu is cy for any constant c and arbitrary input function u. Moreover, this system is additive, since if the response to u_1 is y_1 and the response to u_2 is y_2, then the response to $u_1 + u_2$ is $y_1 + y_2$. Therefore this system is zero-state linear. ∎

(1.29) Example
A squarer is a system characterized by the input-output relation (zero-state response) $y(t) = [u(t)]^2$, where u is a real function of time. (Note: A squarer need not have a state associated with it since it is instantaneous, although zero-state concepts still apply.) This system is not homogeneous, since if y is the response to u, c^2y is the response to cu. Therefore a squarer is zero-state nonlinear. Furthermore, if y_1 is the response to u_1 and y_2 the response to u_2, then since the response to $u_1 + u_2$ is not $y_1 + y_2$, this system is not additive. ∎

(1.30) Example
Consider a system for which the zero-input response is given by the relation

$$y(t) = e^{-(t-t_0)} x(t_0)$$

It is easy to verify that this system is both zero-input homogeneous and additive and, therefore, zero-input linear. ∎

Thus we see that the RC network discussed in Example (1.20), which is characterized by the equation

$$y(t) = \exp\left[-\frac{1}{RC}(t - t_0)\right] x(t_0) + \int_{t_0}^{t} \exp\left[-\frac{1}{RC}(t - \tau)\right] u(\tau)\, d\tau$$

where we have assumed that the capacitance voltage is the output, is both zero-state linear and zero-input linear.

(1.31) Example

The system characterized by the input-state-output relation

$$y(t) = (e^{-(t-t_0)}x(t_0))^2 + \int_{t_0}^{t} e^{-(t-\tau)}u(\tau)\,d\tau$$

is zero-input nonlinear. ▮

Zero-input linearity and zero-state linearity along with the decomposition property are used to define the general concept of linearity.

(1.32) Decomposition property

A system is said to have the *decomposition property* if the following condition is satisfied.

If y_0 is the zero-input response to an arbitrary initial state x_0 and y_u is the zero-state response for an arbitrary input u, then the total response for the same initial state and input is $y_0 + y_u$. ▮

(1.33) Linearity

A system is said to be *linear* if it is zero-state linear, zero-input linear, and satisfies the decomposition property. ▮

(1.34) Example

The systems discussed in Examples (1.30) and (1.31) both have the decomposition property, but only the former is linear. ▮

The above definition of linearity is a useful extension of the frequently encountered input-output statement: If y_1 is the response to u_1 and y_2 is the response to u_2, then the system is (input-output) linear if $\alpha y_1 + \beta y_2$ is the response to $\alpha u_1 + \beta u_2$ for arbitrary constants α and β and arbitrary input functions u_1 and u_2. Input-output linearity may be made to coincide with zero-state linearity in practice. The reason for generalizing the definition to states, as above, is to retain the linearity concept for systems which are characterized by linear differential equations.

(1.35) Example

To appreciate the usefulness of the linearity definition (1.33) consider the RC network of Fig. 1.8*a*. Assume that the capacitance is initially charged to 1 volt and the time interval of interest is $0 \leq t < \infty$. Then for the input-voltage signal function

$$u(t) = 0$$

the accompanying output-voltage signal function is

$$y(t) = e^{-t}$$

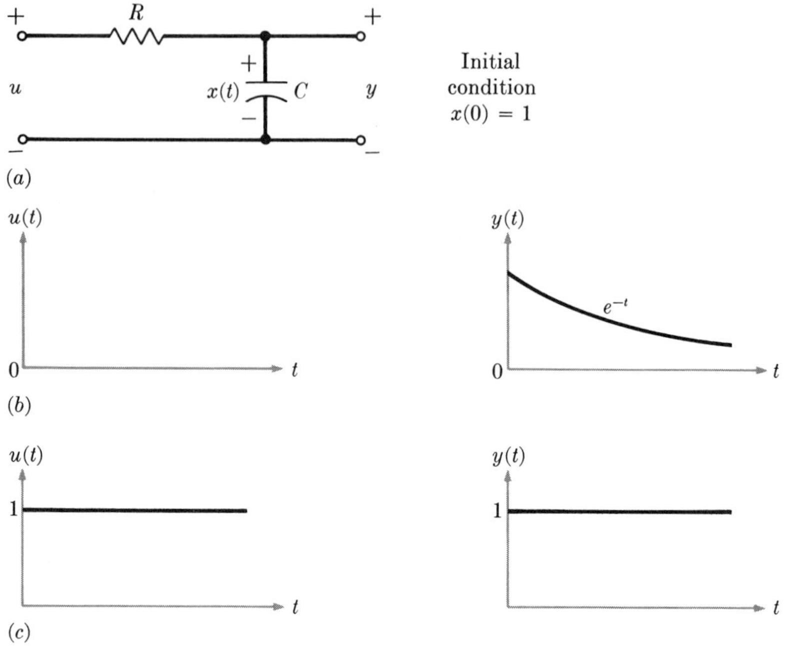

FIG. 1.8 (*a*) A simple single-input-output system which consists of a 1-Ω resistance with a 1-F capacitance with a 1-V initial condition, and (*b*) and (*c*) two possible input-output signal functions.

as is shown in Fig. 1.8*b*. Now let the input-voltage signal function be

$$u(t) = 1$$

then the accompanying output-voltage signal function is

$$y(t) = 1$$

as is shown in Fig. 1.8*c*. The sum of the two input-voltage signal functions considered is merely the latter, i.e.,

$$u(t) = 1$$

however, the sum of the two output-voltage signal functions is

$$y(t) = 1 + e^{-t}$$

which does not correspond to the input-voltage signal function $u \equiv 1$, when the initial capacitance voltage is 1 volt. This simple first-order system fails the (input-output) linearity test even though it is made up of elements which we would like to call linear. The problem is that the initial capacitance voltage constitutes an input which we cannot control. Mathematically, we can consider the addition of the initial conditions in both cases; the output-voltage signal function

$$y(t) = 1 + e^{-t}$$

does correspond to the input-voltage signal function if the initial capacitance voltage is taken to be (the sum) 2 volts. This linear system is linear under definition (1.33). ▮

Most systems in the real world are inherently nonlinear. In other words, one is usually required to characterize a system's behavior by expressions (1.12) and (1.14),

$$(1.36a)\quad \dot{x}(t) = f(x(t),u(t),t)$$
$$(1.36b)\quad y(t) = g(x(t),u(t),t)$$

rather than the simpler linear equation (1.9)

$$(1.37a)\quad \dot{x}(t) = a(t)x(t) + b(t)u(t)$$

and the associated linear-output relation

$$(1.37b)\quad y(t) = c(t)x(t) + d(t)u(t)$$

Often in practice, a nonlinear system can be approximated by a linear representation for some restricted range of operation. For instance, in the study of nonlinear electric networks, e.g., a transistor amplifier, one is often concerned with the "small signal analysis" in the neighborhood of a "quiescent" operating point.

In order to see how an approximate linear model can be derived, assume that solutions $x_0(t)$ and $y_0(t)$ to Eqs. (1.36) are known for a given initial condition $x = \hat{x}_0$ and input function $u_0(t)$, that is,

$$\dot{x}_0(t) = f(x_0(t),u_0(t),t)$$
$$y_0(t) = g(x_0(t),u_0(t),t)$$

and

$$x_0(t_0) = \hat{x}_0$$

Now suppose that the initial state and input are perturbed so that the new state and input become

$$x_1(t) = x_0(t) + \xi(t)$$

and

$$u_1(t) = u_0(t) + \eta(t)$$

The resulting output,

$$y_1(t) = y_0(t) + \nu(t)$$

can be found by solving the perturbed equations

$$\dot{x}_0(t) + \dot{\xi}(t) = f(x_0(t) + \xi(t),\ u_0(t) + \eta(t), t)$$

and

$$y_0(t) + \nu(t) = g(x_0(t) + \xi(t),\ u_0(t) + \eta(t), t)$$

First, we make a Taylor series expansion[1] (at each point in time) about the original solution.

$$\dot{x}_0(t) + \dot{\xi}(t) = f(x_0(t), u_0(t), t) + \left.\frac{\partial f}{\partial x}\right|_{x_0,u_0} \xi(t) + \left.\frac{\partial f}{\partial u}\right|_{x_0,u_0} \eta(t) + 0(\xi^2,\eta^2)$$

and

$$y_0(t) + \nu(t) = g(x_0(t), u_0(t), t) + \left.\frac{\partial g}{\partial x}\right|_{x_0,u_0} \xi(t) + \left.\frac{\partial g}{\partial u}\right|_{x_0,u_0} \eta(t) + 0(\xi^2,\eta^2)$$

where

$$\left.\frac{\partial f}{\partial x}\right|_{x_0,u_0} = \left.\frac{\partial f(x(t),u(t),t)}{\partial x(t)}\right|_{\substack{x(t)=x_0(t)\\ u(t)=u_0(t)}}$$

$$\left.\frac{\partial f}{\partial u}\right|_{x_0,u_0} = \left.\frac{\partial f(x(t),u(t),t)}{\partial u(t)}\right|_{\substack{x(t)=x_0(t)\\ u(t)=u_0(t)}}$$

$$\left.\frac{\partial g}{\partial x}\right|_{x_0,u_0} = \left.\frac{\partial g(x(t),u(t),t)}{\partial x(t)}\right|_{\substack{x(t)=x_0(t)\\ u(t)=u_0(t)}}$$

$$\left.\frac{\partial g}{\partial u}\right|_{x_0,u_0} = \left.\frac{\partial g(x(t),u(t),t)}{\partial u(t)}\right|_{\substack{x(t)=x_0(t)\\ u(t)=u_0(t)}}$$

and $0(\xi^2,\eta^2)$ is used to denote functions higher than first order in ξ and η. We assume here that f and g are twice differentiable in all arguments except possibly time. Then, under the assumption that ξ^2 and η^2 are negligibly small, we subtract the original solution to obtain the following linear approximate equations:

$$\dot{\xi}(t) = \left.\frac{\partial f}{\partial x}\right|_{x_0,u_0} \xi(t) + \left.\frac{\partial f}{\partial u}\right|_{x_0,u_0} \eta(t)$$

and

$$\nu(t) = \left.\frac{\partial g}{\partial x}\right|_{x_0,u_0} \xi(t) + \left.\frac{\partial g}{\partial u}\right|_{x_0,u_0} \eta(t)$$

These expressions may be written as

(1.38a) $\dot{\xi}(t) = a(t)\xi(t) + b(t)\eta(t)$

[1] I. S. Sokolonikoff and R. M. Redheffer, "Mathematics of Physics and Modern Engineering," pp. 143–146, McGraw-Hill, New York, 1950.

and

(1.38b) $\nu(t) = c(t)\xi(t) + d(t)\eta(t)$

where

$$a(t) \equiv \left.\frac{\partial f}{\partial x}\right|_{x_0,u_0} \qquad b(t) \equiv \left.\frac{\partial f}{\partial u}\right|_{x_0,u_0}$$

$$c(t) \equiv \left.\frac{\partial g}{\partial x}\right|_{x_0,u_0} \qquad d(t) \equiv \left.\frac{\partial g}{\partial u}\right|_{x_0,u_0}$$

Expressions (1.37) and (1.38) are seen to be similar in nature. The assumption that η^2 is small is easily met since it is an input (control) deviation. On the other hand, it is not always possible to ensure that ξ^2 is small. The linear system described by (1.37) can be used to characterize the behavior of the nonlinear system described by (1.36) if the region of operation is limited to that where ξ^2 remains small. The question of the magnitude of ξ^2 must be resolved in stability studies.

(1.39) Example

A simple first-order nonlinear network consisting of a linear, time-invariant capacitor and a nonlinear resistor is shown in Fig. 1.9*a*. The differential equation which describes this system is

(1.40) $\dot{x}(t) = -x^2(t)$

It is not too difficult to show that the solution of (1.40) is

$$(1.41) \quad x(t) = -\frac{x(t_0)}{1 - x(t_0)(t - t_0)}$$

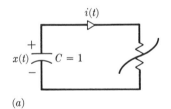

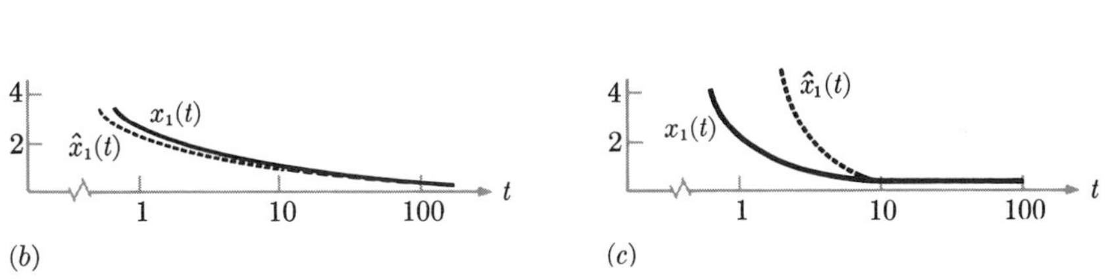

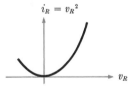

FIG. 1.9 (*a*) A simple nonlinear RC network; (*b*) actual and approximate solutions for small perturbation in initial state; (*c*) actual and approximate solutions for larger perturbations in initial state.

(Note: Singular behavior is possible here if the denominator becomes zero; assume in this instance that such a situation does not arise.) The linearized system associated with (1.40) is

$$\dot{\xi}(t) = \frac{2x(t_0)}{1 - x(t_0)(t - t_0)} \xi(t)$$

the solution of which is easily found to be

$$\xi(t) = \frac{-\xi(t_0)}{(1 - x(t_0)(t - t_0))^2}$$

Recall that if $x_0(t)$ denotes the state function which corresponds to the initial condition $x(t_0)$, and if $x_1(t)$ denotes the state function which corresponds to initial condition $\hat{x}(t_0)$, then

$$(1.42) \quad x_1(t) \approx x_0(t) + \xi(t) = \hat{x}_1(t)$$

where

$$(1.43) \quad \xi(t) = -\frac{x_1(t_0) - x_0(t_0)}{(1 - x(t_0)(t - t_0))^2}$$

as long as $\Delta x = x_1 - x_0$ remains small. Let $t_0 = 0$, $x_0(t_0) = 1$ and consider the following two situations: $x_1(t_0) = 1.1$ and $x_1(t_0) = 2.0$. For the first situation, the actual solution as given by (1.41) is

$$x_1(t) = -\frac{1.1}{1 - 1.1t}$$

while the approximate solution given by (1.42) and (1.43) is

$$\hat{x}_1(t) = \frac{0.1}{1 - t} - \frac{0.1}{(1 - t)^2}$$

Figure 1.9*b* shows that the correspondence between x_1 and $\hat{x}_1$ is fairly good. Note that about the singular point $t = 1$ where

$$\xi(t) = -\frac{0.1}{(1 - t)^2}$$

is undefined, the approximate solution is understandably poor. Now consider the second situation. The exact solution is

$$x_1(t) = \frac{-2}{1 - 2t}$$

while the approximate solution is

$$\hat{x}_1(t) = -\frac{1}{1 - t} - \frac{2}{(1 - t)^2}$$

Figure 1.9c is a graph of x_1 and $\hat{x}_1$ for this situation. Since

$$\xi(t) = \frac{-2}{(1-t)^2}$$

is larger relative to the previous situation, the approximate solution is correspondingly worse. ∎

Another important property that a system may possess is that of time invariance. Qualitatively, a system is *time invariant* if its characteristics do not change with time. For instance, consider application of an input to a time-invariant system in the zero state at time t_0, and record the output for $t \geq t_0$. Then if the same input were applied to this system, again in the zero state at time $t_0 + T$, the observed output would correspond to the one recorded previously, only shifted by T seconds.

In order to facilitate our discussion, we introduce the following notation. If $u(t)$ is a real function of time, then $u_h(t)$ is $u(t)$ shifted forward h seconds in time, that is, $u_h(t)$ is $u(t)$ translated h units to the right along the time axis. The relation between $u(t)$ and $u_h(t)$ is shown in Fig. 1.10. Thus

$$u_h(t) = u(t-h)$$

[Note: It is confusing, but well worth remembering that $u(t-h)$ corresponds to a *positive* translation of the time function $u(t)$ by h seconds.]

(1.44) Time invariance

A system is said to be *time invariant* if the following condition is satisfied:

If $y(t)$ is the response of the system to any input $u(t)$ and any initial state x_0 at time t_0, then $y_h(t)$ is the response to input $u_h(t)$ and initial state x_0 at time $t_0 + h$. ∎

(1.45) Example

Consider again the RC network of Example (1.20). If the capacitance voltage is taken to be the output, then the input-state-output relation for initial time t_0 and input $u(t)$ is

$$y(t) = \exp\left[-\frac{1}{RC}(t-t_0)\right]x(t_0) + \int_{t_0}^{t} \exp\left[-\frac{1}{RC}(t-\tau)\right]u(\tau)\,d\tau$$

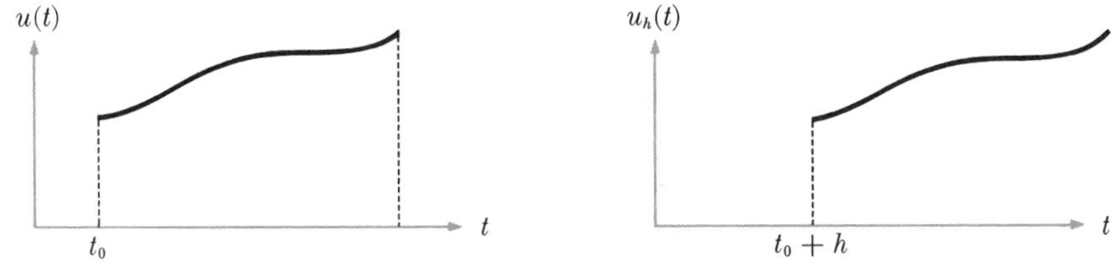

FIG. 1.10 Demonstration of the time-shifting operation.

The response of this system to the input $u_h(t)$ and for initial time t_1 is

$$\hat{y}(t) = \exp\left[-\frac{1}{RC}(t - t_1)\right]x(t_1) + \int_{t_1}^{t} \exp\left[-\frac{1}{RC}(t - \tau)\right]u_h(\tau)\,d\tau$$

but $u_h(t) = u(t - h)$ so that after a change of variables

$$\hat{y}(t) = \exp\left[-\frac{1}{RC}(t - t_1)\right]x(t_1) + \int_{t_1-h}^{t-h} \exp\left[-\frac{1}{RC}(t - h - \sigma)\right]u(\sigma)\,d\sigma$$

Now to check for time invariance, we let $t_1 = t_0 + h$ and $x(t_1) = x(t_0)$. Then

$$\begin{aligned}\hat{y}(t) &= \exp\left[-\frac{1}{RC}(t - h - t_0)\right]x(t_0) \\ &\qquad + \int_{t_0}^{t-h} \exp\left[-\frac{1}{RC}(t - h - \sigma)\right]u(\sigma)\,d\sigma \\ &= y(t-h) = y_h(t)\end{aligned}$$

which demonstrates the time invariance of this system. ▮

We recognize that the translation of the initial condition is critical to this verification of system time invariance. As with linearity, we may entertain the possibility of two related special cases of time invariance.

(1.46) Zero state time invariance

A system is said to be *zero-state time invariant* if it is time invariant when the initial state is a zero state. ▮

(1.47) Zero input time invariance

A system is said to be *zero-input time invariant* if it is time invariant for the zero-input function. ▮

Note that a system which is time invariant is both zero-state time invariant and zero-input time invariant, but the converse is not true in general. We shall demonstrate in a subsequent section that zero-state time invariance and zero-input time invariance imply time invariance only if the system is linear.

Definition (1.44) extends the more usually encountered input-output definition of time invariance. The latter neglects the initial state and defines a system to be time invariant if a constant time shift of the input yields a corresponding constant time shift of the output.

(1.48) Example

To see that definition (1.44) is required, consider the simple network of Fig. 1.11*a*.

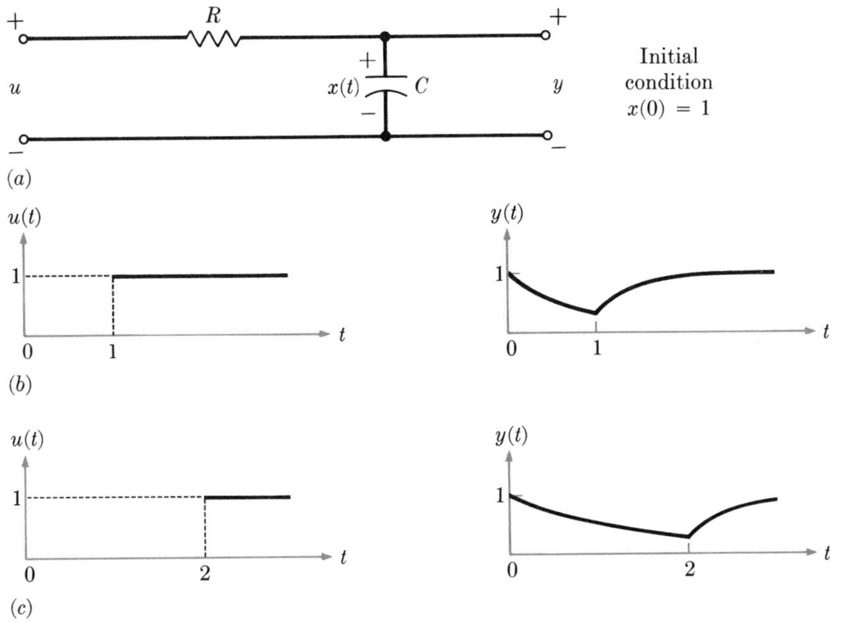

FIG. 1.11 (*a*) A simple single input—single output system that consists of a 1-Ω resistance and a 1-F capacitance with a 1-V initial condition at $t = 0$, and (*b*) and (*c*) two possible admissible signal-function pairs.

The input-voltage signal function

$$u(t) = \begin{cases} 0 & 0 \leq t < 1 \\ 1 & t \geq 1 \end{cases}$$

is accompanied by the output-voltage signal function

$$y(t) = \begin{cases} e^{-t} & 0 \leq t < 1 \\ 1 + (1 - e)e^{-t} & t \geq 1 \end{cases}$$

However, the shifted input-voltage signal function

$$u(t) = \begin{cases} 0 & 0 \leq t < 1 \\ 1 & t \geq 2 \end{cases}$$

is accompanied by the output-voltage signal function

$$y(t) = \begin{cases} e^{-t} & 0 \leq t < 2 \\ 1 + (1 - e^2)e^{-t} & t \geq 2 \end{cases}$$

Portrayal of these signal functions in Figs. 1.11*b* and *c* illustrates that the latter output-voltage signal function does not correspond to a shift by one unit of the former. If, on the other hand, we demand that the 1-volt initial condition occur at $t = 1$ in the second case, the appropriately shifted output-voltage function for $1 \leq t < \infty$ will be obtained. Hence, we must employ the time-invariance definition (1.44) to demonstrate that this "time-invariant" system is indeed time invariant. Again, as with linearity, we recognize the necessity to treat initial states as being roughly equivalent to inputs in order to characterize systems appropriately. ∎

It is most important to recognize that *linearity and time invariance are independent properties.* The following examples illustrate this point.

(1.49) Example

Consider the ideal delay element of Fig. 1.12 which is described by

$$y(t) = u(t - \tau) \qquad \tau > 0$$

To test for linearity, let the output $y_a(t)$ be the zero-state response to input $u_a(t)$, that is,

$$y_a(t) = u_a(t - \tau)$$

and the output $y_b(t)$ be the zero-state response due to input $u_b(t)$, that is,

$$y_b(t) = u_b(t - \tau)$$

Now let the system input be

$$u_{ab}(t) = \alpha u_a(t) + \beta u_b(t)$$

where α and β are arbitrary finite constants; the system's zero-state response is

$$\begin{aligned} y_{ab}(t) &= u_{ab}(t - \tau) \\ &= \alpha u_a(t - \tau) + \beta u_b(t - \tau) \\ &= \alpha y_a(t) + \beta y_b(t) \end{aligned}$$

Hence the system is zero-state linear. To test for zero-state time invariance let the input to the system be

$$u_h(t) = u(t - h)$$

Under this excitation, the output is

$$\hat{y}(t) = u_h(t - \tau) = u((t - \tau) - h)$$

but

$$y_h(t) = y(t - h) = u(t - \tau - h)$$

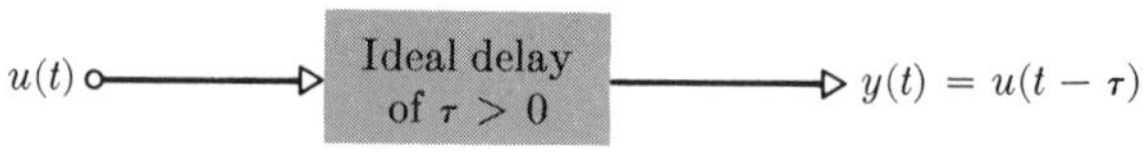

FIG. 1.12 An ideal delay element.

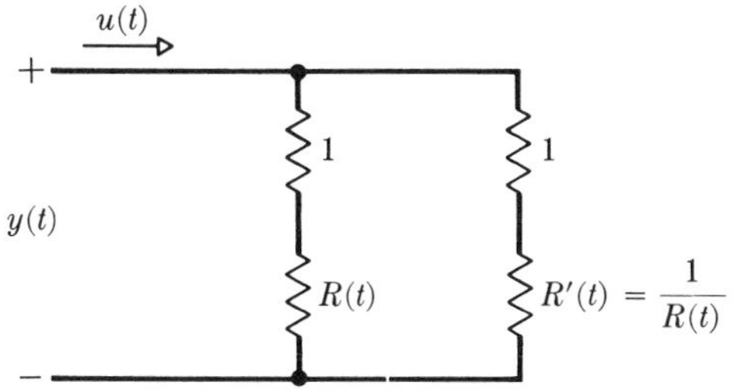

FIG. 1.13 A linear time-invariant network containing time-varying elements.

therefore, since

$$\hat{y}(t) = y_h(t)$$

the ideal delay element is also zero-state time invariant. In summary then, the ideal delay element of Fig. 1.12 is both zero-state linear and time invariant. ∎

(1.50) Example

Consider the network of Fig. 1.13. The input is taken to be the current $u(t)$, and the output is taken to be the voltage $y(t)$. It is simple to show that

$$y(t) = \frac{u(t)}{1/[1 + R(t)] + 1/[1 + 1/R(t)]}$$
$$= u(t)$$

This network is both linear and time invariant even though two of the network elements have time-variable values. ∎

(1.51) Example

A trivial example of a system which appears to be time invariant, but not linear, is one described by

$$y(t) = k = \text{constant}$$

for all inputs. However, if we describe this system by

$$\dot{x}(t) = 0 \qquad x(t_0) = k$$

and

$$y(t) = x(t)$$

then it appears to be both time invariant and linear. This example demonstrates that in actuality, it is a *system's "characterization" which may be linear and/or time invariant; these concepts are not to be applied to the system itself.* ∎

(1.52) Example
Consider the system described by

$$y(t) = \begin{cases} 0 & t < t_0 \\ 2u(t) & t \geq t_0 \end{cases}$$

It is easily verified that this system is linear. To test for time invariance let the input be

$$u_h(t) = u(t - h)$$

Therefore

$$\hat{y}(t) = \begin{cases} 0 & t < t_0 \\ 2u(t - h) & t \geq t_0 \end{cases}$$

But

$$y_h(t) = y(t - h) = \begin{cases} 0 & t - h < t_0 \\ 2u(t - h) & t \geq h - t_0 \end{cases}$$

so that for $t_0 < t < t_0 + h$

$$\hat{y}(t) = 2u(t - h)$$

while

$$y_h(t) = 0 \qquad \text{identically}$$

Thus

$$y(t) \neq y_h(t)$$

in general and hence the system is not time invariant. ∎

We leave it as an exercise (Prob. 1.5) for the reader to show that we can write the standard-form state equations as

(1.53a) $\dot{x}(t) = f(x(t),u(t))$

and

(1.53b) $y(t) = g(x(t),u(t))$

when the system is time invariant;

(1.54a) $\dot{x}(t) = a(t)x(t) + b(t)u(t)$

and

(1.54b) $y(t) = c(t)x(t) + d(t)u(t)$

when the system is linear, and

(1.55a) $\dot{x}(t) = ax(t) + bu(t)$

and

(1.55b) $y(t) = cx(t) + du(t)$

when the system is both linear and time invariant.

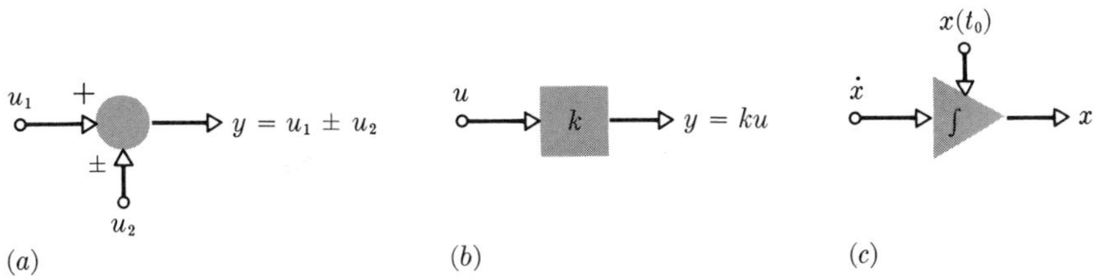

FIG. 1.14 Three basic lumped linear, time-invariant-system building blocks: (a) summer (adder); (b) scaler; (c) integrator.

Block diagrams provide a useful graphical approach to system characterization. For lumped systems, the basic linear blocks are the summer, scaler, and integrator shown in Fig. 1.14. These blocks are simply specified: the summer of Fig. 1.14*a* by

$$(1.56)\quad y(t) = u_1(t) \pm u_2(t)$$

the scaler of Fig. 1.14*b* by

$$(1.57)\quad y(t) = ku(t)$$

and the integrator of Fig. 1.14*c* by

$$(1.58)\quad x(t) = x(t_0) + \int_{t_0}^{t} \dot{x}(\tau)\, d\tau$$

We leave it as an exercise for the reader to verify that these elements are indeed linear. The rules of interconnection of these ideal elements are almost self-evident; in addition to the relations defined above, we need only recognize that any variable may be "picked off" from its common line. For example, the block diagram of Fig. 1.15 represents the standard-form state equations (1.55) with $x(t_0) = x_0$. Because of its particular position in the overall signal-transmission path, the scaler block a is often said to be a *feedback* element. The block-diagram representation is

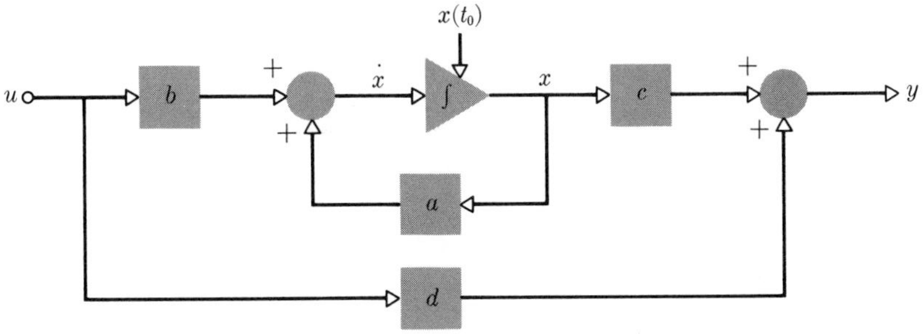

FIG. 1.15 The block-diagram representation of the single input—single output, standard-form, first-order state equations.

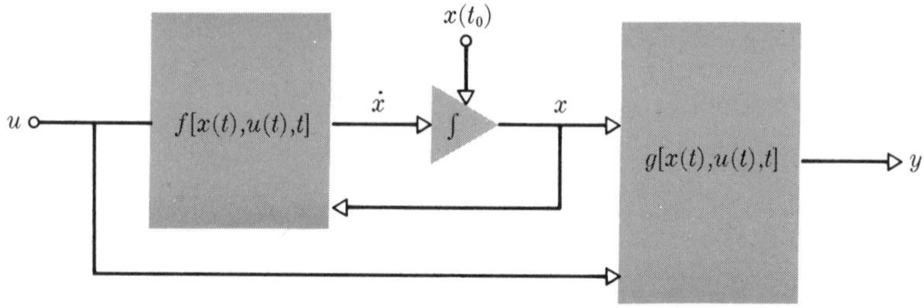

FIG. 1.16 The block-diagram representation of the general first-order, standard-form state equation.

easily extended to nonlinear and time-variable systems upon the introduction of function blocks. For example, Fig. 1.16 represents the general first-order standard-form state equations (1.12) and (1.14)

$$\dot{x}(t) = f(x(t),u(t),t) \qquad x(t_0) = x_0$$

and

$$y(t) = g(x(t),u(t),t)$$

We note that one (linear) ideal integrator block suffices in the characterization of a first-order system, although the converse need not be true.

1.4 MATHEMATICAL PROPERTIES OF FIRST-ORDER SYSTEMS

In this section we derive a general solution for the first-order, linear, standard-form state equations

$$(1.59a) \quad \dot{x}(t) = a(t)x(t) + b(t)u(t)$$

and

$$(1.59b) \quad y(t) = c(t)x(t) + d(t)u(t)$$

The first step is to find the solution to the differential-state equation (1.59*a*). To do so we consider the associated homogeneous (or zero-input) equation, i.e., the equation which results from (1.59*a*) when the input is set to zero:

$$(1.60) \quad \frac{dx(t)}{dt} = a(t)x(t)$$

A solution to the homogeneous equation is easily found by the method of separation of variables. First recognize that (1.60) can be written as

$$(1.61) \quad \frac{dx(t)}{x(t)} = a(t)\,dt$$

Upon integration from τ to t, (1.61) becomes

$$\ln \frac{x(t)}{x(\tau)} = \int_\tau^t a(\xi)\, d\xi$$

or

$$x(t) = \exp\left[\int_\tau^t a(\xi)\, d\xi\right] x(\tau) \tag{1.62}$$

or

$$x(t) = \exp\left[\int_{t_0}^t a(\xi)\, d\xi\right] x(t_0)$$

if the initial state is specified at t_0.

Since the term

$$\exp\left[\int_\tau^t a(\xi)\, d\xi\right]$$

describes the movement of the system's state between times t and τ under zero excitation, it is often referred to as the *state-transition function* and is denoted by $\Phi(t,\tau)$, that is,

$$\Phi(t,\tau) \equiv \exp\left[\int_\tau^t a(\xi)\, d\xi\right] = x(t)x^{-1}(\tau)$$

Observe that the state-transition function has the following two properties:

(1) $\Phi(t,t) = 1$
(2) $\partial\Phi(t,\tau)/\partial t = a(t)\Phi(t,\tau)$

Although the state-transition function will not play a large role in the discussion of first-order systems, it will be of great utility when we discuss higher-order systems. We defer a detailed treatment of the state-transition function until Chap. 4.

We now turn to the particular solution of (1.59*a*). The method of variation of parameters,[1] although unmotivated, is to be employed. Let $\lambda(t)$ denote the homogeneous solution so that

$$\dot{\lambda}(t) = a(t)\lambda(t) \tag{1.63a}$$

and

$$\lambda(t_0) = \lambda_0 \tag{1.63b}$$

It is relatively simple to show that the solution to the homogeneous equation for a given initial condition is unique provided that

$$\int_{t_0}^t a(\tau)\, d\tau < \infty$$

[1] I. S. Sokolnikoff and R. M. Redheffer, "Mathematics of Physics and Modern Engineering," pp. 17–29, McGraw-Hill, 1958.

(see Prob. 1.9) and, moreover, that if the solution vanishes at any finite time, it must vanish for all finite time (see Prob. 1.10). These properties ensure that $\lambda(t)$ is nonzero for all finite time provided only that $\lambda(t_0)$ is nonzero. We try as the particular solution

$$(1.64)\quad x(t) = \lambda(t)\eta(t)$$

where $\eta(t)$ is at this point, an arbitrary function of time, and $\lambda(t)$ is a *nontrivial* (nonzero) solution of the homogeneous equation (1.63*a*). Substitution of (1.64) into (1.59*a*) yields

$$\lambda(t)\dot{\eta}(t) = b(t)u(t)$$

or

$$(1.65)\quad \dot{\eta}(t) = \lambda^{-1}(t)b(t)u(t)$$

and $\lambda^{-1}(t)$ exists for all finite time since $\lambda(t)$ is a nontrivial solution to the homogeneous equation. Expression (1.65) may be integrated and then multiplied by $\lambda(t)$ to yield

$$x(t) = \lambda(t)\eta(t) = \int_{t_0}^{t} \lambda(t)\lambda^{-1}(\tau)b(\tau)u(\tau)\,d\tau$$

(Note that $\eta(t_0) = 0$.) Since $\lambda(t)$ is the solution to the homogeneous equation

$$\lambda(t) = \exp\left[\int_{\tau}^{t} a(\xi)\,d\xi\right]\lambda(\tau)$$

the particular solution may be written as

$$x(t) = \int_{t_0}^{t} \exp\left[\int_{\tau}^{t} a(\xi)\,d\xi\right] b(\tau)u(\tau)\,d\tau$$

The complete solution is the sum of the homogeneous and particular solutions:

$$(1.66)\quad x(t) = \exp\left[\int_{t_0}^{t} a(\xi)\,d\xi\right] x(t_0) + \int_{t_0}^{t} \exp\left[\int_{\tau}^{t} a(\xi)\,d\xi\right] b(\tau)u(\tau)\,d\tau$$

Therefore the input-state-output relation for first-order linear systems becomes

$$(1.67)\quad y(t) = c(t)\exp\left[\int_{t_0}^{t} a(\xi)\,d\xi\right] x(t_0) + \int_{t_0}^{t} c(t)\exp\left[\int_{\tau}^{t} a(\xi)\,d\xi\right] b(\tau)u(\tau)\,d\tau + d(t)u(t)$$

(1.68) Example

We have seen earlier that the state equations for the network of Fig. 1.3 are

$$\dot{x}(t) = -\frac{R_0 + \alpha t}{L}x(t) - \frac{1}{L}v(t)$$

and

$$y(t) = x(t)$$

where $v(t)$ is the input voltage and $x(t)$ is the loop current. For convenience we take $t_0 = 0$. Therefore

$$\int_{t_0}^{t} a(\xi)\, d\xi = \int_0^t -\frac{R_0 + \alpha\xi}{L}\, d\xi = -\frac{2R_0 t + \alpha t^2}{2L}$$

so that from (1.67)

$$x(t) = \exp\left(-\frac{2R_0 t + \alpha t^2}{2L}\right) x_0 - \int_0^t \frac{1}{L} \exp\left[-\frac{2R_0(t-\tau) + \alpha(t^2 - \tau^2)}{2L}\, v(\tau)\, d\tau\right] \blacksquare$$

For the case of first-order, linear, time-invariant systems, the state equations for which are

$$(1.69a) \quad \dot{x}(t) = ax(t) + bu(t)$$

and

$$(1.69b) \quad y(t) = cx(t) + du(t)$$

expressions (1.66) and (1.67) reduce to

$$(1.70) \quad x(t) = e^{a(t-t_0)}x(t_0) + \int_{t_0}^{t} e^{a(t-\tau)}bu(\tau)\, d\tau$$

and

$$(1.71) \quad y(t) = ce^{a(t-t_0)}x(t_0) + \int_{t_0}^{t} ce^{a(t-\tau)}bu(\tau)\, d\tau + du(t)$$

A frequently encountered special case is that for which the system is assumed to be in the zero state, $x_0 = 0$ at the "initial time" $t_0 \to -\infty$. Then from (1.71)

$$y(t) = \int_{-\infty}^{t} ce^{a(t-\tau)}bu(\tau)\, d\tau + du(t)$$

We can rewrite this expression as

$$(1.72) \quad y(t) = \int_{-\infty}^{t} [ce^{a(t-\tau)}b + d\delta(t-\tau)]u(\tau)\, d\tau$$

if we recognize that

$$\int_{-\infty}^{\infty} f(\tau)\delta(t-\tau)\, d\tau = f(t)$$

for any ordinary functions $f(\tau)$. (Note: A more detailed discussion of the properties of the δ function will be undertaken in Chap. 6.)

The function

(1.73) $h(t) = ce^{at}b + d\delta(t)$

is referred to as the *system kernal, system function*, or *impulse response*. Combination of (1.72) and (1.73) results in the familiar *convolution integral*,

(1.74) $y(t) = \int_{-\infty}^{t} h(t - \tau)u(\tau)\, d\tau$

In summary then, we have been able to find a general solution to state equations which describe first-order linear systems. In general, the solution of nonlinear differential equations, even for the first-order case, is a difficult chore, and usually some form of numerical analysis is required. An introduction to some of the pertinent numerical techniques is presented in Chap. 7.

1.5 INTRODUCTION TO STABILITY

The concept of stability of a system or, more precisely, the stability of the response of a system characterization is fundamental to the qualitative study of system behavior. Moreover, stability is usually a desirable property of real engineering systems such as electronic amplifiers or earth satellites. It is therefore appropriate to discuss stability of even the most simple systems, i.e., first-order systems. Although we will limit our discussion here to a heuristic development, sufficient motivation should be provided for the more detailed discussion to come in Chap. 6.

Consider an arbitrary first-order system characterized by the differential-state equation

(1.75) $\dot{x}(t) = f(x(t),u(t),t)$

In order to facilitate the discussion let $\phi_u(t; x_0,t_0)$ denote the solution of (1.75) for initial time t_0, initial state $x(t_0) = x_0$, and a given input function u. Therefore

(1.76) $\dot{\phi}_u(t; x_0,t_0) = f(\phi_u(t; x_0,t_0),u(t),t)$

Any equilibrium state associated with (1.75) will be denoted by $x_e(t)$, so that

$$\dot{x}_e(t) = f(x_e(t),0,t) = 0$$

The two questions one might ask concerning the stability of (1.75) are:

(1) Is the solution of (1.75) for the input $u(t)$ and initial state $x(t_0) = x_0$ stable with respect to deviations in the initial state $x(t_0)$?

(2) For the zero-input function $u(t) = 0$ is the equilibrium state $x_e(t)$ stable?

Consider question (1). We speak of the stability of the solution if "slight" perturbations in the initial state accompany solutions which are "near" the original solution. Let the deviation of a solution $x(t)$ from the known solution $\phi_u(t;\, x_0,t_0)$ be $\xi(t)$, that is,

$$\xi(t) \equiv x(t) - \phi_u(t;\, x_0,t_0) \tag{1.77}$$

At time t_0, the deviation is

$$\xi(t_0) = x(t_0) - \phi_u(t_0;\, x_0,t_0)$$

The stability of the solution can be determined by observing $\xi(t)$. If, for small $\xi(t_0)$, that is, small shifts in the initial state, the magnitude of $\xi(t)$ becomes large as t increases, then the solution would be called *unstable* since $x(t)$ would be diverging from $\phi_u(t;\, x_0,t_0)$. On the other hand, if $\xi(t)$ approached zero as t increased, that is, $x(t)$ becomes indistinguishable from $\phi(t;\, x_0,t_0)$, then the solution would be called *asymptotically stable.* A third possibility is for the magnitude of $\xi(t)$ to remain small as t increases, but not necessarily to approach zero. In this situation, the solution would be called *stable.* Similar concepts apply to the stability of equilibrium states. In fact, we will show that solution-stability studies may be reduced always to equilibrium-state stability studies of associated systems. The above discussion is rather loose and more formal definitions will be given in Chap. 6.

(1.78) Example

Consider the network of Fig. 1.17*a* made up of a linear capacitor and nonlinear resistor. The characteristic of the resistive element is shown in Fig. 1.17*b*. The network may be described by

$$\dot{q}(t) = -i\left(\frac{q(t)}{C}\right) \qquad q(t_0) = q_0$$

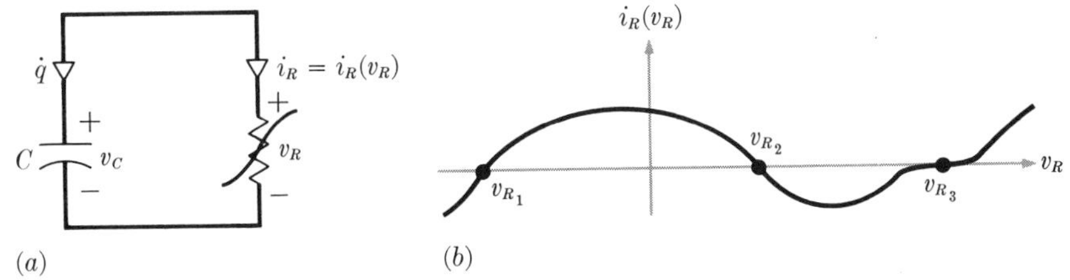

FIG. 1.17 (*a*) A simple nonlinear RC circuit that may be unstable, (*b*) the resistive-element characteristic.

where $q(t)$ is the capacitance charge at time t. The equilibrium states of this homogeneous system, found from the resistive-element characteristic, are

$$q_{e1} = Cv_{e1} \qquad q_{e2} = Cv_{e2} \qquad q_{e3} = Cv_{e3}$$

If the initial state were q_{e3}, and if the state were displaced slightly from q_{e3}, it would remain there; observe that the resistance characteristic is horizontal in the immediate neighborhood of this point. We call q_{e3} a *stable* equilibrium state. If the initial state were q_{e1}, and if the state were displaced slightly from q_{e1}, it would ultimately return to this point; observe that the resistive element is incrementally positive about this point. We call q_{e1} an *asymptotically stable* equilibrium state. If the equilibrium state were q_{e2}, and if the state were displaced slightly from q_{e2}, it would never return to this point; observe that the resistive element is incrementally negative about this point. We call q_{e2} an *unstable* equilibrium state. These stability situations are illustrated in Fig. 1.18. ∎

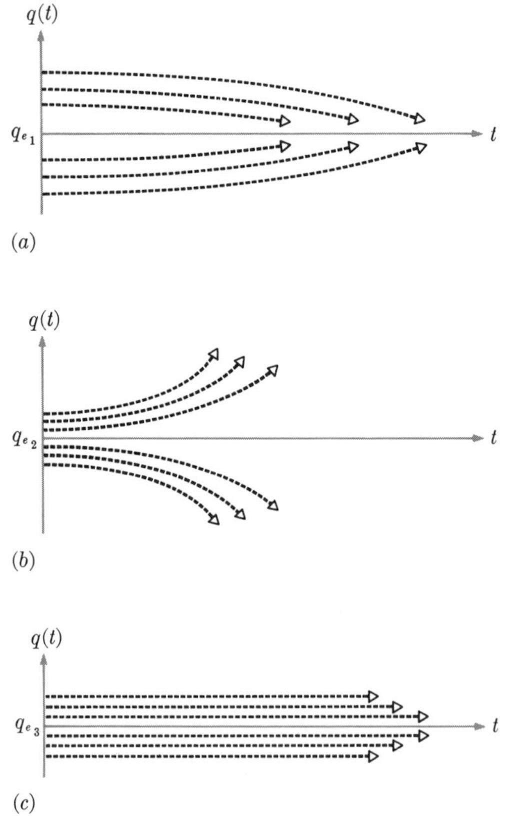

FIG. 1.18 (*a*) q_{e1} is an asymptotically stable state, any state trajectory starting near q_{e1} will approach it; (*b*) q_{e2} is an unstable equilibrium state, any state trajectory starting near q_{e2} will diverge from it; (*c*) q_{e3} is a stable equilibrium state, any state trajectory starting near q_{e3} will remain near it.

Let us consider stability of solutions in some more detail. From (1.77)

$$x(t) = \xi(t) + \phi_u(t;\, x_0,t_0)$$

But $x(t)$ is a solution of (1.75) so that

$$\dot{\xi}(t) + \dot{\phi}_u(t;\, x_0,t_0) = f(\xi(t) + \phi_u(t;\, x_0,t_0),u(t),t)$$

or upon substitution of (1.76)

$$(1.79) \quad \dot{\xi}(t) = f(\xi(t) + \phi_u(t;\, x_0,t_0),u(t),t) - f(\phi_u(t;\, x_0,t_0),u(t),t)$$

Recall that the input function u is known, and since $\phi(t;\, x_0,t_0)$, the original solution is presumed known, the right-hand side of (1.79) is a function only of $\xi(t)$, so we may define

$$(1.80) \quad h(\xi(t),t) \equiv f(\xi(t) + \phi_u(t;\, x_0,t_0),u(t),t) - f(\phi_u(t;\, x_0,t_0),u(t),t)$$

Hence deviations from a *known solution* of the differential-state equation when the *input is known* are described by the homogeneous differential equation

$$(1.81) \quad \dot{\xi}(t) = h(\xi(t),t) \qquad \xi(t_0) = \xi_0$$

Observe that $\xi(t) = 0$ is an equilibrium state, since from (1.80)

$$h(0,t) \equiv 0$$

So we have transformed the problem of determination of stability of a solution to one of determination of stability of an equilibrium state at the origin ($\xi(t) = 0$) of a homogeneous differential equation.

(1.82) Example

Suppose we are interested in studying the stability behavior of a system described by

$$\dot{x}(t) = -3t^2x(t) + [u(t)]^2 \qquad x(0) = 1$$

with

$$u(t) = \begin{cases} t & \text{for } t \geq 0 \\ 0 & \text{for } t < 0 \end{cases}$$

in the neighborhood of the solution

$$\phi_u(t,1,0) = \exp\left(-\int_{t_0}^{t} 3\tau^2\, d\tau\right) x(0) + \int_0^t \exp\left(-\int_0^{\tau} 3s^2\, ds\right) \tau^2\, d\tau$$
$$= \frac{1}{3}(1 + 2e^{-t^3})$$

Therefore we want to effect the transformation

$$\xi(t) = x(t) - \phi_u(t; x_0,t_0)$$

and study the homogeneous system

$$\begin{aligned}\dot{\xi}(t) &= h(\xi(t),t) \\ &= f(\xi(t) + \phi_u(t; x_0,t_0),u(t),t) - f(\phi_u(t; x_0,t_0),u(t),t) \\ &= -3t^2\xi(t)\end{aligned}$$

Observe that $\xi(t) = 0$ is indeed an equilibrium state for the transformed system. ▌

(1.83) Example
Given a system described by

$$\dot{x}(t) = e^{-x(t)} + u(t)$$

the solution for $x(0) = x_0$ and $u \equiv 0$ is

$$\phi_u(t,x_0,0) = \ln (e^{x_0} + t)$$

The associated free system with an equilibrium state at the origin is

$$\dot{\xi}(t) = h(\xi(t),t) = (e^{x_0} + t)(1 - e^{-\xi(t)})$$ ▌

Before continuing with the discussion of the revised problem of studying the associated homogeneous system, let us return to the second stability question, that of stability of equilibrium states. In order to discuss equilibrium states, we assume zero input so that the differential-state equation (1.75) becomes

$$\dot{x}(t) = f(x(t),0,t) = \hat{f}(x(t),t) \tag{1.84}$$

Suppose that this system has n equilibrium states $x_{e1}, x_{e2}, \ldots, x_{en}$. Consider any one of these equilibrium states x_{ek}. Then

$$\hat{f}(x_{ek},t) = 0 \qquad k = 1, 2, \ldots, n$$

by definition (1.24). The deviation from x_{ek} can be defined by $\xi_k(t)$, that is,

$$\xi_k(t) = x(t) - x_{ek}$$

Therefore

$$\dot{\xi}_k(t) = \hat{f}(\xi_k(t) + x_{ek}, t) = h(\xi_k(t),t) \tag{1.85}$$

Observe that (1.85) is a homogeneous differential equation with an equilibrium state at the origin, that is, $\xi_k(t) = 0$. Thus we have shown that the question of stability of an arbitrary equilibrium state can also be discussed in terms of an associated system with an equilibrium state at the origin.

(1.86) Example

Given the differential-state equation

$$\dot{x}(t) = [x(t)]^3 + 6[x(t)]^2 + 11x(t) + 6$$

the equilibrium states are found to be

$$x_{e1} = -1 \qquad x_{e2} = -2 \qquad x_{e3} = -3$$

We are required to make three individual transformations:

$$\xi_1(t) = x(t) - (-1)$$
$$\xi_2(t) = x(t) - (-2)$$
$$\xi_3(t) = x(t) - (-3)$$

Hence

$$\dot{\xi}_1(t) = h_1(\xi_1(t),t) = (\xi_1 - 1)^3 + 6(\xi_1 - 1)^2 + 11(\xi_1 - 1) + 6$$

which becomes

$$\dot{\xi}_1(t) = \xi_1^3(t) + 6\xi_1^2(t) + 2\xi_1(t)$$

And

$$\dot{\xi}_2(t) = h_2(\xi_2(t),t) = (\xi_2 - 2)^3 + 6(\xi_2 - 2)^3 + 11(\xi_2 - 2) + 6$$

which becomes

$$\dot{\xi}_2(t) = \xi_2^2(t) - \xi_2(t)$$

Finally,

$$\dot{\xi}_3(t) = h_3(\xi_3(t),t) = (\xi_3 - 3)^3 + 6(\xi_3 - 3)^2 + 11(\xi_3 - 3) + 6$$

which becomes

$$\dot{\xi}_3(t) = \xi_3^3(t) - 3\xi_3^2(t) + 2\xi_3(t)$$

In each case, there is an equilibrium state at the origin. ∎

Before leaving this introductory discussion of stability, we discuss briefly the implications of stability in terms of a first-order homogeneous, time-invariant, linear system described by the differential-state equation

$$\dot{x}(t) = ax(t)$$

The origin

$$x(t) = 0$$

is an equilibrium state; moreover it is the *only* equilibrium state if $a \neq 0$. Furthermore, the associated homogeneous system to be discussed in the study of the stability of its equilibrium states is identical to the original system, i.e.,

$$\dot{\xi}(t) = a\xi(t) \tag{1.87}$$

or

$$h(\xi(t),t) = a\xi(t)$$

We have already seen that the solution to (1.87) is

$$\xi(t) = e^{a(t-t_0)}\xi(t_0)$$

so that

$$|\xi(t)| = |e^{a(t-t_0)}\xi(t_0)| \leq |e^{a(t-t_0)}|\,|\xi(t_0)|$$

Thus if the real part of a is negative, $|\xi(t)|$ will approach zero as t increases, and the origin would be an asymptotically stable equilibrium state. If the real part of a equals zero, $|\xi(t)| = |\xi(t_0)|$, and the origin would be stable, as would any constant (equilibrium) state. A third possibility is for the real part of a to be positive. Then as t increased, $|\xi(t)|$ could grow without limit, so that the origin would be an unstable equilibrium state.

1.6 DISCRETE-TIME SYSTEMS

There are a class of systems whose inputs and outputs are specified only at regular time intervals rather than for all time and, therefore, are not describable by differential equations. Systems of this type are called *discrete-time systems*. One of the most important examples of such a system is the digital computer, hence the recent increase of interest in this class of systems.

Since the input and output of a discrete-time system are specified only at certain fixed points in time, that is, $t_0, t_1, t_2, \ldots$, they can be represented by the sequences $(u(t_0),u(t_1),u(t_2), \ldots)$ and $(y(t_0),y(t_1),y(t_2), \ldots)$ respectively, or $(u_0,u_1,u_2, \ldots)$ and $(y_0,y_1,y_2, \ldots)$, respectively, where the subscript denotes the time point of interest. These sequences are written most succinctly as $\{u_k\}$ and $\{y_k\}$. A first-order linear, time-invariant discrete-time system can be described by the *first-order linear difference equation*

$$y_{k+1} = ay_k + bu_k \qquad (1.88)$$

Observe that one initial condition y_0 is needed for solution of (1.88). In other words, the output y_n at any time $n \geq 0$ can be found in terms of the initial condition y_0 and the input sequence $(u_0,u_1, \ldots ,u_n)$:

$$\begin{aligned}
y_1 &= ay_0 + bu_0 \\
y_2 &= ay_1 + bu_1 = a(ay_0 + bu_0) + bu_1 \\
&= a^2y_0 + abu_0 + bu_1 \\
y_3 &= ay_2 + bu_2 = a(a^2y_0 + abu_0 + bu_1) + bu_2 \\
&= a^3y_0 + a^2bu_0 + abu_1 + bu_2 \\
&\cdots\cdots\cdots\cdots\cdots
\end{aligned}$$

so

$$y_n = a^n y_0 + a^{n-1} b u_0 + a^{n-2} b u_1 + \cdots + b u_{n-1}$$

or

$$(1.89) \quad y_n = a^n y_0 + \sum_{k=1}^{n} a^{n-k} b u_{k-1}$$

An alternative description of this system is in terms of the *state-difference equation*

$$(1.90a) \quad x_{n+1} = a x_n + b u_n$$

and the *input-state-output relation*

$$(1.90b) \quad y_n = c x_n + d u_n$$

The reader should be able to verify that the solution of (1.90*a*) is

$$(1.91) \quad x_n = a^n x_0 + \sum_{i=0}^{n-1} a^{n-i-1} b u_i$$

so that

$$(1.92) \quad y_n = c a^n x_0 + \sum_{i=0}^{n-1} c a^{n-i-1} b u_i + d u_n$$

Observe the similarity between (1.92) and the solution of the continuous-time state equations (1.71).

Now consider the following simple numerical-analysis problem. Suppose we wish to solve the equation

$$\dot{x}(t) = \alpha x(t)$$

for $x(t_0) = x_0$ on a digital computer. Recall the definition of a derivative[1]

$$\dot{x}(t) = \lim_{\Delta t \to 0} \frac{x(t + \Delta t) - x(t)}{\Delta t}$$

Then for Δt small enough

$$\frac{x(t + \Delta t) - x(t)}{\Delta t} \simeq \alpha x(t)$$

or

$$x(t + \Delta t) \simeq (1 + \alpha\, \Delta t) x(t)$$

If we let x_n denote $x(t + n\,\Delta t)$ and let $a = 1 + \alpha\,\Delta t$, then we arrive at the difference equation

$$x_{n+1} \simeq a x_n$$

[1] A. Schwartz, "Analytic Geometry and Calculus," pp. 20–25, Holt, Rinehart and Winston, Inc., New York, 1960.

Now consider the exact solution to the differential equation:

$$x(t) = e^{\alpha(t-\tau)}x(\tau)$$

or, if we let the difference between t and τ be Δt seconds, we have

$$x(t + \Delta t) = e^{\alpha \Delta t}x(t)$$

or

$$x(t + (n + 1)\,\Delta t) = e^{\alpha \Delta t}x(t + n\,\Delta t)$$

Using the notation introduced above, this equation may be rewritten as

$$x_{n+1} = e^{\alpha \Delta t}x_n$$

Observe that

$$e^{\alpha \Delta t} = 1 + \alpha\,\Delta t + \frac{(\alpha\,\Delta t)^2}{2!} + \cdots$$

therefore

$$x_{n+1} = \left(1 + \alpha\,\Delta t + \frac{(\alpha\,\Delta t)^2}{2!} + \cdots\right)x_n$$

or

$$x_{n+1} \simeq (1 + \alpha\,\Delta t)x_n$$

which agrees with our previous result if second- and higher-order terms are neglected. The above example illustrates the close relation between numerical analysis and discrete-time systems.

Block diagrams are also a useful graphical means for characterization of discrete-time systems. The basic elements of block diagrams for discrete-time systems are the summer, scaler, and unit delayor. (Note that the unit delayor in a discrete-time system block diagram is analogous to an integrator in a continuous-time system block diagram.) The unit delayor shown in Fig. 1.19 is characterized by

$$y_k = u_{k-1}$$

The reader should verify that the block diagram of the discrete-state equations (1.90) is shown in Fig. 1.20. We note that one unit-delayor element suffices in the characterization of a first-order discrete-time system, although the converse need not be true.

1.7 SUMMARY

The intent of this chapter has been to introduce some of the fundamental concepts of system theory without the burdens of excessive detail or

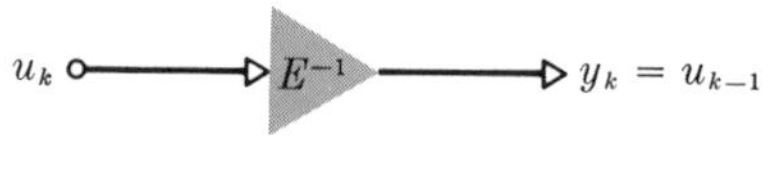

FIG. 1.19 The unit-delayor element used in discrete-time-system block diagrams.

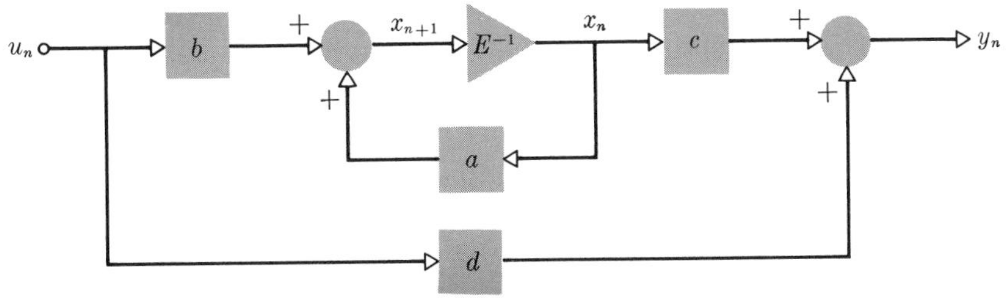

FIG. 1.20 Block diagram of first-order, discrete-time state equations.

mathematical complexity. To do so we have confined discussion to the relatively simple class of first-order systems. Nonetheless, some obviously generalizable concepts should now be apparent.

The system *characterization* associates with a given first-order system a *state,* which is usually simply related to the *initial condition(s).* System analysis problems often simplify considerably upon an appropriate choice of characterization (state).

Linearity and *time invariance* are qualitative system properties of considerable manipulative importance. *Zero-state* response, *zero-input* response, and the *decomposition property* render these concepts applicable to the widest class of system characterizations.

Stability characterizes both system responses and system equilibrium states; simple transformations may always reduce a study of the former to the latter.

Both the closed-form solution of characterizing equations and their discretization for digital-computer simulation are important alternatives to complete system studies.

We must be careful as we proceed to perceive these concepts in their simplicity through the mathematical hierarchy necessitated by increased system complexity.

1.8 PROBLEMS

(1.1) Let A denote the amount of a substance at the beginning of a chemical reaction, and let x be the amount of the substance entering the reaction after t seconds. Assume that the rate of change of the substance is proportional to the amount remaining, and justify that the differential equation which describes this "system" is

$$\dot{x}(t) = -C(x(t) - A)$$

where C is a constant depending on the reaction. If $A = 10$ lb and $C = 0.1\ \text{sec}^{-1}$ how long after the start of the reaction will it be before $x = 0.634$ lb?

(1.2) Suppose that we consider two first-order systems which produce the same response:

(1) $\dot{y}(t) = ay(t) + bu(t) \qquad y(t_0) = y_0$
(2) $\dot{y}(t) = ay(t) + bu(t) + y_0\delta(t - t_0)$

In the first case consider the input to be the function $u(t)$, $t_0 \leq t < \infty$, and in the second case consider the input to be $u(t) + y_0\delta(t - t_0)$, $t_0 \leq t < \infty$. Are these systems (*a*) input-output linear, (*b*) zero-state linear, (*c*) zero-input linear, (*d*) linear?

(1.3) Consider a system characterized by

$$y(t) = f(t) + g(t) \int_{t_0}^{t} h(\tau)u(\tau)\, d\tau$$

Under what conditions on the functions f, g, and h is the system (*a*) linear, (*b*) time invariant, (*c*) linear and time invariant?

(1.4) Example (1.49) has illustrated the *zero-state* linearity and time invariance of the ideal delay element characterized by

$$y(t) = u(t - \tau) \qquad \tau > 0$$

(*a*) Obtain a suitable state which might characterize such a system. (Note: A physical delay element is usually characterized by *partial* differential equations and does not admit of a *finite-dimensional* state space; this is *not* a first-order system.)

(*b*) Show that the ideal delay element is zero-input linear and time invariant and linear and time invariant in general.

(1.5) The most general description given for a first-order system was

$$\dot{x}(t) = f(x(t),u(t),t)$$

and

$$y(t) = g(x(t),u(t),t)$$

(*a*) Show that if the system is time invariant, it could be characterized by

$$\dot{x}(t) = f(x(t),u(t))$$

and

$$y(t) = g(x(t),u(t))$$

(*b*) Show that if the system is linear, it could be characterized by

$$\dot{x}(t) = a(t)x(t) + b(t)u(t)$$

and

$$y(t) = c(t)x(t) + d(t)u(t)$$

(*c*) Finally, show that if the system is both linear and time invariant, it could be characterized by

$$\dot{x}(t) = ax(t) + bu(t)$$

and

$$y(t) = cx(t) + du(t)$$

(1.6) Determine whether or not each of the following systems is linear and/or time invariant.

$$(a)\quad y(t) = 4u(t) + \frac{d}{dt}u(t) \qquad t > 0$$
$$(b)\quad y(t) = tu(t) + u(t^2)$$
$$(c)\quad y(t) = \dot{u}(t) + u^2(t)$$
$$(d)\quad y(t) = \int_{t_1}^{t_2} tu(\tau)\,d\tau$$
$$(e)\quad y(t) = 3u(t+1) + 2u(t)$$
$$(f)\quad y(t) = \int_{-\infty}^{\infty} h(t,\tau)u(\tau)\,d\tau \qquad \text{where } h(t,\tau) = e^{-t}(e^t - e^\tau)$$
$$(g)\quad y(t) = \int_{-\infty}^{\infty} h(t,\tau)u(\tau)\,d\tau \qquad \text{where } h(t,\tau) = e^{\tau}(e^t - e^\tau)$$
$$(h)\quad y(t) = mu(t) + b \qquad m \text{ and } b \text{ are constants}$$
$$(i)\quad y(t) = \min\,[u_1(t),u_2(t)]$$
$$(j)\quad y(t) = \begin{cases} 0 & t < t_0 \\ 2u(t) & t_0 \le t \le t_1 \\ 5u(t) & t \ge t_1 \end{cases}$$

(1.7) A linear, time-invariant system has the zero-state response

$$y(t) = \begin{cases} 0 & t \le 0 \\ 5t^2 & t > 0 \end{cases}$$

to the excitation

$$u(t) = \begin{cases} 0 & t \le 0 \\ t & t > 0 \end{cases}$$

What is the zero-state response to the excitation

$$u(t) = \begin{cases} 0 & t < 2 \\ 1 & t = 2 \\ 2 & 2 < t < 3 \\ 1 & t = 3 \\ 0 & t > 3 \end{cases}$$

(1.8) Given a single input–output system described by the state equations

$$\dot{x}(t) = x(t) + u(t)$$

and

$$y(t) = x(t)u(t) + [u(t)]^2$$

find the equilibrium state. Find the associated linearized system about the equilibrium state and try to determine whether the equilibrium state is stable, asymptotically stable, or unstable.

(1.9) We have shown that the solution to the linear, time-invariant, differential-state equation

(1) $\dot{x}(t) = ax(t) + bu(t)$

is

(2) $x(t) = e^{a(t-t_0)}x(t_0) + \int_{t_0}^{t} e^{a(t-\tau)}bu(\tau)\,d\tau$

by the method of separation of variables. An alternative approach is to use Picard's method of successive approximations.

Integration of (1) yields

(3) $x(t) = x(t_0) + \int_{t_0}^{t} [ax(\tau) + bu(\tau)]\,d\tau$

which is an implicit solution for $x(t)$. Show that if one guesses at the solution of (3), substitutes this estimate back into (3), and repeats the procedure, a sequence of approximate solutions to (3) is generated, and this sequence converges to (2).

(1.10) Using the fact that (Bellman-Gronwell)[1] if

$$\dot{w}(t) \leq k(t)w(t)$$

and

$$w(t_0) = w_0$$

then

$$w(t) \leq w_0 \exp\left[\int_{t_0} k(\xi)\,d\xi\right]$$

derive the fact that if $\int_{t_0}^{t} a(\xi)\,d\xi < \infty$, then the solution to the homogeneous differential equation

$$\dot{x}(t) = a(t)x(t)$$

is unique. (Hint: Assume that two different solutions exist for the same initial conditions, that is, $x_1(t_0) = x_2(t_0) = x_0$, but $x_1(t_1) \neq x_2(t_1)$ for some $t_1 > t_0$, and show a contradiction.)

(1.11) Suppose that $\psi(t)$ is a solution of the homogeneous differential equation

$$\dot{x}(t) = ax(t)$$

[1] L. A. Zadeh and C. A. Desoer, "Linear System Theory," p. 374, McGraw-Hill, New York, 1963.

which vanishes at some time t_1, that is, $\psi(t_1) = 0$. Show that

$$\psi(t) = 0$$

for all t.

(1.12) Consider the homogeneous system derived in Example (1.82) which is described by

$$\dot{\xi}(t) = -3t^2\xi(t)$$

(*a*) Is this system stable, asymptotically stable, or unstable?
(*b*) Determine whether the homogeneous system described by

$$\dot{\xi}(t) = (e^{x_0} + t)(1 - e^{-\xi})$$

is stable (see Example 1.83).

(1.13) Find a solution to the difference equation

$$y_{n+1} + (k - 1)y_n = u$$

where u is a constant input. Try to formulate the stability concept with regard to discrete systems. For what values of k would this system be unstable?

(1.14) As indicated in the text, iterative numerical procedures for solving systems of equations are actually a means of constructing difference equations whose solutions tend to the solution of the set of continuous equations as n tends to infinity. Two basic iterative schemes are
(*a*) *Newton's method* where we write the equation to be solved as

$$f(x) = 0$$

and use the scheme

$$x_{n+1} = x_n - \frac{f(x_n)}{f'(x_n)} \qquad \text{where } f'(x_n) = \left.\frac{df}{dx}\right|_{x=x_n}$$

which is obtained from a Taylor series expansion of $f(x)$ about the point x_n;
(*b*) *Successive approximations* where we write the equation to be solved as

$$g(x) = x$$

and use the scheme

$$x_{n+1} = g(x_n)$$

In general there are no guarantees that either method will converge, i.e.,

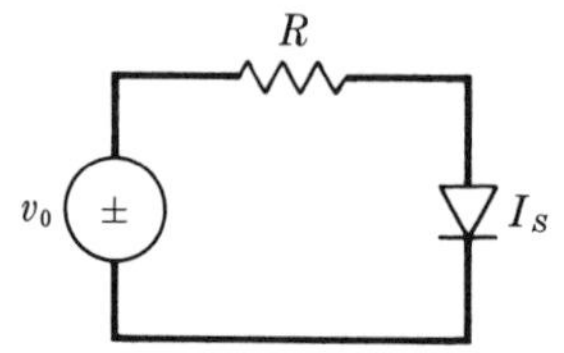

FIG. 1.21 Network for Prob. 1.15.

that the systems are stable. Use both techniques to find $\sqrt{2}$, and try to determine if these methods are stable.

(1.15) Consider the network of Fig. 1.21. The equation for the loop current i is

$$i = I_s \left\{ \exp \left[\frac{q(v_0 - Ri)}{nkT} \right] - 1 \right\}$$

Using Newton's method, indicate how one would find a solution for i. For what values of v_0, R, and initial guess of i would we expect to find a stable solution?

(1.16) Given the continuous-time, linear, time-invariant, first-order system characterized by

$$\dot{x}(t) = ax(t) + bu(t)$$

and

$$y(t) = cx(t) + du(t)$$

the response is

$$y(t) = ce^{at}x_0 + \int_0^t ce^{a(t-\tau)}bu(\tau)\,d\tau + du(t)$$

Sample this output every T seconds beginning at $t = 0$, and find the equivalent discrete-time system $x_{k+1} = \hat{a}x_k + \hat{b}u_k$ and $y_k = \hat{c}x_k + \hat{d}u_k$ and its solution. [Make any assumptions necessary on the nature of the original inputs $u(t)$.] Compare this result with the discrete-time system characterization that follows from using $x(t) \approx [x(t + \Delta t) - x(t)]/\Delta t$ directly in the state equations.

SECOND-ORDER SYSTEMS

2

Technically, second-order systems differ from first-order systems only by degree. Second-order systems are those describable by second-order differential equations, and all the techniques and concepts introduced in the preceding chapter are readily extendable. Second-order systems characterize a variety of physical situations, but their main purpose in this chapter is to indicate the transition from scalar first-order systems to the matrix methods virtually necessitated in the higher-order system studies to follow.

2.1 EXAMPLES OF SECOND-ORDER SYSTEMS AND EXTENSION OF THE CONCEPT OF STATE

Second-order systems are characterized by second-order differential equations. For instance a second-order system with excitation $u(t)$ and response $y(t)$ might be described by

$$\text{(2.1)} \quad \alpha_2 \frac{d^2y(t)}{dt^2} + \alpha_1 \frac{dy(t)}{dt} + \alpha_0 y(t) = \beta_0 u(t) + \beta_1 \frac{du(t)}{dt} + \beta_2 \frac{d^2u(t)}{dt^2}$$

An alternative description of this same second-order system is given by a pair of coupled first-order differential equations of the form

$$\text{(2.2}a\text{)} \quad \dot{x}_1(t) = a_{11}x_1(t) + a_{12}x_2(t) + b_1u(t)$$

and

$$\text{(2.2}b\text{)} \quad \dot{x}_2(t) = a_{21}x_1(t) + a_{22}x_2(t) + b_2u(t)$$

and an input-output equation

$$\text{(2.2}c\text{)} \quad y(t) = c_1x_1(t) + c_2x_2(t) + du(t)$$

Relationships between the coefficients α_2, α_1, α_0, β_2, β_1, β_0 of (2.1) and a_{11}, a_{12}, a_{21}, a_{22}, b_1, b_2, c_1, c_2, d of (2.2) are to be considered later.

(2.3) Example

Consider the second-order differential equation

$$2\frac{d^2y}{dt^2} + 6\frac{dy}{dt} - 4y = u(t)$$

The pair of first-order differential equations

$$\dot{x}_1(t) = x_2(t)$$

and

$$\dot{x}_2(t) = 2x_1(t) - 3x_2(t) + \tfrac{1}{2}u(t)$$

and the relation

$$y(t) = x_1(t)$$

also describe the above system. To see that both characterizations are equivalent, note that

$$\begin{aligned} \ddot{y}(t) &= \ddot{x}_1(t) \\ &= \dot{x}_2(t) \\ &= 2x_1(t) - 3x_2(t) + \tfrac{1}{2}u(t) \\ &= 2y(t) - 3\dot{y}(t) + \tfrac{1}{2}u(t) \end{aligned}$$

or

$$2\ddot{y}(t) + 6\dot{y}(t) - 4y(t) = u(t)$$

∎

Observe that in either instance, whether we are interested in the solution of the second-order differential equation (2.1) or the pair of coupled first-order differential equations (2.2), two initial conditions must be specified. In particular, for (2.2), $x_1(t_0)$ and $x_2(t_0)$ suffice. For the case of first-order systems it was found that the quantity which was specified as the initial condition could be chosen as the system's state as defined by (1.21). In a similar manner, we can consider the pair $(x_1(t),x_2(t))$ to be the state of a second-order system at time t, because knowledge of this pair at any time t_0 and the input for all time $t > t_0$ uniquely determines the state for any subsequent time $t > t_0$, from (2.2a) and (2.2b), and therefore, the output from (2.2c).

If the state of the system is taken to be the pair $(x_1(t),x_2(t))$, then the individual quantities x_1 and x_2 are referred to as *state variables*, the two coupled first-order differential equations which relate the state to the input are called the *differential-state equations*, and the equation which relates the response to the input and state is called the *input-state-output equation*.

In this section, we present several examples of second-order systems. We also indicate how the state variables of a system might be chosen so as to decompose a second-order differential equation into a pair of first-order differential equations. The reason for desiring a system description involving first-order differential equations is that a uniform method of solution results. Further discussion of this point will be given in Chap. 4.

(2.4) Example

Consider the mechanical system shown in Fig. 2.1. A mass m is suspended from a spring and is subjected to viscous damping. The force exerted by

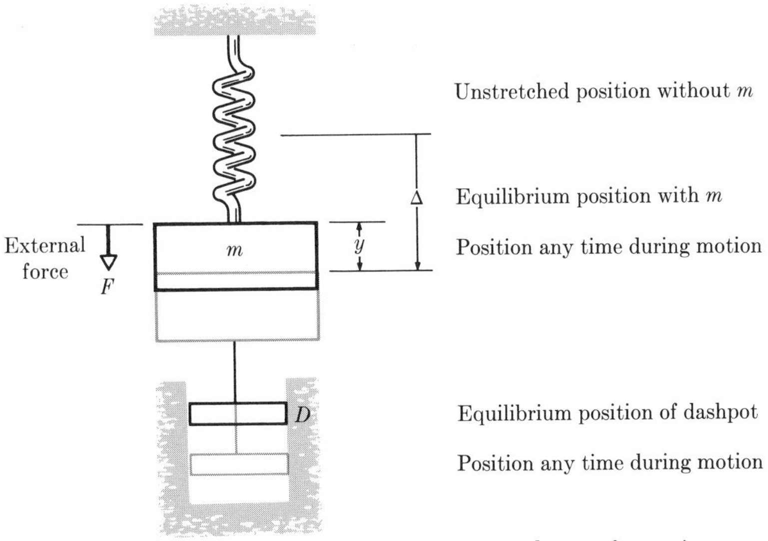

FIG. 2.1 A simple second-order mechanical system made up of a spring, mass, and dashpot.

the spring is proportional to its length while the force exerted by the dashpot is proportional to the velocity of the mass. If F is some external force, then the equation of motion can be written as

$$F + mq - k(y + \Delta) - D\frac{dy}{dt} = m\frac{d^2y}{dt^2}$$

or

$$\frac{d^2y}{dt^2} + \frac{D}{m}\frac{dy}{dt} + \frac{k}{m}y = \frac{1}{m}F \tag{2.5}$$

because, in the equilibrium position,

$$mg = k\Delta$$

▮

Decomposition of second-order differential equations into coupled first-order differential equations and an input-state-output equation is easily accomplished by reference to Chap. 1. Recall that in the study of first-order systems, the quantity specified as the initial condition could be taken to be the state of the system. Therefore we might be motivated to choose as the two state variables necessary for characterization of a second-order system any two quantities which are normally specified as initial conditions. If the coupled first-order equations which result are of the desired form, we have made a suitable choice for state variables; if not, we must look further.

(2.6) Example

Consider again Example (2.4) and Eq. (2.5). One might expect to find the initial displacement $y(t_0)$ and the initial velocity $\dot{y}(t_0)$ specified at the initial time t_0. Therefore we choose as the first state variable, the displacement of the mass from equilibrium at time t,

$$x_1(t) = y(t) \tag{2.7}$$

The velocity of the mass at time t is the second state variable,

$$x_2(t) = \dot{y}(t) \tag{2.8}$$

From (2.5), (2.7), and (2.8) we have the following pair of coupled first-order equations

$$\dot{x}_1(t) = x_2(t) \tag{2.9a}$$

$$\dot{x}_2(t) = -\frac{k}{m}x_1(t) - \frac{D}{m}x_2(t) + \frac{1}{m}F \tag{2.9b}$$

and the input-state-output relation

$$y(t) = x_1(t) \tag{2.9c}$$

▮

It is important to realize that the decomposition of a second-order differential equation into a pair of first-order differential equations need not be unique. For instance, one may wish, for physical reasons, to make some choice of state variables other than those described above. A different set of first-order differential equations would result.

(2.10) Example

Once again consider Example (2.4) and Eq. (2.5). It is easily verified, by direct substitution, that the differential-state equations

$$\dot{x}_1 = -\frac{D}{k}x_1 + x_2 - \frac{D}{k}F$$

$$\dot{x}_2 = -\frac{m}{k}x_1 - \frac{m}{k}F$$

and the input-state-output relation

$$y = \frac{1}{k}x_1 + \frac{1}{k}F$$

also characterize this system. Here we have taken the state variables to be

$$x_1 = ky - F$$

and

$$x_2 = k\dot{y} - \dot{F} + Dy$$

A third possible choice of state variables, and probably the most natural as will be seen in the sequel, is displacement and momentum. Then

$$x_1 = y$$

and

$$x_2 = m\dot{y}$$

The associated state equations are

$$\dot{x}_1 = \frac{1}{m}x_2$$

$$\dot{x}_2 = -x_1 - \frac{D}{m}x_2 + F$$

and the input-output relation is

$$y = x_1$$

∎

(2.11) Example

Usually an electrical network which contains two energy-storage elements is characterized by a second-order differential equation. Consider the

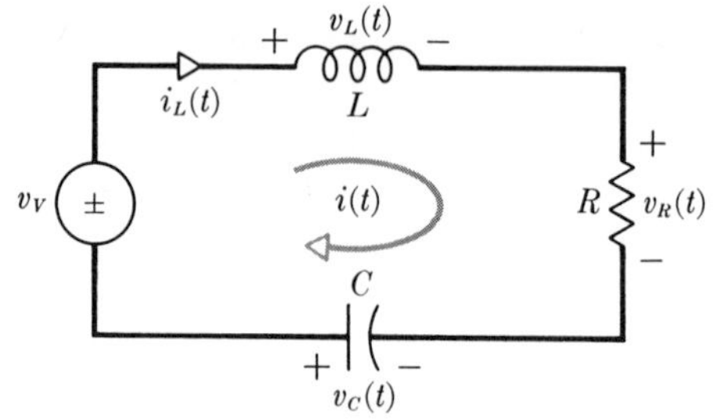

FIG. 2.2 A second-order RLC network.

series RLC network of Fig. 2.2. The Kirchhoff's voltage law loop equation is

$$v_V - v_L - v_R - v_C = 0$$

The following second-order differential equation results upon substitution of the branch relations and the Kirchhoff's current law equations:

$$L\frac{d^2i}{dt^2} + R\frac{di}{dt} + \frac{1}{C}i = \frac{dv_V}{dt}$$

Since two initial conditions, for instance $i(t_0)$ and $\dot{i}(t_0)$, are required for the unique solution of this equation, we might be motivated to choose as the state variables the loop current

$$x_1 = i$$

and the derivative of the loop current

$$x_2 = \frac{di}{dt}$$

This choice leads to the coupled first-order differential equations

$$\dot{x}_1 = x_2$$

and

$$\dot{x}_2 = -\frac{1}{LC}x_1 - \frac{R}{L}x + \dot{v}_V$$

Unfortunately, the derivative of the input $\dot{v}_V(t)$ appears in these expressions, and therefore they are not of the desired form. Whereas in the mechanical system of Example (2.4), the choice of the independent variable and its derivative sufficed as state variables, this choice is inadequate for the electrical system described here. In the case of Example (2.4), the state variables corresponded to physical quantities, i.e., position and velocity, while for the case on hand, only one of the state variables has direct correspondence with a physical quantity, i.e., current.

In order to arrive at expressions with the desired state form, some other pair of state-variable candidates must be chosen. To help in our quest, we ask what physical quantities would most likely be specified as initial conditions for the network of Fig. 2.2. Since inductors and capacitors are energy-storage elements, it is not uncommon to find the initial stored energy specified at the initial time t_0. In actuality, we expect to be given the initial inductance current and the initial capacitance voltage. Therefore another possible choice for state variables would appear to be the capacitance voltage

$$x_1(t) = v_C(t)$$

and the inductance current

$$x_2(t) = i_L(t)$$

With this choice of state variables, the pair of first-order differential equations becomes

$$\text{(2.12}a\text{)}\quad \dot{x}_1(t) = -\frac{1}{C}\,x_2(t)$$

and

$$\text{(2.12}b\text{)}\quad \dot{x}_2(t) = -\frac{1}{L}\,x_1(t) - \frac{R}{L}\,x_2(t) + \frac{1}{L}\,v_V(t)$$

and the input-state-output relation is

$$\text{(2.12}c\text{)}\quad y(t) = x_2(t)$$

These expressions are of the desired form. ▮

It is interesting to note the similarity between state equations (2.9) which describe the mechanical system of Fig. 2.1 and the state equations (2.12) which describe the electrical network of Fig. 2.2. The systems are seen to be described by equivalent state equations if we set up the correspondence of Table 2.1. This correspondence is known as the *force-voltage analogy*. Thus if a solution to the mechanical problem is found, it also serves as the solution to the analogous electrical problem,

TABLE 2.1

Mechanical system	*Electrical system*
Force, F	Voltage, v
Velocity, v	Current, i
Displacement, y	Charge, q
Mass, M	Inductance, L
Damping coefficient, D	Resistance, R
Compliance, K	Capacitance, C

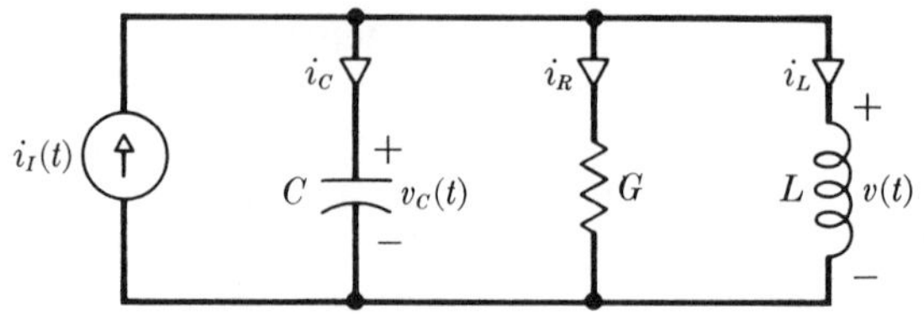

FIG. 2.3 The dual of the network shown in Fig. 2.2.

and vice versa. It is not our intent to pursue this analogy in further detail; we merely wish to point out that such an analogy exists and may be exploited easily.[1]

(2.13) Example

Consider the parallel RLC network of Fig. 2.3. The Kirchhoff's current law node equation is

$$i_I + i_C + i_R + i_L = 0$$

Upon substitution of the branch relationships and Kirchhoff's voltage law equations, the above expression becomes

$$C\frac{d^2v(t)}{dt^2} + G\frac{dv(t)}{dt} + \frac{1}{L}v(t) = -\frac{di_I(t)}{dt} \tag{2.14}$$

a second-order differential equation in terms of $v(t)$, the voltage across the current source. Decomposition of (2.14) into a suitable pair of coupled first-order differential equations is achieved with the choice, once again, of the capacitance voltage and inductance current as state variables. In other words, if

$$x_1(t) = i_L(t)$$

and

$$x_2(t) = v_C(t)$$

then the state equations which result are

$$\dot{x}_1(t) = \frac{1}{L}x_2(t) \tag{2.15a}$$

and

$$\dot{x}_2(t) = -\frac{G}{C}x_1(t) - \frac{1}{C}x_2(t) + i_I(t) \tag{2.15b}$$

and the input-state-output relation is

$$y(t) = x_2(t) \tag{2.15c}$$

▮

[1] For further study see D. K. Cheng, "Analysis of Linear Systems," Chap. 4, Addison-Wesley, Reading, Mass., 1961.

TABLE 2.2

Mechanical system	*Electrical system*
Force, F	Current, i
Velocity, v	Voltage, v
Displacement, y	Flux linkage, ϕ
Mass, M	Capacitance, C
Damping coefficient, D	Conductance, G
Compliance, K	Inductance, L

Comparison of state equations (2.15) and state equations (2.9) indicates that the mechanical system of Fig. 2.1 and the electrical system of Fig. 2.3 are describable by equivalent state equations under the correspondence of Table 2.2. This correspondence is known as the *force-current analogy*.

There remains one more comparison of interest. Consider state equations (2.12) for the network of Fig. 2.2 and state equations (2.15) for the network of Fig. 2.3. These sets of state equations are equivalent under the correspondence of Table 2.3. Networks which possess this correspondence are said to be *duals*.[1]

The above have all been examples of *linear* second-order systems. We now consider a nonlinear system.

(2.16) Example

A particle of mass m is suspended on a cord of length l, as shown in Fig. 2.4. The only forces which act on the particle are its weight, directed vertically downward, and the tension T in the string. The position of this simple pendulum at any time t can be specified in terms of the angle $\theta(t)$. If we choose the "x axis" to be perpendicular to the string (tangent to the

[1] C. A. Desoer and E. S. Kuh, "Basic Circuit Theory," pp. 453–457, McGraw-Hill, New York, 1969.

TABLE 2.3

Variables of network in Fig. 2.2	*Variables of network in Fig. 2.3*
$i(t)$	$v(t)$
$v(t)$	$i(t)$
C	L
G	R
L	C

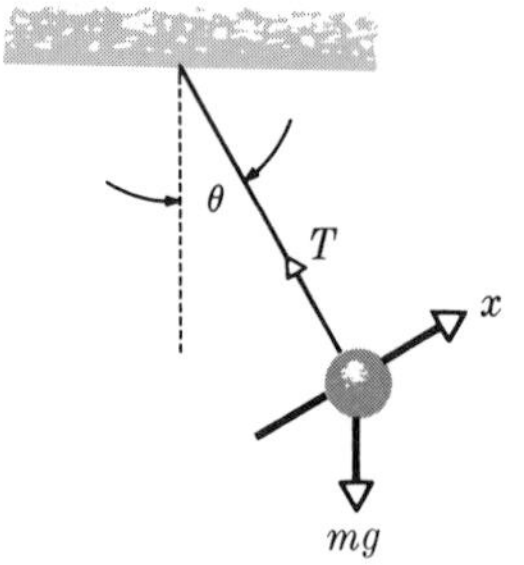

FIG. 2.4 A simple pendulum which can be characterized by a nonlinear, second-order differential equation.

path of the particle) then the sum of forces in the x direction is

$$ma_x = -mg \sin \theta$$

where a_x is the acceleration of the particle along the x axis. Observe that when θ is zero, the acceleration is zero. Let α denote the angular acceleration of the string and particle, then

$$a_x = l\alpha$$

But

$$\alpha(t) = \ddot{\theta}(t)$$

so the force equation becomes

$$\ddot{\theta}(t) = \frac{-g}{l} \sin \theta(t)$$

The motion of a pendulum is seen to be describable by a second-order, nonlinear, differential equation. In order to find an equivalent representation involving two first-order differential equations, we choose as our state variables the angle

$$x_1(t) = \theta(t)$$

and the angular velocity

$$x_2(t) = \dot{\theta}(t)$$

then

$$\dot{x}_1(t) = x_2(t)$$

and

$$\dot{x}_2(t) = \frac{-g}{l} \sin x_1(t)$$ ∎

The first-order equations in Example (2.16) are not of the same form as (2.2); rather, they are similar to the more general form of state equations of second-order systems, namely:

(2.17a) $\dot{x}_1(t) = f_1(x_1(t),x_2(t),u(t),t)$

and

(2.17b) $\dot{x}_2(t) = f_2(x_1(t),x_2(t),u(t),t)$

In correspondence with (2.17a) and (2.17b), the more general form of the input-state-output relation is

$$y(t) = g(x_1(t),x_2(t),u(t),t)$$

We may entertain the possibility of a second-order system having more than one input or output. For instance a two input—two output system would have the following state-equation description:

$$\dot{x}_1 = f_1(x_1,x_2,u_1,u_2,t)$$
$$\dot{x}_2 = f_2(x_1,x_2,u_1,u_2,t)$$

and

$$y_1 = g_1(x_1,x_2,u_1,u_2,t)$$
$$y_2 = g_2(x_1,x_2,u_1,u_2,t)$$

The reader can see that even for the case of a second-order system, the notation introduced thus far is cumbersome. This problem will be alleviated by the use of vector-matrix notation to be discussed in Chap. 3. For the present we limit our attention to single input—single output systems.

2.2 LINEARIZATION OF SECOND-ORDER STATE EQUATIONS

For the most part, we will again restrict our attention to linear second-order systems. Linearity has been defined for first-order systems in the previous chapter. We leave as an exercise the extension of this definition to second-order systems (see Prob. 2.5). Since most nonlinear systems behave linearly over some small operating range, they can be described by linear state equations in this range and are amenable to the same analysis techniques as are linear systems. Before we proceed to the general solution of linear second-order system equations, we discuss the linearization of nonlinear equations in a limited operating range.

A general second-order system can be described by the *standard-form state equations*

(2.18a) $\dot{x}_1(t) = f_1(x_1(t),x_2(t),u(t),t)$
(2.18b) $\dot{x}_2(t) = f_2(x_1(t),x_2(t),u(t),t)$

and

(2.18c) $y(t) = g(x_1(t),x_2(t),u(t),t)$

Assume that $x_{10}(t)$ and $x_{20}(t)$ are known solutions to the differential-state equations for initial state $(\hat{x}_{10},\hat{x}_{20})$ and input $u_0(t)$. Furthermore, let $y_0(t)$

denote the known response of the system with the above initial state and input. Then

$$\begin{aligned}
\dot{x}_{10}(t) &= f_1(x_{10}(t),x_{20}(t),u_0(t),t)\\
\dot{x}_{20}(t) &= f_2(x_{10}(t),x_{20}(t),u_0(t),t)\\
y_0(t) &= g(x_{10}(t),x_{20}(t),u_0(t),t)\\
x_{10}(t_0) &= \hat{x}_{10}
\end{aligned}$$

and

$$x_{20}(t_0) = \hat{x}_{20}$$

Suppose that the initial state and input are perturbed so that the new state and input become

$$\begin{aligned}
x_{11}(t) &= x_{10}(t) + \xi_1(t)\\
x_{21}(t) &= x_{20}(t) + \xi_2(t)
\end{aligned}$$

and

$$u_1(t) = u_0(t) + \eta(t)$$

The system's response

$$y_1(t) = y_0(t) + \nu(t)$$

can be found from the perturbed state equations

$$\begin{aligned}
\dot{x}_{10} + \dot{\xi}_1 &= f_1(x_{10} + \xi_1,\ x_{20} + \xi_2,\ u + \eta,\ t)\\
\dot{x}_{20} + \dot{\xi}_2 &= f_2(x_{10} + \xi_1,\ x_{20} + \xi_2,\ u + \eta,\ t)
\end{aligned}$$

and

$$y_0 + \nu = g(x_{10} + \xi_1,\ x_{20} + \xi_2,\ u + \eta,\ t)$$

Consider a Taylor series expansion of the perturbed state equations about the known solution:

$$\begin{aligned}
\dot{x}_{10} + \dot{\xi}_1 &= f_1(x_{10},x_{20},u_0,t)\\
&\quad + \left.\frac{\partial f_1}{\partial x_1}\right|_{x_{10},x_{20},u_0} \xi_1 + \left.\frac{\partial f_1}{\partial x_2}\right|_{x_{10},x_{20},u_0} \xi_2 + \left.\frac{\partial f_1}{\partial u}\right|_{x_{10},x_{20},u_0} \eta + 0(\xi_1^2,\xi_2^2,\eta^2)\\
\dot{x}_{20} + \dot{\xi}_2 &= f_2(x_{10},x_{20},u_0,t)\\
&\quad + \left.\frac{\partial f_2}{\partial x_1}\right|_{x_{10},x_{20},u_0} \xi_1 + \left.\frac{\partial f_2}{\partial x_2}\right|_{x_{10},x_{20},u_0} \xi_2 + \left.\frac{\partial f_2}{\partial u}\right|_{x_{10},x_{20},u_0} \eta + 0(\xi_1^2,\xi_2^2,\eta^2)
\end{aligned}$$

and

$$\begin{aligned}
y_0 + \nu &= g(x_{10},x_{20},u_0,t)\\
&\quad + \left.\frac{\partial g}{\partial x_1}\right|_{x_{10},x_{20},u_0} \xi_1 + \left.\frac{\partial g}{\partial x_2}\right|_{x_{10},x_{20},u_0} \xi_2 + \left.\frac{\partial g}{\partial u}\right|_{x_{10},x_{20},u_0} \eta + 0(\xi_1^2,\xi_2^2,\eta^2)
\end{aligned}$$

where

$$\left.\frac{\partial f_1}{\partial x_1}\right|_{x_{10},x_{20},u_0} = \left.\frac{\partial f_1(x_1(t),x_2(t),u(t),t)}{\partial x_1(t)}\right|_{\substack{x_1(t)=x_{10}(t)\\ x_2(t)=x_{20}(t)\\ u(t)=u_0(t)}}$$

etc., and $0(\xi_1^2,\xi_2^2,\eta^2)$ denotes terms higher than first order in ξ_1, ξ_2, and η. Observe that we have assumed that the functions f_1, f_2, and g are at least twice differentiable in all arguments except possibly time. We make the assumption that $0(\xi_1^2,\xi_2^2,\eta^2)$, the remainder terms, are negligibly small and subtract the original solution to obtain the approximate equations

$$(2.19a)\quad \dot{\xi}_1(t) = a_{11}(t)\xi_1(t) + a_{12}(t)\xi_2(t) + b_1(t)\eta(t)$$
$$(2.19b)\quad \dot{\xi}_2(t) = a_{21}(t)\xi_1(t) + a_{22}(t)\xi_2(t) + b_2(t)\eta(t)$$

and

$$(2.19c)\quad \nu(t) = c_1(t)\xi_1(t) + c_2(t)\xi_2(t) + d(t)\eta(t)$$

where

$$a_{11}(t) = \frac{\partial f_1}{\partial x_1}\bigg|_{x_{10},x_{20},u_0} \qquad a_{12}(t) = \frac{\partial f_1}{\partial x_2}\bigg|_{x_{10},x_{20},u_0}$$

$$a_{21}(t) = \frac{\partial f_2}{\partial x_1}\bigg|_{x_{10},x_{20},u_0} \qquad a_{22}(t) = \frac{\partial f_2}{\partial x_2}\bigg|_{x_{10},x_{20},u_0}$$

$$b_1(t) = \frac{\partial f_1}{\partial u}\bigg|_{x_{10},x_{20},u_0} \qquad b_2(t) = \frac{\partial f_2}{\partial u}\bigg|_{x_{10},x_{20},u_0}$$

$$c_1(t) = \frac{\partial g}{\partial x_1}\bigg|_{x_{10},x_{20},u_0} \qquad c_2(t) = \frac{\partial g}{\partial x_2}\bigg|_{x_{10},x_{20},u_0}$$

and

$$d(t) = \frac{\partial g}{\partial u}\bigg|_{x_{10},x_{20},u_0}$$

Expressions (2.19) have the form of linear-state equations.

(2.20) Example

A second-order nonlinear system is characterized by the differential equation

$$\ddot{y}(t) - (\dot{y}(t))^3 - y(t) = u(t)$$

If we choose as state variables

$$x_1(t) = y(t)$$

and

$$x_2(t) = \dot{y}(t)$$

then an alternative description in terms of standard-form state equations is

$$\dot{x}_1(t) = x_2(t)$$
$$\dot{x}_2(t) = -x_1(t) - (x_2(t))^3 + u(t)$$

and

$$y(t) = x_1(t)$$

For the input

$$u(t) = (\cos t)^3$$

it can be easily be verified that the particular solution to the differential-state equations is

$$x_1(t) = \sin t$$

and

$$x_2(t) = \cos t$$

so that

$$y(t) = \sin t$$

The linearized version of these equations about the particular solution is

$$\begin{aligned}\dot{\xi}_1(t) &= \xi_2(t)\\ \dot{\xi}_2(t) &= -\xi_1(t) - 3\cos^2 t\ \xi_2(t) + \eta(t)\end{aligned}$$

and

$$\eta(t) = \xi_1(t)$$

which describes a linear *time-variable* system. ∎

(2.21) Example

The linearized version of the state equations

$$\begin{aligned}\dot{x}_1(t) &= -x_1(t) + u(t)\\ \dot{x}_2(t) &= -x_2(t) + [u(t)]^3\end{aligned}$$

and

$$y(t) = x_2{}^3(t) + u^2(t)$$

about the solution

$$\begin{aligned}x_1(t) &= \alpha\\ x_2(t) &= \alpha^3\end{aligned}$$

and

$$u(t) = \alpha$$

where α is a constant, is

$$\begin{aligned}\dot{\xi}_1(t) &= -\xi_1(t) + \eta(t)\\ \dot{\xi}_2(t) &= -\xi_2(t) + 3\alpha^2\eta(t)\\ \nu(t) &= 3\alpha^6\xi_2(t) + 2\alpha\eta(t)\end{aligned}$$

∎

2.3 BLOCK DIAGRAMS AND SYSTEM REPRESENTATIONS

Block diagrams are even more useful for visualization of second-order systems than they are for first-order systems. The summer, scaler, and integrator, introduced in Chap. 1, suffice to graphically represent any linear, time-invariant, second-order system characterized by the general second-order differential-state equation

$$(2.22)\quad \ddot{y}(t) + \alpha_1\dot{y}(t) + \alpha_0 y(t) = \beta_0 u(t) + \beta_1\dot{u}(t) + \beta_2\ddot{u}(t)$$

or by the standard-form state equations

$$(2.23a)\quad \dot{x}_1(t) = a_{11}x_1(t) + a_{12}x_2(t) + b_1u(t)$$
$$(2.23b)\quad \dot{x}_2(t) = a_{21}x_1(t) + a_{22}x_2(t) + b_2u(t)$$

and

$$(2.23c)\quad y(t) = c_1x_1(t) + c_2x_2(t) + du(t)$$

Before proceeding to the general block diagram associated with (2.22), consider the simpler relation

$$\ddot{y}(t) + \alpha_1\dot{y}(t) + \alpha_0 y(t) = u(t)$$

This expression may be rewritten as

$$\ddot{y}(t) = -\alpha_1\dot{y}(t) - \alpha_0 y(t) + u(t)$$

Upon choosing y and $\dot{y}$ as the outputs of two integrators, we obtain the block diagram shown in Fig. 2.5. Now consider the equation

$$(2.24)\quad \ddot{y}(t) + \alpha_1\dot{y}(t) + \alpha_0 y(t) = u + \dot{u}$$

The reader should verify that this expression cannot be simulated by a two-integrator block diagram if y and $\dot{y}$ are chosen to be the outputs of the integrators. Since we are concerned with a second-order system, we know that we need, at most, two integrators to simulate it. Moreover, y and $\dot{y}$ are not the outputs of these integrators. Let us denote the integrator outputs by p and q and consider the block diagram of Fig. 2.6. We have

$$y = p + \gamma_2 u$$
$$\dot{p} = q + \gamma_1 u$$

and

$$\dot{q} = \epsilon_1 p + \epsilon_2 y + \gamma_0 u$$

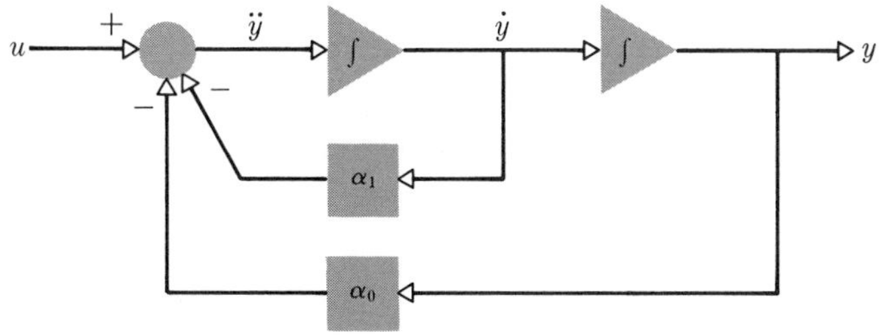

FIG. 2.5 Simulation diagram of the second-order differential equation $\ddot{y} + \alpha_1\dot{y} + \alpha_0 y = u$.

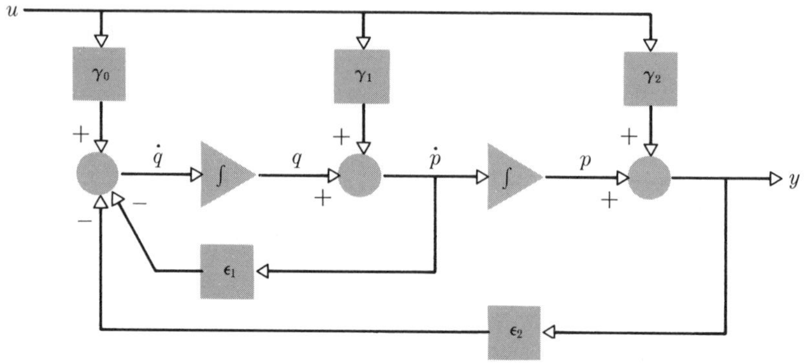

FIG. 2.6 A general second-order-system simulation diagram.

Combination of the above relations yields

$$\ddot{y} + \epsilon_1\dot{y} + \epsilon_2 y = \gamma_2\ddot{u} + (\gamma_1 + \epsilon_1\gamma_2)\dot{u} + \gamma_0 u \tag{2.25}$$

Comparison of (2.25) and (2.24) indicates that the block diagram of Fig. 2.6 can be utilized to simulate expression (2.24) if

$$\epsilon_1 = \alpha_1$$
$$\epsilon_2 = \alpha_0$$
$$\gamma_2 = 0$$
$$\gamma_1 = -1$$

and

$$\gamma_0 = 1$$

This realization is shown in Fig. 2.7. Finally, the simulation diagram of the general second-order differential equation (2.22) can be found by comparing (2.25) with (2.22). Then

$$\epsilon_1 = \alpha_1$$
$$\epsilon_2 = \alpha_0$$
$$\gamma_2 = \beta_2$$
$$\gamma_1 = \beta_1 - \alpha_1\beta_2$$
$$\gamma_0 = \beta_0$$

and the simulation diagram is shown in Fig. 2.8.

Simulation of the state equations is straightforward if x_1 and x_2 are chosen as the outputs of integrators. Figure 2.9 shows the block diagram associated with (2.23).

2.4 SOLUTION OF COUPLED, FIRST-ORDER, DIFFERENTIAL-STATE EQUATIONS

We now turn our attention to the solution of the state equations characterizing second-order systems. Our primary concern is linear, single input

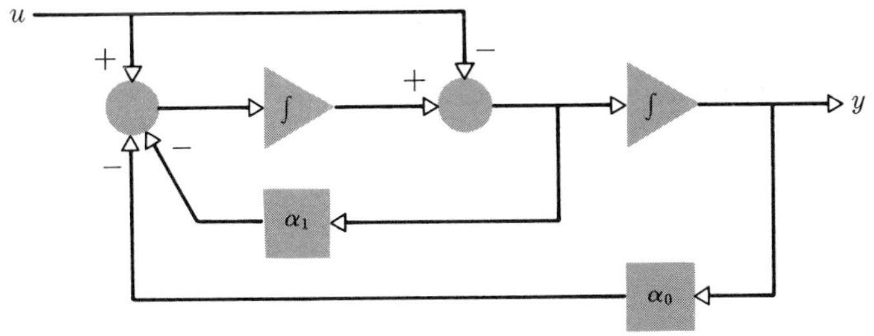

FIG. 2.7 Block-diagram realization of $\ddot{y} + \alpha_1\dot{y} + \alpha_0 y = u + \dot{u}$.

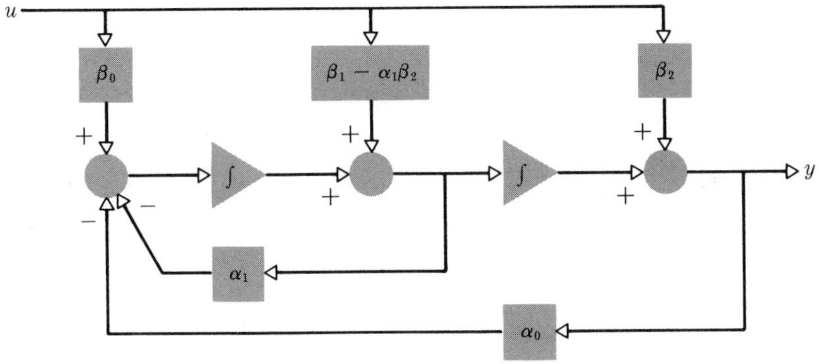

FIG. 2.8 Simulation of $\ddot{y} + \alpha_1\dot{y} + \alpha_0 y = \beta_0 u + \beta_1\dot{u} + \beta_2\ddot{u}$.

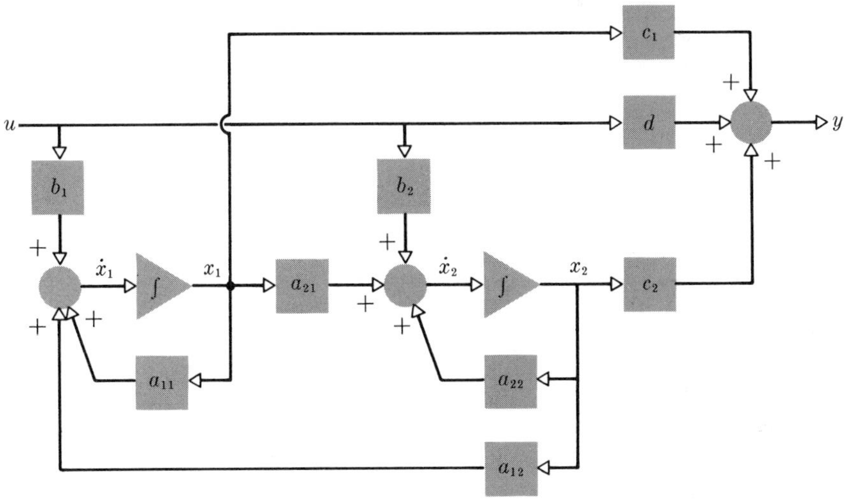

FIG. 2.9 Simulation of standard-form, second-order state equations.

—single output systems which can be described by

$$
\begin{aligned}
&(2.26a)\quad \dot{x}_1(t) = a_{11}(t)x_1(t) + a_{12}(t)x_2(t) + b_1(t)u(t)\\
&(2.26b)\quad \dot{x}_2(t) = a_{21}(t)x_2(t) + a_{22}(t)x_2(t) + b_2(t)u(t)
\end{aligned}
$$

and

$$(2.26c)\quad y(t) = c_1(t)x_1(t) + c_2(t)x_2(t) + d(t)u(t)$$

Initially we restrict ourselves to the linear time-invariant case so that Eqs. (2.26) can be written as

$$
\begin{aligned}
&(2.27a)\quad \dot{x}_1(t) = a_{11}x_1(t) + a_{12}x_2(t) + b_1u(t)\\
&(2.27b)\quad \dot{x}_2(t) = a_{21}x_1(t) + a_{22}x_2(t) + b_2u(t)
\end{aligned}
$$

and

$$(2.27c)\quad y(t) = c_1x_1(t) + c_2x_2(t) + du(t)$$

One of the most common methods of solution of coupled differential equations is to reduce the system of equations to a single differential equation in a single variable. Equations (2.27) can be solved simultaneously to yield

$$(2.28)\quad \ddot{y}(t) + \alpha_1\dot{y}(t) + \alpha_0 y(t) = \beta_0 u(t) + \beta_1\dot{u}(t) + \beta_2\ddot{u}(t)$$

where

$$
(2.29)\quad
\begin{aligned}
\alpha_1 &= -(a_{11} + a_{22})\\
\alpha_0 &= a_{11}a_{22} - a_{12}a_{21}\\
\beta_0 &= (a_{21}c_2b_1 - b_1a_{22}c_1 - b_2a_{11}c_2 + c_1a_{12}b_2 + da_{22}a_{11} - da_{12}a_{21})\\
\beta_1 &= c_1b_1 + b_2c_2 + (a_{11} + a_{22})d
\end{aligned}
$$

and

$$\beta_2 = -d$$

Upon employing the differential operator D, defined by

$$D \equiv \frac{d}{dt}$$

we may write (2.28) most succinctly as

$$(2.30)\quad (D^2 + \alpha_1 D + \alpha_0)y(t) = (\beta_2 D^2 + \beta_1 D + \beta_0)u(t)$$

Solution of (2.30) is undertaken in two steps. First we find the homogeneous solution y_H, and then we find the particular solution y_p. The complete solution is an appropriate sum of these two solutions. The homogeneous equation associated with (2.30) is

$$(2.31)\quad (D^2 + \alpha_1 D + \alpha_0)y(t) = 0$$

We assume the homogeneous solution to be of the form

(2.32) $y_H(t) = e^{st}$

where s is some finite (real or complex) constant. Substitution of (2.32) into (2.31) yields

$$(s^2 + \alpha_1 s + \alpha_0)e^{st} = 0$$

Therefore (2.32) is indeed the solution to the homogeneous equation if s is chosen to satisfy the *characteristic equation*

$$s^2 + \alpha_1 s + \alpha_0 = 0$$

The roots of the characteristic equation are

(2.33*a*) $s_1 = -\frac{\alpha_1}{2} + \left(\left(\frac{\alpha_1}{2}\right)^2 - \alpha_0\right)^{\frac{1}{2}}$

and

(2.33*b*) $s_2 = -\frac{\alpha_1}{2} - \left(\left(\frac{\alpha_1}{2}\right)^2 - \alpha_0\right)^{\frac{1}{2}}$

If $s_1 \neq s_2$ then the homogeneous solution is

(2.34) $y_H(t) = C_1 e^{s_1 t} + C_2 e^{s_2 t}$

where C_1 and C_2 are constants which depend on the two initial conditions. If the two roots of the characteristic equation are equal, that is, $s_1 = s_2$, then (2.34) reduces to

(2.35) $y_H(t) = k_1 e^{s_1 t}$

and only one arbitrary constant is present. Thus (2.35) cannot be the general solution to a second-order differential equation. In order to remedy this situation, we try

(2.36) $y_H(t) = \xi(t)e^{s_1 t}$

where $\xi(t)$ is an arbitrary function of time, as the solution to (2.31). Substitution of (2.36) into (2.31) yields

$$[\ddot{\xi}(t) + (2s_1 + \alpha_1)\dot{\xi}(t) + (s_1{}^2 + \alpha_1 s_1 + \alpha_0)\xi(t)]e^{s_1 t} = 0$$

But

$$s_1{}^2 + \alpha_1 s_1 + \alpha_0 = 0$$

and

$$2s_1 + \alpha_1 = 0$$

since s_1 is a multiple root of the characteristic equation, so that (2.36) is a solution of the homogeneous equation if

$$\ddot{\xi}(t) = 0$$

Certainly if we choose

$$\xi(t) = \hat{k}_1 + \hat{k}_2 t$$

where $\hat{k}_1$ and $\hat{k}_2$ are constants, this requirement is met. Therefore if the characteristic equation has two coincident roots, the solution to the homogeneous equation is

$$y_H(t) = C_1 e^{s_1 t} + C_2 t e^{s_1 t} \tag{2.37}$$

Note, we can always employ one solution to reduce the task of finding the other to the solution of a simpler differential equation. Given

$$\ddot{y} + \alpha_1 y + \alpha_0 y = 0$$

and

$$s_1 = -\frac{\alpha_1}{2} + \left(\left(\frac{\alpha_1}{2}\right)^2 - \alpha_0\right)^{\frac{1}{2}}$$

try

$$y_H(t) = \xi(t) e^{s_1 t}$$

as the homogeneous solution.

$$\dot{y}_H = \dot{\xi} e^{s_1 t} + s_1 \xi e^{s_1 t}$$

and

$$\ddot{y} = \ddot{\xi} e^{s_1 t} + 2 s_1 \dot{\xi} e^{s_1 t} + s_1{}^2 \xi e^{s_1 t}$$

Hence, we have

$$\begin{aligned} \ddot{y}_H + \alpha_1 \dot{y}_H + \alpha_0 y_H &= [(\ddot{\xi} + 2 s_1 \dot{\xi} + s_1{}^2 \xi) + \alpha_1(\dot{\xi} + s_1 \xi) + \alpha_0 \xi] e^{s_1 t} \\ &= [\ddot{\xi} + (2 s_1 + \alpha_1)\dot{\xi} + (s_1{}^2 + \alpha_1 s_1 + \alpha_0)\xi] e^{s_1 t} \end{aligned}$$

But

$$2 s_1 + \alpha_1 = 2\left(\left(\frac{\alpha_1}{2}\right)^2 - \alpha_0\right)^{\frac{1}{2}}$$

and

$$s_1{}^2 + \alpha_1 s_1 + \alpha_0 = 0$$

hence,

$$\ddot{\xi} + 2\left(\left(\frac{\alpha_1}{2}\right)^2 + \alpha_0\right)^{\frac{1}{2}} \dot{\xi} = 0$$

so that

$$\xi(t) = k_2 \exp\left[-2\sqrt{\left(\frac{\alpha_1}{2}\right)^2 + \alpha_0}\right] + k_1$$

Therefore,

$$y_H = k_1 e^{s_1 t} + k_2 e^{s_2 t}$$

where

$$s_2 = -\frac{\alpha_1}{2} - \left(\left(\frac{\alpha_1}{2}\right)^2 - \alpha_0\right)^{\frac{1}{2}}$$

unless

$$\left(\left(\frac{\alpha_1}{2}\right)^2 - \alpha_0\right)^{\frac{1}{2}} = 0$$

in which case

$$y_H = (k_1 + k_2t)e^{s_1t}$$

because

$$\ddot{\xi} = 0$$

This technique is useful in general, for when k solutions of an nth-order, linear, homogeneous differential equation are known, we may reduce the quest for the remaining $(n - k)$ solutions to that of solution of an $(n - k)$-order, linear, homogeneous differential equation.

(2.38) Example

Consider a second-order system described by the standard-form state equations

$$\begin{aligned} \dot{x}_1(t) &= -x_1(t) + x_2(t) \\ \dot{x}_2(t) &= -2x_2(t) + u(t) \end{aligned}$$

and

$$y(t) = x_1(t) + 2x_2(t)$$

These equations can be expressed as the following second-order differential equation:

$$\ddot{y}(t) + 3\dot{y}(t) + 2y(t) = 3u(t) + 2\dot{u}(t)$$

The solution to the homogeneous equation

$$(D^2 + 3D + 2)y = 0$$

is

$$y_1 = C_1e^{-t} + C_2e^{-2t}$$ ∎

We find the particular solution as we did for the first-order case, by variation of parameters. First rewrite the homogeneous solution as

$$y_H(t) = C_1\lambda_1(t) + C_2\lambda_1(t)$$

where

$$\lambda_1(t) = e^{s_1t}$$

and

$$\lambda_2(t) = e^{s_2t}$$

if $s_1 \neq s_2$, or

$$\lambda_1 = e^{s_1 t}$$

and

$$\lambda_2 = te^{s_1 t}$$

if $s_1 = s_2$. Then assume the particular solution to be of the form

$$y_P(t) = \eta_1(t)\lambda_1(t) + \eta_2(t)\lambda_2(t) \tag{2.39}$$

where $\eta_1(t)$ and $\eta_2(t)$ are unknown functions of time. Differentiation of (2.39) yields

$$\dot{y}_P = (\eta_1\dot{\lambda}_1 + \eta_2\dot{\lambda}_2) + (\dot{\eta}_1\lambda_1 + \dot{\eta}_2\lambda_2) \tag{2.40}$$

Since η_1 and η_2 are as yet undefined, let us choose them so that

$$\dot{\eta}_1\lambda_1 + \dot{\eta}_2\lambda_2 = 0 \tag{2.41}$$

then

$$\ddot{y}_P = \eta_1\ddot{\lambda}_1 + \eta_1\ddot{\lambda}_2 + \dot{\eta}_1\dot{\lambda}_1 + \dot{\eta}_2\dot{\lambda}_2 \tag{2.42}$$

Substitution of (2.39), (2.40), and (2.42) into the original differential equation (2.30) yields

$$(\ddot{\lambda}_1 + \alpha_1\dot{\lambda}_1 + \alpha_0\lambda_1)\eta_1 + (\ddot{\lambda}_2 + \alpha_1\dot{\lambda}_2 + \alpha_0\lambda_2)\eta_2 + \dot{\lambda}_1\dot{\eta}_1 + \dot{\lambda}_2\dot{\eta}_2 \\ = \beta_0 u + \beta_1\dot{u} + \beta_2\ddot{u}$$

But since λ_1 and λ_2 are solutions of the homogeneous equation, the above expression reduces to

$$\dot{\lambda}_1\dot{\eta}_1 + \dot{\lambda}_2\dot{\eta}_2 = \beta_0 u + \beta_1\dot{u} + \beta_2\ddot{u} \tag{2.43}$$

Expressions (2.43) and (2.41) may be solved simultaneously to yield

$$\dot{\eta}_1 = (\dot{\lambda}_1 - \lambda_1\lambda_2^{-1}\dot{\lambda}_2)^{-1}(\beta_0 u + \beta_1\dot{u} + \beta_2\ddot{u}) \tag{2.44a}$$

and

$$\eta_2 = (\dot{\lambda}_2 - \lambda_2\lambda_1^{-1}\dot{\lambda}_1)^{-1}(\beta_0 u + \beta_1\dot{u} + \beta_2\ddot{u}) \tag{2.44b}$$

Consider first the case of distinct roots. Then the above expressions reduce to

$$\dot{\eta}_1(t) = \frac{e^{-s_1 t}}{s_1 - s_2}(\beta_0 u + \beta_1\dot{u} + \beta_2\ddot{u})$$

and

$$\dot{\eta}_2(t) = \frac{-e^{-s_2 t}}{s_1 - s_2}(\beta_0 u + \beta_1\dot{u} + \beta_2\ddot{u})$$

so that

$$\eta_1(t) = \int_{t_0}^{t} \frac{e^{-s_1\tau}}{s_1 - s_2}[\beta_0 u(\tau) + \beta_1\dot{u}(\tau) + \beta_2\ddot{u}(\tau)]\,d\tau$$

and

$$\eta_2(t) = \int_{t_0}^{t} \frac{-e^{-s_2\tau}}{s_1 - s_2} [\beta_0 u(\tau) + \beta_1 \dot{u}(\tau) + \beta_2 \ddot{u}(\tau)]\, d\tau$$

Thus, the particular solution for the case of distinct roots is

$$y_P(t) = \int_{t_0}^{t} \frac{1}{s_1 - s_2} (e^{s_1(t-\tau)} - e^{s_2(t-\tau)})[\beta_0 u(\tau) + \beta_1 \dot{u}(\tau) + \beta_2 \ddot{u}(\tau)]\, d\tau$$

If the characteristic equation has repeated roots, then Eqs. (2.44) become

$$\dot{\eta}_1 = -te^{-s_1 t}(\beta_0 u + \beta_1 \dot{u} + \beta_2 \ddot{u})$$

and

$$\dot{\eta}_2 = e^{-s_1 t}(\beta_0 u + \beta_1 \dot{u} + \beta_2 \ddot{u})$$

so that the particular solution is

$$y_P(t) = \int_{t_0}^{t} e^{s_1(t-\tau)}(t - \tau)[\beta_0 u(\tau) + \beta_1 \dot{u}(\tau) + \beta_2 \ddot{u}(\tau)]\, d\tau$$

Therefore the complete solution of the second-order differential equation (2.30) is

$$(2.45)\quad y(t) = C_1 e^{s_1 t} + C_2 e^{s_2 t} + \int_{t_0}^{t} \frac{1}{s_1 - s_2} (e^{s_1(t-\tau)} - e^{s_2(t-\tau)})[\beta_0 u(\tau) + \beta_1 \dot{u}(\tau) + \beta_2 \ddot{u}(\tau)]\, d\tau$$

if $s_1 \neq s_2$ and

$$(2.46)\quad y(t) = (C_1 + C_2 t)e^{s_1 t} + \int_{t_0}^{t} e^{s_1(t-\tau)}(t - \tau)[\beta_0 u(\tau) + \beta_1 \dot{u}(\tau) + \beta_2 \ddot{u}(\tau)]\, d\tau$$

if $s_1 = s_2$. The constants C_1 and C_2 are determined by the initial conditions.

(2.47) Example

Consider again the system described in Example (2.38). The particular solution is

$$y_P(t) = \int_{t_0}^{t} [e^{-(t-\tau)} - e^{-2(t-\tau)}][3u(\tau) + 2\dot{u}(\tau)]\, d\tau$$

so that the complete solution is

$$y(t) = C_1 e^{-t} + C_2 e^{-2t} + \int_{t_0}^{t} [e^{-(t-\tau)} - e^{-2(t-\tau)}][3u(\tau) + 2\dot{u}(\tau)]\, d\tau$$

(2.48) Example

A second-order system is described by the state equations

$$\dot{x}_1 = x_2$$
$$\dot{x}_2 = -6x_1 - 5x_2 + u$$

and

$$y = x_1$$

This system can also be characterized by the second-order differential equation

$$\ddot{y} + 5\dot{y} + 6y = u$$

The two forms of description are related by

(2.49a) $x_1 = y$

and

(2.49b) $x_2 = \dot{y}$

From (2.45) we find the solution of the second-order differential equation to be

$$y(t) = C_1e^{-2t} + C_2e^{-3t} + \int_{t_0}^{t} [e^{-3(t-\tau)} - e^{-2(t-\tau)}]u(\tau)\, d\tau \tag{2.50}$$

It is also possible to find the solution of the state equations from (2.49) and (2.50):

$$x_1(t) = C_1e^{-2t} + C_2e^{-3t} + \int_{t_0}^{t} [e^{-2(t-\tau)} - e^{-3(t-\tau)}]u(\tau)\, d\tau$$

and

$$x_2(t) = -2C_1e^{-2t} - 3C_2e^{-3t} + \int_{t_0}^{t} [-2e^{-2(t-\tau)} + 3e^{-3(t-\tau)}]u(\tau)\, d\tau$$

Since $x_1(t_0) = x_{10}$ and $x_2(t_0) = x_{20}$, then it is relatively easy to show that

$$C_1 = 3e^{2t_0}x_{10} + e^{2t_0}x_{10}$$

and

$$C_2 = -2e^{3t_0}x_{10} - e^{3t_0}x_{10}$$

which can be checked by direct substitution. Therefore,

$$x_1(t) = (3e^{-2(t-t_0)} - 2e^{-3(t-t_0)})x_{10} + (e^{-2(t-t_0)} - e^{-3(t-t_0)})x_{20} + \int_{t_0}^{t} [e^{-2(t-\tau)} - e^{-3(t-\tau)}]u(\tau)\, d\tau$$

and

$$x_2(t) = (-6e^{-2(t-t_0)} + 6e^{-3(t-t_0)})x_{10} + (-2e^{-2(t-t_0)} + 3e^{-3(t-t_0)})x_{20} + \int_{t_0}^{t} [-2e^{-2(t-\tau)} + 3e^{-3(t-\tau)}]u(\tau)\, d\tau$$

∎

When deriving solutions to higher-order systems, we will find it very inconvenient to reduce a set of n first-order differential equations to an nth-order differential equation. Rather, the n first-order equations will be solved directly by matrix methods. By way of introduction to the more general solution, we set up our second-order state equations in matrix form and solve them by analogy with the first-order case.

The two coupled, first-order, differential state equations of a second-order system can be written in matrix form as follows: (Note: A complete discussion of matrices is to be given in Chap. 3.)

$$(2.51)\quad \begin{bmatrix} \dot{x}_1(t) \\ \dot{x}_2(t) \end{bmatrix} = \begin{bmatrix} a_{11} & a_{12} \\ a_{21} & a_{22} \end{bmatrix} \begin{bmatrix} x_1(t) \\ x_2(t) \end{bmatrix} + \begin{bmatrix} b_1 \\ b_2 \end{bmatrix} u(t)$$

or more succinctly as

$$(2.52)\quad \dot{\mathbf{x}}(t) = \mathbf{A}\mathbf{x}(t) + \mathbf{B}\mathbf{u}(t)$$

where

$$\dot{\mathbf{x}}(t) = \begin{bmatrix} x_1(t) \\ x_2(t) \end{bmatrix} \quad \text{is the state vector}$$

$$\mathbf{A} = \begin{bmatrix} a_{11} & a_{12} \\ a_{21} & a_{22} \end{bmatrix}$$

$$\mathbf{b} = \begin{bmatrix} b_1 \\ b_2 \end{bmatrix}$$

Until the reader becomes more familiar with matrix techniques, he should look upon matrices simply as a bookkeeping method. We will attempt to arrive at a solution of (2.52) in a manner analogous to that used to find a solution for the scalar, first-order differential equation

$$(2.53)\quad \dot{x}(t) = ax(t) + bu(t)$$

Consider first the homogeneous equation

$$(2.54)\quad \dot{\mathbf{x}}(t) = \mathbf{A}\mathbf{x}(t)$$

or

$$\begin{bmatrix} \dot{x}_1(t) \\ \dot{x}_2(t) \end{bmatrix} = \begin{bmatrix} a_{11} & a_{12} \\ a_{21} & a_{22} \end{bmatrix} \begin{bmatrix} x_1(t) \\ x_2(t) \end{bmatrix}$$

Recall that the solution to the scalar homogeneous equation associated with (2.53) is

$$x(t) = e^{a(t-t_0)}x_0$$

Therefore we are led to try as the solution to (2.54)

$$(2.55)\quad \mathbf{x}(t) = e^{\mathbf{A}(t-t_0)}\mathbf{x}_0$$

where the matrix $e^{\mathbf{A}t}$ is defined by

$$(2.56)\quad e^{\mathbf{A}t} = \mathbf{1}_2 + \mathbf{A}t + \frac{\mathbf{A}^2}{2!}t^2 + \frac{\mathbf{A}^3}{3!}t^3 + \cdots$$

where

$$\mathbf{1}_2 = \begin{bmatrix} 1 & 0 \\ 0 & 1 \end{bmatrix} \qquad \text{is the } 2 \times 2 \text{ identity matrix,}$$
$$\mathbf{A}^2 = \mathbf{A} \cdot \mathbf{A}$$
$$\mathbf{A}^3 = \mathbf{A} \cdot \mathbf{A}^2 = \mathbf{A} \cdot \mathbf{A} \cdot \mathbf{A} \quad \cdots$$

We can verify that (2.55) is indeed the solution to (2.54) by direct substitution. First, note that upon differentiation, (2.56) becomes

$$\begin{aligned} \frac{d}{dt} e^{\mathbf{A}t} &= \mathbf{A} + \mathbf{A}^2 t + \frac{\mathbf{A}^3}{2!} t^2 + \frac{\mathbf{A}^4}{3!} t^3 + \cdots \\ &= \mathbf{A}[\mathbf{1}_2 + \mathbf{A}t + \frac{\mathbf{A}^2}{2!} t^2 + \frac{\mathbf{A}^3}{3!} t^3 + \cdots] \\ &= \mathbf{A}e^{\mathbf{A}t} \end{aligned}$$

Thus we have

$$\begin{aligned} \frac{d}{dt} \mathbf{x}(t) &= \frac{d}{dt} [e^{\mathbf{A}(t-t_0)} \mathbf{x}(t_0)] \\ &= \left[\frac{d}{dt} e^{\mathbf{A}(t-t_0)} \right] \mathbf{x}(t_0) \\ &= \mathbf{A}e^{\mathbf{A}(t-t_0)} \mathbf{x}(t_0) \\ &= \mathbf{A}\mathbf{x}(t) \end{aligned}$$

which demonstrates the validity of the homogeneous solution (2.55).

(2.57) Example

In Example (2.38) we introduced a system described by

$$\begin{aligned} x_1(t) &= -x_1(t) + x_2(t) \\ \dot{x}_2(t) &= -2x_2(t) + u(t) \end{aligned}$$

and

$$\dot{y}(t) = x_1(t) + 2x_2(t)$$

The **A** matrix is

$$\mathbf{A} = \begin{bmatrix} -1 & 1 \\ 0 & -2 \end{bmatrix}$$

Hence the solution to the homogeneous equation

$$\dot{\mathbf{x}}(t) = \mathbf{A}\mathbf{x}(t)$$

is

$$\mathbf{x}(t) = e^{\mathbf{A}(t-t_0)} \mathbf{x}(t_0)$$

From (2.56)

$$e^{\mathbf{A}t} = \begin{bmatrix} 1 & 0 \\ 0 & 1 \end{bmatrix} + \begin{bmatrix} -1 & 1 \\ 0 & -2 \end{bmatrix} t + \begin{bmatrix} 1 & -3 \\ 0 & 4 \end{bmatrix} \frac{t^2}{2!} + \begin{bmatrix} -1 & 7 \\ 0 & -8 \end{bmatrix} \frac{t^3}{3!} + \cdots$$

$$= \begin{bmatrix} 1 - t + \dfrac{t^2}{2!} - \dfrac{t^3}{3!} + \cdots & 0 + t - \dfrac{3}{2!} + \dfrac{7}{3!} t^3 + \cdots \\ 0 & 1 - 2t + \dfrac{4t^2}{2!} - \dfrac{8t^3}{3!} \end{bmatrix}$$

$$= \begin{bmatrix} e^{-t} & e^{-t} - e^{-2t} \\ 0 & e^{-2t} \end{bmatrix}$$

Therefore, the homogeneous solution becomes

$$\begin{bmatrix} x_1(t) \\ x_2(t) \end{bmatrix} = \begin{bmatrix} e^{-(t-t_0)} & e^{-(t-t_0)} - e^{-2(t-t_0)} \\ 0 & e^{-2(t-t_0)} \end{bmatrix} \begin{bmatrix} x_1(t_0) \\ x_2(t_0) \end{bmatrix}$$

Combining the above result with the input-state-output relation, we have

$$y(t) = \hat{C}_1 e^{-t} + \hat{C}_2 e^{-2t}$$

where the constants $\hat{C}_1$ and $\hat{C}_2$ are defined as

$$\hat{C}_1 \equiv e^{t_0}(x_1(t_0) + x_2(t_0))$$

and

$$\hat{C}_2 \equiv e^{2t_0} x(t_0)$$

Observe that the above result agrees with that obtained in Example (2.38). ▮

(2.58) Example

Consider again the system discussed in Example (2.48) which was described by the state equations

$$\dot{x}_1 = x_2$$

and

$$\dot{x}_2 = -6x_1 - 5x_2 + u$$

These equations may be rewritten as

$$\begin{bmatrix} \dot{x}_1 \\ \dot{x}_2 \end{bmatrix} = \begin{bmatrix} 0 & 1 \\ -6 & -5 \end{bmatrix} \begin{bmatrix} x_1 \\ x_2 \end{bmatrix} + \begin{bmatrix} 0 \\ 1 \end{bmatrix} u$$

and the homogeneous equation is

$$\dot{\mathbf{x}} = \mathbf{A}\mathbf{x}$$

where

$$\mathbf{A} = \begin{bmatrix} 0 & 1 \\ -6 & -5 \end{bmatrix}$$

From (2.56)

$$e^{\mathbf{A}t} = \begin{bmatrix} 1 & 0 \\ 0 & 1 \end{bmatrix} + \begin{bmatrix} 0 & 1 \\ -6 & 2 \end{bmatrix} t + \begin{bmatrix} -6 & 2 \\ 30 & -16 \end{bmatrix} \frac{t^2}{2!} + \begin{bmatrix} 30 & -16 \\ -114 & 68 \end{bmatrix} \frac{t^3}{3!} + \cdots$$

$$= \begin{bmatrix} 1 - \frac{6t^2}{2!} + \frac{30t^3}{3!} - \cdots & t + \frac{2t^2}{2!} + \frac{16t^3}{3!} + \cdots \\ -6t + \frac{30t^2}{2!} - \frac{114}{3!} t^3 + \cdots & 1 + 2t - \frac{16t^2}{2!} + \frac{68t^3}{3!} - \cdots \end{bmatrix}$$

which is seen to be

$$e^{\mathbf{A}t} = \begin{bmatrix} 3e^{-2t} - 2e^{-3t} & e^{-2t} - e^{-3t} \\ -6e^{-2t} + 6e^{-3t} & -2e^{-2t} + 3e^{-3t} \end{bmatrix}$$

Therefore the solution of the homogeneous equation is

$$\begin{bmatrix} x_1(t) \\ x_2(t) \end{bmatrix} = \begin{bmatrix} 3e^{-2(t-t_0)} - 2e^{-3(t-t_0)} & e^{-2(t-t_0)} - e^{-3(t-t_0)} \\ -6e^{-2(t-t_0)} + 6e^{-3(t-t_0)} & -2e^{-2(t-t_0)} + 3e^{-3(t-t_0)} \end{bmatrix} \begin{bmatrix} x_{10} \\ x_{20} \end{bmatrix}$$

This result agrees with that of Example (2.48). ▮

Let us now turn to the complete solution. In Chap. 1, the complete solution to the scalar, first-order differential equation (2.53) was found to be

$$x(t) = e^{a(t-t_0)}x(t_0) + \int_{t_0}^{t} e^{a(t-\tau)}bu(\tau)\, d\tau$$

By analogy then, we try as the complete solution to the matrix differential equation (2.52)

$$\text{(2.59)} \quad \mathbf{x}(t) = e^{\mathbf{A}(t-t_0)}\mathbf{x}(t_0) + \int_{t_0}^{t} e^{\mathbf{A}(t-\tau)}\mathbf{b}u(\tau)\, d\tau$$

(Note: When performing any linear operation on a matrix, such as integration or differentiation, the operation must be applied individually to each element of the matrix.) This equation is seen to be the correct solution upon differentiation:

$$\dot{\mathbf{x}}(t) = \frac{d}{dt}[e^{\mathbf{A}(t-t_0)}\mathbf{x}(t_0)] + e^{\mathbf{A}(t-t)}\mathbf{b}\mathbf{u}(t) + \int_{t_0}^{t} \frac{d}{dt} e^{\mathbf{A}(t-\tau)}\mathbf{b}u(\tau)\, d\tau$$

but

$$\frac{d}{dt} e^{\mathbf{A}t} = \mathbf{A}e^{\mathbf{A}t}$$

and

$$e^{\mathbf{A}(t-t)} = \mathbf{1}$$

so that

$$\begin{aligned}\dot{\mathbf{x}}(t) &= \mathbf{A}\left[\mathbf{e}^{\mathbf{A}(t-t_0)}\mathbf{x}(t_0) + \int_{t_0}^{t} e^{\mathbf{A}(t-\tau)}\mathbf{b}u(\tau)\,d\tau\right] + \mathbf{b}u(\tau)\\ &= \mathbf{A}\mathbf{x}(t) + \mathbf{b}u(t)\end{aligned}$$

(2.60) Example

Let us find the complete response of the system discussed in Examples (2.38) and (2.57) for $t_0 = 0$ and $u(t) = 1$. The state equations are

$$\begin{aligned}\dot{x}_1 &= -x_1 + x_2\\ \dot{x}_2 &= -2x_2 + u\end{aligned}$$

and

$$y = x_1 + 2x_2$$

Therefore

$$\begin{aligned}\int_0^t e^{\mathbf{A}(t-\tau)}\mathbf{b}u(\tau)\,d\tau &= \int_0^t \begin{bmatrix} e^{-(t-\tau)} & e^{-(t-\tau)} - e^{-2(t-\tau)} \\ 0 & e^{-2(t-\tau)} \end{bmatrix}\begin{bmatrix}0\\1\end{bmatrix} u(\tau)\,d\tau\\ &= \begin{bmatrix} \frac{1}{2} - e^{-t} + \frac{e^{-2t}}{2} \\ \frac{1}{2} - \frac{e^{-2t}}{2} \end{bmatrix}\end{aligned}$$

Assume the initial conditions

$$\mathbf{x}(t_0) = \begin{bmatrix}-1\\0\end{bmatrix}$$

then combining the above result with that of Example (2.57), the complete solution is found to be

$$\mathbf{x}(t) = \begin{bmatrix} \frac{1}{2} - 2e^{-t} + \frac{e^{-2t}}{2} \\ \frac{1}{2} - \frac{e^{-2t}}{2} \end{bmatrix}$$

and the input-state-output relation becomes

$$y(t) = \tfrac{3}{2} - 2e^{-t} - \tfrac{1}{2}e^{-2t}$$ ∎

In Chap. 1 we had no particular difficulty finding a solution to first-order, linear, *time-variable* systems. Unfortunately, extension of this solution to the second-order case is not as straightforward as what we have outlined above for time-invariant systems. Since sufficient background in matrix theory has not been presented as yet, it is not possible to show exactly where problems arise in extending the first-order time-variable solution to second-order systems. This topic will be investigated in Chap. 4.

2.5 THE PHASE PLANE: A GEOMETRIC ANALYSIS OF SECOND-ORDER SYSTEMS

In this section we present a geometric interpretation of the solution of the second-order state equations

$$(2.61a)\quad \dot{x}_1(t) = f_1(x_1(t),x_2(t),u(t),t)$$

and

$$(2.61b)\quad \dot{x}_2(t) = f_2(x_1(t),x_2(t),u(t),t)$$

Since the state variables $x_1(t)$ and $x_2(t)$ are independent, we can think of them as being the two coordinates of a two-dimensional cartesian coordinate system with parameter t. This association leads to the following definition.

(2.62) State space

The two-dimensional *state space* or *phase plane* of a second-order system is the plane defined by considering the two state variables as rectangular coordinates in a two-dimensional space. ∎

For convenience, we will use vector notation and let the state variables $x_1(t)$ and $x_2(t)$ be denoted by the two-dimensional *state vector* $x(t)$:

$$x(t) = \begin{bmatrix} x_1(t) \\ x_2(t) \end{bmatrix}$$

Any state vector can be represented in the phase plane as shown in Fig. 2.10.

We can plot on the phase plane the locus of points generated by the tip of the state vector as time increases. Such a plot is referred to as the motion or *trajectory* of a system. It is important to indicate the direction of the trajectory on a phase-plane plot. The direction of the trajectory can be found by calculating its slope at any point

$$\frac{dx_1}{dx_2}$$

An example of a system trajectory is shown in Fig. 2.11.

Before continuing our discussion about the phase plane, we extend the definition of an equilibrium state to include second-order systems.

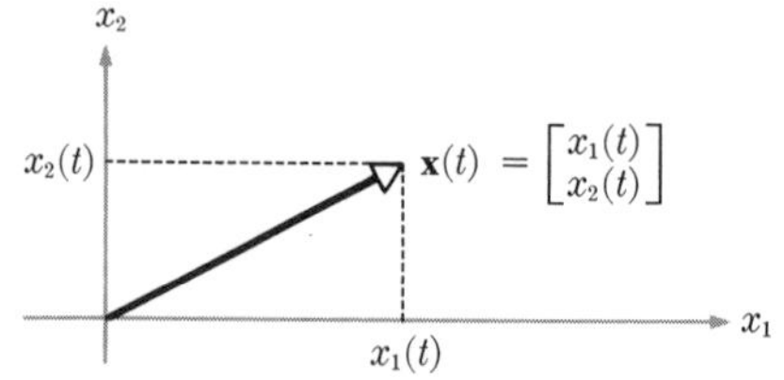

FIG. 2.10 The two-dimensional state space or phase plane defined by the state variables x_1 and x_2 and an arbitrary state vector $x(t)$.

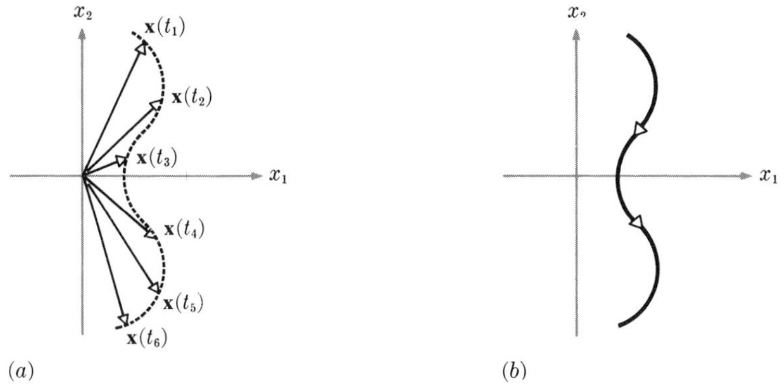

FIG. 2.11 (*a*) The motion of the state vector as time increases, and (*b*) the trajectory system.

(2.63) Equilibrium state

An *equilibrium state* is any state $\mathbf{x}_e = \begin{bmatrix} x_{e1} \\ x_{e2} \end{bmatrix}$ in which the system remains when subject to the zero input; because $\dot{x}_{e1} = 0$ and $\dot{x}_{e2} = 0$, the equilibrium states (if any) can be found from

$$f_1(x_{e1},x_{e2},0,t) = 0$$

and

$$f_2(x_{e1},x_{e2},0,t) = 0$$

for any $t_0 \le t < \infty$. ∎

Equilibrium states are sometimes called *critical, singular*, or *null points*.

Note that no trajectories can cross each other in the state space. This fact follows from uniqueness of the solution of the differential-state equations. Moreover, since an equilibrium point is itself a trajectory, that is, $\mathbf{x}(t) = \mathbf{x}_e(t)$ is a solution of the differential-state equation, no trajectory can pass through an equilibrium state, although trajectories may get arbitrarily close to singular points as time goes to infinity.

In order to pursue the idea of one vector approaching another, we must define in some suitable manner what we mean by "length" in two dimensions.

(2.64) Norm of a vector

The "size," or "length," of a two-dimensional vector $\mathbf{x}$, denoted by $\|\mathbf{x}\|$, is called the norm of $\mathbf{x}$. The *norm of a vector* is a real, nonnegative number $\|\mathbf{x}\|$ which has the properties

(1) $\|\mathbf{x}\| = 0$ if and only if $\mathbf{x} = \mathbf{0}$, that is, $x_1 = 0$ and $x_2 = 0$.
(2) $\|c\mathbf{x}\| = |c|\,\|\mathbf{x}\|$ for all scalars c and all vectors $\mathbf{x}$.

(3) $\|\mathbf{x}_1 + \mathbf{x}_2\| \leq \|\mathbf{x}_1\| + \|\mathbf{x}_2\|$ for all $\mathbf{x}_1$, $\mathbf{x}_2$ (this relation is known as the triangle inequality). ∎

Three of the most common norms are

$$\|\mathbf{x}\|_1 = |x_1| + |x_2|$$

$$\|\mathbf{x}\|_2 = \sqrt{x_1^2 + x_2^2}$$

and

$$\|\mathbf{x}\|_\infty = \max\,(|x_1|,|x_2|)$$

We leave it as an exercise for the reader (Prob. 2.12) to show that these norms do indeed satisfy the requisite properties given by definition (2.64).

The idea of trajectories approaching equilibrium states can now be formalized. A trajectory $\mathbf{x}(t)$ is said to *approach* an equilibrium state $\mathbf{x}_e$ as $t \rightarrow \pm\infty$ if

$$\lim_{t \rightarrow \pm\infty} \|\mathbf{x}(t) - \mathbf{x}_e(t)\| = 0 \tag{2.65}$$

A trajectory $\mathbf{x}(t)$ is said to *enter* an equilibrium state $\mathbf{x}_e$ as $t \rightarrow \pm\infty$ if it approaches $\mathbf{x}_e$, and if the following limits exist:

$$\lim_{t \rightarrow \pm\infty} \frac{x_1(t) - x_{1e}(t)}{\|\mathbf{x}(t) - \mathbf{x}_e(t)\|} < \infty \tag{2.66a}$$

and

$$\lim_{t \rightarrow \pm\infty} \frac{x_2(t) - x_{2e}(t)}{\|\mathbf{x}(t) - \mathbf{x}_e(t)\|} < \infty \tag{2.66b}$$

Note that if the *euclidean norm* is used,

$$\|\mathbf{x}\|_2 = \sqrt{x_1^2 + x_2^2}$$

then the ratios defined by (2.66*a*) and (2.66*b*) are *direction cosines* of the trajectory as it approaches $\mathbf{x}_e$. Hence, if a trajectory *enters* a singular point, its direction of entrance is well defined at that point. The concepts of a trajectory approaching a point and entering a point are shown in Fig. 2.12.

It is convenient to define several types of points in the phase plane. Any point in the phase plane through which a trajectory may pass is called a *regular* point. Note that an equilibrium point is *not* a regular point. An equilibrium point is said to be *isolated* if there are only regular points in a small neighborhood about it. Most systems encountered have only isolated equilibrium points, although there are some cases of interest when this is not true.

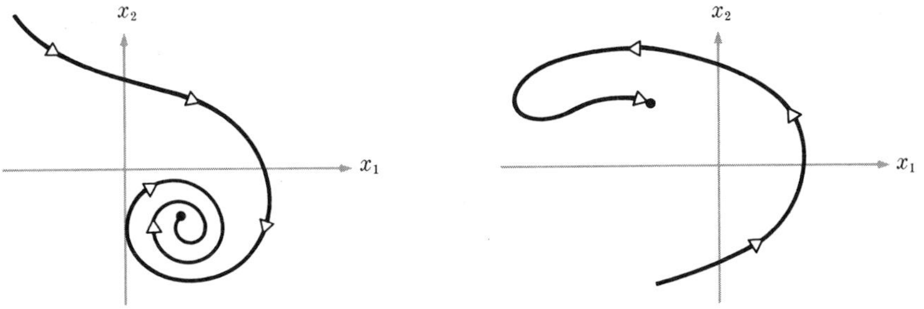

(a) (b)

FIG. 2.12 Examples of trajectories which (a) approach and (b) enter equilibrium points.

(2.67) Example

Consider a system described by

$$\dot{x}_1 = x_1 + 2x_2$$

and

$$\dot{x}_2 = 2x_1 + 4x_2$$

To find the equilibrium states, we must solve the dependent equations

$$x_1 + 2x_2 = 0$$

and

$$2x_1 + 4x_2 = 0$$

Any point on the line

$$x_2 = -\tfrac{1}{2}x_1$$

is an equilibrium state! Hence they are not isolated. ∎

Note that for linear time-invariant systems, described by

$$\dot{x}_1 = a_{11}x_1 + a_{12}x_2$$
$$\dot{x}_2 = a_{21}x_1 + a_{22}x_2$$

the origin is the unique equilibrium state, and hence isolated, if

$$a_{11}a_{22} - a_{12}a_{21} \neq 0$$

An equilibrium state $\mathbf{x}_e$ of a second-order system described by

$$\dot{x}_1 = f_1(x_1,x_2,t)$$

and

$$\dot{x}_2 = f_2(x_1,x_2,t)$$

is said to be *simple* if the corresponding *jacobian* determinant is nonzero:

$$\left.\frac{\partial f_1}{\partial x_1}\right|_e \left.\frac{\partial f_2}{\partial x_2}\right|_{\mathbf{x}_e} - \left.\frac{\partial f_1}{\partial x_2}\right| \left.\frac{\partial f_2}{\partial x_1}\right|_{\mathbf{x}_e} \neq 0$$

otherwise, it is *nonsimple.* If an equilibrium point is simple, it is isolated; the converse is not necessarily true, except for linear time-invariant systems.

For the remainder of our studies of the phase plane, we assume that the linear time-invariant system under consideration is characterized by the second-order differential equation

$$(2.68) \quad \ddot{y} + \alpha_1\dot{y} + \alpha_0 y = 0$$

It is easy to ascertain that the following differential-state equations also describe the system:

$$\dot{x}_1 = x_2$$
$$\dot{x}_2 = -\alpha_0 x_1 - \alpha_1 x_2$$

i.e., we have taken

$$x_1 = y$$

and

$$x_2 = \dot{y}$$

as the state variables. We know from earlier considerations that the characteristic equation associated with Eq. (2.68) is

$$(2.69) \quad s^2 + \alpha_1 s + \alpha_0 = 0$$

and that the solution to (2.68) is

$$y_1 = C_1 e^{s_1 t} + C_2 e^{s_2 t}$$

if $s_1 \neq s_2$ and

$$y_1 = C_1 e^{s_1 t} + C_2 t e^{s_1 t}$$

if $s_1 = s_2$ where

$$s_1 = \frac{-\alpha_1}{2} + \sqrt{\left(\frac{\alpha_1}{2}\right)^2 - \alpha_0}$$

and

$$s_2 = \frac{-\alpha_1}{2} - \sqrt{\left(\frac{\alpha_1}{2}\right)^2 - \alpha_0}$$

Expressions for the state solutions are easily obtained as

$$(2.70a) \quad x_1(t) = \begin{cases} C_1 e^{s_1 t} + C_2 e^{s_2 t} & \text{if } s_1 \neq s_2 \\ C_1 e^{s_1 t} + C_2 t e^{s_1 t} & \text{if } s_1 = s_2 \end{cases}$$

and

$$(2.70b) \quad x_2(t) = \begin{cases} C_1 s_1 e^{s_1 t} + C_2 s_2 e^{s_2 t} & \text{if } s_1 \neq s_2 \\ (C_1 s_1 + C_2) e^{s_1 t} + C_2 s_1 t e^{s_1 t} & \text{if } s_1 = s_2 \end{cases}$$

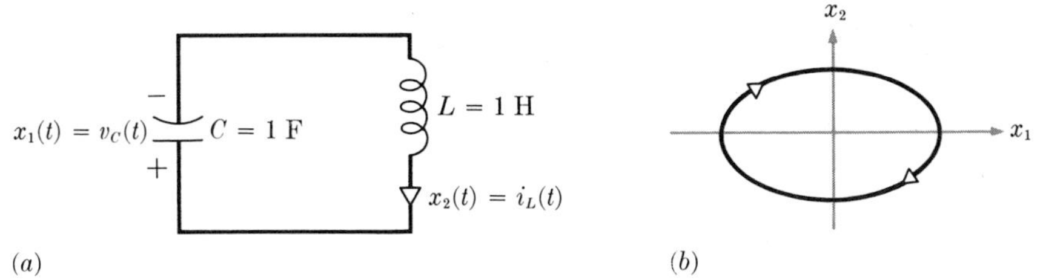

FIG. 2.13 (a) A second-order oscillatory system, and (b) its phase-plane plot.

The phase-plane trajectory for this system will vary considerably depending on the values of α_1 and α_0. Several examples illustrate this fact.

(2.71) Example
Consider the system in Fig. 2.13a which is described by

$$\dot{x}_1 = x_2 \qquad x_1(0) = x_{10}$$

and

$$\dot{x}_2 = -x_1 \qquad x_2(0) = x_{20}$$

or by

$$\ddot{y} + y = 0 \qquad y(0) = x_{10} \qquad \dot{y}(0) = x_{20}$$

The solution to the second-order differential equation is

$$y(t) = C_1e^{-jt} + C_2e^{jt}$$

so that

$$x_1(t) = C_1e^{-jt} + C_2e^{jt}$$

and

$$x_2(t) = -jC_1e^{-jt} + jC_2e^{jt}$$

The constants C_1 and C_2 may be ascertained by evaluating $x_1(t)$ and $x_2(t)$ at the initial condition $t = 0$:

$$x_1(0) = C_1 + C_2 = x_{10}$$
$$x_2(0) = -jC_1 + jC_2 = x_{20}$$

Thus

$$x_1(t) = \tfrac{1}{2}(x_{10} + jx_{20})e^{-jt} + \tfrac{1}{2}(x_{10} - jx_{20})e^{jt}$$

and

$$x_2(t) = \tfrac{1}{2}(x_{20} - jx_{10})e^{-jt} + \tfrac{1}{2}(x_{20} + jx_{10})e^{jt}$$

and finally

$$x_1(t) = x_{10}\cos t + x_{20}\sin t$$

and

$$x_2(t) = x_{20}\cos t - x_{10}\sin t$$

The motion of the system is oscillatory, and the phase-plane plot is shown in Fig. 2.13b. The simple equilibrium state **0** is called a center. Notice that the trajectory does not enter or approach this equilibrium state. Also, since any motion which starts near the equilibrium state always remains near it, the system is said to be *stable,* but not *asymptotically stable.* (Compare with stability of first-order systems discussed in the preceding chapter.) ▮

(2.72) Example

Consider the RLC network shown in Fig. 2-14*a*. The differential-state equations can be written as

$$\dot{x}_1(t) = x_2(t) \qquad x_1(0) = x_{10}$$

and

$$\dot{x}_2(t) = -x_1(t) - Rx_2(t) \qquad x_2(0) = x_{20}$$

which reduces to the second-order differential equation

$$\ddot{y} + R\dot{y} + y = 0 \qquad y(0) = x_{10} \qquad \dot{y}(0) = x_{20}$$

The associated characteristic equation is

$$s^2 + Rs + 1 = 0$$

so that the solution is

$$y(t) = C_1e^{s_1t} + C_2e^{s_2t}$$

where

$$s_1 = \frac{-R}{2} + \sqrt{\left(\frac{R}{2}\right)^2 - 1}$$

and

$$s_2 = \frac{-R}{2} - \sqrt{\left(\frac{R}{2}\right)^2 - 1}$$

After some manipulation we have that

$$x_1(t) = \begin{cases} \dfrac{x_{20} - s_2x_{10}}{s_1 - s_2}e^{s_1t} + \dfrac{s_1x_{10} - x_{20}}{s_1 - s_2}e^{s_2t} & \text{if } s_1 \neq s_2 \\ x_{10}e^{s_1t} + (x_{20} - s_1x_{10})te^{s_1t} & \text{if } s_1 = s_2 \end{cases}$$

and

$$x_2(t) = \begin{cases} \dfrac{s_1(x_{20} - s_2x_{10})}{s_1 - s_2}e^{s_1t} + \dfrac{s_2(s_1x_{10} - x_{20})}{s_1 - s_2}e^{s_2t} & \text{if } s_1 \neq s_2 \\ s_1x_{10}e^{s_1t} + (x_{20} - s_1x_{10})(1 + s_1t)e^{s_1t} & \text{if } s_1 = s_2 \end{cases}$$

Assume that R is greater than 2 Ω, in particular let $R = 3$ Ω, then

$$s_1 = -0.62 \qquad s_2 = -2.62$$

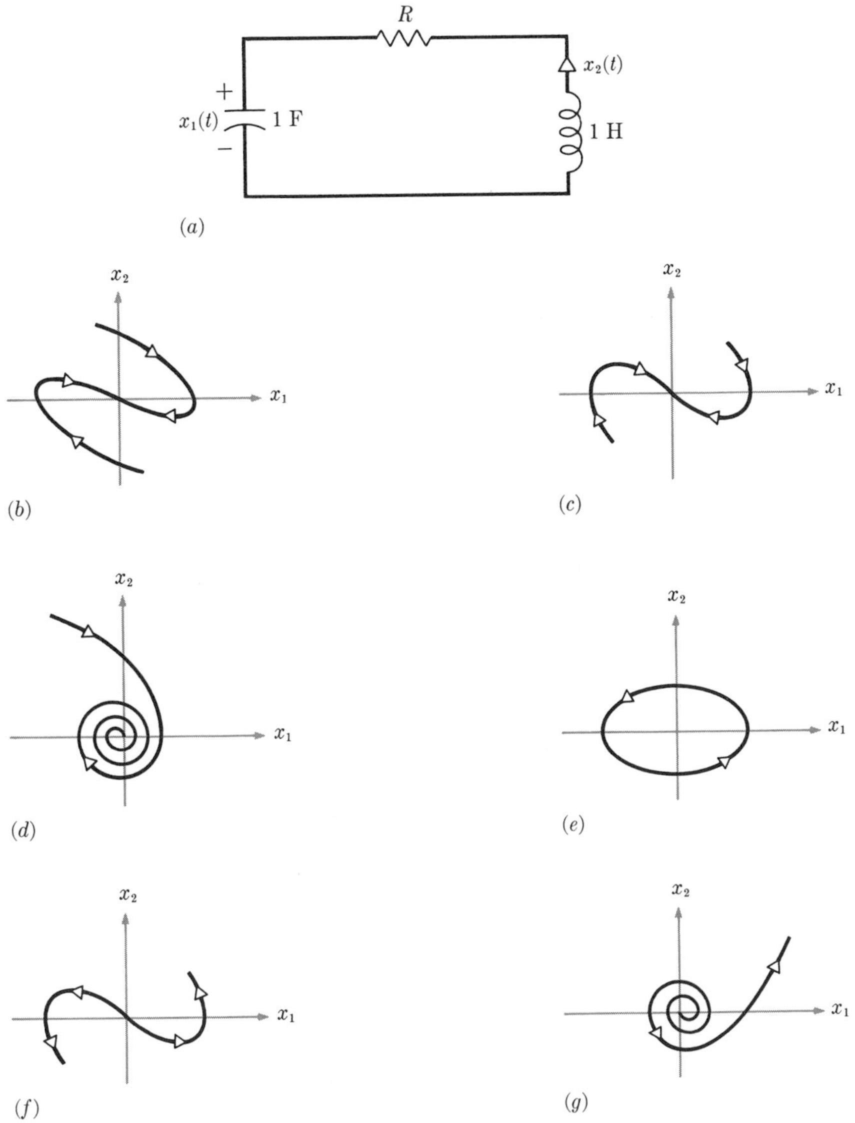

FIG. 2.14 (*a*) A simple RLC network and possible phase-plane trajectories, (*b*) and (*c*) show stable nodes for $R \geq 2$, (*d*) shows a stable focus for $0 < R < 2$, (*e*) shows a center for $R = 0$, (*f*) shows an unstable node for $R \leq -2$, (*g*) shows an unstable focus for $-2 < R < 0$.

For convenience let $x_{10} = 1$ and $x_{20} = 1$, then

$$x_1(t) = \frac{3.62}{2} e^{-0.62t} - \frac{0.62}{2} e^{-2.62t}$$

and

$$x_2(t) = \frac{-2.24}{2} e^{-0.62t} + \frac{4.24}{2} e^{-2.62t}$$

The motion of the system is exponential decay (overdamped), and the trajectory enters the isolated equilibrium point as $t \to \infty$. This equilibrium point is asymptotically stable and is called a *stable node*. The trajectory is shown in Fig. 2.14*b*.

Now assume $R = 2\ \Omega$, then

$$s_1 = s_2 = -1$$

and if $x_{10} = 1$ and $x_{20} = 1$ then

$$x_1(t) = e^{-t} + 2te^{-t}$$

and

$$x_2(t) = e^{-t} + 2te^{-t}$$

The trajectory is shown in Fig. 2.14*c*, and the equilibrium state is once again a stable node. This situation is that of critical damping.

If $R > 0$ but $R < 2$, for example, let $R = 1$, the resulting motion is underdamped. We have for this case,

$$s_1 = \frac{-1 + j\sqrt{3}}{2} \qquad s_2 = \frac{-1 - j\sqrt{3}}{2}$$

and if $x_{10} = 1$ and $x_{20} = 1$, then

$$x_{10} = e^{-\frac{1}{2}t} \left[\cos \frac{\sqrt{3}}{2} t + \frac{2}{\sqrt{3}} \sin \frac{\sqrt{3}}{2} t \right]$$

and

$$x_{20} = e^{-\frac{1}{2}t} \left[\cos \frac{\sqrt{3}}{2} t - \frac{2}{\sqrt{3}} \sin \frac{\sqrt{3}}{2} t \right]$$

This motion corresponds to damped oscillation as shown in Fig. 2.14*d*. The equilibrium state is known as a *stable focus* and is asymptotically stable. We leave it as an exercise for the reader to show that

(1) If $R = 0$, the simple equilibrium point is stable (called a *center*) and the trajectory neither approaches nor enters this point (see Fig. 2.14*e*).
(2) If $R \leq -2$, the trajectory "enters" the *unstable node* at $t \to -\infty$. This situation is shown in Fig. 2.14*f*.
(3) If $-2 < R < 0$, the trajectory "approaches" the *unstable focus* at $t \to -\infty$. This situation is shown in Fig. 2.14*g*. ∎

2.6 DISCRETE-TIME SYSTEMS

Second-order, linear, time-invariant, discrete-time systems are characterized by second-order difference equations of the form

$$(2.73)\quad y(k+2) + \alpha_1 y(k+1) + \alpha_0 y(k) = \beta_0 u(k) + \beta_1 u(k+1) + \beta_2 u(k+2)$$

or by discrete-time state equations of the form

$$(2.74a)\quad x_1(k+1) = a_{11}x_1(k) + a_{12}x_2(k) + b_1 u(k)$$
$$(2.74b)\quad x_2(k+1) = a_{21}x_1(k) + a_{22}x_2(k) + b_2 u(k)$$

and

$$(2.74c)\quad y(k) = c_1 x_1(k) + c_2 x_2(k) + du(k)$$

We leave as an exercise for the reader the solution of (2.73) and undertake here the solution of (2.74). First let us rewrite (2.74) in matrix form as

$$(2.75a)\quad \mathbf{x}(k+1) = \mathbf{A}\mathbf{x}(k) + \mathbf{b}u(k)$$

and

$$(2.75b)\quad y(k) = \mathbf{C}\mathbf{x}(k) + du(k)$$

where

$$\mathbf{x}(k) = \begin{bmatrix} x_1(k) \\ x_2(k) \end{bmatrix} \qquad \mathbf{b} = \begin{bmatrix} b_1 \\ b_2 \end{bmatrix}$$

$$\mathbf{A} = \begin{bmatrix} a_{11} & a_{12} \\ a_{21} & a_{22} \end{bmatrix}$$

and

$$\mathbf{C} = [c_1 \quad c_2]$$

Then we have

$$\mathbf{x}(1) = \mathbf{A}\mathbf{x}(0) + \mathbf{b}u(0)$$
$$\mathbf{x}(2) = \mathbf{A}\mathbf{x}(1) + \mathbf{b}u(1) = \mathbf{A}^2\mathbf{x}(0) + \mathbf{A}\mathbf{b}u(0) + \mathbf{b}u(1)$$
$$\mathbf{x}(3) = \mathbf{A}\mathbf{x}(2) + \mathbf{b}u(2) = \mathbf{A}^3\mathbf{x}(0) + \mathbf{A}^2\mathbf{b}u(0) + \mathbf{A}\mathbf{b}u(1) + \mathbf{b}u(2)$$

or in general

$$\mathbf{x}(k) = \mathbf{A}^k\mathbf{x}(0) + \sum_{j=0}^{k-1} \mathbf{A}^j\mathbf{b}u(k-1-j)$$

Therefore solution of (2.75) is

$$(2.76)\quad \mathbf{y}(k) = \mathbf{C}\mathbf{A}^k\mathbf{x}(0) + \sum_{j=0}^{k-1} \mathbf{C}\mathbf{A}^j\mathbf{b}u(k-1-j) + du(k)$$

We depart from completion of the discussion of second-order systems until after some elementary matrix techniques are introduced in the next chapter. These methods will be helpful in evaluation of the indicated summation of expression (2.76).

2.7 SUMMARY

The introduction of second-order systems has allowed us to demonstrate a little more clearly the fundamental concepts of system theory. Inherently, there is an increase of mathematical complexity, and the scalar notation of Chap. 1 has become cumbersome in this second-order study. This problem was reduced by using *matrix notation.*

Second-order differential equations can be transformed to coupled, first-order differential equations. This transformation is not unique, and the first-order equations which result may not have the desired standard state-equation form.

Linearity and *time-invariance* concepts are easily extended to second-order systems.

Standard-form, linear, time-invariant state equations can be solved by analogy with the first-order case.

The *phase-plane* plot provides a useful geometric interpretation of the behavior of state variables, and system stability can be determined from it.

2.8 PROBLEMS

(2.1) By choosing the capacitance *voltages* as state variables, determine the standard-form state equations for the network of Fig. 2.15.

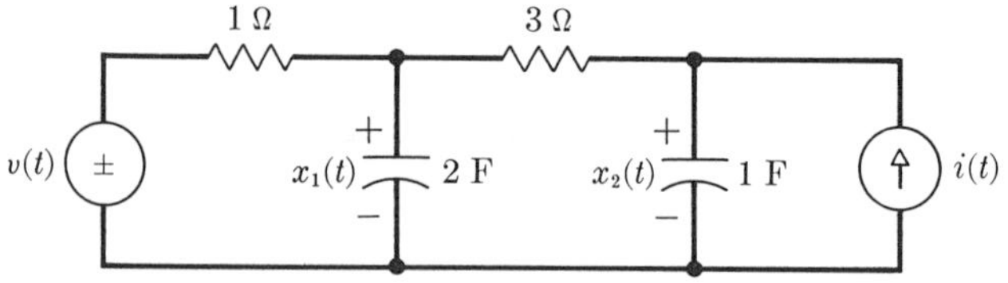

FIG. 2.15 Probs. 2.1 and 2.2.

(2.2) Choose the capacitance *charges* as state variables and again write the standard-form state equations for the network of Fig. 2.15.

(2.3) Find standard-form state equations for the network of Fig. 2.16.

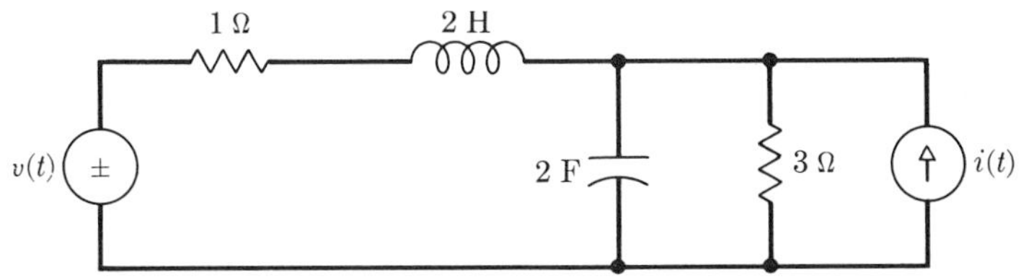

FIG. 2.16 Prob. 2.3.

(2.4) We have shown how to transform a constant-coefficient, linear, second-order differential equation into a pair of coupled, first-order differential equations. Try to generalize this method to allow for variable coefficients. In particular, transform

$$\ddot{y}(t) + t\dot{y}(t) + t^2 y(t) = u(t)$$

and

$$\ddot{y}(t) + t\dot{y}(t) + t^2 y(t) = u(t) + t\dot{u}(t)$$

into a pair of coupled, first-order differential equations.

(2.5) Extend the definition of linearity given for first-order systems in Chap. 1 (1.33) to include second-order systems.

(2.6) (*a*) Write state equations to describe the network of Fig. 2.17. Take the output to be $y = -x_1 + x_2$. Assume that the diodes are ideal (that is, $v \equiv 0$ for $i \geq 0$, and $i \equiv 0$ for $v \leq 0$).

(*b*) Is the system zero-state linear, zero-input linear, linear?

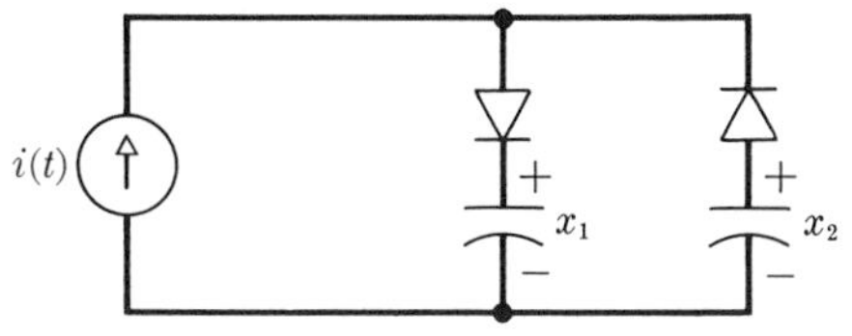

FIG. 2.17 Prob. 2.6.

(2.7) Find a block-diagram realization for the mathematical system described by

$$\ddot{y}(t) + 3\dot{y}(t) + 2y(t) = \ddot{u}(t) + 6\dot{u}(t) + 5u(t)$$

(2.8) The differential equation

$$\ddot{y}(t) + y(t) + y^3(t) = \cos^3 t$$

has the particular solution

$$y(t) = \cos t$$

Linearize the second-order differential equation about this solution.

Express the linearized equation as a second-order equation and also as a pair of first-order equations.

(2.9) Consider a time-variable system which is characterized by

$$\ddot{y}(t) + 5\dot{y}(t) + 6y(t) = u(t) + f(t)\dot{u}(t)$$

Find a state-variable characterization for this system.

(2.10) A system is characterized by the nonlinear second-order equation

$$\dot{y}(t)\ddot{y}(t) + \frac{1}{3\dot{y}(t)} = u(t)$$

The substitution of $\dot{z} = \dot{y}^3$ transforms this equation into the linear equation

$$\ddot{z}(t) + \dot{z}(t) = 3u(t)$$

If we choose $x_1 = z$ and $x_2 = \dot{z}$ as state variables, then the second-order equation is transformed into

$$\begin{aligned}\dot{x}_1(t) &= x_2(t)\\ \dot{x}_2(t) &= -x_1(t) + 3u(t)\end{aligned}$$

In order to completely characterize the system, we must be able to express the output y in terms of the states and the input. Does there exist a function g such that

$$y(t) = g(x_1(t),x_2(t))$$

(2.11) Write state equations for the networks shown in Fig. 2.18. Find the solution of these equations and determine the zero states, equilibrium states, and ground state (if it exists) in each case.

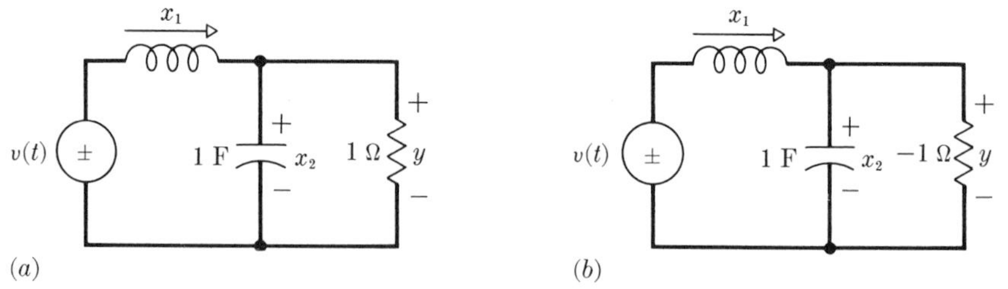

FIG. 2.18 Prob. 2.11.

(2.12) Consider the network of Fig. 2.19a. The nonlinear resistance is characterized by the $v - i$ characteristic.

$$v_0 = 24i_0 - 9i_0^2 + i_0^3$$

Take the voltage v to be the input and current i to be the output and write a set of state equations which describe the system. For each of the loading situations shown in Fig. 2.19*b* to *d*, find the equilibrium states and linearize the state equations about these points. Determine whether these linearized systems are asymptotically stable, stable, or unstable by drawing the phase-plane trajectories.

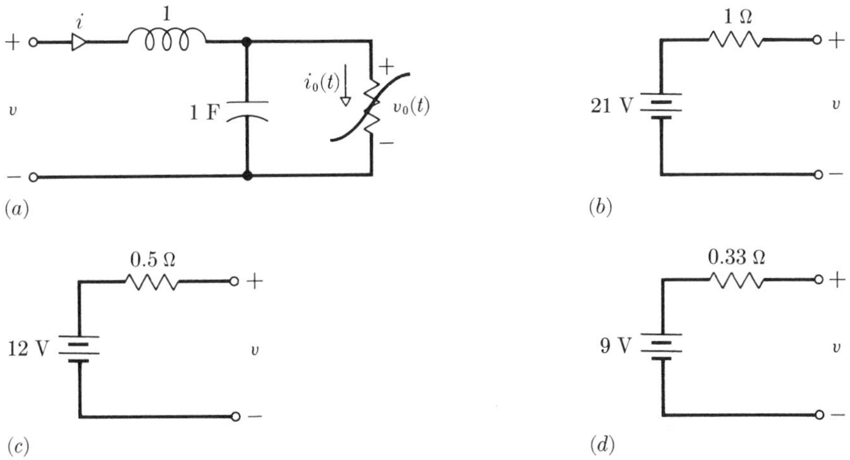

FIG. 2.19 Prob. 2.12.

(2.13) A second-order system is characterized by the state equations

$$\dot{x}_1(t) = x_2(t)$$
$$\dot{x}_2(t) = -2x_1(t) - 3x_2(t) + u(t)$$

and

$$y(t) = x_1(t)$$

Find the second-order differential equation which also describes this system. For $u(t) = 0$, determine x_2 as a function of x_1, and plot the phase-plane trajectories for a few initial values of x_1 and x_2.

(2.14) Prove that no two trajectories in the state space may cross each other. (Hint: Use uniqueness.)

(2.15) Show that the following norms satisfy the necessary properties:

(*a*) $\|\mathbf{x}\|_1 = |x_1| + |x_2|$
(*b*) $\|\mathbf{x}\|_2 = \sqrt{x_1^2 + x_2^2}$
(*c*) $\|\mathbf{x}\|_\infty = \max(|x_1|,|x_2|)$

where

$$\mathbf{x} = (x_1,x_2)'$$

(2.16) Show that if an equilibrium state of a second-order system described by

$$\dot{x}_1(t) = f_1(x_1,x_2,t)$$

and

$$\dot{x}_2(t) = f_2(x_1,x_2,t)$$

is simple, it is isolated. Why isn't the converse true?

(2.17) Sketch the solution in the phase plane of the system

$$\begin{bmatrix} \dot{x}_1 \\ \dot{x}_2 \end{bmatrix} = \begin{bmatrix} 0 & 1 \\ -1 & -1 \end{bmatrix} \begin{bmatrix} x_1 \\ x_2 \end{bmatrix} \qquad \begin{bmatrix} x_1(0) \\ x_2(0) \end{bmatrix} = \begin{bmatrix} 0 \\ 1 \end{bmatrix}$$

(2.18) Find the values of $u(0)$ and $u(1)$ which take the state of the discrete-time system

$$\begin{bmatrix} x_1(k+1) \\ x_2(k+1) \end{bmatrix} = \begin{bmatrix} 0 & 1 \\ -2 & -3 \end{bmatrix} \begin{bmatrix} x_1(k) \\ x_2(k) \end{bmatrix} + \begin{bmatrix} 0 \\ 1 \end{bmatrix} u(k)$$

with

$$\mathbf{x}(0) = \begin{bmatrix} 0 \\ 1 \end{bmatrix}$$

to the origin at $k = 2$.

ELEMENTARY MATRIX THEORY

3

We observed in the last chapter that vector-matrix notation greatly facilitates the discussion of second-order systems. With higher-order systems, the vector-matrix approach is virtually indispensable. Aside from the matrix manipulations though, the philosophy underlying our study of higher-order systems remains identical to that which we employed for first- and second-order systems. So that matrices enhance, rather than obscure, our subsequent system studies, in this chapter we digress to study them in some detail.

3.1 MATRICES AND OPERATIONS ON THEM

For motivational purposes, consider the set of m linear algebraic equations in terms of n unknowns:

$$
\begin{aligned}
&a_{11}x_1 + a_{12}x_2 + \cdots + a_{1n}x_n = y_1 \\
(3.1)\qquad &a_{21}x_1 + a_{22}x_2 + \cdots + a_{2n}x_n = y_2 \\
&a_{m1}x_1 + a_{m2}x_2 + \cdots + a_{mn}x_n = y_m
\end{aligned}
$$

where the x_j ($j = 1, 2, \ldots, n$) are the dependent variables, y_i ($i = 1, 2, \ldots, m$) are the independent variables, and the a_{ij} ($i = 1, 2, \ldots, m$; $j = 1, 2, \ldots, n$) are constants. These equations may also be conveniently rewritten as

$$\sum_{j=1}^{n} a_{ij}x_j = y_i \qquad i = 1, 2, \ldots, m$$

But even the use of summation notation is cumbersome. A simpler shorthand notation is the matrix notation

$$(3.2)\qquad \mathbf{Ax} = \mathbf{y}$$

where the $m \times n$ matrix $\mathbf{A}$ is defined by the rectangular array of numbers

$$\mathbf{A} \equiv \begin{bmatrix} a_{11} & a_{12} & \cdots & a_{1n} \\ a_{21} & a_{22} & \cdots & a_{2n} \\ \cdots & \cdots & \cdots & \cdots \\ a_{m1} & a_{m2} & \cdots & a_{mn} \end{bmatrix}$$

the $n \times 1$ matrix $\mathbf{x}$ is defined by

$$\mathbf{x} = \begin{bmatrix} x_1 \\ x_2 \\ \cdot \\ \cdot \\ \cdot \\ x_n \end{bmatrix}$$

and the $m \times 1$ matrix $\mathbf{y}$ is defined by

$$\mathbf{y} = \begin{bmatrix} y_1 \\ y_2 \\ \cdot \\ \cdot \\ \cdot \\ y_m \end{bmatrix}$$

We then say that we multiply the matrix **x** by the matrix **A** to obtain the matrix **y**. Before proceeding further let us formalize these ideas.

(3.3) Matrix

A rectangular array of elements having m rows and n columns is called an $(m \times n)$ *matrix*. When $m = n$, the matrix is called *square* and the number $(n(= m))$ is its *order*. ▮

An $m \times n$ matrix is denoted by a capital (boldface) letter, for example, **A**. The elements of **A** are written as a_{ij} where the first subscript i denotes the row number and the second subscript j denotes the column number. We may define a matrix as follows:

$$\mathbf{A} \equiv [a_{ij}]$$

where the square brackets indicate the array, a typical element of which is a_{ij}.

(3.4) Vector

An $(n \times 1)$ matrix is called a *column matrix, column vector, n vector*, or just *vector*. Vectors are denoted by lowercase (boldface) letters, for example, **a**. A vector may also be defined by its elements:

$$\mathbf{a} = \begin{bmatrix} a_1 \\ a_2 \\ \cdot \\ \cdot \\ \cdot \\ a_n \end{bmatrix}$$

▮

There are some specific names attached to special types of matrices. An $(n \times n)$ square matrix is called *diagonal* if $a_{ij} = 0$ for $i \neq j$ and is sometimes denoted by diag $(a_{11}, a_{22}, \ldots, a_{nn})$. The *identity matrix*, denoted by $\mathbf{1}$ or $\mathbf{1}_n$, is an $(n \times n)$ diagonal matrix with all diagonal elements equal to unity. The *zero* or *null matrix*, denoted by $\mathbf{0}$, is a matrix of arbitrary dimensions with all elements equal to zero.

(3.5) Matrix product

The *product* of the $(n \times m)$ matrix **A** and the $(m \times r)$ matrix **B** is the $(n \times r)$ matrix **C** where

$$c_{ij} \equiv \sum_{k=1}^{m} a_{ik} b_{kj}$$

for all $i = 1, 2, \ldots, n$ and for all $j = 1, 2, \ldots, r$. ▮

(3.6) Example
Given the matrices

$$\mathbf{A} = \begin{bmatrix} 1 & 2 \\ 1 & -1 \end{bmatrix}$$

and

$$\mathbf{B} = \begin{bmatrix} 1 & 0 & -1 \\ 1 & -1 & 1 \end{bmatrix}$$

the product of **A** and **B** is the matrix **C**:

$$\mathbf{C} = \mathbf{AB} = \begin{bmatrix} 3 & -2 & 1 \\ 0 & 1 & -1 \end{bmatrix}$$

∎

(3.7) Example
Given the matrices

$$\mathbf{A} = \begin{bmatrix} 1 & 2 & 3 & -1 \\ -2 & 1 & 3 & 5 \\ -1 & 3 & 1 & 2 \end{bmatrix}$$

and

$$\mathbf{B} = \begin{bmatrix} 1 & 2 \\ -1 & 1 \\ 0 & 1 \\ 1 & 0 \end{bmatrix}$$

the product of **A** and **B** is the matrix **C**:

$$\mathbf{C} = \begin{bmatrix} -2 & 7 \\ 2 & 0 \\ -2 & 2 \end{bmatrix}$$

∎

It is important to observe the order of multiplication of matrices as illustrated by the following example.

(3.8) Example
Consider the two matrices

$$\mathbf{A} = \begin{bmatrix} 1 & 3 \\ 2 & 1 \end{bmatrix}$$

and

$$\mathbf{B} = \begin{bmatrix} 2 & 1 \\ 1 & 1 \end{bmatrix}$$

The matrix product **AB** is

$$\mathbf{AB} = \begin{bmatrix} 5 & 4 \\ 5 & 3 \end{bmatrix}$$

while the matrix product **BA** is

$$\mathbf{BA} = \begin{bmatrix} 4 & 7 \\ 3 & 4 \end{bmatrix}$$

Therefore

$$\mathbf{AB} \neq \mathbf{BA} \qquad \blacksquare$$

Two $(n \times n)$ matrices are said to *commute* if **AB** equals **BA**.

Observe that we cannot effect a multiplication of arbitrary matrices. The two matrices to be multiplied must be *conformable*, i.e., the number of columns of the first must equal the number of rows of the second. Under the above definitions, the set of simultaneous algebraic equations (3.1) can adequately be represented by the matrix equation (3.2).

Consider the following situation. In addition to the m equations in n unknowns represented by (3.2), we are also given the set of n equations in r unknowns represented by the matrix equation

$$\mathbf{Bz} = \mathbf{x}$$

that is, **B** is $(n \times r)$. Since (3.2) relates **x** and **y**, and the above relation relates **x** and **z**, it is desirable to have an expression that relates **y** and **z** directly, i.e.,

$$\mathbf{Cz} = \mathbf{y}$$

where **C** is $(m \times r)$. Observe that

$$\mathbf{Ax} = \mathbf{ABz} = \mathbf{y}$$

so that

$$\mathbf{C} = \mathbf{AB}$$

Thus matrix multiplication as defined above arises naturally in the solution of sets of simultaneous algebraic equations. We sometimes say that in the product

$$\mathbf{AB}$$

A is *postmultiplied* by **B** or that **B** is *premultiplied* by **A**.

Certainly this notation will only be useful if it is easily manipulatable. To this end we investigate matrix operations that may be performed. The reader should constantly bear in mind that the operations to be discussed are defined so that when they are performed on matrices, they correspond to the operations as if they were performed on sets of simultaneous equations.

(3.9) Product of matrix by a scalar
Given the $(n \times m)$ matrix $\mathbf{A}$ and the scalar α, the product of $\alpha\mathbf{A}$ is the $(n \times m)$ matrix $\mathbf{C}$ where

$$c_{ij} = \alpha a_{ij}$$

for all $i = 1, 2, \ldots, n$ and all $j = 1, 2, \ldots, m$. ∎

(3.10) Example
The product of the matrix

$$\begin{bmatrix} 1 & 5 \\ -2 & 7 \end{bmatrix}$$

by the scalar 3 is

$$3\begin{bmatrix} 1 & 5 \\ -2 & 7 \end{bmatrix} = \begin{bmatrix} 3 & 15 \\ -6 & 21 \end{bmatrix}$$ ∎

(3.11) Equality
Two $(m \times n)$ matrices,

$$\mathbf{A} = [a_{ij}]$$
$$\mathbf{B} = [b_{ij}]$$

are said to be *equal* if and only if

$$a_{ij} = b_{ij}$$

for all $i = 1, 2, \ldots, m$ and all $j = 1, 2, \ldots, n$. (Note: Matrix equality may only be defined for matrices of equal size.) ∎

(3.12) Matrix addition
The *sum* of two $(m \times n)$ matrices

$$\mathbf{A} = [a_{ij}]$$

and

$$\mathbf{B} = [b_{ij}]$$

is the $(m \times n)$ matrix

$$\mathbf{C} = \mathbf{A} + \mathbf{B} \tag{3.13}$$

where

$$c_{ij} = a_{ij} + b_{ij}$$

for all $i = 1, 2, \ldots, m$, and all $j = 1, 2, \ldots, n$. ∎

Observe the following identities:

$$\mathbf{A} \cdot \mathbf{1} = \mathbf{1} \cdot \mathbf{A} = \mathbf{A}$$

for any square matrix $\mathbf{A}$; and

$$\mathbf{A} + \mathbf{0} = \mathbf{0} + \mathbf{A} = \mathbf{A}$$

for any $(m \times n)$ matrix $\mathbf{A}$.

It is left as an exercise for the reader to show that the following rules are satisfied by matrix operations.

(1) *Distributive rules*

$$(\mathbf{A} + \mathbf{B})\mathbf{C} = \mathbf{AC} + \mathbf{BC}$$

where $\mathbf{A}$ and $\mathbf{B}$ are $(n \times m)$ and $\mathbf{C}$ is $(m \times r)$;

$$\mathbf{A}(\mathbf{B} + \mathbf{C}) = \mathbf{AB} + \mathbf{AC}$$

where $\mathbf{A}$ is $(n \times m)$ and $\mathbf{B}$ and $\mathbf{C}$ are $(m \times r)$;

$$(\alpha + \beta)\mathbf{A} = \alpha\mathbf{A} + \beta\mathbf{A}$$

where α and β are scalars;

$$\alpha(\mathbf{A} + \mathbf{B}) = \alpha\mathbf{A} + \alpha\mathbf{B}$$

where α is a scalar and $\mathbf{A}$ and $\mathbf{B}$ are $(n \times m)$.

(2) *Associative rules*

$$\alpha\mathbf{A} = \mathbf{A}\alpha \qquad \text{or} \qquad (\alpha\mathbf{A})\mathbf{B} = \alpha\mathbf{AB} = \mathbf{A}(\alpha\mathbf{B})$$

where $\mathbf{A}$ is $(n \times m)$, $\mathbf{B}$ is $(m \times r)$, and α is a scalar;

$$\mathbf{A}(\mathbf{BC}) = (\mathbf{AB})\mathbf{C}$$

where $\mathbf{A}$ is $(n \times m)$, $\mathbf{B}$ is $(m \times r)$, $\mathbf{C}$ is $(r \times s)$;

$$(\mathbf{A} + \mathbf{B}) + \mathbf{C} = \mathbf{A} + (\mathbf{B} + \mathbf{C})$$

where $\mathbf{A}$, $\mathbf{B}$, and $\mathbf{C}$ are $(n \times m)$.

(3) *Commutative rules*

$$\mathbf{A} + \mathbf{B} = \mathbf{B} + \mathbf{A}$$

where $\mathbf{A}$ and $\mathbf{B}$ are $(n \times m)$.

3.2 DETERMINANTS AND MATRIX INVERSION

Consider the two simultaneous algebraic equations in two unknowns

$$\begin{aligned} a_{11}x_1 + a_{12}x_2 &= y_1 \\ a_{21}x_1 + a_{22}x_2 &= y_2 \end{aligned} \tag{3.14}$$

or in matrix form

$$\mathbf{A}\mathbf{x} = \mathbf{y} \tag{3.15}$$

where

$$\mathbf{A} = \begin{bmatrix} a_{11} & a_{12} \\ a_{21} & a_{22} \end{bmatrix}$$

Using simple algebraic techniques, it is easy to ascertain expressions for x_1 and x_2 in terms of y_1 and y_2:

$$\begin{aligned} x_1 &= \frac{a_{22}}{a_{11}a_{22} - a_{12}a_{21}} y_1 - \frac{a_{12}}{a_{11}a_{22} - a_{12}a_{21}} y_2 \\ x_2 &= \frac{-a_{21}}{a_{11}a_{22} - a_{12}a_{21}} y_1 + \frac{a_{11}}{a_{11}a_{22} - a_{12}a_{21}} y_2 \end{aligned} \tag{3.16}$$

if the quantity $(a_{11}a_{22} - a_{12}a_{21})$ is nonzero. The quantity $(a_{11}a_{22} - a_{12}a_{21})$ is known as the *determinant* of the matrix **A** and is denoted by det (**A**), that is,

$$\det(\mathbf{A}) = a_{11}a_{22} - a_{12}a_{21}$$

Thus we can say that the set of simultaneous equations represented by (3.15) can be solved for **x** if det (**A**) is nonzero, i.e., if they are "determinant."

As seen above, the determinant of a matrix plays an important role in the solution of simultaneous equations. (In Chap. 7 we will investigate numerical solutions to matrix equations.) Formally we define determinants as follows.

(3.17) Determinant

A determinant of first order consists of a single element a and has the value a. A determinant of second order consists of a 2×2 square array

$$\begin{vmatrix} a_{11} & a_{12} \\ a_{21} & a_{22} \end{vmatrix}$$

and has the value

$$a_{11}a_{22} - a_{12}a_{21}$$

A determinant of third order is defined in terms of second-order determinants:

$$\begin{vmatrix} a_{11} & a_{12} & a_{13} \\ a_{21} & a_{22} & a_{23} \\ a_{31} & a_{32} & a_{33} \end{vmatrix} = a_{11} \begin{vmatrix} a_{22} & a_{23} \\ a_{32} & a_{33} \end{vmatrix} - a_{12} \begin{vmatrix} a_{21} & a_{23} \\ a_{31} & a_{33} \end{vmatrix} + a_{13} \begin{vmatrix} a_{21} & a_{22} \\ a_{31} & a_{32} \end{vmatrix}$$

In general, if $\mathbf{A}$ represents a square $n \times n$ matrix, the *determinant* of $\mathbf{A}$ is given by the Laplace expansion

$$\det(\mathbf{A}) \equiv \sum_{j=1}^{n} a_{ij}\Delta_{ij} \qquad \text{or} \qquad \det(\mathbf{A}) \equiv \sum_{j=1}^{n} a_{ji}\Delta_{ji}$$

for any i where Δ_{ij} is the cofactor of a_{ij}. The cofactor of a_{ij} is defined by

$$\Delta_{ij} = (-1)^{i+j}M_{ij}$$

where M_{ij} is the *minor* of a_{ij}, that is, it is the determinant found from the square matrix obtained by deleting the ith row and jth column from $\mathbf{A}$. ▮

(3.18) Example

The determinant of the 3 × 3 matrix

$$\begin{bmatrix} 1 & 2 & 3 \\ 1 & 1 & 1 \\ 2 & 1 & 3 \end{bmatrix}$$

is found as follows

$$\det\begin{bmatrix} 1 & 2 & 3 \\ 1 & 1 & 1 \\ 2 & 1 & 3 \end{bmatrix} = (1)\det\begin{bmatrix} 1 & 1 \\ 1 & 3 \end{bmatrix} - (2)\det\begin{bmatrix} 1 & 1 \\ 2 & 3 \end{bmatrix}$$
$$+ (3)\det\begin{bmatrix} 1 & 1 \\ 2 & 1 \end{bmatrix} = (1)[(1)(3) - (1)(1)]$$
$$+ (2)[(1)(3) - (1)(2)] + (3)[(1)(1) - (1)(2)] = -3$$ ▮

We leave it as an exercise to show that if $\mathbf{A}$ and $\mathbf{B}$ are $n \times n$ matrices, then

$$\det(\mathbf{AB}) = \det(\mathbf{A})\det(\mathbf{B})$$

Consider again Eqs. (3.14) and the solution (3.16). Rewriting (3.16) in matrix form, we have

$$\mathbf{x} = \mathbf{By} \tag{3.19}$$

where

$$\mathbf{B} = \frac{1}{\det \mathbf{A}}\begin{bmatrix} a_{22} & -a_{12} \\ -a_{21} & a_{11} \end{bmatrix}$$

Consideration of (3.15) and (3.19) yields

$$\mathbf{x} = \mathbf{BAx}$$

and

$$\mathbf{BA} = \mathbf{1}$$

as expected. It is also easy to see that

$$\mathbf{AB} = \mathbf{1}$$

that is, **A** and **B** commute. The matrix **B** is called the *inverse* of **A** and is denoted by $\mathbf{A}^{-1}$.

Let us be a little more general. Suppose we are given a set of n independent algebraic equations in terms of n unknowns

$$\sum_{j=1}^{n} a_{ij}x_j = y_i \qquad i = 1, 2, \ldots, n$$

where the a_{ij} and y_i are known constants and the x_j are unknown. These equations can be written in matrix form as

$$\begin{bmatrix} a_{11} & a_{12} & \cdots & a_{1j} & \cdots & a_{1n} \\ a_{21} & a_{22} & \cdots & a_{2j} & \cdots & a_{2n} \\ \cdots & \cdots & \cdots & \cdots & \cdots & \cdots \\ a_{i1} & a_{i2} & \cdots & a_{ij} & \cdots & a_{in} \\ \cdots & \cdots & \cdots & \cdots & \cdots & \cdots \\ a_{n1} & a_{n2} & \cdots & a_{nj} & \cdots & a_{nn} \end{bmatrix} \begin{bmatrix} x_1 \\ x_2 \\ \cdot \\ \cdot \\ \cdot \\ x_n \end{bmatrix} = \begin{bmatrix} y_1 \\ y_2 \\ \cdot \\ \cdot \\ \cdot \\ y_n \end{bmatrix}$$

or

$$\mathbf{Ax} = \mathbf{y} \tag{3.20}$$

Cramer's rule can be employed to find values for the x's:

$$x_j = \frac{1}{\Delta} \sum_{i=1}^{n} y_i \Delta_{ij} \qquad j = 1, 2, \ldots, n \tag{3.21}$$

where $\Delta = \det(\mathbf{A}) \neq 0$. In Chap. 7 we will find that the use of Cramer's rule is computationally inefficient, but it suffices for the present. [Observe that $\det(\mathbf{A}) \neq 0$, because the equations were assumed to be independent. We will return to this point later.] We rewrite (3.21) as

$$\sum_{i=1}^{n} \frac{\Delta_{ij}}{\Delta} y_i = x_j \qquad j = 1, 2, \ldots, n$$

or in matrix form

$$\mathbf{By} = \mathbf{x} \tag{3.22}$$

where we have defined

$$\mathbf{B} = \left[\frac{\Delta_{ji}}{\Delta}\right]$$

that is,

$$b_{ij} = \frac{\Delta_{ji}}{\Delta}$$

Now observe that

$$\begin{aligned}\mathbf{ABy} &= \mathbf{Ax}\\ &= \mathbf{y}\\ &= \mathbf{1y}\end{aligned}$$

so that

$$\mathbf{AB} = \mathbf{1} \tag{3.23}$$

Similarly, since

$$\mathbf{x} = \mathbf{By}$$

we have

$$\mathbf{x} = \mathbf{BAy}$$

so that

$$\mathbf{BA} = \mathbf{1} \tag{3.24}$$

Any matrix **B** such that (3.23) and (3.24) are true is called the *inverse of* **A** and is denoted by $\mathbf{A}^{-1}$. Therefore

$$\mathbf{A}^{-1} = \left[\frac{\Delta_{ji}}{\Delta}\right] \tag{3.25}$$

and

$$\mathbf{AA}^{-1} = \mathbf{A}^{-1}\mathbf{A} = \mathbf{1} \tag{3.26}$$

Moreover, observe that $\mathbf{A}^{-1}$ exists if and only if det $(\mathbf{A}) \neq 0$, that is, **A** is *nonsingular*.

Another important concept, which is closely associated to the matrix inverse, is the *rank* of a matrix. Rank is defined in terms of the minors of a matrix. In general, a minor of order p of an arbitrary $(n \times m)$ matrix **A** is the determinant of any $(p \times p)$ submatrix of **A**.

(3.27) Example

Let **A** be the (3×4) matrix

$$\mathbf{A} = \begin{bmatrix} 1 & 1 & 2 & 3\\ 3 & 1 & -1 & 0\\ -2 & -1 & 1 & 5\end{bmatrix}$$

Then one possible second-order minor of **A** is

$$\det\begin{bmatrix} 1 & 3\\ -2 & 5\end{bmatrix} = 11$$

A third-order minor is

$$\det \begin{bmatrix} 1 & 2 & 3 \\ 3 & -1 & 0 \\ -2 & 1 & 5 \end{bmatrix} = -32$$

∎

The *rank* of a matrix is the largest among the orders of the nonzero minors. If r is the rank of a rectangular matrix $\mathbf{A}$ of dimension $(n \times m)$, then obviously, $r \leq \min(n,m)$.

(3.28) Example
Given the matrix

$$\mathbf{A} = \begin{bmatrix} 1 & 1 & 2 \\ 2 & 1 & 4 \\ 3 & 0 & 6 \end{bmatrix}$$

then

$$\det(\mathbf{A}) = 0$$

so that the rank of $\mathbf{A}$ must be less than 3. Since one possible second-order minor is

$$\det \begin{bmatrix} 1 & 1 \\ 2 & 1 \end{bmatrix} = -1$$

the rank of $\mathbf{A}$ is 2. ∎

(3.29) Example
Given the rectangular matrix

$$\mathbf{A} = \begin{bmatrix} 1 & 2 & 1 \\ -1 & 1 & 1 \end{bmatrix}$$

then since the second-order minor

$$\det \begin{bmatrix} 1 & 1 \\ -1 & 1 \end{bmatrix} = 2$$

is nonzero, $\mathbf{A}$ is of rank 2. ∎

An $(n \times n)$ matrix is *nonsingular* if and only if its *rank* is equal to its *order*.

(3.30) Example
Consider the third-order matrix

$$\mathbf{A} = \begin{bmatrix} 1 & 2 & -1 \\ 2 & 1 & 0 \\ -1 & 0 & 1 \end{bmatrix}$$

Since

$$\det(\mathbf{A}) = 4$$

A is of rank 3, and its inverse exists:

$$\mathbf{A}^{-1} = \begin{bmatrix} -\frac{1}{4} & \frac{1}{2} & -\frac{1}{4} \\ \frac{1}{2} & 0 & \frac{1}{2} \\ -\frac{1}{4} & \frac{1}{2} & \frac{3}{4} \end{bmatrix}$$

▮

We leave it as an exercise for the reader to show that a matrix has a unique inverse only when it is nonsingular. Moreover, the product of two nonsingular matrices is nonsingular.

There is one other useful matrix operation that will be of value in the sequel.

(3.31) Transpose

The *transpose* of an $(n \times m)$ matrix $\mathbf{A} = [a_{ij}]$ is the $(m \times n)$ matrix $\mathbf{A}' = [a_{ji}]$, that is, the rows and columns of **A** are interchanged to obtain $\mathbf{A}'$. ▮

(3.32) Example

The transpose of the (2×3) matrix

$$\mathbf{A} = \begin{bmatrix} 1 & -3 & 2 + j1 \\ 9 & -4.2 & 0 \end{bmatrix}$$

is the (3×2) matrix

$$\mathbf{A}' = \begin{bmatrix} 1 & 9 \\ -3 & -4.2 \\ 2 + j1 & 0 \end{bmatrix}$$

The transpose of the three-vector

$$\mathbf{a} = \begin{bmatrix} -0.5 \\ 15 \\ j\sqrt{3} \end{bmatrix}$$

is

$$\mathbf{a}' = [-0.5 \quad 15 \quad j\sqrt{3}]$$

▮

We leave it as an exercise for the reader to show that

(1) $(\mathbf{A} + \mathbf{B})' = \mathbf{A}' + \mathbf{B}'$

where **A** and **B** are $(n \times m)$.

(2) $(\mathbf{AB})' = \mathbf{B}'\mathbf{A}'$

where **A** is $(n \times m)$ and **B** is $(m \times r)$.

If **A** and **B** are nonsingular square matrices, then

(3) $(\mathbf{AB})^{-1} = \mathbf{B}^{-1}\mathbf{A}^{-1}$
(4) $(\mathbf{A}^{-1})^{-1} = \mathbf{A}$
(5) $(\mathbf{A}^{-1})' = (\mathbf{A}')^{-1}$

3.3 LINEAR VECTOR SPACES

In the sequel we will spend a great deal of time working with vectors, and the concept of a linear vector space will enhance our studies.

In order to discuss linear vector spaces, we must define a field.

(3.33) Field

A *field* is any set of numbers which also contains the *sum*, *difference*, *product*, and *quotient* (excluding division by zero) of any two numbers in the field. ∎

For example, the set of real numbers is a field, so is the set of rational numbers and the set of all complex numbers.

(3.34) Linear vector spaces

A set of vectors $\mathcal{L}$ is a *linear vector space* if the two operations, "addition" and "multiplication" of vectors by scalars in a field Φ, are defined and the following axioms are satisfied (we use ε to mean "is a member of").

(1) *Additivity:* If $\mathbf{f} \in \mathcal{L}$ and $\mathbf{g} \in \mathcal{L}$, then $\mathbf{f} + \mathbf{g} \in \mathcal{L}$, for all $\mathbf{f}, \mathbf{g} \in \mathcal{L}$; moreover,

(1*a*) Commutivity:

$$\mathbf{f} + \mathbf{g} = \mathbf{g} + \mathbf{f} \qquad \text{for all } \mathbf{f}, \mathbf{g} \in \mathcal{L}$$

(1*b*) Associativity:

$$(\mathbf{f} + \mathbf{g}) + \mathbf{h} = \mathbf{f} + (\mathbf{g} + \mathbf{h}) \qquad \text{for all } \mathbf{f}, \mathbf{g}, \mathbf{h} \in \mathcal{L}$$

(1*c*) Existence of the zero element:
There exists a $\mathbf{0} \in \mathcal{L}$ such that

$$\mathbf{f} + \mathbf{0} = \mathbf{f} \qquad \text{for all } \mathbf{f} \in \mathcal{L}$$

(1*d*) Additive inverse:
For all $\mathbf{f} \in \mathcal{L}$, there exists a $\mathbf{g} \in \mathcal{L}$ such that

$$\mathbf{f} + \mathbf{g} = 0$$

(2) *Homogeneity:* If $\mathbf{f} \in \mathcal{L}$ and $\alpha \in \Phi$, then $\alpha\mathbf{f} \in \mathcal{L}$, for all $\mathbf{f} \in \mathcal{L}$, and for all $\alpha \in \Phi$; moreover,

(2*a*) Associativity:

$$\alpha(\beta\mathbf{f}) = (\alpha\beta)\mathbf{f} \qquad \text{for all } \alpha, \beta \in \Phi, \mathbf{f} \in \mathfrak{L}$$

(2*b*) Distributivity:

$$(\alpha + \beta)\mathbf{f} = \alpha\mathbf{f} + \beta\mathbf{f} \qquad \text{for all } \alpha, \beta \in \Phi, \mathbf{f} \in \mathfrak{L}$$
$$\alpha(\mathbf{f} + \mathbf{g}) = \alpha\mathbf{f} + \alpha\mathbf{g} \qquad \alpha \in \Phi, \mathbf{f}, \mathbf{g} \in \mathfrak{L}$$

(2*c*) Existence of an identity element:

$$1 \cdot \mathbf{f} = \mathbf{f} \qquad \text{for all } \mathbf{f} \in \mathfrak{L}, \mathbf{1} \in \Phi$$ ▮

One of the simplest linear vector spaces which we may envision is that which is made up of all ordered pairs of real numbers,

$$\mathbf{x}' = (\xi_1,\xi_2) \qquad \xi_1 \in R^1, \xi_2 \in R^1$$

A pictorial representation of this linear vector space is the plane of Fig. 3.1. It is reasonable to call this plane euclidean two-space or

$$R^2 = R^1 \times R^1$$

where the symbol "×" indicates the *cartesian product.* That is, the cartesian product of two spaces is obtained by adjoining one orthogonally to the other, as when two real lines are adjoined to form a real plane. Similarly, euclidean three-space consists of all ordered triples of real numbers,

$$\mathbf{x}' = (\xi_1,\xi_2,\xi_3) \qquad \xi_1 \in R^1, \xi_2 \in R^1, \xi_3 \in R^1$$

and is denoted by

$$R^3 = R^1 \times R^1 \times R^1 = R^2 \times R^1$$

Complex two-space, the space made up of all ordered pairs of complex numbers, is denoted by

$$\mathcal{C}^2 = \mathcal{C}^1 \times \mathcal{C}^1$$

We note that it would actually require four dimensions to represent such a space pictorially, since the complex numbers alone require a plane. None-

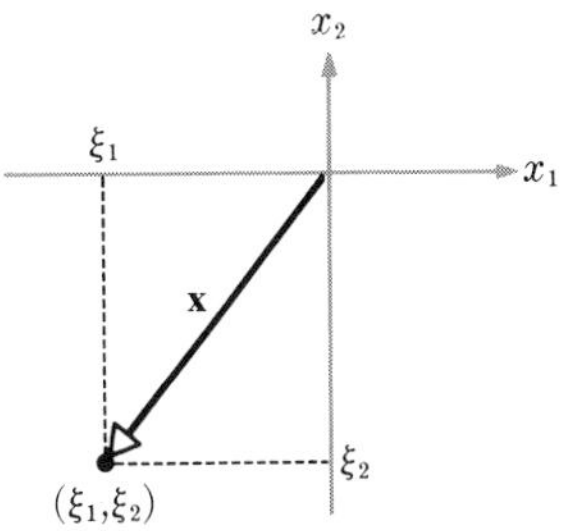

FIG. 3.1 The (real) plane is formed of the cartesian product of two real lines. Since they are in one-to-one correspondence, we may speak interchangeably of the vector $x = (\xi_1,\xi_2)'$ and the point (ξ_1,ξ_2).

theless, we persist in accepting

$$\mathbf{x}' = (\xi_1, \xi_2) \qquad \xi_1 \in \mathcal{C}^1,\ \xi_2 \in \mathcal{C}^1$$

as a complex-valued two-vector, in that for most practical studies, complex two-spaces arise quite naturally in the study of (real) euclidean two-spaces. Finally, we consider two abstract linear vector spaces of great utility: euclidean n space,

$$R^n = \underbrace{R^1 \times R^1 \times \cdots \times R^1}_{n \text{ times}} = R^{n-1} \times R$$

which is made up of all ordered n-tuples of real numbers; and complex n space,

$$\mathcal{C}^n = \underbrace{\mathcal{C}^1 \times \mathcal{C}^1 \times \cdots \times \mathcal{C}^1}_{n \text{ times}} = \mathcal{C}^{n-1} \times \mathcal{C}$$

which is comprised of all ordered n-tuples of complex numbers.

Just as we may adjoin the set of real numbers, a one-dimensional linear vector space, to itself to form a two-dimensional linear vector space, we may form a two-dimensional linear vector space of functions from a one-dimensional linear vector space of functions adjoined to itself in a similar manner. Some examples of frequently encountered sets of functions are

(1) $L_1(T)$, the set of all (measurable) real-valued functions which are absolutely integrable over the time interval T, that is,

$$f \in L_1(T) \Leftrightarrow \int_T |f(t)|\, dt < \infty$$

where $\Leftrightarrow$ means "implies and is implied by"

(2) $L_2(T)$, the set of all (measurable) real-valued functions which are square integrable over time interval T, that is,

$$f \in L_2(T) \Leftrightarrow \left[\int_T |f(t)|^2\, dt\right]^{\frac{1}{2}} < \infty$$

(3) $L_p(T)$, the set of all (measurable) real-valued functions which are p integrable over the time interval T, that is,

$$f \in L_P(T) \Leftrightarrow \left[\int_T |f(t)|^P\, dt\right]^{1/P} < \infty$$

(4) $L_\infty(T)$, the set of all (measurable) real-valued functions for which the *supremum* (or the *least upper bound*—the absolute maximum, if it exists) over the time interval T is finite, i.e.,

$$f \in L_\infty(T) \Leftrightarrow \sup_{t \in T} |f(t)| < \infty$$

Thus we have the following n-dimensional *linear vector spaces of functions:*

$$\begin{aligned} L_1{}^n(T) &= L_1{}^{n-1}(T) \times L(T) \\ L_2{}^n(T) &= L_2{}^{n-1}(T) \times L(T) \\ L_p{}^n(T) &= L_p{}^{n-1}(T) \times L_p(T) \\ L_\infty{}^n(T) &= L_\infty{}^{n-1}(T) \times L_\infty(T) \end{aligned} \qquad n = 2, 3, \ldots$$

Thus, if we consider the n-vector signal function

$$\mathbf{f}' \equiv (f_1, f_2, \ldots, f_n)'$$

we say

$$\begin{aligned} \mathbf{f} \in L_1{}^n(T) &\Leftrightarrow f_k \in L_1(T) \\ \mathbf{f} \in L_2{}^n(T) &\Leftrightarrow f_k \in L_2(T) \\ \mathbf{f} \in L_p{}^n(T) &\Leftrightarrow f_k \in L_p(T) \\ \mathbf{f} \in L_\infty{}^n(T) &\Leftrightarrow f_k \in L_\infty(T) \end{aligned} \qquad k = 1, 2, \ldots, n$$

In general we will often refer to these n-vector signal functions as *points* (or, usually, merely "signals") in the signal space in analogy with the vector-point isomorphism in ordinary euclidean n space. For convenience, we will usually assume that all possible attributes of the n-vector signal functions with which we may deal are subsumed in the statement

$$\mathbf{f} \in \mathfrak{F}^n$$

or more explicitly,

$$[\mathbf{f}(t) : t \in T] \in \mathfrak{F}^n$$

That is, the function space $\mathfrak{F}^n$ contains all signals that we care to distinguish.

We now state and prove a number of theorems that are easily deduced from the above definitions.

(3.35) Theorem

For every linear vector space $\mathcal{L}$, the *zero element* $\mathbf{0} \in \mathcal{L}$ is *unique.*

Proof

We know from axiom (1c) that there is at least one zero element; now suppose there are two, $\mathbf{0}_1 \in \mathcal{L}$ and $\mathbf{0}_2 \in \mathcal{L}$. Since axiom (1$c$) states

$$\mathbf{f} + \mathbf{0} = \mathbf{f} \qquad \text{for all } \mathbf{f} \in \mathcal{L}$$

we have (taking $\mathbf{f} = \mathbf{0}_1$ and $\mathbf{0} = \mathbf{0}_2$)

$$\mathbf{0}_1 + \mathbf{0}_2 = \mathbf{0}_1$$

and (similarly, taking $\mathbf{f} = \mathbf{0}_2$ and $\mathbf{0} = \mathbf{0}_1$)

$$\mathbf{0}_2 + \mathbf{0}_1 = \mathbf{0}_2$$

But, from axiom (1*a*)

$$\mathbf{0}_1 + \mathbf{0}_2 = \mathbf{0}_2 + \mathbf{0}_1$$

therefore

$$\mathbf{0}_1 = \mathbf{0}_2$$

and **0** is unique. ∎

(3.36) Theorem
For every element **f** in a linear vector space $\mathcal{L}$, $\mathbf{f} \in \mathcal{L}$, the negative element, or more precisely, the additive inverse, is *unique*.

Proof
We know from axiom (1*d*) that there is at least one negative element for **f**: $\mathbf{g} \in \mathcal{L}$; now suppose there are two, $\mathbf{g}_1 \in \mathcal{L}$ and $\mathbf{g}_2 \in \mathcal{L}$. But, from axioms (1*a*) to (1*c*) and the preceding theorem,

$$\mathbf{g}_2 = \mathbf{g}_2 + (\mathbf{f} + \mathbf{g}_1) = (\mathbf{g}_2 + \mathbf{f}) + \mathbf{g}_1 = (\mathbf{f} + \mathbf{g}_2) + \mathbf{g}_1 = \mathbf{g}_1$$

and **g** is unique. ∎

(3.37) Theorem
For every element **f** in a linear vector space $\mathcal{L}$, $\mathbf{f} \in \mathcal{L}$, the relation

$$0 \cdot \mathbf{f} = \mathbf{0}$$

is satisfied.

Proof
Consider the element $0 \cdot \mathbf{f} + 1 \cdot \mathbf{f}$; from axiom (2*b*) we may write

$$0 \cdot \mathbf{f} + 1 \cdot \mathbf{f} = (0 + 1)\mathbf{f} = 1 \cdot \mathbf{f} = \mathbf{f}$$

while from axiom (2*c*) alone, we may write

$$0 \cdot \mathbf{f} + 1 \cdot \mathbf{f} = 0 \cdot \mathbf{f} + \mathbf{f}$$

As a consequence, we have

$$\mathbf{f} = \mathbf{0} \cdot \mathbf{f} + \mathbf{f}$$

which, upon the addition to both sides of this equation of the unique negative element $\mathbf{g} \in \mathcal{L}$ such that $\mathbf{f} + \mathbf{g} = \mathbf{0}$, becomes

$$\mathbf{0} + \mathbf{f} + \mathbf{g} = (0 \cdot \mathbf{f} + \mathbf{f}) + \mathbf{g} = 0 \cdot \mathbf{f} + (\mathbf{f} + \mathbf{g}) = 0 \cdot \mathbf{f} + \mathbf{0} = 0 \cdot \mathbf{f}$$

or

$$\mathbf{0} = 0 \cdot \mathbf{f}$$ ∎

(3.38) Theorem
For every element $\mathbf{f}$ in a linear vector space $\mathcal{L}$, $\mathbf{f} \in \mathcal{L}$, the element

$$\mathbf{g} = (-1) \cdot \mathbf{f}$$

is the *unique negative* which is to be denoted by $-\mathbf{f}$.

Proof
As a consequence of the above theorems and the original axioms, we may write

$$\mathbf{f} + \mathbf{g} = 1 \cdot \mathbf{f} + (-1) \cdot \mathbf{f} = (1 - 1) \cdot \mathbf{f} = 0 \cdot \mathbf{f} = \mathbf{0}$$

or

$$\mathbf{f} + (-1) \cdot \mathbf{f} = \mathbf{0}$$ ∎

It is natural, in view of this result, to introduce the notion of subtraction, i.e.,

$$\mathbf{f} - \mathbf{g} \equiv \mathbf{f} + (-1) \cdot \mathbf{g}$$

It becomes necessary in many aspects of the study of systems to have some scalar measure for the correspondence of two vector-valued quantities. For example, when two vectors (points) coincide, it is convenient to say that the "distance" between them is zero. Distance, however, is an intuitive concept which must be properly defined in order to be effectively employed. To this end, we have the following definition.

(3.39) Metric
Given two vectors $\boldsymbol{\xi}$ and $\boldsymbol{\eta}$, the distance between them is given by a *metric* $\rho(\boldsymbol{\xi},\boldsymbol{\eta})$, which must possess the following properties:

(1) $\rho(\boldsymbol{\xi},\boldsymbol{\eta}) = 0$ if and only if $\boldsymbol{\xi} = \boldsymbol{\eta}$;
(2) $\rho(\boldsymbol{\xi},\boldsymbol{\eta}) = \rho(\boldsymbol{\eta},\boldsymbol{\xi})$ axiom of symmetry;
(3) $\rho(\boldsymbol{\xi},\boldsymbol{\eta}) + \rho(\boldsymbol{\eta},\boldsymbol{\lambda}) \geq \rho(\boldsymbol{\xi},\boldsymbol{\lambda})$ triangle inequality. ∎

Let $\boldsymbol{\xi}$ and $\boldsymbol{\eta}$ be two-vectors in R^2, that is,

$$\boldsymbol{\xi} = \begin{bmatrix} \xi_1 \\ \xi_2 \end{bmatrix} \quad \text{and} \quad \boldsymbol{\eta} = \begin{bmatrix} \eta_1 \\ \eta_2 \end{bmatrix}$$

then the ordinary notion of distance is represented by the metric

$$\rho_2(\boldsymbol{\xi},\boldsymbol{\eta}) \equiv |\sqrt{(\xi_1 - \eta_1)^2 + (\xi_2 - \eta_2)^2}|$$

which obviously satisfies the above three conditions. Alternately, we may consider

$$\rho_1(\boldsymbol{\xi},\boldsymbol{\eta}) \equiv |\xi_1 - \eta_1| + |\xi_2 - \eta_2|$$

and

$$\rho_\infty(\boldsymbol{\xi},\boldsymbol{\eta}) \equiv \max \{|\xi_1 - \eta_1|, |\xi_2 - \eta_2|\}$$

both of which satisfy the above three conditions and are sometimes more conveniently employed.

(3.40) Example
To illustrate these metrics, we take, for example, the following three real-valued two-vectors:

$$\boldsymbol{\xi} = \begin{bmatrix} 1 \\ 4 \end{bmatrix} \qquad \boldsymbol{\eta} = \begin{bmatrix} 2 \\ -3 \end{bmatrix} \qquad \text{and} \qquad \boldsymbol{\lambda} = \begin{bmatrix} -1 \\ 0 \end{bmatrix}$$

Hence,

$$\rho_2(\boldsymbol{\xi},\boldsymbol{\eta}) = \sqrt{50} \qquad \rho_2(\boldsymbol{\xi},\boldsymbol{\lambda}) = \sqrt{20} \qquad \text{and} \qquad \rho_2(\eta,\boldsymbol{\lambda}) = \sqrt{18}$$

similarly

$$\rho_1(\boldsymbol{\xi},\boldsymbol{\eta}) = 8 \qquad \rho_1(\boldsymbol{\xi},\boldsymbol{\lambda}) = 6 \qquad \text{and} \qquad \rho_1(\boldsymbol{\eta},\boldsymbol{\lambda}) = 6$$

and, moreover

$$\rho_\infty(\boldsymbol{\xi},\boldsymbol{\eta}) = 7 \qquad \rho_\infty(\boldsymbol{\xi},\boldsymbol{\lambda}) = 4 \qquad \text{and} \qquad \rho_\infty(\boldsymbol{\eta},\boldsymbol{\lambda}) = 3$$ ∎

We may consider the unit "circle" under each of these metrics to be the locus of all points for which the distance to the origin $\rho(\boldsymbol{\xi},\mathbf{0})$ is 1. The illustration of Fig. 3.2, then, provides a convenient visualization of the three metrics.

Although they are not so easy to visualize, the above notions readily extend to complex n space $\mathcal{C}^n$.

Associated with the concept of distance is that of length.

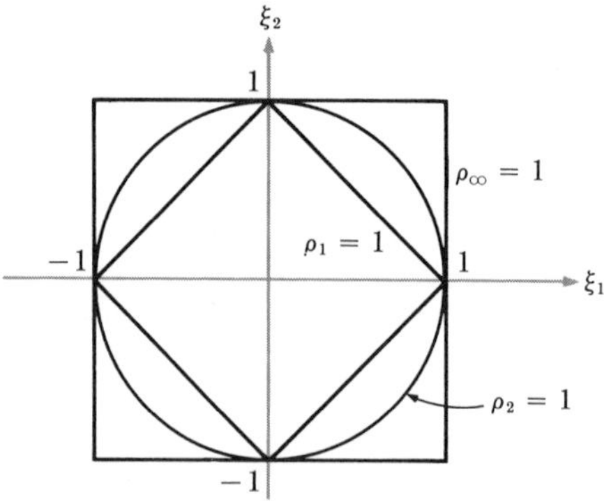

FIG. 3.2 The unit "circle" in real two-space, defined by the metric distance from the origin $\rho(\boldsymbol{\xi},0) = 1$, for ρ_1, ρ_2, and ρ_∞.

(3.41) Norm

Suppose that ξ is a complex n vector,

$$\xi = \begin{bmatrix} \xi_1 \\ \xi_2 \\ \cdot \\ \cdot \\ \cdot \\ \xi_n \end{bmatrix}$$

then we speak of the *norm* of ξ, denoted by $\|\xi\|$, as the "length" of the vector ξ (or the distance of the point ξ from the origin). The notion of norm is actually applied to far more general linear vector spaces in that it, like the metric, can be introduced axiomatically. ▮

(3.42) Normed space

A linear vector space $\mathcal{L}$ is said to be *normed* if to each element $\mathbf{f} \in \mathcal{L}$ there is made to correspond a nonnegative number $\|\mathbf{f}\|$ which is called the *norm* of $\mathbf{f}$ and possesses the following properties:

(1) $\|\mathbf{f}\| = 0$ if and only if $\mathbf{f} = 0$;
(2) $\|\alpha\mathbf{f}\| = |\alpha| \, \|\mathbf{f}\|$
(3) $\|\mathbf{f} + \mathbf{g}\| \leq \|\mathbf{f}\| + \|\mathbf{g}\|$ ▮

In particular, in $\mathcal{C}^n$ we have the $l_1{}^n$ norm

$$\|\xi\|_1 \equiv \sum_{k=1}^{n} |\xi_k|$$

the $l_2{}^n$ norm

$$\|\xi\|_2 \equiv \left| \sqrt{\sum_{k=1}^{n} |\xi_k|^2} \right| = |\sqrt{\xi'\xi}|$$

and the $l_\infty{}^n$ norm

$$\|\xi\|_\infty \equiv \max_k \{|\xi_k|\}$$

We name the linear vector space with which we are dealing according to the norm which we impose; hence, we have $l_1{}^n$ space, $l_2{}^n$ space, and $l_\infty{}^n$ space, among others. Similarly, we measure distance in a given space according to the norm imposed, i.e.,

$$\rho(\xi,\mathbf{n}) = \|\xi - \mathbf{n}\|$$

satisfies all the conditions for a metric. The natural tendency is to work in $l_2{}^n$ space, for which the notion of distance seems the most natural;

however, in many instances l_1^n space and l_∞^n space are significantly more accommodating.

3.4 LINEAR INDEPENDENCE, DIMENSIONALITY, AND BASIS VECTORS

We now formalize the concept of linear dependence referred to earlier.

(3.43) Linear dependence and independence
The set of n vectors $\{\mathbf{x}_1,\mathbf{x}_2, \ldots ,\mathbf{x}_k\}$ is said to be *linearly dependent* if there exists a set of scalars $\{c_1,c_2, \ldots ,c_k\}$, not all equal to zero, such that

$$c_1\mathbf{x}_1 + c_2\mathbf{x}_2 + \cdots + c_k\mathbf{x}_k = \mathbf{0}$$

The set of vectors $\{\mathbf{x}_1,\mathbf{x}_2, \ldots ,\mathbf{x}_k\}$ is said to be *linearly independent* if

$$c_1\mathbf{x}_1 + c_2\mathbf{x}_2 + \cdots + c_k\mathbf{x}_k = 0$$

occurs only if

$$c_1 = c_2 = \cdots = c_k = 0$$ ▮

Several conclusions are easily drawn from the above definition.

(3.44) Lemma
If some of the vectors $\mathbf{x}_1, \mathbf{x}_2, \ldots, \mathbf{x}_k$ are linearly dependent, the whole set $\{\mathbf{x}_1,\mathbf{x}_2, \ldots ,\mathbf{x}_k\}$ is also linearly dependent. ▮

(3.45) Lemma
The set of vectors $\{\mathbf{x}_1,\mathbf{x}_2, \ldots ,\mathbf{x}_k\}$ is linearly dependent if and only if one of the vectors can be expressed as a linear combination of the others. ▮

We leave it as an exercise for the reader to demonstrate the validity of lemmas (3.44) and (3.45).

(3.46) Dimension
The linear vector space $\mathcal{L}$ is called *finite dimensional,* and the number n is called the *dimension of the space* if there exist n linearly independent vectors in $\mathcal{L}$ while any $n + 1$ vectors in $\mathcal{L}$ are linearly dependent. If the space contains linearly independent systems of arbitrary numbers of vectors, then it is said to be *infinite dimensional.* ▮

In the sequel we essentially consider only finite-dimensional vector spaces, except in a few examples for motivational purposes.

(3.47) Basis
A set of linearly independent vectors $\{\xi_1,\xi_2, \ldots ,\xi_n\}$ in a linear vector space $\mathcal{L}$ is said to be a *basis* for $\mathcal{L}$ if for every vector $\mathbf{x}$ in $\mathcal{L}$ there exists an

expansion

$$\mathbf{x} = a_1\xi_1 + a_2\xi_2 + \cdots + a_n\xi_n$$

where $a_1, a_2, \ldots, a_n$ are scalars.

(3.48) Lemma

The coefficients of the expansion of any vector in terms of a basis is unique.

Proof

The lemma is easily proven by contradiction. Suppose there are two expansions for the vector x:

$$\mathbf{x} = a_1\xi_1 + a_2\xi_2 + \cdots + a_n\xi_n$$

and

$$\mathbf{x} = b_1\xi_1 + b_2\xi_2 + \cdots + b_n\xi_n$$

hence

$$\mathbf{0} = (a_1 - b_1)\xi_1 + (a_2 - b_2)\xi_2 + \cdots (a_n - b_n)\xi_n$$

But, since the set of vectors $\{\xi_1,\xi_2, \ldots ,\xi_n\}$ is linearly independent

$$a_1 = b_1,\ a_2 = b_2,\ \ldots,\ a_n = b_n$$

which contradicts the original hypothesis. ∎

The uniquely defined numbers $a_1, a_2, \ldots, a_n$ are called *components of the vector* **x** *with respect to the basis* $\{\xi_1,\xi_2, \ldots ,\xi_n\}$. That is, we say

$$\mathbf{x} = \begin{bmatrix} a_1 \\ a_2 \\ \cdot \\ \cdot \\ \cdot \\ a_n \end{bmatrix}$$

with respect to the basis $\{\xi_1,\xi_2, \ldots ,\xi_n\}$ if

$$\mathbf{x} = a_1\xi_1 + a_2\xi_2 + \cdots + a_n\xi_n$$

The following three theorems, stated without proof, are useful for vector manipulations.

(3.49) Theorem

When two vectors of a space $\mathcal{L}$ are added, their components (with respect to the same arbitrary basis) are added. When a vector is multiplied by a number λ, all its components are multiplied by λ. ∎

(3.50) Theorem

In a space $\mathcal{L}$ of dimension n there exists a basis consisting of n vectors; moreover, any set of n linearly independent vectors of the n-dimensional space $\mathcal{L}$ is a basis for the space.

(3.51) Theorem

If there is a basis in the space $\mathcal{L}$, then the dimension of $\mathcal{L}$ equals the number of basis vectors. ∎

3.5 LINEAR TRANSFORMATIONS

In the discussion that follows, we let E^n denote either euclidean n space R^n or complex n space $\mathcal{C}^n$. In Chap. 4 we will find it convenient to think of matrices in terms of how they "transform" vectors in one space into vectors in another space. The following discussion is pertinent.

(3.52) Transformation

A *transformation* T is an operator that maps E^n into E^m, written

$$T: E^n \longrightarrow E^m$$

that is, the transformation associates to every n vector $\mathbf{x} \in E^n$ at least one m vector $\mathbf{y} \in E^m$, written $\mathbf{y} = T\mathbf{x}$. The transformation T is said to be *single valued* if the $\mathbf{y}$ associated by it with each $\mathbf{x}$ is unique. The transformation T is said to be *linear* if

$$\mathbf{y}_a = T\mathbf{x}_a \qquad \text{and} \qquad \mathbf{y}_b = T\mathbf{x}_b$$

imply

$$\alpha\mathbf{y}_a + \beta\mathbf{y}_b = T(\alpha\mathbf{x}_a + \beta\mathbf{x}_b)$$

for all complex scalars α and β. ∎

We now show that single-valued, linear transformations

$$T: E^n \longrightarrow E^m$$

may be associated with an $m \times n$ matrix. Let $\{\mathbf{e}_1,\mathbf{e}_2, \ldots ,\mathbf{e}_n\}$ constitute a basis set of vectors in E^n and $\{\mathbf{f}_1,\mathbf{f}_2, \ldots ,\mathbf{f}_m\}$ constitute a basis set of vectors in E^m. Let us apply the operator T to the basis vector $\mathbf{e}_k$ ($k = 1, 2, \ldots , n$) and let the coordinates in the basis $(\mathbf{f}_1,\mathbf{f}_2, \ldots ,\mathbf{f}_m)$ of the vector $T\mathbf{e}_k$ be denoted by $\mathbf{a}_{1k}, \mathbf{a}_{2k}, \ldots , \mathbf{a}_{mk}$ ($k = 1, 2, \ldots , n$):

$$(3.53) \quad T\mathbf{e}_k = \sum_{i=1}^{m} a_{ik}\mathbf{f}_k \qquad (k = 1, 2, \ldots , n)$$

We can now multiply both sides of (3.53) by x_k and sum from $k = 1$ to $k = n$:

$$\sum_{k=1}^{n} x_k T\mathbf{e}_k = T \sum_{i=1}^{m} \left(\sum_{k=1}^{n} a_{ik}x_k\right) \mathbf{f}_i$$

hence

$$\mathbf{y} = T\mathbf{x} = T \sum_{k=1}^{n} x_k\mathbf{e}_k = \sum_{k=1}^{n} x_k T\mathbf{e}_k$$

where

$$\mathbf{y} = \sum_{i=1}^{m} y_i\mathbf{f}_i$$

and

$$y_i = \sum_{k=1}^{n} a_{ik}x_k$$

or T can be represented by the matrix

$$\begin{bmatrix} a_{11} & a_{12} & \cdots & a_{1n} \\ a_{21} & a_{22} & \cdots & a_{2n} \\ \cdots & \cdots & \cdots & \cdots \\ a_{m1} & a_{m2} & \cdots & a_{mn} \end{bmatrix}$$

The converse is also true; i.e., any $n \times m$ matrix can be associated with a single-valued, linear transformation T. Let $T: E^n \to E^m$ be a single-valued, linear transformation. Moreover let $\{\mathbf{e}_1,\mathbf{e}_2, \ldots ,\mathbf{e}_n\}$ be a basis in E^n, $\{\mathbf{f}_1,\mathbf{f}_2, \ldots ,\mathbf{f}_m\}$ be a basis in E^m, and $\mathbf{A}$ be the matrix which represents the linear transformation T on this basis. That is, if

$$\mathbf{x} = \begin{bmatrix} x_1 \\ x_2 \\ \cdot \\ \cdot \\ \cdot \\ x_n \end{bmatrix}$$

with respect to $\{\mathbf{e}_1,\mathbf{e}_2, \ldots ,\mathbf{e}_n\}$,

$$\mathbf{x} = x_1\mathbf{e}_1 + x_2\mathbf{e}_2 + \cdots + x_n\mathbf{e}_n$$

and

$$y = \begin{bmatrix} \mathbf{y}_1 \\ \mathbf{y}_2 \\ \cdot \\ \cdot \\ \cdot \\ \mathbf{y}_m \end{bmatrix}$$

with respect to $\{\mathbf{f}_1,\mathbf{f}_2, \ldots ,\mathbf{f}_m\}$,

$$\mathbf{y} = y_1\mathbf{f}_1 + y_2\mathbf{f}_2 + \cdots + y_m\mathbf{f}_m$$

then the matrix-vector equation

$$\mathbf{Ax} = \mathbf{y}$$

is equivalent to

$$\sum_{j=1}^{n} a_{ij}x_j = y_i \qquad (i = 1, 2, \ldots, n)$$

This set of linear relations represents a single-valued, linear transformation.

3.6 EIGENVECTORS AND EIGENVALUES

An alternative means of characterizing a linear transformation is in terms of the "preferred" eigen (sometimes called proper or characteristic) directions for the linear transformation in E^n.

(3.54) Linear subspace
$M \subset E^n$ is said to be a linear subspace (*or linear manifold*) if

$$\alpha\mathbf{x}_a + \beta\mathbf{x}_b \in M$$

for all $\mathbf{x}_a$ and $\mathbf{x}_b \in M$, and for all scalars α and β. ▮

(3.55) Example
Consider euclidean two-space R^2. Each of the following is easily shown to be a subspace in R^2:

(1) The origin (a single point)
(2) Any straight line through the origin
(3) The entire plane

In euclidean three-space R^3, the following are seen to be subspaces:

(1) The whole space
(2) Any plane through the origin
(3) Any straight line through the origin (intersection of two nonparallel planes through the origin)
(4) The origin (a single point)

In complex n space $\mathcal{C}^n$, the linear subspaces are complex $(n-1)$-dimensional hyperplanes through the origin $\{$actually $[2(n-1)]$ dimensions$\}$ and arbitrary intersections thereof. ▮

(3.56) Invariant subspace
$M \subset E^n$ is said to be an invariant subspace (or invariant manifold) under the transformation T if

$$\mathbf{x} \in M$$

implies

$$\mathbf{Tx} \in M$$

Observe that the origin and the entire space E^n are always invariant subspaces. ▮

Let us consider one-dimensional invariant subspaces of the n-dimensional vector space E^n. For instance, in complex n space $\mathcal{C}^n$, a complex one-dimensional subspace can be represented by a fixed complex nonzero n vector $\boldsymbol{\xi}$ multiplied by an arbitrary scalar α, that is, the locus of points generated by $\alpha\boldsymbol{\xi}$ is a complex one-dimensional subspace. In real n space R^n, with the real field, a one-dimensional subspace is a straight line through the origin. If $\alpha\boldsymbol{\xi}$ is to represent an invariant subspace for the linear transformation T, then we must have as a consequence of definition (3.56),

$$T(\alpha\boldsymbol{\xi}) = \lambda_\alpha(\alpha\boldsymbol{\xi})$$

where λ_α is a scalar (possibly complex) which depends on α. Equivalently, using the matrix representation of the operator, we have

$$\mathbf{A}(\alpha\boldsymbol{\xi}) = \lambda_\alpha(\alpha\boldsymbol{\xi}) \tag{3.57}$$

or

$$(\mathbf{A} - \lambda_\alpha\mathbf{1})\boldsymbol{\xi} = \mathbf{0}$$

and since α cancels from the homogeneous equation (3.57), λ_α must be independent of α, so we write

$$\mathbf{A}\boldsymbol{\xi} = \lambda\boldsymbol{\xi}$$

or

$$(\mathbf{A} - \lambda\mathbf{1})\boldsymbol{\xi} = \mathbf{0}$$

If we can find a nonzero vector which satisfies this relation, then we can conclude that any constant real or complex multiple of it does also; hence, the nonzero vector $\boldsymbol{\xi}$ defines a one-dimensional invariant subspace of E^n for the linear operator T represented in the basis $\{\mathbf{e}_1,\mathbf{e}_2, \ldots ,\mathbf{e}_n\}$ by the matrix $\mathbf{A}$.

Recall that the matrix equation

$$(\mathbf{A} - \lambda\mathbf{1})\boldsymbol{\xi} = \mathbf{0}$$

actually represents a set of simultaneous algebraic equations. This set of equations may be solved for a unique $\boldsymbol{\xi}$ by Cramer's rule if

$$\det (\mathbf{A} - \lambda\mathbf{1}) \neq 0$$

In this instance, the only solution is $\boldsymbol{\xi} \equiv 0$. On the other hand if

$$\det(\mathbf{A} - \lambda\mathbf{1}) = \mathbf{0},$$

then the solution is nonunique and, as we shall see, nontrivial, i.e., a solution $\boldsymbol{\xi} \neq 0$ exists.

We define the *characteristic polynomial* as

$$q(\lambda) \equiv \det(\mathbf{A} - \lambda\mathbf{1}) = q_0 + q_1\lambda + \cdots + q_n\lambda^n$$

where $q_0 = \det(\mathbf{A})$ and $q_n = (-1)^n$. The roots of the *characteristic equation*

$$q(\lambda) = 0$$

are called *eigenvalues* (or characteristic values). From the *fundamental theorem of algebra,* we recognize that the characteristic equation

$$q_0 + q_1\lambda + \cdots + q_n\lambda^n = 0$$

has n roots (some of which may coincide and some of which may be complex). Corresponding to each of the *eigenvalues*

$$\{\lambda_1,\lambda_2, \ldots ,\lambda_n\}$$

is the corresponding member from the set of *eigenvectors*

$$\{\boldsymbol{\xi}_1,\boldsymbol{\xi}_2, \ldots ,\boldsymbol{\xi}_n\}$$

where equal eigenvalues *may* correspond to equal eigenvectors. That is, the eigenvector $\boldsymbol{\xi}_k$ may be taken to be any *nonzero* solution of the homogeneous algebraic equation

$$(\mathbf{A} - \lambda_k\mathbf{1})\boldsymbol{\xi}_k = \mathbf{0}$$

Observe that such solutions are not unique; since the equations are homogeneous, any scalar multiple of a solution vector is also a solution vector—this and other sources of ambiguity are presently to be cleared up.

(3.58) Theorem

If the eigenvalues are numbered so that the first k $(1 \leq k \leq n)$ are distinct, then the corresponding eigenvectors $\boldsymbol{\xi}_1, \boldsymbol{\xi}_2, \ldots, \boldsymbol{\xi}_k$ are linearly independent.

Proof

This theorem is proved by induction. The first eigenvector $\boldsymbol{\xi}_1$ is linearly independent (trivially), because it is nonzero by definition, i.e.,

$$c_1\boldsymbol{\xi}_1 = \mathbf{0} \text{ if and only if } c_1 = 0$$

Now assume the first $l - 1(2 \leq l \leq k)$ eigenvectors are linearly independent but the first l are not. Then

(3.59) $c_1\xi_1 + c_2\xi_2 + \cdots c_l\xi_l = \mathbf{0}$

for some set of constant $\{c_1, c_2, \ldots, c_l\}$, not all of which are zero. Now, consider

$$\mathbf{A}(c_1\xi_1 + c_2\xi_2 + \cdots + c_l\xi_l) = \mathbf{0}$$

which implies

(3.60) $c_1\lambda_1\xi_1 + c_2\lambda_2\xi_2 + \cdots + c_l\lambda_l\xi_l = \mathbf{0}$

Multiplication of the originally assumed linear dependence relation (3.59) by λ_l and subtraction of the result from (3.60) yields

$$c_1(\lambda_1 - \lambda_l)\xi_1 + c_2(\lambda_2 - \lambda_l)\xi_2 + \cdots + c_l(\lambda_{l-1} - \lambda_l)\xi_{l-1} = \mathbf{0}$$

But the first $l - 1$ eigenvectors were assumed to be linearly independent, therefore,

$$c_1(\lambda_1 - \lambda_l) = c_2(\lambda_2 - \lambda_l) = \cdots = c_l(\lambda_{l-1} - \lambda_l) = 0$$

Since the eigenvalues $\lambda_1, \lambda_2, \ldots, \lambda_l$ are distinct,

$$c_1 = c_2 = \cdots = c_{l-1} = 0$$

which contradicts the assumed linear dependence of the first l eigenvectors, because

$$c_l\xi_l = 0$$

can only hold for $c_l = 0$ as well. ∎

Note that Theorem (3.58) says nothing of the eigenvectors which correspond to nondistinct eigenvalues, which may or may not be linearly independent of the others. If $k = n$, that is, if all eigenvalues are distinct, the n corresponding eigenvectors $\xi_1, \xi_2, \ldots, \xi_n$ are linearly independent and may be taken to be a basis in E^n.

(3.61) Example

Consider a linear transformation that is characterized by the matrix

$$\mathbf{A} = \begin{bmatrix} 0 & 1 \\ -2 & -3 \end{bmatrix}$$

The characteristic polynomial is

$$\begin{aligned} q(\lambda) &= \det(\mathbf{A} - \lambda\mathbf{1}) \\ &= \det \begin{bmatrix} -\lambda & 1 & \\ -2 & -3 & -\lambda \end{bmatrix} \\ &= \lambda^2 + 3\lambda + 2 \end{aligned}$$

and the eigenvalues obtained from the characteristic equation

$$\lambda^2 + 3\lambda + 2 = 0$$

or

$$(\lambda + 1)(\lambda + 2) = 0$$

are

$$\lambda_1 = -1 \qquad \text{and} \qquad \lambda_2 = -2$$

To find an eigenvector associated with λ_1, we consider

$$(\mathbf{A} - \lambda_1\mathbf{1})\boldsymbol{\xi}_1 = \mathbf{0}$$

or

$$\begin{bmatrix} 1 & 1 \\ -2 & -2 \end{bmatrix} \begin{bmatrix} \xi_{11} \\ \xi_{21} \end{bmatrix} = \begin{bmatrix} 0 \\ 0 \end{bmatrix}$$

Therefore

$$\xi_{11} + \xi_{21} = 0 \tag{3.62}$$

One solution of (3.62) is

$$\xi_{11} = 1 \qquad \text{and} \qquad \xi_{21} = -1$$

so that an eigenvector associated with $\lambda_1 = -1$ is

$$\boldsymbol{\xi}_1 = \begin{bmatrix} 1 \\ -1 \end{bmatrix}$$

Observe that this choice for the eigenvector is not unique since

$$\boldsymbol{\xi}_1 = \begin{bmatrix} 2 \\ -2 \end{bmatrix}$$

also satisfies (3.62). Now consider

$$(\mathbf{A} - \lambda_2\mathbf{1})\boldsymbol{\xi}_2 = \mathbf{0}$$

or

$$\begin{bmatrix} 2 & 1 \\ -2 & -1 \end{bmatrix} \begin{bmatrix} \xi_{12} \\ \xi_{22} \end{bmatrix} = \begin{bmatrix} 0 \\ 0 \end{bmatrix}$$

so that

$$2\xi_{12} + \xi_{22} = 0$$

We can take

$$\xi_{12} = 1 \qquad \text{and} \qquad \xi_{22} = -2$$

i.e., the eigenvector associated with $\lambda_2 = -2$ is

$$\boldsymbol{\xi}_2 = \begin{bmatrix} 1 \\ -2 \end{bmatrix}$$

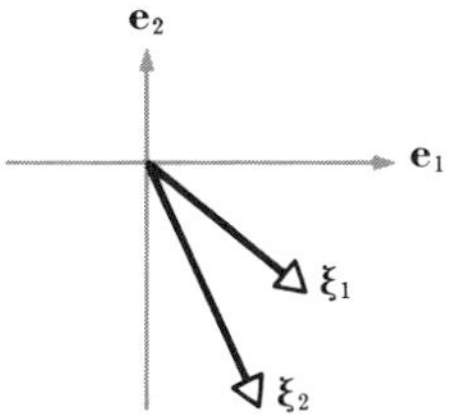

FIG. 3.3 Two eigenvectors which constitute a basis in two-space.

These eigenvectors are shown in Fig. 3.3. Observe that although the eigenvectors are not orthogonal, they *do* constitute a basis since they are linearly independent. ∎

When we consider the expansion of an arbitrary vector $\mathbf{z}$ in terms of a basis made up of eigenvectors which correspond to distinct eigenvalues,

$$\mathbf{z} = z_1\xi_1 + z_2\xi_2 + \cdots + z_n\xi_n$$

or

$$\mathbf{z} = \begin{bmatrix} z_1 \\ z_2 \\ \cdot \\ \cdot \\ \cdot \\ z_n \end{bmatrix}$$

with respect to the basis $\{\xi_1, \xi_2, \ldots, \xi_n\}$, we recognize that the effect of the linear transformation T on this vector is simply computed as

$$\mathbf{W} = T\mathbf{z}$$

or

$$\mathbf{W} = z_1\lambda_1\xi_1 + z_2\lambda_2\xi_2 + \cdots + z_n\lambda_n\xi_n$$

Consideration of the case for which the eigenvalues are not distinct will be postponed since a much more complicated theory prevails. In the meantime, we may discuss all the pertinent results in terms of the *usual* special case in which all n eigenvalues are distinct. Before we proceed to do so, we consider a second example which motivates the use of complex space.

(3.63) Example

The linear transformation which is represented by the real matrix

$$\mathbf{A} = \begin{bmatrix} \cos\theta & \sin\theta \\ -\sin\theta & \cos\theta \end{bmatrix}$$

is the rotation of every vector in *real* two-space through the angle θ. The characteristic polynomial is

$$q(\lambda) = \det\begin{bmatrix} \cos\theta - \lambda & \sin\theta \\ -\sin\theta & \cos\theta - \lambda \end{bmatrix}$$
$$= \lambda^2 - 2\lambda\cos\theta + 1$$

and the eigenvalues, obtained from the characteristic equation

$$\lambda^2 - 2\lambda\cos\theta + 1 = 0$$

are

$$\lambda_1 = \cos\theta + j\sin\theta = e^{j\theta}$$

and

$$\lambda_2 = \cos\theta - j\sin\theta = e^{-j\theta}$$

In general, the eigenvalues are complex conjugates. The eigenvectors are obtained as follows:

$$\begin{bmatrix} -j\sin\theta & \sin\theta \\ -\sin\theta & -j\sin\theta \end{bmatrix}\begin{bmatrix} \xi_{11} \\ \xi_{21} \end{bmatrix} = \begin{bmatrix} 0 \\ 0 \end{bmatrix}$$

so that

$$\xi_1 = (1\ j)';$$
$$\begin{bmatrix} j\sin\theta & \sin\theta \\ -\sin\theta & j\sin\theta \end{bmatrix}\begin{bmatrix} \xi_{12} \\ \xi_{21} \end{bmatrix} = \begin{bmatrix} 0 \\ 0 \end{bmatrix}$$

so that

$$\xi_2 = (1\ -j)'$$

Thus, use of the complex space allows us to represent a rotation by means of a multiplication. Consider a 90° rotation, $\theta = \pi/2$; then

$$\mathbf{A} = \begin{bmatrix} 0 & 1 \\ -1 & 0 \end{bmatrix}$$

and the eigenvectors become

$$\xi_1 = \begin{bmatrix} 1 \\ j \end{bmatrix} \qquad \text{and} \qquad \xi_2 = \begin{bmatrix} 1 \\ -j \end{bmatrix}$$

Note that

$$j\xi_1 = \begin{bmatrix} j \\ 1 \end{bmatrix} \qquad \text{and} \qquad \xi_1 = \begin{bmatrix} 1 \\ j \end{bmatrix}$$

are 90° apart as are

$$-j\xi_2 = \begin{bmatrix} -j \\ 1 \end{bmatrix} \qquad \text{and} \qquad \xi_2 = \begin{bmatrix} 1 \\ -j \end{bmatrix}$$

(to visualize, consider real and imaginary parts separately). With complex coefficients any real two-vector can be expanded in terms of ξ_1 and ξ_2. In general, we may consider separately the real and imaginary parts of the eigenvectors and the vectors into which they are transformed. For instance

$$\xi_1 = (1\ j)'$$

implies

$$\text{Re}\,\{\xi_1\} = (1\ 0)' \qquad \text{and} \qquad \text{Im}\,\{\xi_1\} = (0\ 1)'$$

$$e^{j\theta}\xi_1 = (e^{j\theta}\ je^{j\theta})'$$

implies

$$\text{Re}\,\{e^{j\theta}\xi_1\} = \begin{bmatrix} \cos\theta \\ -\sin\theta \end{bmatrix} \qquad \text{and} \qquad \text{Im}\,\{e^{j\theta}\xi_1\} = \begin{bmatrix} \sin\theta \\ \cos\theta \end{bmatrix}$$

$$\xi_2 = (1\ -j)'$$

implies

$$\text{Re}\,\{\xi_2\} = (1\ 0)' \qquad \text{and} \qquad \text{Im}\,\{\xi_2\} = (0\ -1)'$$

and finally,

$$e^{-j\theta}\xi_2 = (e^{-j\theta}\ -je^{-j\theta})'$$

implies

$$\text{Re}\,\{e^{-j\theta}\xi_2\} = \begin{bmatrix} \cos\theta \\ -\sin\theta \end{bmatrix} \qquad \text{and} \qquad \text{Im}\,\{e^{-j\theta}\xi_2\} = \begin{bmatrix} -\sin\theta \\ -\cos\theta \end{bmatrix}$$

We see then that, in general, a rotation in real two-space can be represented as a complex multiplication in complex two-space. All the pertinent pairs of two-vectors discussed above differ by the angle θ in real two-space. These concepts extend readily to complex n space since n-space rotations can be expressed in terms of multiple two-space rotations. ∎

The introduction of the complex space does not yield any more information about a real matrix **A**, but manipulations are much easier since all operations can be represented by multiplications.

(3.64) Theorem

If **A** is an $n \times n$ *real* matrix with the complex eigenvalue λ corresponding to the complex eigenvector ξ, then $\bar{\lambda}$ is also a complex eigenvalue, and it corresponds to the complex eigenvector $\bar{\xi}$.

Proof

If ξ is an eigenvector associated with the eigenvalue λ, then

$$\mathbf{A}\xi = \lambda\xi$$

Taking the complex conjugate of this equation yields

$$\bar{\mathbf{A}}\bar{\xi} = \bar{\lambda}\bar{\xi}$$

But **A** is real, therefore

$$\mathbf{A}\bar{\xi} = \bar{\lambda}\bar{\xi}$$

∎

Observe that the immediately preceding example (3.63) verifies this property.

There is some ambiguity associated with the selection of eigenvectors, because their length is not determined by the homogeneous defining relation; i.e.,

$$(\mathbf{A} - \lambda\mathbf{1})\boldsymbol{\xi} = 0$$

implies

$$(\mathbf{A} - \lambda\mathbf{1})(k\boldsymbol{\xi}) = \mathbf{0}$$

for arbitrary complex constants k. Some of the ambiguity can be removed by normalizing the eigenvectors to unit length. The normalized set of eigenvectors $\mathbf{e}_k$ are formed as follows:

$$\mathbf{e}_k \equiv \frac{1}{\sqrt{\boldsymbol{\xi}_k^* \boldsymbol{\xi}_k}} \boldsymbol{\xi}_k \qquad (k = 1, 2, \ldots, n)$$

(where * indicates complex conjugate transpose, $\boldsymbol{\xi}_k^* = \bar{\boldsymbol{\xi}}_k'$) then, $\mathbf{e}_k^*\mathbf{e}_k = 1$. It is still true that the eigenvectors are not unambiguously defined, since if $\mathbf{e}_k$ is an eigenvector of unit length, so is $e^{j\theta}\mathbf{e}_k$, where θ is an arbitrary real constant. We need not worry about the normalization of eigenvectors in the following exposition.

Unless otherwise stated, we will assume that the eigenvalues $\lambda_1, \lambda_2, \ldots, \lambda_n$ are distinct so that the corresponding set of eigenvectors $\{\boldsymbol{\xi}_1,\boldsymbol{\xi}_2, \ldots ,\boldsymbol{\xi}_n\}$ constitutes a basis in E^n.

3.7 DIAGONALIZATION OF A MATRIX

Consider the matrix expression

$$\mathbf{Ax} = \mathbf{y}$$

and the associated basis of eigenvectors $\{\boldsymbol{\xi}_1,\boldsymbol{\xi}_2, \ldots ,\boldsymbol{\xi}_n\}$ which correspond to the distinct eigenvalues $\lambda_1, \lambda_2, \ldots, \lambda_n$. Suppose we assume that both the vectors $\mathbf{x}$ and $\mathbf{y}$ can be represented in this basis by

$$\mathbf{x} = \hat{x}_1\boldsymbol{\xi}_1 + \hat{x}_2\boldsymbol{\xi}_2 + \cdots + \hat{x}_n\boldsymbol{\xi}_n$$

and

$$\mathbf{y} = \hat{y}_1\boldsymbol{\xi}_1 + \hat{y}_2\boldsymbol{\xi}_2 + \cdots + \hat{y}_n\boldsymbol{\xi}_n$$

Then the relation

$$\mathbf{Ax} - \mathbf{y} = \mathbf{0}$$

becomes

$$(\lambda_1\hat{x}_1 - \hat{y}_1)\boldsymbol{\xi}_1 + (\lambda_2\hat{x}_2 - \hat{y}_2)\boldsymbol{\xi}_2 + \cdots + (\lambda_n\hat{x}_n + \hat{y}_n)\boldsymbol{\xi}_n = 0$$

Since the eigenvectors are linearly independent,

$$\lambda_k \hat{x}_k - \hat{y}_k = 0 \qquad (k = 1, 2, \ldots, n)$$

If **A** is nonsingular, i.e., det (**A**) $\neq 0$ so that the first term of the characteristic equation is nonzero, then

$$\lambda_k \neq 0 \qquad (k = 1, 2, \ldots, n)$$

and we can solve trivially for $\hat{x}_k$ in terms of $\hat{y}_k$:

$$\hat{x}_k = \frac{1}{\lambda_k} \hat{y}_k$$

Thus in the *eigenvector basis*, the linear transformation T which corresponds to the matrix **A** in the original basis is represented by the diagonal matrix

$$\mathbf{\Lambda} = \begin{bmatrix} \lambda_1 & 0 & 0 & \cdots & 0 \\ 0 & \lambda_2 & 0 & \cdots & 0 \\ 0 & 0 & \lambda_3 & \cdots & 0 \\ \cdot & \cdot & \cdot & \cdots & \cdot \\ 0 & 0 & 0 & \cdots & \lambda_n \end{bmatrix}$$

or

$$\mathbf{\Lambda} = \text{diag}\,(\lambda_1, \lambda_2, \ldots, \lambda_n)$$

Now consider two arbitrary sets of basis vectors in E^n:

$$\{\mathbf{b}_1, \mathbf{b}_2, \ldots, \mathbf{b}_n\}$$

and

$$\{\mathbf{d}_1, \mathbf{d}_2, \ldots, \mathbf{d}_n\}$$

Since all the vectors $\mathbf{d}_k$, $k = 1, 2, \ldots, n$ can be represented in terms of the basis $\{\mathbf{b}_1, \mathbf{b}_2, \ldots, \mathbf{b}_n\}$, and all the vectors $\mathbf{b}_k$, $k = 1, 2, \ldots, n$ can be represented in terms of the basis $\{\mathbf{d}_1, \mathbf{d}_2, \ldots, \mathbf{d}_n\}$, the bases are related by an $n \times n$ nonsingular matrix (transformation) **W**:

$$\mathbf{D} = \mathbf{W}\mathbf{B}$$

or

$$\mathbf{B} = \mathbf{W}^{-1}\mathbf{D} \tag{3.65}$$

where we have defined

$$\mathbf{B} \equiv \begin{pmatrix} \mathbf{b}_1 & \mathbf{b}_2 & \cdots & \mathbf{b}_n \\ \downarrow & \downarrow & & \downarrow \end{pmatrix}$$

and

$$\mathbf{D} \equiv \begin{pmatrix} \mathbf{d}_1 & \mathbf{d}_2 & \cdots & \mathbf{d}_n \\ \downarrow & \downarrow & & \downarrow \end{pmatrix}$$

The columns of these matrices are linearly independent so that det (**B**) $\neq$

0 and det (**D**) $\neq$ 0. Therefore **W** and $\mathbf{W}^{-1}$ are uniquely defined by

$$\mathbf{W} \equiv \mathbf{DB}^{-1} \qquad \text{and} \qquad \mathbf{W}^{-1} \equiv \mathbf{BD}^{-1}$$

This fact will be used to demonstrate that the eigenvalues (but not the eigenvectors) of a matrix (linear transformation) are independent of the choice of basis.

Let **x** and **y** be two vectors characterized by

$$\mathbf{x} = (x_1,x_2, \ldots ,x_n)' \qquad \text{and} \qquad \mathbf{y} = (y_1,y_2, \ldots ,y_n)'$$

with respect to the basis $\{\mathbf{b}_1,\mathbf{b}_2, \ldots ,\mathbf{b}_n\}$, and

$$\hat{\mathbf{x}} = (\hat{x}_1,\hat{x}_2, \ldots ,\hat{x}_n)' \qquad \text{and} \qquad \hat{\mathbf{y}} = (\hat{y}_1,\hat{y}_2, \ldots ,\hat{y}_n)'$$

with respect to the basis $\{\mathbf{d}_1,\mathbf{d}_2, \ldots ,\mathbf{d}_n\}$. Furthermore, let T be a linear transformation represented by the matrix **A** in the basis $\{b_1,b_2, \ldots ,b_n\}$ such that

$$\mathbf{Ax} = \mathbf{y} \tag{3.66}$$

From (3.65)

$$\mathbf{x} = \mathbf{W}^{-1}\hat{\mathbf{x}}$$

and

$$\mathbf{y} = \mathbf{W}^{-1}\hat{\mathbf{y}}$$

so that

$$\mathbf{AW}^{-1}\hat{\mathbf{x}} = \mathbf{W}^{-1}\hat{\mathbf{y}}$$

or

$$\mathbf{WAW}^{-1}\hat{\mathbf{x}} = \hat{\mathbf{y}}$$

in the new basis, $\{\mathbf{d}_1,\mathbf{d}_2, \ldots ,\mathbf{d}_n\}$. In other words, the transformation T is represented by the matrix

$$\hat{\mathbf{A}} = \mathbf{WAW}^{-1}$$

with respect to the second basis. Consider the characteristic polynomial associated with $\hat{\mathbf{A}}$:

$$\begin{aligned}
\det(\hat{\mathbf{A}} - \lambda\mathbf{1}) &= \det(\mathbf{WAW}^{-1} - \lambda\mathbf{1}) \\
&= \det(\mathbf{WAW}^{-1} - \lambda\mathbf{WW}^{-1}) \\
&= \det(\mathbf{W}(\mathbf{A} - \lambda\mathbf{1})\mathbf{W}^{-1}) \\
&= \det(\mathbf{W}) \det(\mathbf{A} - \lambda\mathbf{1}) \det(\mathbf{W}^{-1}) \\
&= \det(\mathbf{A} - \lambda\mathbf{1})
\end{aligned}$$

which is the characteristic polynomial associated with the matrix **A**. Thus the set of eigenvalues is invariant under a change in basis for a given transformation T.

In summary, any matrix **A** corresponds to a linear transformation T. The eigenvalues associated with this linear transformation are invariant under a change in basis, and the transformation is represented by a diagonal matrix in the eigenvector basis if the eigenvalues are distinct. Thus the eigenvector basis seems to be the natural basis to represent any matrix, and we now demonstrate how to transform any matrix with distinct eigenvalues into diagonal form. These manipulations will be extremely useful when we discuss functions of a matrix.

Consider the matrix relation

$$\mathbf{A}\mathbf{x} = \mathbf{y} \tag{3.67}$$

where the basis is arbitrary. Construct the *modal matrix* **S**, the columns of which are the n linearly independent eigenvectors (in this arbitrary basis):

$$\mathbf{S} = \begin{pmatrix} \xi_1 & \xi_2 & \cdots & \xi_n \\ \downarrow & \downarrow & & \downarrow \end{pmatrix}$$

Then take

$$\mathbf{W} = \mathbf{S}^{-1}$$

so that from (3.65), the vector **x** with respect to the eigenvector basis is

$$\hat{\mathbf{x}} = \mathbf{S}^{-1}\mathbf{x}$$

or

$$\mathbf{x} = \mathbf{S}\hat{\mathbf{x}}$$

Observe that the eigenvectors are linearly independent, and therefore, **S** is nonsingular. Now, consider $\mathbf{S}^{-1}$ to be constructed of row vectors

$$\mathbf{S}^{-1} \equiv \begin{bmatrix} \mathbf{n}_1' \rightarrow \\ \mathbf{n}_2' \rightarrow \\ \mathbf{n}_n' \rightarrow \end{bmatrix}$$

where the $\mathbf{n}_k$ are called the *reciprocal basis.* Since $\mathbf{S}^{-1}\mathbf{S} = \mathbf{1}$, it follows that

$$\mathbf{n}_k'\xi_k = \begin{cases} 0 & \text{if } k \neq l \\ 1 & \text{if } k = l \end{cases}$$

Hence, if in terms of the eigenvector basis $\xi_1, \xi_2, \ldots, \xi_n$, the representation of **x** is

$$\mathbf{x} = \hat{x}_1\xi_1 + \hat{x}_2\xi_2 + \cdots + \hat{x}_n\xi_n$$

then

$$\hat{\mathbf{x}} = \mathbf{S}^{-1}\mathbf{x} = \begin{bmatrix} \mathbf{n}_1 \rightarrow \\ \mathbf{n}_2 \rightarrow \\ \cdot \\ \cdot \\ \cdot \\ \mathbf{n}_n \rightarrow \end{bmatrix} (\hat{x}_1\xi_1 + \hat{x}_2\xi_2 + \cdots + \hat{x}_n\xi_n) = \begin{bmatrix} \hat{x}_1 \\ \hat{x}_2 \\ \cdot \\ \cdot \\ \cdot \\ \hat{x}_n \end{bmatrix}$$

That is, given any $\mathbf{x}$, $\mathbf{S}^{-1}\mathbf{x}$ becomes the desired representation. Similarly, if

$$\mathbf{y} = \hat{y}_1\xi_1 + \hat{y}_2\xi_2 + \cdots \hat{y}_n\xi_n$$

then

$$\hat{\mathbf{y}} = \mathbf{S}^{-1}\mathbf{y} = \begin{bmatrix} \mathfrak{n}_1 \rightarrow \\ \mathfrak{n}_2 \rightarrow \\ \cdot \\ \cdot \\ \cdot \\ \mathfrak{n}_n \rightarrow \end{bmatrix} (\hat{y}_1\xi_1 + \hat{y}_2\xi_2 + \cdots + \hat{y}_n\xi_n) = \begin{bmatrix} \hat{y}_1 \\ \hat{y}_2 \\ \cdot \\ \cdot \\ \cdot \\ \hat{y}_n \end{bmatrix}$$

The matrix relation (3.67) becomes, in the new basis,

$$\mathbf{AS}\hat{\mathbf{x}} = \mathbf{S}\hat{\mathbf{y}}$$

or

$$\mathbf{S}^{-1}\mathbf{AS}\hat{\mathbf{x}} = \hat{\mathbf{y}}$$

Consider first

$$\mathbf{AS} = \mathbf{A}\begin{pmatrix} \xi_1 & \xi_2 & \cdots & \xi_n \\ \downarrow & \downarrow & & \downarrow \end{pmatrix} = \begin{pmatrix} \lambda_1\xi_1 & \lambda_2\xi_2 & \cdots & \lambda_n\xi_n \\ \downarrow & \downarrow & & \downarrow \end{pmatrix}$$

$$= \begin{pmatrix} \xi_1 & \xi_2 & \cdots & \xi_n \\ \downarrow & \downarrow & & \downarrow \end{pmatrix} \begin{bmatrix} \lambda_1 & 0 & \cdots & 0 \\ 0 & \lambda_2 & \cdots & 0 \\ \cdot & \cdot & \cdots & \cdot \\ 0 & 0 & \cdots & \lambda_n \end{bmatrix}$$

$$= \mathbf{S\Lambda}$$

where

$$\mathbf{\Lambda} = \text{diag}\,(\lambda_1,\lambda_2, \ldots ,\lambda_n)$$

Hence,

$$\mathbf{S}^{-1}\mathbf{AS} = \mathbf{S}^{-1}\mathbf{S\Lambda} = \mathbf{\Lambda}$$

Therefore, the diagonal matrix $\mathbf{\Lambda}$ represents the linear transformation T in the eigenvector basis $\{\xi_1,\xi_2, \ldots ,\xi_n\}$.

(3.68) Example

In example (3.61) we found that the matrix

$$\mathbf{A} = \begin{bmatrix} 0 & 1 \\ -2 & -3 \end{bmatrix}$$

had the eigenvalues

$$\lambda_1 = -1 \qquad \text{and} \qquad \lambda_2 = -2$$

and the eigenvectors

$$\xi_1 = \begin{bmatrix} 1 \\ -1 \end{bmatrix} \qquad \text{and} \qquad \xi_2 = \begin{bmatrix} 1 \\ -2 \end{bmatrix}$$

The modal matrix is

$$\mathbf{S} = \begin{bmatrix} 1 & 1 \\ -1 & -2 \end{bmatrix}$$

and

$$\mathbf{S}^{-1} = \begin{bmatrix} 2 & 1 \\ -1 & -1 \end{bmatrix}$$

Therefore,

$$\begin{aligned} \mathbf{S}^{-1}\mathbf{A}\mathbf{S} &= \begin{bmatrix} 2 & 1 \\ -1 & -1 \end{bmatrix}\begin{bmatrix} 0 & 1 \\ -2 & -3 \end{bmatrix}\begin{bmatrix} 1 & 1 \\ -1 & -2 \end{bmatrix} \\ &= \begin{bmatrix} -1 & 0 \\ 0 & -2 \end{bmatrix} \end{aligned}$$

(3.69) Example
Consider the matrix

$$\mathbf{A} = \begin{bmatrix} 1 & 2 \\ 2 & 1 \end{bmatrix}$$

The eigenvalues are $\lambda_1 = -1$ and $\lambda_2 = 3$ and the corresponding eigenvectors may be taken to be

$$\boldsymbol{\xi}_1 = \begin{bmatrix} 1 \\ -1 \end{bmatrix} \quad \text{and} \quad \boldsymbol{\xi}_2 = \begin{bmatrix} 1 \\ 1 \end{bmatrix}$$

so that

$$\mathbf{S} = \begin{bmatrix} 1 & 1 \\ -1 & 1 \end{bmatrix} \quad \text{and} \quad \mathbf{S}^{-1} = \frac{1}{2}\begin{bmatrix} 1 & -1 \\ 1 & 1 \end{bmatrix}$$

It is easy to verify that

$$\mathbf{S}^{-1}\mathbf{A}\mathbf{S} = \begin{bmatrix} -1 & 0 \\ 0 & 3 \end{bmatrix}$$

∎

We note finally the *dyadic representation* for a given matrix **A** with distinct eigenvalues in terms of the eigenvectors and their corresponding reciprocal basis

$$\mathbf{A} = \lambda_1\boldsymbol{\xi}_1\mathbf{n}_1' + \lambda_2\boldsymbol{\xi}_2\mathbf{n}_2' + \cdots + \lambda_n\boldsymbol{\xi}_n\mathbf{n}_n'$$

is equivalent to the matrix relation

$$\mathbf{A} = \mathbf{S}\boldsymbol{\Lambda}\mathbf{S}^{-1}$$

For instance in Example (3.61), we have

$$\mathbf{A} = \begin{bmatrix} 0 & 1 \\ -2 & -3 \end{bmatrix} = -1\begin{bmatrix} 1 \\ 1 \end{bmatrix}(2 \quad 1) - 2\begin{bmatrix} 1 \\ -2 \end{bmatrix}(-1 \quad -1)$$

while in Example (3.63), we have

$$\mathbf{A} = \begin{bmatrix} 1 & 2 \\ 2 & 1 \end{bmatrix} = -1 \begin{bmatrix} 1 \\ -1 \end{bmatrix} (\tfrac{1}{2} \quad -\tfrac{1}{2}) + 3 \begin{bmatrix} 1 \\ 1 \end{bmatrix} (\tfrac{1}{2} \quad \tfrac{1}{2})$$

Similarly,

$$\begin{bmatrix} \cos\theta & \sin\theta \\ -\sin\theta & \cos\theta \end{bmatrix} = e^{j\theta} \begin{bmatrix} 1 \\ j \end{bmatrix} (\tfrac{1}{2} \quad -j\tfrac{1}{2}) + e^{j\theta} \begin{bmatrix} 1 \\ -j \end{bmatrix} (\tfrac{1}{2} \quad j\tfrac{1}{2})$$

3.8 THE CAYLEY-HAMILTON THEOREM AND FUNCTIONS OF SQUARE MATRICES

We have seen the importance of the quantity e^{at} in the solution of first-order systems. In the study of second-order systems, the matrix $e^{\mathbf{A}t}$ where $\mathbf{A}$ is a 2×2 matrix played an important role. To this juncture, the only means presented for evaluation of $e^{\mathbf{A}t}$ has been in terms of an infinite series. A much more palatable means for evaluating $e^{\mathbf{A}t}$ emerges as a result of the eminently useful Cayley-Hamilton theorem.

(3.70) Theorem

Every $n \times n$ matrix satisfies its characteristic equation; i.e., if

$$\det(\mathbf{A} - \lambda\mathbf{1}) = q(\lambda) = q_0 + q_1\lambda + \cdots + q_n\lambda^n$$

then

$$q(\mathbf{A}) = q_0\mathbf{1} + q_1\mathbf{A} + \cdots + q_n\mathbf{A}^n = \mathbf{0}$$

where $\mathbf{1} = \mathbf{A}^0$, of course.

Proof

(We prove at this point only the special case for distinct eigenvalues, reserving the general proof for a subsequent section.) Consider an arbitrary vector $\mathbf{x} \in E^n$, and let the set of linearly independent eigenvectors $\{\boldsymbol{\xi}_1, \boldsymbol{\xi}_2, \ldots, \boldsymbol{\xi}_n\}$ correspond to the distinct eigenvalues $\lambda_1, \lambda_2, \ldots, \lambda_n$ of $\mathbf{A}$. Then we can express $\mathbf{x}$ as

$$\mathbf{x} = \hat{x}_1\boldsymbol{\xi}_1 + \hat{x}_2\boldsymbol{\xi}_2 + \cdots + \hat{x}_n\boldsymbol{\xi}_n$$

Consider also

$$(3.71) \quad q(\mathbf{A})\mathbf{x} = (q_0\mathbf{1} + q_1\mathbf{A} + \cdots + q_n\mathbf{A}^n)(\hat{x}_1\boldsymbol{\xi}_1 + \hat{x}_2\boldsymbol{\xi}_2 + \cdots + \hat{x}_n\boldsymbol{\xi}_n)$$

Since

$$\mathbf{A}\boldsymbol{\xi}_k = \lambda_k\boldsymbol{\xi}_k$$

it follows that

$$\mathbf{A}^r\boldsymbol{\xi}_k = \lambda_k{}^r\boldsymbol{\xi}_k \qquad (r = 0, 1, 2, \ldots)$$

Therefore, (3.71) becomes

$$q(\mathbf{A})\mathbf{x} = q(\lambda_1)\hat{x}_1\xi_1 + q(\lambda_2)\hat{x}_2\xi_2 + \cdots + q(\lambda_n)\hat{x}_n\xi_n$$

But

$$q(\lambda_k) = 0 \qquad k = 1, 2, \ldots, n$$

because $\lambda_1, \lambda_2, \ldots, \lambda_n$ are eigenvalues (roots of the characteristic equation). Thus,

$$q(\mathbf{A})\mathbf{x} = \mathbf{0}$$

for arbitrary vectors $\mathbf{x} \in E^n$, so $q(\mathbf{A})$ must be the zero matrix

$$q(\mathbf{A}) = \mathbf{0}$$ ∎

The fundamental result

$$q_0\mathbf{1} + q_1\mathbf{A} + \cdots + q_n\mathbf{A}^n = \mathbf{0} \tag{3.72}$$

is extremely powerful. Observe that *we can compute any positive integer power of* **A** *in terms of the zeroth through the* $(n-1)$*st integer power* of **A**. First,

$$\mathbf{A}^n = -\frac{1}{q_n}(q_0\mathbf{1} + q_1\mathbf{A} + \cdots + q_{n-1}\mathbf{A}^{n-1})$$

since division by $q_n = (-1)^n$ is always possible. Now note

$$\begin{aligned}\mathbf{A}^{n+1} &= -\frac{1}{q_n}(q_0\mathbf{A} + q_1\mathbf{A}^2 + \cdots + q_{n-1}\mathbf{A}^n)\\ &= -\frac{1}{q_n}\Big[q_0\mathbf{A} + q_1\mathbf{A}^2 + \cdots + q_{n-2}\mathbf{A}^{n-1}\\ &\qquad - \frac{q_{n-1}}{q_n}(q_0\mathbf{1} + q_1\mathbf{A} + \cdots + q_{n-1}\mathbf{A}^{n-1})\Big]\end{aligned}$$

Any higher power of **A** may be computed recursively in this manner; for our purpose it suffices merely to know that there exists a set of complex scalars $\{\alpha_{k0},\alpha_{k1}, \ldots ,\alpha_{k,n-1}\}$ such that

$$\mathbf{A}^k = \alpha_{k0}\mathbf{1} + \alpha_{k1}\mathbf{A} + \cdots + \alpha_{k,n-1}\mathbf{A}^{n-1}$$

for any complex $(n \times n)$ matrix **A**. If it exists, we can also find an expression for $\mathbf{A}^{-1}$ in a similar fashion.

$$\mathbf{A}^{-1}(q_0\mathbf{1} + q_1\mathbf{A} + \cdots + q_n\mathbf{A}^n) = \mathbf{0}$$

so

$$\mathbf{A}^{-1} = \frac{1}{q_0}(q_1\mathbf{1} + q_2\mathbf{A} + \cdots + q_n\mathbf{A}^{n-1})$$

This expression makes sense so long as $q_0 = \det(\mathbf{A}) \neq 0$, which is the condition that the inverse exists. With this result, we recognize that any integer power of $\mathbf{A}$ (positive or negative) which exists may be expressed as a linear combination of the zeroth through $(n - 1)$st powers of $\mathbf{A}$.

We now turn our attention to what is meant by a function of a square matrix. Suppose we are given a scalar function $f(t)$, and we wish to obtain the corresponding $(n \times n)$ matrix function $f(\mathbf{A})$ of the $(n \times n)$ matrix $\mathbf{A}$. We recognize that polynomial functions are easily defined as the corresponding polynomial in the matrix (e.g., the characteristic polynomial). Following this observation, we *first* define the function of a matrix in terms of a power series; i.e.,

$$f(\mathbf{A}) = \sum_{k=0}^{\infty} \frac{1}{k!} f_k \mathbf{A}^k$$

when $f(t)$ has the same power series

$$f(t) = \sum_{k=0}^{\infty} \frac{1}{k!} f_k t^k$$

provided that the matrix series converges. Alternatively, consider

$$\left[f(\mathbf{A}) - \sum_{k=0}^{\infty} \frac{1}{k!} f_k \mathbf{A}^k = \mathbf{0} \right]$$

if we apply this zero matrix to an arbitrary vector in the space (expanded in terms of the eigenvector basis)

$$\mathbf{x} = \hat{x}_1 \xi_1 + \hat{x}_2 \xi_2 + \cdots + \hat{x}_n \xi_n$$

we obtain

$$[f(\mathbf{A}) - f(\lambda_1)\mathbf{1}]\hat{x}_1 \xi_1 + \cdots + [f(\mathbf{A}) - f(\lambda_n)\mathbf{1}]\hat{x}_n \xi_n = \mathbf{0}$$

Hence, we may define the function of an $(n \times n)$ matrix $\mathbf{A}$ (with distinct eigenvalues) in terms of its scalar-function behavior on each of the one-dimensional invariant subspaces (eigenvectors):

$$f(\mathbf{A})\xi_k = f(\lambda_k)\xi_k \qquad (k = 1, 2, \ldots, n)$$

so $f(\mathbf{A})$ exists if $f(\lambda_k)$ exists for $k = 1, 2, \ldots, n$. We may again take advantage of the Cayley-Hamilton theorem and discuss a simplified means for computing the function of a matrix. Since we have assumed that $f(\mathbf{A})$ can be represented by an infinite power series of $\mathbf{A}$, it can be represented by a finite series in terms of the zeroth through $(n - 1)$st powers of $\mathbf{A}$:

$$f(\mathbf{A}) = \alpha_0\mathbf{1} + \alpha_1\mathbf{A} + \cdots + \alpha_{n-1}\mathbf{A}^{n-1}$$

If we can compute the n unknown coefficients in this expansion, then we can easily display $f(\mathbf{A})$. We take advantage of the behavior of $f(\mathbf{A})$ on the one-dimensional invariant subspaces represented by the eigenvectors:

$$f(\mathbf{A}) = \alpha_0\mathbf{1} + \alpha_1\mathbf{A} + \cdots + \alpha_{n-1}\mathbf{A}^{n-1}$$

implies

$$f(\mathbf{A})\xi_k = (\alpha_0\mathbf{1} + \alpha_1\mathbf{A} + \cdots + \alpha_{n-1}\mathbf{A}^{n-1})\xi_k$$

which implies

$$f(\lambda_k)\xi_k = (\alpha_0 + \alpha_1\lambda_k + \cdots + \alpha_{n-1}\lambda_k^{n-1})\xi_k$$

which implies

$$\alpha_0 + \lambda_k\alpha_1 + \lambda_k^2\alpha_2 + \cdots + \lambda_k^{n-1}\alpha_{n-1} = f(\lambda_k)$$

Hence, we have n equations in n unknowns, $\alpha_0, \alpha_1, \ldots, \alpha_{n-1}$. These equations may be represented by the single matrix equation

$$\begin{bmatrix} 1 & \lambda_1 & \lambda_1^2 & \cdots & \lambda_1^{n-1} \\ 1 & \lambda_2 & \lambda_2^2 & \cdots & \lambda_2^{n-1} \\ \cdot & \cdot & \cdot & \cdots & \cdot \\ 1 & \lambda_n & \lambda_n^2 & \cdots & \lambda_n^{n-1} \end{bmatrix} \begin{bmatrix} \alpha_0 \\ \alpha_1 \\ \cdot \\ \cdot \\ \cdot \\ \alpha_{n-1} \end{bmatrix} = \begin{bmatrix} f(\lambda_1) \\ f(\lambda_2) \\ \cdot \\ \cdot \\ \cdot \\ f(\lambda_n) \end{bmatrix} \tag{3.73}$$

which has a solution if the Vandermonde determinant (determinant of the $n \times n$ Vandermonde matrix on the left-hand side of the equation) is nonzero. The Vandermonde determinant is nonzero if and only if the eigenvalues are distinct, which is the case under consideration. If the eigenvalues are not distinct, more powerful theories must be employed.

We now demonstrate the above technique in terms of several examples.

(3.74) Example

We have already seen that the matrix

$$\mathbf{A} = \begin{bmatrix} 0 & 1 \\ -2 & -3 \end{bmatrix}$$

has the eigenvalues $\lambda_1 = -1$ and $\lambda_2 = -2$. Let us calculate the function

$$f(\mathbf{A}) = \mathbf{A}^{-1}$$

Since $\mathbf{A}$ is 2×2, we may write

$$\mathbf{A}^{-1} = \alpha_0 \mathbf{1} + \alpha_1 \mathbf{A}$$

and from (3.73)

$$\begin{bmatrix} 1 & \lambda_1 \\ 1 & \lambda_2 \end{bmatrix} \begin{bmatrix} \alpha_0 \\ \alpha_1 \end{bmatrix} = \begin{bmatrix} f(\lambda_1) \\ f(\lambda_2) \end{bmatrix}$$

which implies

$$\begin{bmatrix} 1 & -1 \\ 1 & -2 \end{bmatrix} \begin{bmatrix} \alpha_0 \\ \alpha_1 \end{bmatrix} = \begin{bmatrix} -1 \\ -\frac{1}{2} \end{bmatrix}$$

Hence, $\alpha_0 = -\frac{3}{2}$ and $\alpha_1 = -\frac{1}{2}$ and

$$\mathbf{A}^{-1} = -\frac{3}{2} \begin{bmatrix} 1 & 0 \\ 0 & 1 \end{bmatrix} - \frac{1}{2} \begin{bmatrix} 0 & 1 \\ -2 & -3 \end{bmatrix}$$

or

$$\mathbf{A}^{-1} = \begin{bmatrix} -\frac{3}{2} & -\frac{1}{2} \\ 1 & 0 \end{bmatrix}$$

Note the coefficients α_0 and α_1 check with the characteristic polynomial

$$q(1) = 2 + 3\lambda + \lambda^2$$

since

$$\alpha_0 = -\frac{q_1}{q_0} = -\frac{3}{2}$$

and

$$\alpha_1 = -\frac{q_2}{q_0} = -\frac{1}{2}$$

and

$$\mathbf{A}^{-1} = -\frac{1}{q_0} (q_1 \mathbf{1} + q_2 \mathbf{A})$$

∎

(3.75) Example

The matrix

$$\mathbf{A} = \begin{bmatrix} 1 & 2 \\ 2 & 1 \end{bmatrix}$$

has eigenvalues $\lambda_1 = -1$ and $\lambda_2 = 3$. Then

$$f(\mathbf{A}) = \mathbf{A}^{-1} = \alpha_0 \mathbf{1} + \alpha_1 \mathbf{A}$$

and from (3.73)

$$\begin{bmatrix} 1 & -1 \\ 1 & 3 \end{bmatrix} \begin{bmatrix} \alpha_0 \\ \alpha_1 \end{bmatrix} = \begin{bmatrix} -1 \\ \frac{1}{3} \end{bmatrix}$$

so that $\alpha_0 = -\frac{2}{3}$ and $\alpha_1 = \frac{1}{3}$. Hence

$$A^{-1} = -\tfrac{2}{3}\begin{bmatrix} 1 & 0 \\ 0 & 1 \end{bmatrix} + \tfrac{1}{3}\begin{bmatrix} 1 & 2 \\ 2 & 1 \end{bmatrix}$$

or

$$A^{-1} = \begin{bmatrix} -\frac{1}{3} & \frac{2}{3} \\ \frac{2}{3} & -\frac{1}{3} \end{bmatrix}$$

Again, the result checks with the characteristic polynomial

$$q(\lambda) = -3 - 2\lambda + \lambda^2$$

since

$$\alpha_0 = -\frac{q_1}{q_0} = -\frac{2}{3}$$

and

$$\alpha_1 = -\frac{q_2}{q_0} = \frac{1}{3}$$

∎

(3.76) Example

The matrix

$$\mathbf{A} = \begin{bmatrix} \cos\theta & \sin\theta \\ -\sin\theta & \cos\theta \end{bmatrix}$$

has eigenvalues $\lambda_1 = e^{j\theta}$ and $\lambda_2 = e^{-j\theta}$. Then

$$f(\mathbf{A}) = \mathbf{A}^{-1} = \alpha_0\mathbf{1} + \alpha_1\mathbf{A}$$

and from (3.73)

$$\begin{bmatrix} 1 & e^{j\theta} \\ 1 & e^{-j\theta} \end{bmatrix}\begin{bmatrix} \alpha_0 \\ \alpha_1 \end{bmatrix} = \begin{bmatrix} e^{-j\theta} \\ e^{j\theta} \end{bmatrix}$$

so that $\alpha_0 = 2\cos\theta$ and $\alpha_1 = -1$. Hence

$$\mathbf{A}^{-1} = 2\cos\theta\begin{bmatrix} 1 & 0 \\ 0 & 1 \end{bmatrix} - 1\begin{bmatrix} \cos\theta & \sin\theta \\ -\sin\theta & \cos\theta \end{bmatrix}$$

or

$$\mathbf{A}^{-1} = \begin{bmatrix} \cos\theta & -\sin\theta \\ \sin\theta & \cos\theta \end{bmatrix}$$

Again, the result checks with the characteristic polynomial since

$$q(\lambda) = 1 - 2\cos\theta + \lambda^2$$

$$\alpha_0 = -\frac{q_1}{q_0} = 2\cos\theta$$

and

$$\alpha_1 = -\frac{q_2}{q_0} = -1$$

∎

In the study of second-order, linear, time-invariant systems, the function of a matrix $e^{\mathbf{A}t}$ was of interest. This function will be of considerable importance when we undertake the study of higher-order systems. We have already demonstrated the infinite-series method to determine $e^{\mathbf{A}t}$. This function can be evaluated more easily by the techniques presented above.

(3.77) Example
We wish to evaluate the function

$$f(\mathbf{A}) = e^{\mathbf{A}t}$$

for

$$\mathbf{A} = \begin{bmatrix} 0 & 1 \\ -2 & -3 \end{bmatrix}$$

As a result of the Cayley-Hamilton theorem

$$f(\mathbf{A}) = e^{\mathbf{A}t} = \alpha_0(t)\mathbf{1} + \alpha_1(t)\mathbf{A}$$

This computation can be done point-by-point in time, or $\mathbf{A}t$ can be considered to be the matrix in question. The former approach is preferable, then we have

$$\begin{bmatrix} 1 & -1 \\ 1 & -2 \end{bmatrix} \begin{bmatrix} \alpha_0 \\ \alpha_1 \end{bmatrix} = \begin{bmatrix} e^{-t} \\ e^{-2t} \end{bmatrix}$$

so that

$$\alpha_0(t) = 2e^{-t} - e^{-2t} \qquad \text{and} \qquad \alpha_1(t) = e^{-t} - e^{-2t}$$

Hence

$$e^{\mathbf{A}t} = (2e^{-t} - e^{-2t}) \begin{bmatrix} 1 & 0 \\ 0 & 1 \end{bmatrix} + (e^{-t} - e^{-2t}) \begin{bmatrix} 0 & 1 \\ -2 & -3 \end{bmatrix}$$

or

$$e^{\mathbf{A}t} = \begin{bmatrix} 2e^{-t} - e^{-2t} & e^{-t} - e^{-2t} \\ -2e^{-t} + 2e^{-2t} & -e^{-t} + 2e^{-2t} \end{bmatrix}$$

or

$$e^{\mathbf{A}t} = e^{-t} \begin{bmatrix} 2 & 1 \\ -2 & -1 \end{bmatrix} + e^{-2t} \begin{bmatrix} -1 & -1 \\ 2 & 2 \end{bmatrix}$$ ∎

Note that each of the constant matrices involved is a one-term dyad. In fact, we have in general

$$e^{\mathbf{A}t} = e^{\lambda_1 t}\boldsymbol{\xi}_1\mathbf{n}_1' + \cdots + e^{\lambda_n t}\boldsymbol{\xi}_n\mathbf{n}_n'$$

where $\{\boldsymbol{\xi}_1, \ldots, \boldsymbol{\xi}_n\}$ is the eigenvector basis and $\{\mathbf{n}_1', \ldots, \mathbf{n}_n'\}$ is the reciprocal basis (for the case in which the eigenvalues are distinct).

(3.78) Example

The eigenvalues for the matrix

$$\mathbf{A} = \begin{bmatrix} 1 & 2 \\ 2 & 1 \end{bmatrix}$$

are $\lambda_1 = -1$ and $\lambda_2 = 3$. Hence to evaluate

$$f(\mathbf{A}) = e^{\mathbf{A}t} = \alpha_0(t)1 + \alpha_1(t)\mathbf{A}$$

we solve for α_0 and α_1 from

$$\begin{bmatrix} 1 & -1 \\ 1 & 3 \end{bmatrix} \begin{bmatrix} \alpha_0 \\ \alpha_1 \end{bmatrix} = \begin{bmatrix} e^{-t} \\ e^{3t} \end{bmatrix}$$

It is easy to ascertain that

$$\alpha_0 = \tfrac{1}{4}(3e^{-t} + e^{3t})$$

and

$$\alpha_1 - \tfrac{1}{4}(e^{-t} - e^{3t})$$

so that

$$e^{\mathbf{A}t} = \frac{1}{2}\begin{bmatrix} e^{-t} + e^{3t} & -e^{-t} + e^{3t} \\ -e^{-t} + e^{3t} & e^{-t} + e^{3t} \end{bmatrix}$$

or

$$e^{\mathbf{A}t} = e^{-t}\begin{bmatrix} \frac{1}{2} & -\frac{1}{2} \\ -\frac{1}{2} & \frac{1}{2} \end{bmatrix} + e^{3t}\begin{bmatrix} \frac{1}{2} & \frac{1}{2} \\ \frac{1}{2} & \frac{1}{2} \end{bmatrix}$$ ∎

Much difficulty in evaluation of the function of a matrix can be avoided upon recognition of the fact that

$$f(\mathbf{W}^{-1}\mathbf{A}\mathbf{W}) = \mathbf{W}^{-1}f(\mathbf{A})\mathbf{W}$$

for any nonsingular matrix $\mathbf{W}$. That is, since

$$(\mathbf{W}^{-1}\mathbf{A}\mathbf{W})^r = \mathbf{W}^{-1}\mathbf{A}^r\mathbf{W}$$

and

$$f(\mathbf{A}) = \alpha_0\mathbf{1} + \alpha_1\mathbf{A} + \cdots + \alpha_{n-1}\mathbf{A}^{n-1}$$

we have

$$\begin{aligned} f(\mathbf{W}^{-1}\mathbf{A}\mathbf{W}) &= \alpha_0\mathbf{1} + \alpha_1\mathbf{W}^{-1}\mathbf{A}\mathbf{W} + \cdots + \alpha_{n-1}\mathbf{W}^{-1}\mathbf{A}^{n-1}\mathbf{W} \\ &= \mathbf{W}^{-1}(\alpha_0\mathbf{1} + \alpha_1\mathbf{A} + \cdots + \alpha_{n-1}\mathbf{A}^{n-1})\mathbf{W} \\ &= \mathbf{W}^{-1}f(\mathbf{A})\mathbf{W} \end{aligned}$$

We may apply a similar argument to the infinite-series representation for the function of a matrix.

Recall that if **S** is the modal matrix associated with the matrix **A**, and **A** has distinct eigenvalues

$$\mathbf{S}^{-1}\mathbf{A}\mathbf{S} = \mathbf{\Lambda} = \text{diag}\,(\lambda_1,\lambda_2, \ldots ,\lambda_n)$$

Therefore

$$\mathbf{A} = \mathbf{S}\mathbf{\Lambda}\mathbf{S}^{-1}$$

and

$$f(\mathbf{A}) = \mathbf{S}f(\mathbf{\Lambda})\mathbf{S}^{-1} = \mathbf{S}[\text{diag}\,(f(\lambda_1), f(\lambda_2), \ldots , f(\lambda_n)]\mathbf{S}^{-1}$$

or in dyadic representation

$$f(\mathbf{A}) = f(\lambda_1)\boldsymbol{\xi}_1\mathbf{n}_1' + f(\lambda_2)\boldsymbol{\xi}_2\mathbf{n}_2' + \cdots + f(\lambda_n)\boldsymbol{\xi}_n\mathbf{n}_n'$$

where $\{\boldsymbol{\xi}_1, \ldots ,\boldsymbol{\xi}_n\}$ is the eigenvector basis, and $\{\mathbf{n}_1', \ldots ,\mathbf{n}_n'\}$ is the corresponding reciprocal basis. In particular

$$e^{\mathbf{A}t} = e^{\lambda_1 t}\boldsymbol{\xi}_1\mathbf{n}_1' + e^{\lambda_2 t}\boldsymbol{\xi}_2\mathbf{n}_2' + \cdots + e^{\lambda_n t}\boldsymbol{\xi}_n\mathbf{n}_n'$$

3.9 MULTIPLE EIGENVALUES

Strictly for motivation, consider the possibility that a given $(n \times n)$ matrix **A** has a multiple eigenvalue λ which is associated with a one-dimensional invariant subspace. For example,

$$\mathbf{A} = \begin{bmatrix} 2 & 1 \\ 0 & 2 \end{bmatrix}$$

has the characteristic equation

$$q(\lambda) = (2 - \lambda)^2 = 0$$

and the coincident eigenvalues $\lambda_1 = \lambda_2 = 2$. There is only one eigenvector corresponding to this eigenvalue:

$$\begin{bmatrix} 0 & 1 \\ 0 & 0 \end{bmatrix}\begin{bmatrix} \xi_1 \\ \xi_1 \end{bmatrix} = \begin{bmatrix} 0 \\ 0 \end{bmatrix}$$

which implies

$$\boldsymbol{\xi}_1 = \boldsymbol{\xi}_2 = \begin{bmatrix} 1 \\ 0 \end{bmatrix}$$

If, on the other hand, we consider

$$\mathbf{A} = \begin{bmatrix} 2 & 0 \\ 0 & 2 \end{bmatrix}$$

with the same characteristic equation

$$q(\lambda) = (2 - \lambda)^2 = 0$$

and the same eigenvalues $\lambda_1 = \lambda_2 = 2$; we see that *any* vector may be an eigenvector. Two possible eigenvectors, which form a basis, are

$$\boldsymbol{\xi}_1 = \begin{bmatrix} 1 \\ 0 \end{bmatrix} \quad \text{and} \quad \boldsymbol{\xi}_2 = \begin{bmatrix} 0 \\ 1 \end{bmatrix}$$

In the first case we may complete the basis with any nonzero vector

$$\hat{\boldsymbol{\xi}}_2 = \begin{bmatrix} \hat{\xi}_1 \\ \hat{\xi}_2 \end{bmatrix}$$

so long as $\xi_2 \neq 0$; the question is "what is the best such vector?" Let us return to the general problem and consider the case when two coincident eigenvalues λ correspond to a single eigenvector $\boldsymbol{\xi}$, so

$$\mathbf{A}\boldsymbol{\xi} = \lambda\boldsymbol{\xi}$$

Now suppose that a slight perturbation in the matrix $\mathbf{A}$ to $\mathbf{A}_\varepsilon$ results in a pair of distinct eigenvalues λ and $\lambda + \varepsilon$ which correspond to linearly independent eigenvectors $\boldsymbol{\xi}$ and $\boldsymbol{\xi} + \delta\mathbf{v}$, respectively, where $0(\varepsilon) \approx 0(\delta)$ [note that $0(\cdot)$ means "is the order of"] since they must go to zero together. Hence, we have the two relations

$$\mathbf{A}_\varepsilon\boldsymbol{\xi} = \lambda\boldsymbol{\xi}$$

and

$$\mathbf{A}_\varepsilon(\boldsymbol{\xi} + \delta\mathbf{v}) = (\lambda + \varepsilon)(\boldsymbol{\xi} + \delta\mathbf{v})$$

If we subtract the first relation from the second, we obtain

$$\delta\mathbf{A}_\varepsilon\mathbf{v} = \delta\lambda\mathbf{v} + \varepsilon\boldsymbol{\xi} + \delta\varepsilon\mathbf{v}$$

Upon division by δ

$$\mathbf{A}_\varepsilon\mathbf{v} = \lambda\mathbf{v} + \frac{\varepsilon}{\delta}\boldsymbol{\xi} + \varepsilon\mathbf{v}$$

Now in the limit as $\varepsilon \to 0$, $\mathbf{A}_\varepsilon \to \mathbf{A}$ and $\varepsilon/\delta \to$ a constant (say one) since ε and δ are of the same order. Hence, we have

$$\mathbf{A}\mathbf{v} = \lambda\mathbf{v} + \boldsymbol{\xi}$$

and we can think of $\mathbf{v}$ as a *generalized* eigenvector corresponding to the eigenvalue λ. That is, the eigenvector is a nonzero solution of

$$(\mathbf{A} - \lambda\mathbf{1})\boldsymbol{\xi} = \mathbf{0}$$

while the generalized eigenvector is the solution of

$$(\mathbf{A} - \lambda\mathbf{1})^2\,\mathbf{v} = (\mathbf{A} - \lambda\mathbf{1})\boldsymbol{\xi} = 0$$

or

$$(\mathbf{A} - \lambda\mathbf{1})\mathbf{v} = \boldsymbol{\xi}$$

We may formalize this argument with the following definition.

(3.79) Generalized eigenvector
A vector $\xi_{lk} \neq 0$ for which

$$(\mathbf{A} - \lambda_l \mathbf{1})^{k-1}\xi_{lk} \neq \mathbf{0}$$

but

$$(\mathbf{A} - \lambda_l \mathbf{1})^{k}\xi_{lk} = \mathbf{0}$$

is called a *generalized eigenvector of rank k* corresponding to the eigenvalue λ_l. ∎

(3.80) Example
Consider the matrix

$$\mathbf{A} = \begin{bmatrix} 2 & 1 \\ 0 & 2 \end{bmatrix}$$

We have seen that the coincident eigenvalues are $\lambda_1 = 2$ and $\lambda_2 = 2$ and one eigenvector is

$$\xi = \begin{bmatrix} 1 \\ 0 \end{bmatrix}$$

We find the generalized eigenvector from (3.79) as follows:

$$(\mathbf{A} - 2\mathbf{1})\mathbf{v} = \begin{bmatrix} 0 & 1 \\ 0 & 0 \end{bmatrix} \begin{bmatrix} \nu_1 \\ \nu_2 \end{bmatrix} = \begin{bmatrix} 1 \\ 0 \end{bmatrix}$$

so that

$$\mathbf{v} = \begin{bmatrix} 0 \\ 1 \end{bmatrix}$$

among other possibilities, since ν_1 is arbitrary. Note the two vectors ξ and $\mathbf{v}$ constitute a basis in two-space. ∎

In general we define a chain of eigenvectors $\xi_{k1}, \xi_{k2}, \ldots, \xi_{kl}$ associated with the eigenvalue λ_k of multiplicity l by

$$\begin{aligned}
(\mathbf{A} - \lambda_k \mathbf{1})\xi_{k1} &= \mathbf{0} \\
(\mathbf{A} - \lambda_k \mathbf{1})\xi_{k2} &= \xi_{k1} \\
(\mathbf{A} - \lambda_k \mathbf{1})\xi_{k3} &= \xi_{k2} \\
&\cdots\cdots\cdots \\
(\mathbf{A} - \lambda_k \mathbf{1})\xi_{kl} &= \xi_{k,l-1}
\end{aligned}$$

Note: If the invariant subspace originally associated with the eigenvalue λ_k is of m dimensions, there may be as many as m such chains of various lengths. We may augment the linearly independent eigenvectors associated with the distinct eigenvalues with generalized eigenvectors from these chains.

We now show, by induction, that the generalized eigenvectors in a chain associated with an eigenvector λ are linearly independent. Consider a chain of length l. Obviously the assertion is true for $l = 1$. We now assume that the first $k - 1$ $(2 \leq k \leq l)$ are linearly independent and show that the first k are. Suppose that the first k are not, so

$$c_1\xi_1 + c_2\xi_2 + \cdots + c_k\xi_k = \mathbf{0}$$

where not all $\{c_1,c_2, \ldots ,c_k\}$ are zero. Then

$$\mathbf{A}(c_1\xi_1 + c_2\xi_2 + \cdots + c_k\xi_k) = \mathbf{0}$$

or

$$(c_1\lambda + c_2)\xi_1 + (c_2\lambda + c_3)\xi_2 + \cdots + (c_{k-1}\lambda + c_k)\xi_{k-1} + c_k\lambda\xi_k = \mathbf{0}$$

Subtract

$$c_1\lambda\xi_1 + c_2\lambda\xi_2 + \cdots + c_{k-1}\lambda\xi_{k-1} + c_k\lambda\xi_k = \mathbf{0}$$

from the last relation to obtain

$$c_2\xi_1 + c_3\xi_3 + \cdots + c_k\xi_{k-1} = \mathbf{0}$$

since the first $k - 1$ eigenvectors are linearly independent,

$$c_2 = c_2 = \cdots = c_{k-1} = c_k = 0$$

so that the original expression reduces to

$$c_1\xi_1 = 0$$

which may only be true if $c_1 = 0$, contradicting the original linear-independence supposition. Hence, we may create a chain of linearly independent eigenvectors

$$\begin{aligned} \mathbf{A}\xi_1 &= \lambda\xi_1 \\ \mathbf{A}\xi_2 &= \lambda\xi_2 + \xi_1 \\ &\cdots\cdots\cdots \\ \mathbf{A}\xi_l &= \lambda\xi_l + \xi_{l-1} \end{aligned}$$

which terminates when

$$\mathbf{A}\xi_{l+1} = \lambda\xi_{l+1} + \xi_l$$

has no solution. We have not shown the linear independence of the chains themselves. This task is more difficult and is omitted.

(3.81) Example

Consider again the matrix

$$\mathbf{A} = \begin{bmatrix} 2 & 1 \\ 0 & 2 \end{bmatrix}$$

which has the multiple eigenvalue $\lambda_1 = \lambda_2 = 2$. There is one eigenvector

$$\xi_1 = \begin{pmatrix} 1 \\ 0 \end{pmatrix}$$

and one generalized eigenvector

$$\xi_2 = \begin{pmatrix} 0 \\ 1 \end{pmatrix}$$

To see that there are no more generalized eigenvectors, i.e., that the chain terminates, let us try to find a second generalized eigenvector:

$$\begin{pmatrix} 0 & 1 \\ 0 & 0 \end{pmatrix} \begin{pmatrix} \xi_{13} \\ \xi_{23} \end{pmatrix} = \begin{pmatrix} 0 \\ 1 \end{pmatrix}$$

But, this expression yields the equation

$$1 = 0$$

a contradiction we cannot accept. Hence the chain is terminated. ∎

We assume in the sequel that the eigenvectors augmented by the generalized eigenvectors form a basis in E^n.[1]

A modal matrix may also be constructed for $(n \times n)$ matrices that have nondistinct eigenvalues. Both eigenvectors and generalized eigenvectors are used:

$$\mathbf{S} = \begin{bmatrix} \xi_{11} & \xi_{12} & \cdots & \xi_{1k} & \xi_{21} & \xi_{22} & \cdots & \xi_{2k} & \cdots & \xi_{l1} & \xi_{l2} & \cdots & \xi_{lk_l} \\ \downarrow & \downarrow & & \downarrow & \downarrow & \downarrow & & \downarrow & & \downarrow & \downarrow & & \downarrow \end{bmatrix}$$

where $k_1 + k_2 + \cdots + k_l = n$. Observe that $\mathbf{S}$ is nonsingular. Although the transformation $\mathbf{S}^{-1}\mathbf{AS}$ is not diagonal when $\mathbf{A}$ has repeated eigenvalues, there is an associated canonical form:

$$\mathbf{J} = \mathbf{S}^{-1}\mathbf{AS} = \begin{bmatrix} \mathbf{J}_1 & \mathbf{0} & \mathbf{0} & \cdots & \mathbf{0} \\ \mathbf{0} & \mathbf{J}_2 & \mathbf{0} & \cdots & \mathbf{0} \\ \cdot & \cdot & \cdot & \cdots & \cdot \\ \mathbf{0} & \mathbf{0} & \mathbf{0} & \cdots & \mathbf{J}_l \end{bmatrix}$$

where $\mathbf{J}_m$ is a $k_m \times k_m$ square matrix of the following form

$$\mathbf{J}_m = \begin{bmatrix} \lambda_m & 1 & 0 & 0 & \cdots & 0 & 0 \\ 0 & \lambda_m & 1 & 0 & \cdots & 0 & 0 \\ 0 & 0 & 0 & \lambda_m & \cdots & 0 & 0 \\ \cdots & \cdots & \cdots & \cdots & \cdots & \cdots & \cdots \\ 0 & 0 & 0 & 0 & \cdots & \lambda_m & 1 \\ 0 & 0 & 0 & 0 & \cdots & 0 & \lambda_m \end{bmatrix}$$

[1] The proof may be found in any standard text, for example, B. Friedman, "Principles and Techniques of Applied Mathematics," chap. 2, Wiley, New York, 1956.

Note that two different "Jordan blocks" $\mathbf{J}_m$ may be associated with the same eigenvalue, depending on the dimension of the original invariant subspace defined by

$$(\mathbf{A} - \lambda\mathbf{1})\boldsymbol{\xi} = \mathbf{0}$$

The following example illustrates this point.

(3.82) Example
Consider the matrices

$$\mathbf{A} = \begin{bmatrix} 2 & 0 & 0 \\ 0 & 2 & 0 \\ 0 & 0 & 2 \end{bmatrix} \qquad \mathbf{B} = \begin{bmatrix} 2 & 1 & 0 \\ 0 & 2 & 0 \\ 0 & 0 & 2 \end{bmatrix}$$

and

$$\mathbf{C} = \begin{bmatrix} 2 & 1 & 0 \\ 0 & 2 & 1 \\ 0 & 0 & 2 \end{bmatrix}$$

all of which have as their only eigenvalue $\lambda = 2$. The eigenvectors of **A** are obtained from

$$(3.83) \quad (\mathbf{A} - \lambda\mathbf{1})\boldsymbol{\xi} = \begin{bmatrix} 0 & 0 & 0 \\ 0 & 0 & 0 \\ 0 & 0 & 0 \end{bmatrix} \boldsymbol{\xi} = \mathbf{0}$$

We may choose

$$\boldsymbol{\xi}_1 = \begin{bmatrix} 1 \\ 0 \\ 0 \end{bmatrix} \qquad \boldsymbol{\xi}_2 = \begin{bmatrix} 0 \\ 1 \\ 0 \end{bmatrix} \qquad \boldsymbol{\xi}_3 = \begin{bmatrix} 0 \\ 0 \\ 1 \end{bmatrix}$$

as three linearly independent vectors which satisfy (3.83); thus the dimension of the invariant subspace is three, and we will have three 1×1 Jordan blocks. Indeed

$$\mathbf{J} = \mathbf{S}^{-1}\mathbf{A}\mathbf{S} = \begin{bmatrix} 2 & 0 & 0 \\ 0 & 2 & 0 \\ 0 & 0 & 2 \end{bmatrix}$$

Let us find the eigenvectors of **B**:

$$(\mathbf{B} - \lambda\mathbf{1})\boldsymbol{\xi} = \begin{bmatrix} 0 & 1 & 0 \\ 0 & 0 & 0 \\ 0 & 0 & 0 \end{bmatrix} \begin{bmatrix} \xi_{11} \\ \xi_{21} \\ \xi_{31} \end{bmatrix} = \mathbf{0}$$

Thus $\xi_{21} = 0$, and we are free to choose ξ_{11} and ξ_{31}. Two linearly independent eigenvectors emerge:

$$\boldsymbol{\xi}_1 = \begin{bmatrix} 1 \\ 0 \\ 0 \end{bmatrix} \quad \text{and} \quad \boldsymbol{\xi}_2 = \begin{bmatrix} 0 \\ 0 \\ 1 \end{bmatrix}$$

So we have two Jordan blocks, one (1×1) and the other (2×2). To find the one generalized eigenvector consider

$$(\mathbf{B} - \lambda\mathbf{1})\mathbf{v} = \boldsymbol{\xi}_1$$

or

$$\begin{bmatrix} 0 & 1 & 0 \\ 0 & 0 & 0 \\ 0 & 0 & 0 \end{bmatrix} \begin{bmatrix} \nu_1 \\ \nu_2 \\ \nu_3 \end{bmatrix} = \begin{bmatrix} 1 \\ 0 \\ 0 \end{bmatrix}$$

Then

$$\nu_2 = 1$$

so that

$$\mathbf{v} = (0 \quad 1 \quad 0)'$$

To see that this is the only generalized eigenvector consider

$$(\mathbf{B} - \lambda\mathbf{1})\hat{\mathbf{v}} = \boldsymbol{\xi}_2$$

or

$$\begin{bmatrix} 0 & 1 & 0 \\ 0 & 0 & 0 \\ 0 & 0 & 0 \end{bmatrix} \begin{bmatrix} \hat{\nu}_1 \\ \hat{\nu}_2 \\ \hat{\nu}_3 \end{bmatrix} = \begin{bmatrix} 0 \\ 0 \\ 1 \end{bmatrix}$$

which implies

$$0 = 1$$

a contradiction. Hence the modal matrix is

$$\mathbf{S} \begin{bmatrix} \boldsymbol{\xi}_1 & \mathbf{v} & \boldsymbol{\xi}_2 \\ \downarrow & \downarrow & \downarrow \\ & & \end{bmatrix} = \begin{bmatrix} 1 & 0 & 0 \\ 0 & 1 & 0 \\ 0 & 0 & 1 \end{bmatrix}$$

and the Jordan canonical form is

$$\mathbf{J} = \mathbf{S}^{-1}\mathbf{A}\mathbf{S} = \begin{bmatrix} 2 & 1 & 0 \\ 0 & 2 & 0 \\ 0 & 0 & 2 \end{bmatrix}$$

The eigenvectors for $\mathbf{C}$ are obtained from

$$(\mathbf{C} - \lambda\mathbf{1})\boldsymbol{\xi} = \begin{bmatrix} 0 & 1 & 0 \\ 0 & 0 & 1 \\ 0 & 0 & 0 \end{bmatrix} \begin{bmatrix} \xi_{11} \\ \xi_{21} \\ \xi_{31} \end{bmatrix} = \mathbf{0}$$

which requires ξ_{21} and $\xi_{31} = 0$ so that only one eigenvector exists

$$\boldsymbol{\xi}_1 = (1 \quad 0 \quad 0)'$$

the invariant subspace is one dimensional, and there is one 3 × 3 Jordan block. The two generalized eigenvectors are seen to be

$$\boldsymbol{\xi}_{12} = \begin{bmatrix} 0 \\ 1 \\ 0 \end{bmatrix} \quad \text{and} \quad \boldsymbol{\xi}_{13} = \begin{bmatrix} 0 \\ 0 \\ 1 \end{bmatrix}$$

and the Jordan canonical form is

$$\mathbf{J} = \mathbf{S}^{-1}\mathbf{A}\mathbf{S} = \begin{bmatrix} 2 & 1 & 0 \\ 0 & 2 & 1 \\ 0 & 0 & 2 \end{bmatrix}$$

∎

(3.84) Example

Let us find the Jordan canonical form for the matrix

$$\mathbf{A} = \begin{bmatrix} 5 & 0 & 0 \\ -j\frac{1}{4} & 5 & \frac{1}{2} \\ 0 & 0 & 5 \end{bmatrix}$$

The three eigenvalues are $\lambda_1 = \lambda_2 = \lambda_3 = 5$. The eigenvectors are found from

$$(\mathbf{A} - \lambda\mathbf{1})\boldsymbol{\xi} = \begin{bmatrix} 0 & 0 & 0 \\ -j\frac{1}{4} & 0 & \frac{1}{2} \\ 0 & 0 & 0 \end{bmatrix} \begin{bmatrix} \xi_1 \\ \xi_2 \\ \xi_3 \end{bmatrix} = \mathbf{0}$$

so that

$$-j\frac{1}{4}\xi_1 + \frac{1}{2}\xi_3$$

and ξ_2 is arbitrary. The invariant subspace is two dimensional, *spanned* by the eigenvectors

$$\boldsymbol{\xi}_1 = \begin{bmatrix} 0 \\ 1 \\ 0 \end{bmatrix} \quad \text{and} \quad \boldsymbol{\xi}_2 = \begin{bmatrix} -j2 \\ 0 \\ 1 \end{bmatrix}$$

We must find one generalized eigenvector

$$(\mathbf{A} - \lambda\mathbf{1})\mathbf{v} = \boldsymbol{\xi}_1$$

or

$$\begin{bmatrix} 0 & 0 & 0 \\ -j\frac{1}{4} & 0 & \frac{1}{2} \\ 0 & 0 & 0 \end{bmatrix} \begin{bmatrix} \nu_1 \\ \nu_2 \\ \nu_3 \end{bmatrix} = \begin{bmatrix} 0 \\ 1 \\ 0 \end{bmatrix}$$

and find

$$-j\frac{1}{4}\nu_1 + \frac{1}{2}\nu_3 = 1$$

so that the generalized eigenvector is

$$\mathbf{v} = \begin{bmatrix} j2 \\ 0 \\ 1 \end{bmatrix}$$

as might be expected. The modal matrix is

$$\mathbf{S} = \begin{bmatrix} 0 & j & -j2 \\ 1 & 0 & 0 \\ 0 & 1 & 1 \end{bmatrix}$$

so that

$$\mathbf{S}^{-1} = \begin{bmatrix} 0 & 1 & 0 \\ -j\frac{1}{4} & 0 & \frac{1}{2} \\ j\frac{1}{4} & 0 & \frac{1}{2} \end{bmatrix}$$

Therefore the Jordan canonical form is

$$\mathbf{J} = \mathbf{S}^{-1}\mathbf{A}\mathbf{S} = \begin{bmatrix} 5 & 1 & 0 \\ 0 & 5 & 0 \\ 0 & 0 & 5 \end{bmatrix}$$ ∎

In summary then, a matrix with a multiple eigenvalue may have more than one Jordan block associated with this eigenvalue. In fact, if the dimensionality of the general solution $\boldsymbol{\xi}$ to

$$(\mathbf{A} - \lambda\mathbf{1})\boldsymbol{\xi} = \mathbf{0}$$

is r, then there are r Jordan blocks associated with the eigenvalue λ. We need not labor these points since we are able to evolve simple computational means for obtaining the Jordan canonical form.

The basic tool for dealing with matrices with indistinct eigenvalues remains the Cayley-Hamilton theorem, which we now proceed to prove in general.

(3.85) Theorem

Every $(n \times n)$ matrix $\mathbf{A}$ satisfies its characteristic equation; i.e., if

$$\det(\mathbf{A} - \lambda\mathbf{1}) \equiv q(\lambda) = q_0 + q_1\lambda + \cdots + q_n\lambda^n$$

then

$$q(\mathbf{A}) = q_0\mathbf{1} + q_1\mathbf{A} + \cdots + q_n\mathbf{A}^n = \mathbf{0}$$

Proof

Consider $(\mathbf{A} - \lambda\mathbf{1})^{-1}$ which exists almost everywhere [except at the n roots of the characteristic equation $q(\lambda) = 0$]; then

$$(\mathbf{A} - \lambda\mathbf{1})^{-1} = \frac{1}{q(\lambda)}\,\mathbf{C}(\lambda)$$

where $\mathbf{C}(\lambda)$ is the *adjunct* matrix consisting of cofactors of $(\mathbf{A} - \lambda\mathbf{1})$. Since the elements of $\mathbf{C}(\lambda)$ are each (signed) determinants of $(n-1) \times (n-1)$ submatrices of $(\mathbf{A} - \lambda\mathbf{1})$, we have in general,

$$\mathbf{C}(\lambda) = \mathbf{C}_0 + \mathbf{C}_1\lambda + \mathbf{C}_2\lambda^2 + \cdots + \mathbf{C}_{n-1}\lambda^{n-1}$$

where the $\mathbf{C}_0, \mathbf{C}_1, \ldots, \mathbf{C}_{n-1}$ are $n \times n$ matrices. We may write

$$(\mathbf{A} - \lambda\mathbf{1})\mathbf{C}(\lambda) = q(\lambda)\mathbf{1}$$

which also verifies that the highest power of λ in the matrix expansion of $\mathbf{C}(\lambda)$ is λ^{n-1}. So

$$\mathbf{AC}(\lambda) - \lambda\mathbf{C}(\lambda) = q(\lambda)\mathbf{1}$$

or

$$\sum_{k=0}^{n-1} \mathbf{AC}_k\lambda^k - \sum_{k=0}^{n-1} \mathbf{C}_k\lambda^{k+1} = \sum_{k=0}^{n} q_k\lambda^k\mathbf{1}$$

or

$$\sum_{k=0}^{n-1} \mathbf{AC}_k\lambda^k - \sum_{k=1}^{n} \mathbf{C}_{k-1}\lambda^k = \sum_{k=0}^{n} q_k\lambda^k\mathbf{1}$$

or

$$(\mathbf{AC}_0 - q_0\mathbf{1}) + \sum_{k=1}^{n-1} (\mathbf{AC} - \mathbf{C}_{k-1} - q_k\mathbf{1})\lambda^k - (\mathbf{C}_{n-1} + q_n\mathbf{1})\lambda^n = \mathbf{0}$$

Equating the matrix coefficients of like powers of λ we obtain

$$\begin{aligned}
\mathbf{AC}_0 &= q_0\mathbf{1} \\
\mathbf{AC}_1 - \mathbf{C}_0 &= q_1\mathbf{1} \\
&\cdots\cdots\cdots \\
\mathbf{AC}_{n-1} - \mathbf{C}_{n-2} &= q_{n-1}\mathbf{1} \\
- \mathbf{C}_{n-1} &= q_n\mathbf{1}
\end{aligned}$$

Multiply these expressions by $\mathbf{A}^0 = \mathbf{1}, \mathbf{A}, \ldots, \mathbf{A}^{n-1}$, respectively, to obtain

$$\begin{aligned}
\mathbf{AC}_0 &= q_0\mathbf{1} \\
\mathbf{A}^2\mathbf{C}_1 - \mathbf{AC}_0 &= q_1\mathbf{A} \\
&\cdots\cdots\cdots
\end{aligned}$$

$$\mathbf{A}^n\mathbf{C}_{n-1} - \mathbf{A}^{n-1}\mathbf{C}_{n-2} = q_{n-1}\mathbf{A}^{n-1} - \mathbf{A}^n\mathbf{C}_{n-1} = q_n\mathbf{A}^n$$

The sum of these equations is

$$\mathbf{0} = q_0\mathbf{1} + q_1\mathbf{A} + \cdots + q_{n-1}\mathbf{A}^{n-1} + q_n\mathbf{A}^n \qquad \blacksquare$$

The problem with which we are most often concerned is the computation of the function of a matrix $f(\mathbf{A})$, especially $e^{\mathbf{A}t}$, which can now be accomplished in general by means of the Cayley-Hamilton theorem:

$$f(\mathbf{A}) = \alpha_0\mathbf{1} + \alpha_1\mathbf{A} + \cdots + \alpha_{n-1}\mathbf{A}^{n-1}$$

and $f(\mathbf{A})$ exists so long as $f(\lambda_k)$ ($k = 1, 2, \ldots, n$) exists. By reasoning identical to that employed in the case of distinct eigenvalues, it follows that

$$f(\lambda_k) = \alpha_0 + \alpha_1\lambda_k + \cdots + \alpha_{n-1}\lambda_k^{n-1}$$

for n equations in the n unknown scalar coefficients $\alpha_0, \alpha_1, \ldots, \alpha_{n-1}$. But the equations corresponding to coincident eigenvalues are not independent, so further manipulations must be undertaken before we may effect a solution. Consider two distinct eigenvalues which are "close," λ and $\lambda + \varepsilon$; then

$$f(\lambda + \varepsilon) = \alpha_0 + \alpha_1(\lambda + \varepsilon) + \cdots + \alpha_{n-1}(\lambda + \varepsilon)^{n-1}$$

and

$$f(\lambda) = \alpha_0 + \alpha_1\lambda + \cdots + \alpha_{n-1}\lambda^{n-1}$$

Hence,

$$\lim_{\varepsilon \to 0} \frac{f(\lambda + \varepsilon) - f(\lambda)}{\varepsilon} = f'(\lambda)$$

which provides a relation independent of the original equation. In general, if λ_l is an eigenvalue of multiplicity k, we augment the expression

$$f(\lambda_l) = \alpha_0 + \alpha_1\lambda_l + \cdots + \alpha_{n-1}\lambda_l^{n-1}$$

by its first through $(k-1)$st derivative with respect to λ_l. In particular, if $f(\mathbf{A}) = e^{\mathbf{A}t}$ we have

$$\begin{aligned} e^{\lambda_l t} &= \alpha_0(t) + \alpha_1(t)\lambda_l + \cdots + \alpha_{n-1}(t)\lambda_l^{n-1} \\ te^{\lambda_l t} &= \alpha_1(t) + 2\alpha_2(t)\lambda_l + \cdots + (n-1)\alpha_{n-1}(t)\lambda_l^{n-2} \\ t^2e^{\lambda_l t} &= 2\alpha_2(t) + 6\alpha_3(t)\lambda_l + \cdots \\ &\qquad + (n-1)(n-2)\alpha_{n-1}(t)\lambda_l^{n-3} \quad \ldots \end{aligned}$$

If we take derivatives of order k or greater the results are trivial.

(3.86) Example
Find $e^{\mathbf{A}t}$ when

$$\mathbf{A} = \begin{bmatrix} 2 & 0 \\ 0 & 2 \end{bmatrix}$$

A has the eigenvalue $\lambda = 2$ of multiplicity 2. We know that

$$e^{\mathbf{A}t} = \alpha_0(t)\mathbf{1} + \alpha_1(t)\mathbf{A}$$

where $\alpha_0(t)$ and $\alpha_1(t)$ are such that

$$e^{2t} = \alpha_0(t) + 2\alpha_1(t)$$

and

$$te^{2t} = \alpha_1(t)$$

Therefore

$$\alpha_0(t) = (1 - 2t)e^{2t}$$

and

$$\alpha_1(t) = te^{2t}$$

so that

$$e^{\mathbf{A}t} = (1 - 2t)e^{2t}\begin{bmatrix} 1 & 0 \\ 0 & 1 \end{bmatrix} + te^{2t}\begin{bmatrix} 2 & 0 \\ 0 & 2 \end{bmatrix}$$

or

$$e^{\mathbf{A}t} = \begin{bmatrix} e^{2t} & 0 \\ 0 & e^{2t} \end{bmatrix}$$

We note that although a specific value for $\alpha_1(t)$ has been found, it is immaterial, since

$$\alpha_0(t) = e^{2t} - 2\alpha_1(t)$$

provides an adequate solution because $\alpha_1(t)$ cancels from the final expression. This result occurs because the original invariant subspace is one dimensional. If we consider the modal expansion, we have

$$e^{\mathbf{A}t} = e^{2t}\begin{bmatrix} 1 & 0 \\ 0 & 1 \end{bmatrix} = e^{2t}\begin{bmatrix} 1 \\ 0 \end{bmatrix}(1 \quad 0) + e^{2t}\begin{bmatrix} 0 \\ 1 \end{bmatrix}(0 \quad 1)$$

among other possibilities so that the eigenvectors may be taken to be

$$\boldsymbol{\xi}_1 = \begin{bmatrix} 1 \\ 0 \end{bmatrix} \quad \text{and} \quad \boldsymbol{\xi}_2 = \begin{bmatrix} 0 \\ 1 \end{bmatrix}$$ ▮

(3.87) Example

Find $e^{\mathbf{A}t}$ when

$$\mathbf{A} = \begin{bmatrix} 2 & 1 \\ 0 & 2 \end{bmatrix}$$

It is easy to ascertain that

$$\alpha_0(t) = (1 - 2t)e^{2t}$$

and

$$\alpha_1(t) = te^{2t}$$

so that

$$e^{\mathbf{A}t} = (1 - 2t)e^{2t}\begin{bmatrix} 1 & 0 \\ 0 & 1 \end{bmatrix} + te^{2t}\begin{bmatrix} 2 & 1 \\ 0 & 2 \end{bmatrix}$$

or

$$e^{\mathbf{A}t} = \begin{bmatrix} e^{2t} & te^{2t} \\ 0 & e^{2t} \end{bmatrix} = e^{2t}\begin{bmatrix} 1 & t \\ 0 & 1 \end{bmatrix}$$

Consider the modal expansion (dyad representation)

$$\begin{aligned} e^{\mathbf{A}t} &= e^{2t}\begin{bmatrix} 1 & 0 \\ 0 & 1 \end{bmatrix} + te^{2t}\begin{bmatrix} 0 & 1 \\ 0 & 0 \end{bmatrix} \\ &= e^{2t}\begin{bmatrix} 1 \\ 0 \end{bmatrix}(1 \quad 0) + e^{2t}\begin{bmatrix} 0 \\ 1 \end{bmatrix}(0 \quad 1) + te^{2t}\begin{bmatrix} 1 \\ 0 \end{bmatrix}(0 \quad 1) \end{aligned}$$

Hence,

$$\xi_1 = \begin{bmatrix} 1 \\ 0 \end{bmatrix}$$

is the eigenvalue and

$$\xi_2 = \begin{bmatrix} 0 \\ 1 \end{bmatrix}$$

is the generalized eigenvector.

Recall that if $\mathbf{W}$ is a nonsingular matrix

$$f(\mathbf{W}^{-1}\mathbf{A}\mathbf{W}) = \mathbf{W}^{-1}f(\mathbf{A})\mathbf{W}$$

For the case of distinct eigenvalues, we took

$$\mathbf{W} = \mathbf{S}$$

and

$$\mathbf{S}^{-1}\mathbf{A}\mathbf{S} = \mathbf{\Lambda}$$

where $\mathbf{\Lambda} = \text{diag}\,(\lambda_1,\lambda_2, \ldots ,\lambda_n)$. For the general case when eigenvalues may be repeated, we may again take

$$\mathbf{W} = \mathbf{S}$$

where the $\mathbf{S}$ is the generalized modal matrix and

$$\mathbf{S}^{-1}\mathbf{A}\mathbf{S} = \mathbf{J}$$

where $\mathbf{J} = \text{diag}\,(\mathbf{J}_1,\mathbf{J}_2, \ldots ,\mathbf{J}_m)$ is the Jordan canonical form of $\mathbf{A}$. Hence

$$e^{\mathbf{A}t} = \mathbf{S}e^{\mathbf{J}t}\mathbf{S}^{-1}$$

Let us consider $e^{\mathbf{J}t}$:

$$e^{\mathbf{J}t} = \begin{bmatrix} e^{\mathbf{J}_1 t} & 0 & 0 & \cdots & 0 \\ 0 & e^{\mathbf{J}_2 t} & 0 & \cdots & 0 \\ \cdots & \cdots & \cdots & \cdots & \cdots \\ 0 & 0 & 0 & \cdots & e^{\mathbf{J}_m t} \end{bmatrix}$$

where each $\mathbf{J}_k$ is of the form

$$\mathbf{J}_k = \begin{bmatrix} \lambda & 1 & 0 & 0 & \cdots & 0 \\ 0 & \lambda & 1 & 0 & \cdots & 0 \\ \cdots & \cdots & \cdots & \cdots & \cdots & \cdots \\ 0 & 0 & 0 & 0 & \cdots & \lambda \end{bmatrix}$$

Recall the series expansion for $e^{\mathbf{J}_k t}$:

$$e^{\mathbf{J}_k t} = \mathbf{1} + \mathbf{J}_k t + \mathbf{J}_k{}^2 \frac{t^2}{2!} + \mathbf{J}_k{}^3 \frac{t^3}{3!} + \cdots$$

$$= \begin{bmatrix} 1 & 0 & 0 & \cdots & 0 & 0 \\ 0 & 1 & 0 & \cdots & 0 & 0 \\ 0 & 0 & 1 & \cdots & 0 & 0 \\ \cdots & \cdots & \cdots & \cdots & \cdots & \cdots \\ 0 & 0 & 0 & \cdots & 1 & 0 \\ 0 & 0 & 0 & \cdots & 0 & 1 \end{bmatrix} + \begin{bmatrix} \lambda t & t & 0 & \cdots & 0 & 0 \\ 0 & \lambda t & t & \cdots & 0 & 0 \\ 0 & 0 & \lambda t & \cdots & 0 & 0 \\ \cdots & \cdots & \cdots & \cdots & \cdots & \cdots \\ 0 & 0 & 0 & \cdots & \lambda t & t \\ 0 & 0 & 0 & \cdots & 0 & \lambda t \end{bmatrix}$$

$$+ \frac{1}{2} \begin{bmatrix} (\lambda t)^2 & 2\lambda t^2 & t^2 & \cdots & 0 & 0 \\ 0 & (\lambda t)^2 & 2\lambda t^2 & \cdots & 0 & 0 \\ 0 & 0 & (\lambda t)^2 & \cdots & 0 & 0 \\ \cdots & \cdots & \cdots & \cdots & \cdots & \cdots \\ 0 & 0 & 0 & \cdots & (\lambda t)^2 & 2\lambda t^2 \\ 0 & 0 & 0 & \cdots & 0 & (\lambda t)^2 \end{bmatrix}$$

$$+ \frac{1}{3} \begin{bmatrix} (\lambda t)^3 & 3\lambda^2 t^3 & 3\lambda t^3 & \cdots & 0 & 0 \\ 0 & (\lambda t)^3 & 3\lambda^2 t^3 & \cdots & 0 & 0 \\ 0 & 0 & (\lambda t)^3 & \cdots & 0 & 0 \\ \cdots & \cdots & \cdots & \cdots & \cdots & \cdots \\ 0 & 0 & 0 & \cdots & (\lambda t)^3 & 3\lambda^2 t^3 \\ 0 & 0 & 0 & \cdots & 0 & (\lambda t)^3 \end{bmatrix} + \cdots$$

$$= e^{\lambda t} \begin{bmatrix} 1 & t & \dfrac{t^2}{2!} & \cdots & \dfrac{t^{n-1}}{(n-1)!} \\ 0 & 1 & t & \cdots & \dfrac{t^{n-2}}{(n-2)!} \\ \cdots & \cdots & \cdots & \cdots & \cdots \\ 0 & 0 & 0 & \cdots & 1 \end{bmatrix}$$

(3.88) Example

Given

$$\mathbf{A} = \begin{bmatrix} 2 & 0 & 0 \\ 0 & 2 & 0 \\ 0 & 0 & 2 \end{bmatrix}$$

then

$$e^{\mathbf{A}t} = \begin{bmatrix} e^{2t} & 0 & 0 \\ 0 & e^{2t} & 0 \\ 0 & 0 & e^{2t} \end{bmatrix}$$

given

$$\mathbf{A} = \begin{bmatrix} 2 & 1 & 0 \\ 0 & 2 & 0 \\ 0 & 0 & 2 \end{bmatrix}$$

then

$$e^{\mathbf{A}t} = \begin{bmatrix} e^{2t} & te^{2t} & 0 \\ 0 & e^{2t} & 0 \\ 0 & 0 & e^{2t} \end{bmatrix}$$

and finally, given

$$\mathbf{A} = \begin{bmatrix} 2 & 1 & 0 \\ 0 & 2 & 1 \\ 0 & 0 & 2 \end{bmatrix}$$

then

$$e^{\mathbf{A}t} \begin{bmatrix} e^{2t} & te^{2t} & \frac{t^2}{2} e^{2t} \\ 0 & e^{2t} & te^{2t} \\ 0 & 0 & e^{2t} \end{bmatrix}$$

3.10 THE NORM OF A LINEAR TRANSFORMATION (MATRIX)

Consider a linear transformation $T\colon E^n \to E^n$ where E^n is an n-dimensional normed linear vector space. Let the matrix $\mathbf{A}$ represent T with respect to some basis $\mathbf{e}_1, \mathbf{e}_2, \ldots, \mathbf{e}_n$, and let $\mathbf{x}$ be some vector in E^n. If we define

$$\mathbf{y} = \mathbf{A}\mathbf{x}$$

then $\mathbf{y} \in E^n$ and the norm of $\mathbf{y}$,

$$\|\mathbf{y}\| = \|\mathbf{A}\mathbf{x}\|$$

is a well-defined number.

(3.89) Norm of a matrix
The norm of the matrix is defined as

$$\|\mathbf{A}\| = \inf \{\mu : \|\mathbf{Ax}\| \leq \mu\|\mathbf{x}\| \text{ for all } \mathbf{x} \in E^n\} \tag{3.90}$$ ▌

(Note: inf or infinum is the greatest lower bound.) We leave it as an exercise for the reader to show that the above definition of a norm of a matrix does indeed satisfy the axiomatic definition of a norm.

An immediate consequence of this definition is that

$$\|\mathbf{Ax}\| \leq \|\mathbf{A}\| \, \|\mathbf{x}\| \qquad \text{for all } \mathbf{x} \in E^n$$

Observe that (3.90) can also be written as

$$\|\mathbf{A}\| = \inf \left\{\mu : \left\| \mathbf{A} \frac{\mathbf{x}}{\|\mathbf{x}\|} \right\| \leq \mu \text{ for all } \mathbf{x} \in E^n\right\}$$

by the properties of norms, or more succinctly as

$$\|\mathbf{A}\| = \inf \{\mu : \|\mathbf{Ax}\| \leq \mu \text{ for all } \mathbf{x} \in E^n \|\mathbf{x}\| = 1\}$$

or

$$\|\mathbf{A}\| = \sup_{\|\mathbf{x}\| = 1} \|\mathbf{Ax}\|$$

(Note: sup or supremum is the least upper bound.) In words then, the norm of the matrix $\mathbf{A}$, $\|\mathbf{A}\|$, is the maximum length of all the vectors $\mathbf{y} = \mathbf{Ax}$ when $\mathbf{x}$ ranges over the unit sphere in E^n, that is, $\|\mathbf{x}\| = 1$.

3.11 SUMMARY

This chapter constitutes an elementary investigation of matrix theory and manipulations.

Eigenvalues are used to find the *eigenvector*, or natural *basis*, for a square matrix. The *modal* matrix is used to find the *Jordan canonical* form which in turn greatly reduces the complexity of calculation needed to find a *function of a matrix*. The *Cayley-Hamilton theorem* is of prime importance in alternate calculations of square matrix functions.

The matrix techniques introduced here allow for ease of manipulation and notation in our subsequent study of higher-order systems.

3.12 PROBLEMS

(3.1) Prove that matrices obey the distributive laws listed on page 97.

(3.2) Prove that matrices obey the associative laws on page 97.

(3.3) Prove that

$$(\mathbf{A} + \mathbf{B})' = \mathbf{A}' + \mathbf{B}'$$

and

$$(\mathbf{AB})' = \mathbf{B}'\mathbf{A}'$$

(3.4) Evaluate the matrix products

(*a*) $\begin{bmatrix} 1 & -1 \\ -1 & 0 \\ 1 & 1 \end{bmatrix} \begin{bmatrix} -1 & 2 \\ 1 & 1 \end{bmatrix}$

(*b*) $\begin{bmatrix} 1 & 2 & 1 \\ 4 & 6 & 1 \\ 1 & 1 & 0 \end{bmatrix} \begin{bmatrix} 6 & 0 & -2 \\ 2 & 2 & 1 \\ 3 & 1 & 1 \end{bmatrix}$

(*c*) $\mathbf{a}'\mathbf{b}$ and $\mathbf{ab}'$

where

$$a = \begin{bmatrix} a_1 \\ a_2 \\ \cdot \\ \cdot \\ \cdot \\ a_n \end{bmatrix} \quad \text{and} \quad b = \begin{bmatrix} b_1 \\ b_2 \\ \cdot \\ \cdot \\ \cdot \\ b_n \end{bmatrix}$$

(3.5) Given the matrix

$$\mathbf{A} = \begin{bmatrix} 1 & 0 & -1 \\ 0 & 1 & 2 \\ -1 & 2 & 1 \end{bmatrix}$$

find

(*a*) $\mathbf{A}'$
(*b*) det $(\mathbf{A})$
(*c*) $\mathbf{A}^{-1}$
(*d*) eigenvalues of $\mathbf{A}$
(*e*) eigenvectors of $\mathbf{A}$

(3.6) Given the following matrices

$$\mathbf{A} = \begin{bmatrix} 5 & 1 & 3 \\ 8 & 0 & 1 \\ -2 & 6 & 3 \end{bmatrix} \qquad \mathbf{B} = \begin{bmatrix} 4 & 2 & 1 \\ 3 & 1 & 5 \\ 2 & 8 & 6 \end{bmatrix} \qquad \mathbf{C} = \begin{bmatrix} 2 & 1 & 9 \\ 0 & 2 & 1 \\ 3 & 8 & 4 \end{bmatrix}$$

find

(*a*) the determinant of $\mathbf{A}$, $\mathbf{B}$, and $\mathbf{C}$
(*b*) $\mathbf{B}^{-1}$, if it exists, and $\mathbf{B}'$
(*c*) $\mathbf{A} \cdot \mathbf{C}$ and $\mathbf{C} \cdot \mathbf{A}$
(*d*) $\mathbf{A}(\mathbf{B} + \mathbf{C})$ and $\mathbf{AB} + \mathbf{AC}$
(*e*) $[\mathbf{AB}]^{-1}$ and $(\mathbf{AB})'$

(3.7) Show that every nontrivial field must contain a zero element and a 1 element. Is it possible to formulate operations of $+$, $-$, $\times$, $\div$ to obtain a binary field containing just a zero and a 1? How?

(3.8) (*a*) Show that the set of solutions of the set of *homogeneous* linear algebraic equations

$$\begin{aligned} a_{11}x_1 + a_{12}x_2 + \cdots + a_{1n}x_n &= 0 \\ a_{21}x_1 + a_{22}x_2 + \cdots + a_{2n}x_n &= 0 \\ \cdots\cdots\cdots\cdots\cdots\cdots\cdots \\ a_{m1}x_1 + a_{m2}x_2 + \cdots + a_{mn}x_n &= 0 \end{aligned}$$

is a linear vector space.

(*b*) Show that the set of solutions (arbitrary initial conditions) of the homogeneous linear differential equation

$$b_n x^{(n)}(t) + b_{n-1}x^{(n-1)}(t) + \cdots + b_1 x^{(1)}(t) + b_0 x(t) = 0$$

is a linear vector space.

(3.9) (*a*) Is the set of solutions of the inhomogeneous set of linear algebraic equations

$$\begin{aligned} x_1 - 2x_2 &= 3 \\ -2x_1 + 4x_2 &= -6 \end{aligned}$$

a linear vector space?

(*b*) Is the set of solutions (arbitrary initial conditions) of the inhomogeneous linear differential equation

$$\dot{x}(t) + x(t) = 1 \qquad 0 \le t < \infty$$

a linear vector space?

(3.10) Show that the following satisfy the definition of a metric (3.39):

$$\begin{aligned} &(a) \quad \rho(\boldsymbol{\xi},\mathbf{n}) = |\sqrt{(\xi_1 - \eta_1)^2 + (\xi_2 - \eta_2)^2}| \\ &(b) \quad \rho(\boldsymbol{\xi},\mathbf{n}) = |\xi_1 - \eta_1| + |\xi_2 - \eta_2| \\ &(c) \quad \rho_\infty(\boldsymbol{\xi},\mathbf{n}) = \max\{|\xi_1 - \eta_1|, |\xi_2 - \eta_2|\} \end{aligned}$$

where $\boldsymbol{\xi} = \begin{pmatrix} \xi_1 \\ \xi_2 \end{pmatrix}$ and $\mathbf{n} = \begin{pmatrix} \eta_1 \\ \eta_2 \end{pmatrix}$

(3.11) Show that the following have the properties of a norm (3.42):

$$\begin{aligned} &(a) \quad \|\boldsymbol{\xi}\|_1 = |\xi_1| + |\xi_2| \\ &(b) \quad \|\boldsymbol{\xi}\|_2 = |\sqrt{\xi_1^2 + \xi_2^2}| \\ &(c) \quad \|\boldsymbol{\xi}\|_\infty = \max\{|\xi_1|, |\xi_2|\} \end{aligned}$$

where $\boldsymbol{\xi} = \begin{pmatrix} \xi_1 \\ \xi_2 \end{pmatrix}$.

(3.12) A linear transformation is represented by the matrix

$$A = \begin{bmatrix} 4 & 1 & 3 \\ 2 & 1 & 5 \\ 6 & 3 & 1 \\ 0 & 1 & 4 \\ 2 & 5 & 1 \end{bmatrix}$$

If

$$x_1 = \begin{bmatrix} 2 \\ 4 \\ -9 \end{bmatrix}$$

what is $\|\mathbf{x}_2\|_1$, $\|\mathbf{x}_2\|_2$, and $\|\mathbf{x}_2\|_\infty$ if

$$\mathbf{x}_2 = \mathbf{A}\mathbf{x}_1$$

(3.13) Prove that the Vandermonde determinant associated with a matrix with distinct eigenvalues is nonzero.

(3.14) For each matrix **A** below, find the eigenvalues, eigenvectors, generalized eigenvectors, and Jordan canonical form for **A** and $e^{\mathbf{A}t}$.

(*a*)
$$\mathbf{A} = \begin{bmatrix} 2 & 1 & 0 & 0 \\ 0 & 2 & 0 & 0 \\ 0 & 0 & 2 & 1 \\ 0 & 0 & 0 & 2 \end{bmatrix}$$

(*b*)
$$\mathbf{A} = \begin{bmatrix} 5 & -1 & 1 & 1 & 0 & 0 \\ 1 & 3 & -1 & -1 & 0 & 0 \\ 0 & 0 & 4 & 0 & 1 & 1 \\ 0 & 0 & 0 & 4 & -1 & -1 \\ 0 & 0 & 0 & 0 & 3 & 1 \\ 0 & 0 & 0 & 0 & 1 & 3 \end{bmatrix}$$

(3.15) (*a*) Given the complex n vector $\mathbf{x}$ and the complex n vector $\mathbf{y}$, determine the eigenvectors and eigenvalues of the $n \times n$ complex matrix (dyad) $\mathbf{y}'\mathbf{x}$.

(*b*) Find an explicit form for the inverse of the matrix $(\mathbf{1} + \mathbf{y}'\mathbf{x})$.

(*c*) Given $\mathbf{x}$, $\mathbf{y}$, $\hat{\mathbf{x}}$, and $\hat{\mathbf{y}}$, find an explicit form for the inverse of the matrix $(\mathbf{1} + \mathbf{y}'\mathbf{x} + \hat{\mathbf{y}}'\hat{\mathbf{x}})$.

(3.16) The rotation of a rigid body (about its center of mass, for example) can be described by the matrix $\mathbf{A} \equiv \mathbf{BCD}$, where

$$\mathbf{D} \equiv \begin{bmatrix} \cos\phi & \sin\phi & 0 \\ -\sin\phi & \cos\phi & 0 \\ 0 & 0 & 1 \end{bmatrix}$$

$$\mathbf{C} \equiv \begin{bmatrix} 1 & 0 & 0 \\ 0 & \cos\theta & \sin\theta \\ 0 & -\sin\theta & \cos\theta \end{bmatrix}$$

$$\mathbf{B} \equiv \begin{bmatrix} \cos\psi & \sin\psi & 0 \\ -\sin\psi & \cos\psi & 0 \\ 0 & 0 & 1 \end{bmatrix}$$

(ϕ, θ, and ψ are the Euler angles of classical mechanics). Describe by means of a series of sketches the evolution of this rotational transformation. (Hint: Find the invariant subspaces for **D**, **C**, and **B**, respectively.)

(3.17) Given

$$\mathbf{A} = \begin{bmatrix} 1 & -1 & 1 & -1 \\ -3 & 3 & -5 & 4 \\ 8 & -4 & 3 & -4 \\ 15 & -10 & 11 & -11 \end{bmatrix}$$

(*a*) Find **J**, the Jordan canonical form of **A**.
(*b*) What is $e^{\mathbf{J}t}$?

(3.18) Given

$$\mathbf{A} = \begin{bmatrix} 1 & 1 & 0 & 0 & 0 & 0 & 0 \\ 0 & 1 & 0 & 0 & 0 & 0 & 0 \\ 0 & 0 & 5 & 0 & 0 & 0 & 0 \\ 0 & 0 & 0 & -2 & 1 & 0 & 0 \\ 0 & 0 & 0 & 0 & -2 & 1 & 0 \\ 0 & 0 & 0 & 0 & 0 & -2 & 0 \\ 0 & 0 & 0 & 0 & 0 & 0 & 3 \end{bmatrix}$$

(*a*) What is the Jordan canonical form, **J**?
(*b*) What is $e^{\mathbf{J}t}$?
(*c*) Find the modal matrix **S** and the reciprocal basis.

(3.19) In our definition of determinants, we defined a third-order determinant in terms of second-order determinants:

$$\begin{vmatrix} a_{11} & a_{12} & a_{13} \\ a_{21} & a_{22} & a_{23} \\ a_{31} & a_{32} & a_{33} \end{vmatrix} = a_{11}\begin{vmatrix} a_{22} & a_{23} \\ a_{32} & a_{33} \end{vmatrix} a_{12}\begin{vmatrix} a_{21} & a_{23} \\ a_{31} & a_{33} \end{vmatrix} + a_{13}\begin{vmatrix} a_{21} & a_{22} \\ a_{31} & a_{32} \end{vmatrix}$$

Verify that if any other row or column were used in this expansion, the same result would be obtained. Prove that this result holds for determinants of order n.

4 HIGHER-ORDER SYSTEMS

In Chaps. 1 and 2 we were able to discuss the state-variable approach to system theory while resorting minimally to vector-matrix concepts. However, even in the case of second-order systems covered in Chap. 2, we have seen that matrix techniques often offer an attractive alternative to the more cumbersome detailed notation entailed in their absence. In consequence, in Chap. 3 we have undertaken a lengthy mathematical digression in order to prepare for the ensuing study of higher-order systems.

Conceptually, there is little to be added in this chapter, although in the course of this study of higher-order systems, the more compact vector-matrix notation occasionally may make it appear otherwise. As

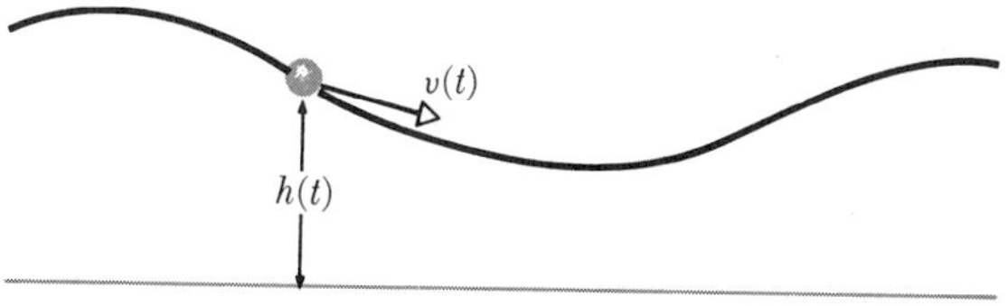

FIG. 4.1 A two-output system: a point mass sliding without friction on a wire where height and velocity are outputs.

we proceed it will be well to keep firmly in mind the corresponding system-theoretic concepts as they were introduced in terms of first- and second-order systems. Probably the most important point to be recalled is that in this chapter, and in system studies in general, we often employ the term "system" in lieu of the more precise phrase "possible mathematical characterization of the system." Moreover, alternate characterizations of the same physical system do not necessarily possess the same system-theoretic properties. It is a major task of system theorists to choose from among these alternatives that mathematical representation most tractable in any given study.

4.1 STANDARD-FORM STATE EQUATIONS

It is easy to visualize a system which has more than one input and more than one output. For instance, consider a point mass sliding without friction on a wire as shown in Fig. 4.1. Two quantities which may be of interest, and thus considered to be outputs, are the height above some reference level and velocity along the wire of the point mass. As an example of a multiple-input system, consider the transistor amplifier in Fig. 4.2. The inputs to this system can be taken to be the dc voltage source, E, and the ac signal v. A television set is an example of a multiple input-output system. The audio and video rf signals and the ac supply voltage are

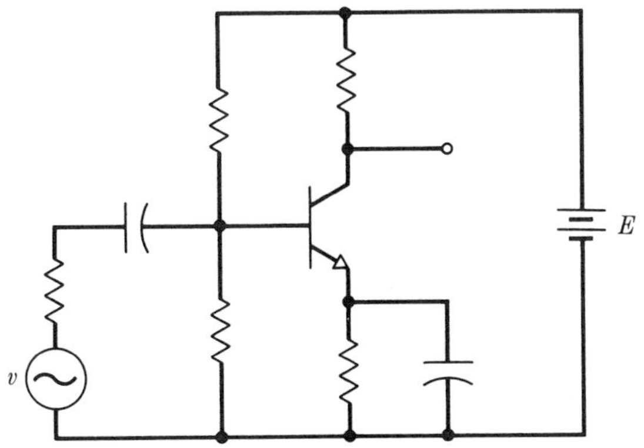

FIG. 4.2 A multiple-input system: transistor amplifier with dc voltage E and ac signal v as inputs.

inputs while the responses are the audio signal fed to the speaker and video signal fed to the picture tube.

In general, we assume that a system has r inputs and m outputs. For notational convenience, we will denote the r inputs by the r vector $\mathbf{u}$, henceforth called the input vector, or merely the input, and the m outputs by the m vector $\mathbf{y}$, henceforth called the output vector or merely the output. Therefore

$$\mathbf{u}(t) = [u_1(t),u_2(t), \ . \ . \ . \ ,u_r(t)]'$$

and

$$\mathbf{y}(t) = [y_1(t),y_2(t), \ . \ . \ . \ ,y_m(t)]'$$

We may sometimes write $\mathbf{u}(t)$ and $\mathbf{y}(t)$ to emphasize their time dependence.

(4.1) State
A *state* of a system at time t_0 is any amount of information which, together with any possible input functions specified for $t_f \geq t \geq t_0$, is adequate to determine uniquely the output functions for $t_f \geq t \geq t_0$, for any $t_f \geq t_0$. ▌

To allow for the possibility that the representation of the state of a system may require several variables, as in the case of second-order systems, we denote the state by the n vector $\mathbf{x}$. The n components of $\mathbf{x}$, that is,

$$\mathbf{x}(t) = [x_1(t),x_2(t), \ . \ . \ . \ ,x_n(t)]'$$

represent the *state variables* of the system. Since $\mathbf{x}$ is a function of time, we sometimes write $\mathbf{x}(t)$. Our experience in earlier sections has been that the state of a first-order system can be described by a single state variable while the state of a second-order system requires two state variables. In the sequel, if a system requires n variables to characterize its state, we call it an nth-order system. The *state space* of a system is the space which is *spanned* by the vector $\mathbf{x}(t)$ as time t varies, i.e., the space in which the basis vectors may be chosen from the set of vectors $\{\mathbf{x}(t)\}$.

There are systems for which an infinite number of state variables are required to specify the state completely. For instance, the unit delayor mentioned in Chap. 1 is an example of such a system. These systems are said to have an *infinite-dimensional state space.* All systems for which a state representation can be found, whether finite or infinite, are said to *admit* a state-space description.

Observe that by our definition, the present state of a system $\mathbf{x}(t_0)$ and the present and future inputs to a system $[\mathbf{u}(t), t \geq t_0]$ suffice to determine the present and future outputs of a system $[\mathbf{y}(t),t \geq t_0]$. Hence, the manner in which a system reaches its present state does not, in any way, affect the future output. In other words, we can say that the state separates past and future behavior of a system or that all past behavior is summarized by the present state of the system.

If a given system admits a state-space description and is describable by ordinary differential equations, the state description can be reduced to

$$\dot{\mathbf{x}}(t) = \mathbf{f}(\mathbf{x}(t),\mathbf{u}(t),t) \tag{4.2}$$

and

$$\mathbf{y}(t) = \mathbf{g}(\mathbf{x}(t),\mathbf{u}(t),t) \tag{4.3}$$

where the n-vector function $\mathbf{f}$ and the m-vector function $\mathbf{g}$ are single valued. Although this fact is not obvious, the reader is asked to assume its truth.[1] Equations (4.2) and (4.3) are known as *standard-form state equations.*

To see that not all systems can be described by finite-dimensional state equations consider again the unit delayor characterized by

$$y(t) = u(t - 1)$$

To find the output for all $t \geq t_0$, not only must $u(t)$ be known for $t \geq t_0$, but $u(t)$ for $t_0 - 1 \leq t \leq t_0$ must also be known, i.e., no satisfactory finite-dimensional state can be found to satisfy our definition; rather we require a function space. A system which admits a finite-dimensional state space description is known as a *finite system* or *lumped system.*

Another example of a system which does not have a finite-dimensional state space associated with it is the differentiator described by

$$y(t) = \frac{d}{dt}\,u(t)$$

This relation can be rewritten as

$$y(t) = \lim_{h \to 0} \frac{(u(t) - u(t - h))}{h}$$

and, as in the case of the unit delayor, the output at time t depends on a *segment* of the input function.

Thus far, there has been no indication as to how many state variables are required to characterize a given system; it must be possible to "overstate" the case by means of inclusion of superfluous states. For this reason, we must consider the possibility of having two or more equivalent states.

[1] For a more detailed explanation of this statement see L. A. Zadeh and C. A. Desoer, "Linear System Theory, The State Space Approach," pp. 67–70, McGraw-Hill, New York, 1963.

(4.4) State equivalence
Given a system with the state space $\mathfrak{X}$, suppose that $\mathbf{y}_1(t)$ is the system response for the initial state $\mathbf{x}_1(t_0) \in \mathfrak{X}$ and input $\mathbf{u}(\tau)$, $t_0 \leq \tau \leq t$, and that $\mathbf{y}_2(t)$ is the system response for the initial state $\mathbf{x}_2(t_0) \in \mathfrak{X}$ and the *same* input $\mathbf{u}(\tau)$, $t_0 \leq \tau \leq t$. The two states $\mathbf{x}_1$ and $\mathbf{x}_2$ are said to be *equivalent*, written

$$\mathbf{x}_1 \simeq \mathbf{x}_2$$

provided that

$$\mathbf{y}_1(\tau) = \mathbf{y}_2(\tau) \qquad t_0 \leq \tau \leq t$$

for all possible initial times t_0 and all admissible inputs $\mathbf{u}$. ∎
In other words, the states $\mathbf{x}_1$ and $\mathbf{x}_2$ are equivalent if the output of the system is identical for all admissible inputs $\mathbf{u}(\tau)$, $t_0 \leq \tau \leq t$, no matter in which of the states $\mathbf{x}_1$ or $\mathbf{x}_2$ the system starts.

If a finite-system characterization has no equivalent states, we say it is *reduced*. Moreover, if a lumped system is reduced, its differential-state equations

$$\dot{\mathbf{x}} = \mathbf{f}(\mathbf{x},\mathbf{u},t)$$

and its input-state-output equations

$$\mathbf{y} = \mathbf{g}(\mathbf{x},\mathbf{u},t)$$

are said to be *canonical*.

(4.5) Example
Consider the network shown in Fig. 4.3*a*. The input is the voltage-source voltage $u(t)$ and the output is the voltage-source current $y(t)$. We take as the two state variables the voltage across the capacitor and the current

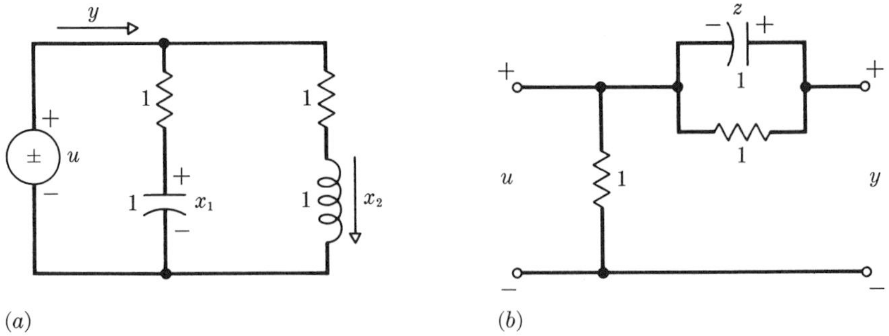

FIG. 4.3 (*a*) A two-state system that is not reduced, and (*b*) a one-state equivalent reduced system.

through the inductor. The differential-state equations are

$$\dot{x}_1(t) = -x_1(t) + u(t)$$

and

$$\dot{x}_2(t) = -x_2(t) + u(t)$$

and the input-state-output equation is

$$y(t) = -x_1(t) + x_2(t) + u(t)$$

The methods of Chap. 2 can be used to show that the general solution of the pair of uncoupled, differential-state equations is

$$x_1(t) = e^{-(t-t_0)}x_1(t_0) + \int_{t_0}^{t} e^{-(t-\tau)}u(\tau)\,d\tau$$

and

$$x_2(t) = e^{-(t-t_0)}x_2(t_0) + \int_{t_0}^{t} e^{-(t-\tau)}u(\tau)\,d\tau$$

therefore, the input-state-output relation becomes

$$y(t) = e^{-(t-t_0)}(-x_1(t) + x_2(t)) + u(t)$$

Hence, any two states $\mathbf{x}_a(t)$ and $\mathbf{x}_b(t)$ will be equivalent by our definition if

$$-x_{a1}(t) + x_{a2}(t) = -x_{b1}(t) + x_{b2}(t)$$

A reduced characterization would be given by the state equations

$$\dot{z}(t) = -z(t)$$

and

$$y(t) = -z(t) + u(t)$$

where the state variable $z(t)$ is taken to be the current through the inductor less the voltage across the capacitor. A first-order network which may be characterized by the reduced-state equations is shown in Fig. 4.3b. ▮

(4.6) Example

Now consider the resistance-capacitance network of Fig. 4.4a, and choose as state variables the two capacitance voltages x_1 and x_2. The pair of

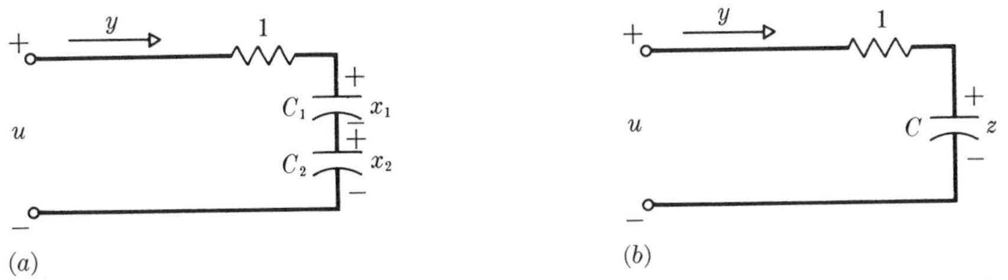

FIG. 4.4 The two-state system (a) is not reduced and is equivalent to the (reduced) single-state system (b).

differential-state equations which describe the system are

$$\dot{x}_1 = -\frac{1}{C_1}x_1 - \frac{1}{C_1}x_2 + \frac{1}{C_1}u$$

and

$$\dot{x}_2 = -\frac{1}{C_2}x_1 - \frac{1}{C_2}x_2 + \frac{1}{C_2}u$$

while the input-state-output equation is

$$y = -x_1 - x_2 + u$$

The solution of the state equations is

$$y(t) = -\exp\left[-\left(\frac{1}{C_1} + \frac{1}{C_2}\right)(t - t_0)\right](x_1(t_0) + x_2(t_0))$$
$$-\left(\frac{1}{C_1} + \frac{1}{C_2}\right)\int_{t_0}^{t} \exp\left[-\left(\frac{1}{C_1} + \frac{1}{C_2}\right)(t - \tau)\right]u(\tau)\,d\tau + u(t)$$

Therefore any pair of state vectors $\mathbf{x}_a$ and $\mathbf{x}_b$ such that

$$x_{a1} + x_{a2} = x_{b1} + x_{b2}$$

are equivalent. A reduced characterization would be

$$\dot{z} = -\left(\frac{1}{C_1} + \frac{1}{C_2}\right)z + \left(\frac{1}{C_1} + \frac{1}{C_2}\right)u$$

and

$$y = -z + u$$

where $z(t)$ is taken to be the sum of the voltages across each capacitor. A system describable by these reduced-state equations is shown in Fig. 4.4*b*. ▮

Just as it is possible to have equivalent states, it is possible to have equivalent systems. Two systems are said to be equivalent if they cannot be distinguished by means of multiple experiments.

(4.7) System equivalence

Two finite systems with state spaces $\mathfrak{X}_a$ and $\mathfrak{X}_b$ and responses $\mathbf{y}_a$ and $\mathbf{y}_b$, respectively, are said to be *equivalent* if for every state $\mathbf{x}_a(t_0) \in \mathfrak{X}_a$, there exists a state $\mathbf{x}_b(t_0) \in \mathfrak{X}_b$ such that for all possible t_0, $\mathbf{u}$ and $t \geq t_0$,

$$\mathbf{u}_a(\tau) = \mathbf{u}_b(\tau) = \mathbf{u}(\tau) \qquad t_0 \leq \tau \leq t$$

implies that

$$\mathbf{y}_a(\tau) = \mathbf{y}_b(\tau) \qquad t_0 \leq \tau \leq t$$

and conversely if for every state $\hat{\mathbf{x}}_b(t_0) \in \mathfrak{X}_b$ there exists a state $\hat{\mathbf{x}}_a(t_0) \in \mathfrak{X}_a$ such that for all possible t_0, $\mathbf{u}$ and $t \geq t_0$,

$$\mathbf{u}_b(\tau) = \mathbf{u}_a(\tau) = \mathbf{u}(\tau) \qquad t_0 \leq \tau \leq t$$

implies that

$$\mathbf{y}_b(\tau) = \mathbf{y}_a(\tau) \qquad t_0 \leq \tau \leq t$$

▮

(4.8) Example

Consider a system described by the differential-state equation

$$\dot{z} = -z$$

and the input-state-output equation

$$y = z + u$$

Such a system is shown in Fig. 4.3*b*. Solution of these equations yields

$$y(t) = e^{-(t-t_0)}z(t_0) + u(t_0)$$

Observe that the second-order system described in Example (4.5) is equivalent to the first-order system described here with

$$z \equiv -x_1 + x_2$$

Note that the above second-order system is equivalent to a first-order system only for the choice of output shown. If a different quantity were chosen to be the output, the equivalence described might be unjustified. For example, suppose that the quantity of interest for the network of Fig. 4.3*a* were the current flowing through the capacitor. Then the output would be

$$\hat{y} = -x_1 + u$$

or

$$\hat{y}(t) = -e^{(t-t_0)}x_1(t_0) + \int_{t_0}^{t} e^{(t-\tau)}u(\tau)\,d\tau + u(t)$$

This characterization is not equivalent to the network of Fig. 4.3*b*. ▮

(4.9) Example

Consider a system characterized by the differential-state equation

$$\dot{z} = -\frac{1}{C}z + \frac{1}{C}u$$

and the input-state-output equation

$$y = -z + u$$

where $1/C \equiv (1/C_1) + (1/C_2)$. Such a system is shown in Fig. 4.4*b*. The solution of these equations is

$$y(t) = -\exp\left[-\frac{1}{C}(t - t_0)\right] z(t_0) + \frac{1}{C}\int_{t_0}^{t} \exp\left[-\frac{1}{C}(t - \tau)\right] u(\tau)\, d\tau + u(t)$$

Comparison of this result with that of Example (4.6) shows that the system described by the second-order, standard-form state equations of Example (4.6) is equivalent to the system described by the first-order, standard-form state equations here with

$$z \equiv x_1 + x_2$$

i.e., the reduced system is equivalent to the original system. ▮

It must be reemphasized that state and system equivalence are heavily dependent on the choice of inputs and outputs. Other input-output—dependent system properties are to be discussed in Chap. 5 on the macroscopic approach to system characterization.

4.2 WRITING STATE EQUATIONS

We now turn our attention to the writing of state equations. Although no universal technique is to be introduced, the exposure to a number of examples will allow us to write state equations to characterize a great variety of the physical systems ordinarily encountered in practice.

Consider first the simplest mechanical system, a point mass m moving with one spatial degree of freedom. The motion of the point mass may be described by a pair of coupled, first-order governing differential equations:

$$p(t) \equiv m\dot{x}(t) \qquad \text{or} \qquad \dot{x}(t) = \frac{1}{m}p(t)$$

defines the momentum p, and

$$\dot{p}(t) = f(t)$$

where f is the force applied on the mass point, is Newton's second law of motion. Now, we can certainly account for all possibilities if we suppose that the force f on the mass point may be attributed to the position x (for example, the force provided by an attached spring), the momentum p (for example, the force provided by friction), and external agents u and time t. Hence, the differential-state equations describing one-dimensional motion of a mass point take the form

$$\dot{x}(t) = \frac{1}{m} p(t)$$

and

$$\dot{p}(t) = f(x(t),p(t),u(t),t)$$

in general, where x and p are state variables. A mass point moving in three dimensions may be associated with three pairs of first-order differential equations similar to the above, where coupling may be evidenced through the second member of each pair.

(4.10) Example

A simple example for the writing of state equations to describe the motion of a mass point in one dimension is provided by the mechanical system of Fig. 4.5. The particle slides without friction along a wire fixed in the vertical plane and described by the function $\xi(x)$, $-\infty < x < \infty$, which is single valued and differentiable. The particle is subjected to an external vertical force $u(x,t) - g$, where g is gravity (a constant). The equation of motion is

$$\dot{x}(t) = \frac{1}{m\sqrt{1 + [\xi'(x)]^2}} p(t)$$

where p is the momentum of the particle directed along the wire and where

$$\xi'(x) \equiv \frac{d}{dx}[\xi(x)]$$

Moreover, the time derivative of the momentum directed along the wire is that component of the vertical force which is directed along the wire:

$$\dot{p}(t) = \frac{\xi'(x)}{\sqrt{1 + [\xi'(x)]^2}} [u(x,t) - g]$$

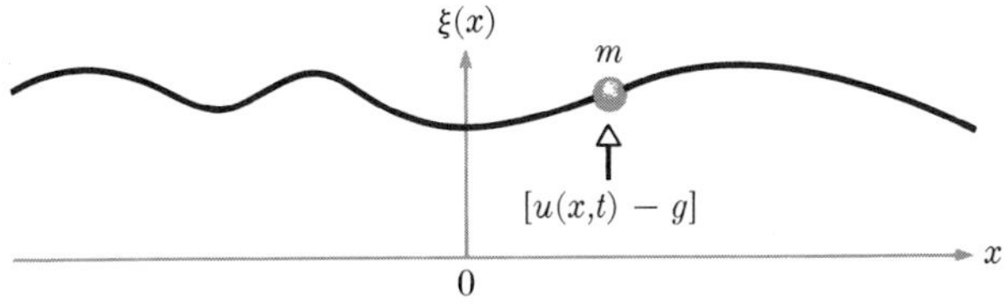

FIG. 4.5 A mass point slides (without friction) on the wire described by the function ξ while subjected to the vertical force $[u(x,t) - g]$.

If we consider the zero-input situation, conservation of energy yields the first integral

$$\tfrac{1}{2}m\{1 + [\xi'(x)]^2\}[\dot{x}(t)]^2\} + mg\xi(x) = \mathcal{E}$$

where the constant $\mathcal{E}$, the total energy in the system, is determined by initial conditions (height and velocity directed along wire). We have, then, the alternative description

$$\dot{x}(t) = \left(\frac{(2/m)\mathcal{E} - 2g\xi(x)}{1 + [\xi'(x)]^2}\right)^{\frac{1}{2}}$$

hence, we see that the system may be characterized by an alternative pair of state variables, the horizontal position x, and the total energy $\mathcal{E}$ (a constant). This pair of state variables is more convenient for this problem than the position and momentum originally chosen, because it reduces the characterization essentially to first order. In a vast number of physical-system studies, energy becomes a more convenient state-variable choice than some position or momentum, because of the conservative (i.e., energy is constant) nature of the system. In particular, in statistical and quantum-mechanical studies, energy is almost invariably employed as a state variable. ▮

(4.11) Example

Consider the system of Fig. 4.6 which consists of the motion of a point mass in a central force field $u(r)$. As a first choice of state variables, consider the angle θ, the angular momentum p_θ, the radius r, and the linear momentum p_r. Four first-order differential equations that relate these parameters are

$$\dot{\theta} = \frac{1}{mr^2} p_\theta$$ conservation of angular momentum in a central force field

$$\dot{p}_\theta = 0$$

$$\dot{r} = \frac{1}{m} pr$$

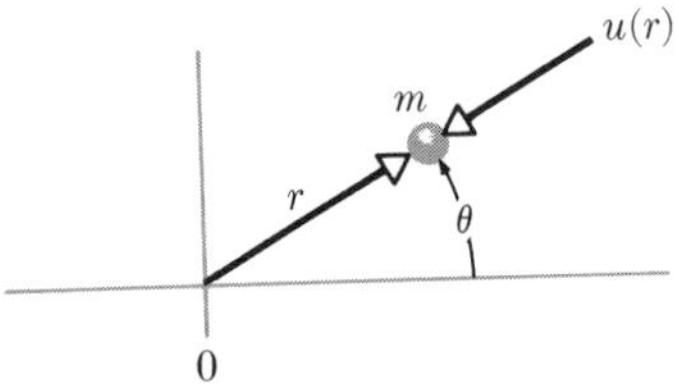

FIG. 4.6 A mass point is attracted to the origin with a force $u(r)$ in a central force field.

and

$$\dot{p}_r = \frac{1}{mr} p_\theta^2 + u(r)$$

We recognize that the angular momentum is constant

$$p_\theta = l$$

The total energy of the system is

$$\mathcal{E} = \frac{1}{2} m\dot{r}^2 + \frac{1}{2} \frac{l^2}{mr^2} + V(r)$$

where $V(r)$ is the potential energy which describes the central force field

$$V(r) = \int_r^\infty u(\xi)\, d\xi$$

or

$$u(r) = -\frac{d}{dr} V(r)$$

An alternative state description of this system is achieved by choosing θ, r, p_θ, and $\mathcal{E}$ as the state variables, then

$$\dot{\theta} = \frac{1}{mr^2} p_\theta$$

$$\dot{r} = \left(\frac{2}{m}\left[\mathcal{E} - V(r) - \frac{p_\theta}{2mr^2}\right]\right)^{\frac{1}{2}}$$

$$\dot{p}_\theta = 0$$

and

$$\dot{\mathcal{E}} = 0 \qquad \text{conservation of energy}$$ ▮

The above two examples illustrate that the choice of state variables is not unique, and that some choices may be more convenient than others.

(4.12) Example

Consider the mass point m_1 sliding without friction on a horizontal plane shown in Fig. 4.7. The coordinates on the plane are the radius r and angle

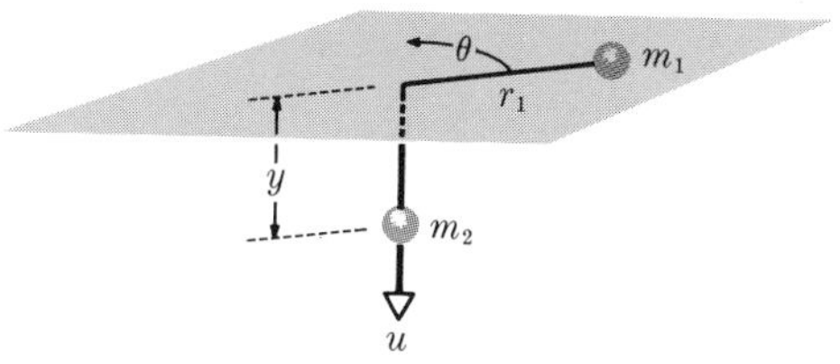

FIG. 4.7 A mass m_1 sliding without friction on a horizontal plane.

θ. Another mass point m_2 is connected to mass point m_1 by means of an incompressible string of length l which goes through a small hole at the origin in the horizontal plane. The string hangs vertically. Let u, the vertical force on m_2 be the input and y, the distance between mass point m_2 and the plane, be the output.

Since we can relate y, l, and r by

$$y = l - r$$

and m_1, m_2 by

$$\frac{p_r}{m_1} = -\frac{p_y}{m_2}$$

where p_r and p_y are linear momentum, only four variables, r, p_r, θ, p_θ, remain as candidates for state variables. Note that all other variables are easily determined from knowledge of these quantities and the input.

From the conservation of angular momentum

$$\dot{p}_\theta = 0$$

moreover,

$$p_\theta = mr^2 = m\dot{\theta}r^2$$

so that

$$\dot{\theta} = \frac{1}{mr^2} p_\theta$$

For convenience, let f denote the *inward* force on the mass point m_1, then

$$f = -\dot{p}_r$$

This force is transmitted through the string and must equal the external force u, and the force due to gravity m_2g, less the outward centrifugal force p_θ/r:

$$f = u + m_2g - \frac{p_\theta}{r} = -\dot{p}_r$$

thus

$$\dot{p}_r = \frac{p_\theta}{r} - (u + m_2g)$$

Finally, we have the relation

$$\dot{r} = \frac{p_r}{m_1}$$

Thus the four differential-state equations are

$$\dot{p}_\theta = 0$$

$$\dot{\theta} = \frac{1}{m_1 r^2} p_\theta$$

$$\dot{r} = \frac{1}{m_1} p_r$$

and

$$\dot{p}_r = \frac{p_\theta}{r} - (u + m_2 g)$$

and the input-state-output relation is

$$y = l - r$$ ∎

In Chap. 2, we found that state equations for electrical networks were easily written if capacitance voltages (or charges) and inductance currents (or fluxes) were chosen to be the state variables. For general networks, we again attempt to employ this choice. The differential-state equations result from the application of Kirchhoff's voltage and current laws and the network-branch relations to eliminate all nonstate variables, except of course, the input functions (independent voltage- or current-source signals). That is, the capacitance relation

$$\frac{d}{dt}[\mathbf{C}\mathbf{v}_C(t)] = \mathbf{i}_C(t)$$

dictates that we solve algebraically for capacitance currents in terms of input functions, capacitance voltages, and inductance currents; similarly, the inductance relation

$$\frac{d}{dt}[\mathbf{L}\mathbf{i}_L(t)] = \mathbf{v}_L(t)$$

dictates that we solve algebraically for inductance voltages in terms of input functions, inductance currents, and capacitance voltages. The simplest means of visualization of the writing of network-state equations is given in Fig. 4.8a. We must have

$$\frac{d}{dt}[\mathbf{C}\mathbf{v}_C(t)] = \mathbf{i}_C(t) = \mathbf{f}_C(\mathbf{v}_C(t),\mathbf{i}_L(t),\mathbf{v}_S(t),\mathbf{i}_S(t),t)$$

and

$$\frac{d}{dt}[\mathbf{L}\mathbf{i}_L(t)] = \mathbf{v}_L(t) = \mathbf{f}_L(\mathbf{v}_C(t),\mathbf{i}_L(t),\mathbf{v}_S(t),\mathbf{i}_S(t),t)$$

The two vector functions $\mathbf{f}_C$ and $\mathbf{f}_L$, which describe the network that

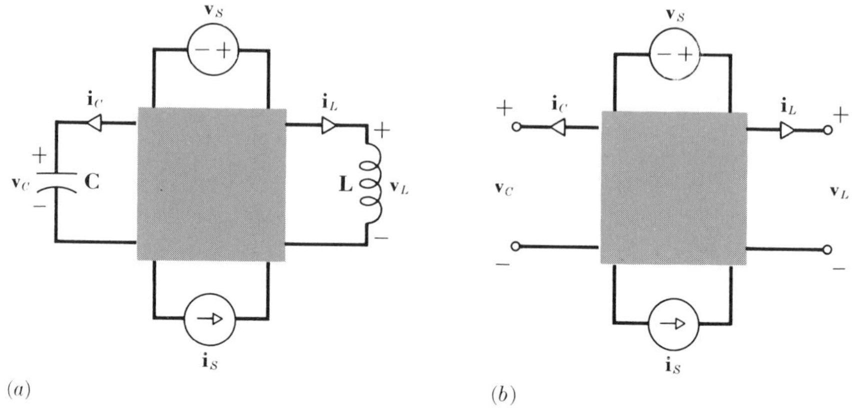

FIG. 4.8 A convenient means for visualizing the development of the state equations for a lumped network: (*a*) the reactances are extracted at artificially created ports; and (*b*) it remains then only to find the instantaneous-transfer characteristic for the remaining memoryless network.

remains when the capacitances and inductances are artificially removed at ports, are not necessarily easily obtained; in fact, they may not even exist in general. However, they are merely algebraic since the elements which are left to remain in the network (resistances, transformers, gyrators, and controlled sources) impose only instantaneous constraints—even if they are nonlinear and time variable. Hence, we must assume that the transfer characteristics of the network shown in Fig. 4.8*b*,

$$\mathbf{i}_C(t) = \mathbf{f}_C(\mathbf{v}_C(t), i_L(t), \mathbf{v}_S(t), \mathbf{i}_S(t), t)$$

and

$$\mathbf{v}_L(t) = \mathbf{f}_L(\mathbf{v}_C(t), \mathbf{i}_L(t), \mathbf{v}_S(t), \mathbf{i}_S(t), t)$$

exist; if they do not, more subtle methods must be employed. There are some obvious instances in which the extraction of reactance elements renders the remaining network noncharacterizable in the sense desired. Two capacitances in parallel as shown in Fig. 4.9 leave a remaining network which prescribes the constraint

$$v_{C1}(t) = v_{C2}(t)$$

but there is no means for solving for the capacitance currents algebraically in terms of the capacitance voltages. There is, however, no need to do so, since only one of the capacitance voltages qualifies as a state variable in the reduced equivalent system. In general, if after short-circuiting all voltage sources and open-circuiting all current sources and removing from the remaining network all capacitances along with the nodes to

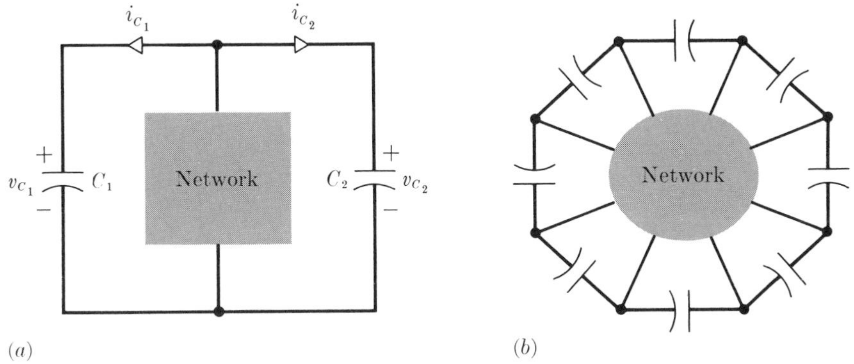

FIG. 4.9 (*a*) Two capacitances in parallel are such that a voltage constraint $v_{C_1} = v_{C_2}$ is provided, but only the sum of currents $i_{C_1} + i_{C_2}$ is uniquely determined by the remaining network (one of the capacitance voltages is not to be considered as a state variable in the reduced equivalent system); (*b*) in general, if the network contains capacitance loops, enough capacitance voltages must be excluded from consideration as state variables to remove all such loops.

which they are attached, external-capacitance loops are observed as shown in Fig. 4.9*b*, enough capacitance voltages must be removed from consideration as state variables (i.e., their associated capacitances replaced by open circuits) until no loops remain.

Two inductances in series as shown in Fig. 4.10*a* leave a remaining network which prescribes the constraints

$$i_{L_1}(t) = -i_{L_2}(t)$$

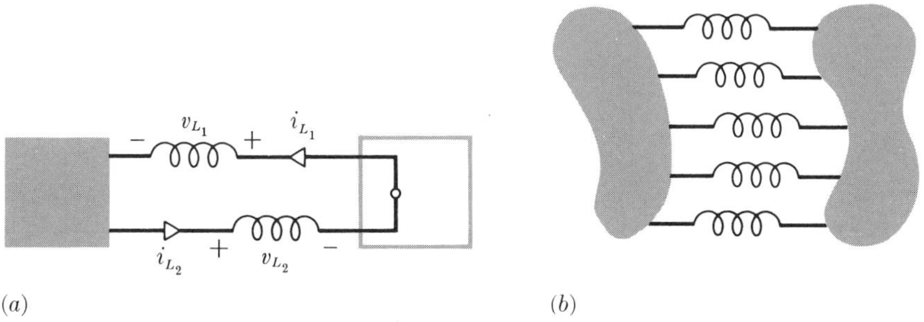

FIG. 4.10 (*a*) Two inductances in series are such that a current constraint $i_{L_1} = i_{L_2}$ is provided, but only the sum of voltages $v_{L_1} + v_{L_2}$ is uniquely determined by the remaining network (one of the inductance currents is not to be considered as a state variable in the reduced equivalent system); (*b*) in general, if the network contains inductance cut-sets, enough inductance currents must be excluded from consideration as state variables to remove all such cut-sets.

but there is no means for solving for the inductance voltages algebraically in terms of the inductance currents. There is, however, no need to do so since only one of the inductance currents qualifies as a state variable in the reduced equivalent system. In general, if, after short-circuiting all voltage sources and open-circuiting all current sources and removing from the network all inductances while leaving to the remaining network the nodes to which they are attached, the network is observed to be divided into separate parts as shown in Fig. 4.10*b*, enough inductance currents must be removed from consideration as state variables (i.e., their associated inductances replaced by short circuits) until the remaining network is in one part.

(4.13) Example

Consider the electrical network of Fig. 4.11. The input is the voltage source $u(t)$, and the output $y(t)$ is the voltage across resistor R_3. We choose as state-variable candidates the two capacitance voltages $v_0(t)$ and $v_1(t)$, and we wish to obtain the differential-state equations and input-state-output equation

$$\begin{aligned} \dot{v}_0(t) &= f_1(v_0(t),v_1(t),u(t),t) \\ \dot{v}_1(t) &= f_2(v_0(t),v_1(t),u(t),t) \end{aligned}$$

and

$$y(t) = g(v_0(t),v_1(t),u(t),t)$$

The nodal equations for nodes (1) and (2) are

$$[u - v_0]\frac{1}{R_1} = C_1\frac{dv_1}{dt} + v_0\frac{1}{R_2} + C_2\frac{dv_1}{dt}$$

and

$$C_2\frac{dv_1}{dt} = g_m v_0 + (v_0 - v_1)\frac{1}{R_3}$$

We can substitute for $C_2(dv_1/dt)$ in the first equation to obtain

$$C_1\frac{dv_0}{dt} = [u - v_0]\frac{1}{R_1} - v_0\frac{1}{R_2} - \left[g_m v_0 + (v_0 - v_1)\frac{1}{R_3}\right]$$

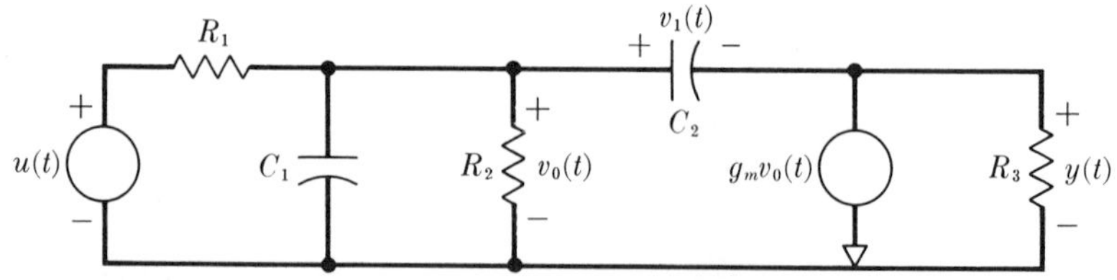

FIG. 4.11 An electrical network with two state variables.

Upon rearrangement, we obtain the differential-state equations

$$\frac{dv_0}{dt} = \frac{1}{C_1}\left\{\frac{u}{R_1} + \left[-\left(g_m + \frac{1}{R_1} + \frac{1}{R_2} + \frac{1}{R_3}\right)\right] v_0 + \frac{v_1}{R_3}\right\}$$

and

$$\frac{dv_1}{dt} = \frac{1}{C_2}\left[\left(g_m + \frac{1}{R_3}\right) v_0 - \frac{v_1}{R_3}\right]$$

The input-output-state equation is given by

$$y = v_0 - v_1$$ ∎

(4.14) Example
Consider the network of Fig. 4.12. The voltage sources u_1 and u_2 are the inputs, and the voltages across resistances R_1 and R_5 are the outputs. We choose as the three state-variable candidates the currents through the two inductors and the voltage across the capacitor.

The Kirchhoff's current law node equation for node 3 is

$$C_3 \frac{dx_2}{dt} + x_1 + x_3 = 0$$

or

$$\dot{x}_2 = -\frac{1}{C_3} x_1 - \frac{1}{C_3} x_3$$

or

$$\dot{x}_2 = -x_1 - x_2$$

The Kirchhoff's voltage law loop equations for loops 1 and 2 are

$$L_2 \frac{dx_1}{dt} + R_1 x_1 - u_1 - x_2 = 0$$

or

$$\dot{x}_1 = -\frac{R_1}{L_2} x_1 + \frac{1}{L_2} x_2 + \frac{1}{L_1} u$$

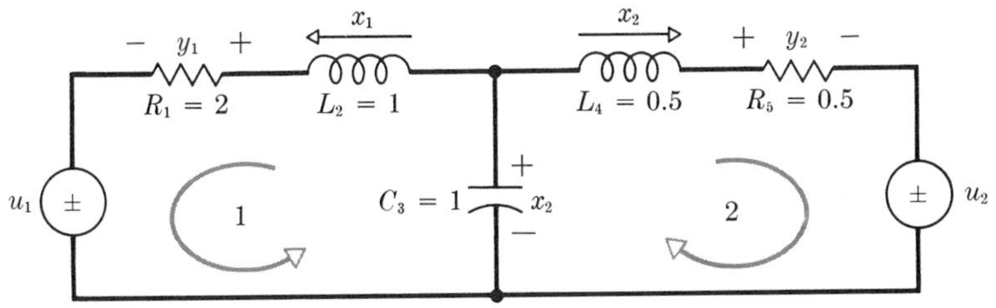

FIG. 4.12 A network for which there are three state variables.

or

$$\dot{x}_1 = -2x_1 + x_2 + u_1$$

and

$$L_4 \frac{dx_3}{dt} + R_5 x_3 - u_2 - x_2 = 0$$

or

$$\dot{x}_3 = \frac{1}{L_4} x_2 - \frac{R_5}{L_4} x_3 + \frac{1}{L_4} u_2$$

or

$$\dot{x}_3 = 2x_2 - x_3 + 2u_2$$

Finally, we have that

$$y_1 = R_1 x_1 = 2x_1$$

and

$$y_2 = R_5 x_3 = \tfrac{1}{2} x_3$$

By defining

$$\mathbf{x} \equiv \begin{pmatrix} x_1 \\ x_2 \\ x_3 \end{pmatrix} \qquad \text{as the state vector}$$

$$\mathbf{u} \equiv \begin{pmatrix} u_1 \\ u_2 \end{pmatrix} \qquad \text{as the input vector}$$

and

$$\mathbf{y} \equiv \begin{pmatrix} y_1 \\ y_2 \end{pmatrix} \qquad \text{as the output vector}$$

we can write the differential-state equation as

$$\dot{\mathbf{x}} = \mathbf{A}\mathbf{x} + \mathbf{B}\mathbf{u}$$

where

$$\mathbf{A} = \begin{pmatrix} -2 & 1 & 0 \\ -1 & -1 & 0 \\ 0 & 2 & -1 \end{pmatrix}$$

and

$$\mathbf{B} = \begin{pmatrix} 1 & 0 \\ 0 & 0 \\ 0 & 2 \end{pmatrix}$$

the input-state-output equation is

$$\mathbf{y} = \mathbf{Cx}$$

where

$$\mathbf{C} = \begin{pmatrix} 2 & 0 & 0 \\ 0 & 0 & \frac{1}{2} \end{pmatrix}$$ ∎

There is a general set of rules to be followed when writing state equations for electrical networks. A detailed exposé on these rules is beyond the scope of this text.[1]

4.3 STATE EQUATIONS IN COMPANION FORM, AND BLOCK-DIAGRAM REPRESENTATION

An nth-order, linear, time-invariant system is also characterized by an nth-order differential equation of the form

$$a_n y^{(n)} + a_{n-1} y^{(n-1)} + \cdots + a_1 y^{(1)} + a_0 y = b_0 u + b_1 u^{(1)} + \cdots + b_{n-1} u^{(n-1)} + b_n u^{(n)}$$

where

$$u^{(k)} \equiv \frac{d^k u}{dt} \qquad \text{and} \qquad y^{(k)} \equiv \frac{d^k y}{dt}$$

Therefore the decomposition of an nth-order, linear, time-invariant differential equation into the coupled set of n standard-form, first-order state equations is of interest. We first consider a simple nth-order, linear, time-invariant differential system with a single input and a single output:

$$a_n y^{(n)} + a_{n-1} y^{(n-1)} + \cdots + a_1 y^{(1)} + a_0 y = u$$

where $a_n \neq 0$ and the a_k ($k = 0, 1, \ldots n$) are constants. (Note: If $a_n = 0$, this equation would characterize an $(n - 1)$st-order system.) Recall the first-order version of this problem,

$$\dot{y} = ay + bu$$

or

$$\frac{1}{b}\dot{y} - \frac{a}{b}y = u$$

the output y qualifies as the state. That is, we could write the state equa-

[1] For further discussion see R. A. Rohrer, "Circuit Theory: An Introduction to the State Variable Approach," McGraw-Hill, New York, 1970.

tions in standard form as

$$\dot{x} = ax + bu$$

and

$$y = x$$

Returning to the nth-order differential system, we recognize that there are n independently specifiable initial conditions which uniquely determine the output function for a given input function: $y(t)$, $\dot{y}(t)$, . . . , $y^{(n-2)}(t)$, and $y^{(n-1)}(t)$ (or some nonsingular transformation on this set). This set of variables may qualify as the state at time t. Hence, we try the following simple association of state variables with the output function:

$$\begin{aligned}
x_1 &\equiv y \\
x_2 &\equiv \dot{y} = \dot{x}_1 \\
x_3 &\equiv \ddot{y} = \dot{x}_2 \\
&\cdots\cdots \\
x_n &\equiv y^{(n-1)} = \dot{x}_{n-1}
\end{aligned}$$

thus,

$$\dot{x}_n = y^{(n)} = -\frac{a_0}{a_n}x_1 - \frac{a_1}{a_n}x_2 - \cdots - \frac{a_{n-1}}{a_n}x_n + \frac{1}{a_n}u$$

From the above, we may easily write the state equations in standard form,

$$\dot{\mathbf{x}} = \mathbf{A}\mathbf{x} + \mathbf{B}\mathbf{u}$$

and

$$\mathbf{y} = \mathbf{C}\mathbf{x} + \mathbf{D}\mathbf{u}$$

where

$$\mathbf{x} \equiv \begin{bmatrix} x_1 \\ x_2 \\ \cdot \\ \cdot \\ \cdot \\ x_n \end{bmatrix}$$

$$\mathbf{A} = \begin{bmatrix} 0 & 1 & 0 & 0 & \cdots & 0 & 0 \\ 0 & 0 & 1 & 0 & \cdots & 0 & 0 \\ 0 & 0 & 0 & 1 & \cdots & 0 & 0 \\ \cdots & \cdots & \cdots & \cdots & \cdots & \cdots & \cdots \\ 0 & 0 & 0 & 0 & \cdots & 0 & 1 \\ \dfrac{-a_0}{a_n} & \dfrac{-a_1}{a_n} & \dfrac{-a_2}{a_n} & \dfrac{-a_3}{a_n} & \cdots & \dfrac{-a_{n-1}}{a_n} & \dfrac{-a_{n-2}}{a_n} \end{bmatrix}$$

$$\mathbf{B} = \begin{bmatrix} 0 \\ 0 \\ 0 \\ 0 \\ \cdot \\ \cdot \\ \cdot \\ 0 \\ \dfrac{1}{a_n} \end{bmatrix}$$

$$\mathbf{C} = [1 \quad 0 \quad 0 \quad 0 \quad \cdots \quad 0 \quad 0]$$

and

$$\mathbf{D} = 0$$

When the matrices for an nth-order, single input—single output system attain this form, the system is said to be characterized in *companion form;* i.e.,

$$\begin{aligned}
&a_{kl} = 0(l \neq k + 1;\ k = 1, 2, \ldots, n - 1)\\
&a_{kl} = 1(l = k + 1;\ k = 1, 2, \ldots, n - 1)\\
&a_{nl} \text{ arbitrary } (l = 1, 2, \ldots, n)\\
&b_k = 0\ (k = 1, 2, \ldots, n - 1)\\
&b_n \text{ arbitrary}\\
&c_1 = 1
\end{aligned}$$

and

$$c_l = 0\ (l = 2, 3, \ldots, n)$$

This method of characterization of a system in companion form works equally well when the coefficients a_k $(k = 0, 1, 2, \ldots, n)$ are functions of time. To see that we may characterize the system

$$a_n(t)y^{(n)}(t) + a_{n-1}(t)y^{(n-1)}(t) + \cdots + a_1(t)y(t) + a_0(t)y(t) = u(t)$$

$(a_n(t) \neq 0)$ by the above method, we need only review the above development to recognize that at no point has the assumption of time invariance of the coefficients been required.

As we have seen in earlier sections, it is often convenient for purposes of visualization to associate a block-diagram representation (schematic diagram for an analog-computer simulation) with a given system. We consider the state equations for a linear, time-invariant, nth-

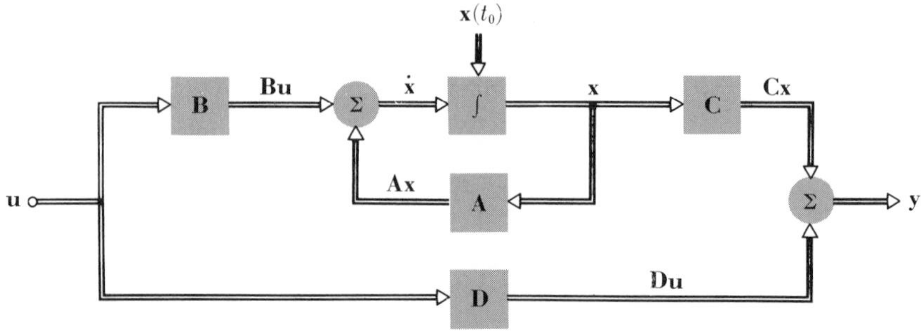

FIG. 4.13 The general block-diagram representation for system-state equations in standard form.

order system in standard form,

$$\dot{\mathbf{x}} = \mathbf{Ax} + \mathbf{Bu}$$

and

$$\mathbf{y} = \mathbf{Cx} + \mathbf{Du}$$

and implicitly integrate the differential-state equation to obtain

$$\mathbf{x}(t) = \mathbf{x}(t_0) + \int_{t_0}^{t} [\mathbf{Ax}(\tau) + \mathbf{Bu}(\tau)]\, d\tau$$

It becomes clear then that the system may be represented by the *vector-block* diagram shown in Fig. 4.13. We may also associate a block diagram with the linear, time-invariant, nth-order differential system described by the input-output relation

$$a_n y^{(n)} + a_{n-1} y^{(n-1)} + \cdots + a_1 \dot{y} + a_0 y = u$$

as shown in Fig. 4.14.

Suppose that we are asked to write standard-form state equations for a single input—single output, linear, time-invariant differential system which is characterized by

$$\sum_{k=0}^{n} a_k y^{(k)}(t) = \sum_{k=0}^{m} b_k u^{(k)}(t) \qquad (a_n \neq 0)$$

Superficially, we could write state equations in *extended form:*

$$\dot{\mathbf{x}} = \mathbf{Ax} + \mathbf{Bu} + \mathbf{B}_1\mathbf{u}^{(1)} + \cdots + \mathbf{B}_m\mathbf{u}^{(m)}$$

and

$$\mathbf{y} = \mathbf{Cx}$$

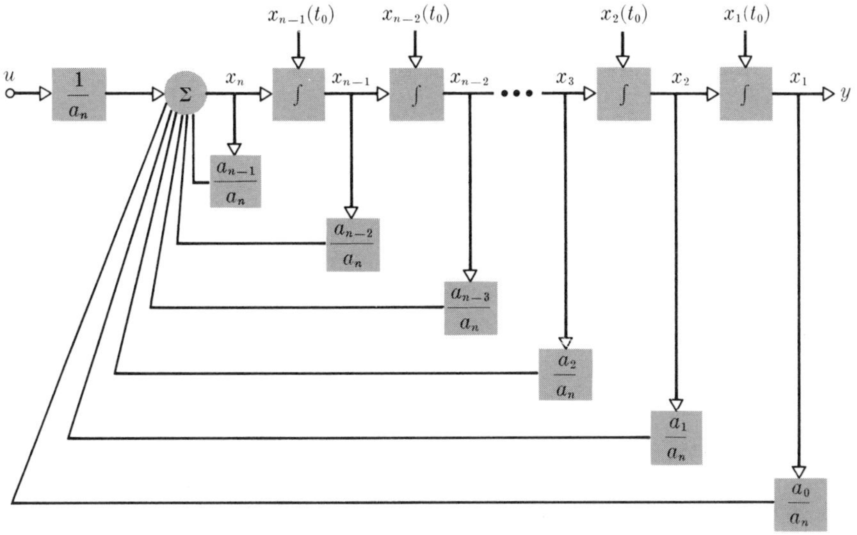

FIG. 4.14 The all-integrator block-diagram representation for the nth-order linear, differential, single input—single output system $a_n y^{(n)} + a_{n-1}{}^{(n-1)} + \cdots + a_1 y + a_0 y = u$ represented in companion form.

where the matrices **A**, **B**, and **C** are in companion form and

$$\mathbf{B}_k = \begin{bmatrix} 0 \\ 0 \\ 0 \\ 0 \\ \cdot \\ \cdot \\ \cdot \\ 0 \\ \dfrac{b_k}{a_n} \end{bmatrix} \qquad (k = 1, 2, \ldots, m)$$

Actually, the state concept (in the strict sense) applies so long as $m \leq n$; we must, however, choose the state variables more carefully than we have above. Suppose that we have

$$\sum_{k=0}^{n} a_k y^{(k)}(t) = \sum_{k=0}^{m} b_k u^{(k)}(t) \qquad (a_n \neq 0 \text{ and } a_0 \neq 0)$$

First write

$$\sum_{k=0}^{n} [a_k y^{(k)}(t) - b_k u^{(k)}(t)] = 0$$

then take

$$x_1 = a_0 y - b_0 u$$

since we must now anticipate taking n derivatives of u as well as y. Next take

$$x_2 = a_0 \dot{y} - b_0 \dot{u} + a_1 y - b_1 u$$

or

$$x_2 = \dot{x}_1 + a_1 y - b_1 u$$

or

$$x_2 = \dot{x}_1 + \frac{a_1}{a_0} x_1 - \frac{1}{a_0} (a_0 b_1 - b_0 a_1) u$$

In general choose the $(k + 1)$st state variable so that

$$x_{k+1} = \dot{x}_k + a_k y - b_k u \qquad (k = 1, 2, \ldots, n - 1)$$

or

$$\dot{x}_k = \frac{1}{a_0} [(-a_k x_1 + a_0 x_{k+1}) + (a_0 b_k - b_0 a_k) u] \qquad (k = 1, 2, \ldots, n - 1)$$

We may now verify directly that the original equation is satisfied with

$$\dot{x}_n = -\frac{a_n}{a_0} x_1 + \frac{1}{a_0} (a_0 b_n - b_0 a_n) u$$

The resulting standard-form characterization yields the following matrices:

$$\mathbf{A} = \frac{1}{a_0} \begin{bmatrix} -a_1 & a_0 & 0 & 0 & \cdots & 0 & 0 \\ -a_2 & 0 & a_0 & 0 & \cdots & 0 & 0 \\ -a_3 & 0 & 0 & a_0 & \cdots & 0 & 0 \\ \cdots & \cdots & \cdots & \cdots & \cdots & \cdots & \cdots \\ -a_{n-1} & 0 & 0 & 0 & \cdots & 0 & a_0 \\ -a_n & 0 & 0 & 0 & \cdots & 0 & 0 \end{bmatrix}$$

$$\mathbf{B} = \frac{1}{a_0} \begin{bmatrix} a_0 b_1 - b_0 a_1 \\ a_0 b_2 - b_0 a_2 \\ a_0 b_3 - b_0 a_3 \\ \cdot \\ \cdot \\ \cdot \\ a_0 b_{n-1} - b_0 a_{n-1} \\ a_0 b_n - b_0 a_n \end{bmatrix}$$

$$\mathbf{C} = \begin{pmatrix} \frac{1}{a_0} & 0 & 0 & 0 & \cdots & 0 & 0 \end{pmatrix}$$

$$\mathbf{D} = \begin{pmatrix} \frac{b_0}{a_0} \end{pmatrix}$$

The all-integrator block diagram for this system given in Fig. 4.15 shows the system to be reduced.

In the event that a_0 is zero, alternative forms of these matrices are

$$\mathbf{A} = \begin{bmatrix} 0 & 1 & 0 & 0 & \cdots & 0 & 0 \\ 0 & 0 & 1 & 0 & \cdots & 0 & 0 \\ 0 & 0 & 0 & 1 & \cdots & 0 & 0 \\ \cdot & \cdot & \cdot & \cdot & \cdot & \cdot & \cdot \\ 0 & 0 & 0 & 0 & \cdots & 0 & 1 \\ -\frac{a_{n-1}}{a_n} & -\frac{a_{n-2}}{a_n} & -\frac{a_{n-3}}{a_n} & -\frac{a_{n-4}}{a_n} & \cdots & -\frac{a_1}{a_n} & -\frac{a_n}{a_n} \end{bmatrix}$$

$$\mathbf{B} = \begin{bmatrix} 0 \\ 0 \\ \cdot \\ \cdot \\ \cdot \\ 0 \\ \frac{1}{a_n} \end{bmatrix}$$

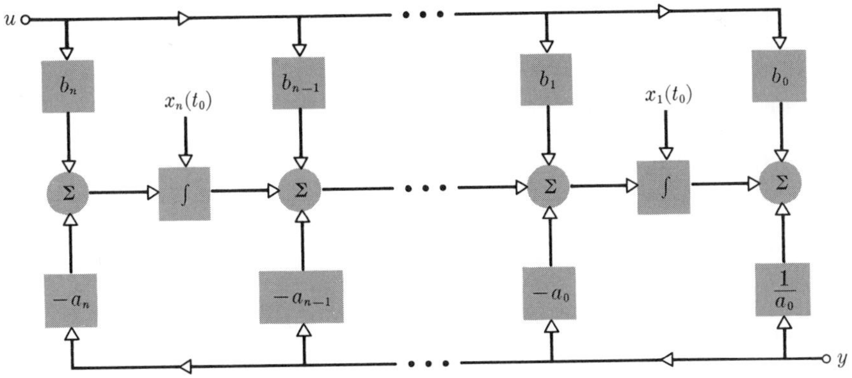

FIG. 4.15 The all-integrator block-diagram representation for the nth-order linear differential, single input—single output system

$$\sum_{k=0}^{n} a_k y^{(k)} = \sum_{k=0}^{n} b_k u^{(k)} \qquad (a_n \neq 0 \text{ and } a_0 \neq 0)$$

$$\mathbf{C} = \left(b_0 - \frac{a_0 b_n}{a_n}, b_1 - \frac{a_1 b_n}{a_n}, \ldots, b_{n-1} - \frac{a_{n-1} b_n}{a_n}\right)$$

$$\mathbf{D} = \left(\frac{b_n}{a_n}\right)$$

There are, of course, many other equivalent realizations. Moreover, the above approach can be extended to time-variable systems—with difficulty! Finally, if

$$\sum_{k=0}^{n} a_k y^{(k)}(t) = \sum_{k=0}^{m} b_k u^{(k)}(t)$$

is given and $m \geq n$, we must employ state equations in the extended form to obtain an equivalent characterization.

4.4 LINEARIZATION

In Chaps. 1 and 2 we have discussed the need for the study of the behavior of nonlinear systems operating about some quiescent point. A Taylor series expansion was used to find state equations which describe this "small-signal" behavior. In this section we generalize the procedure to nth-order systems and the use of matrix notation.

Consider a nonlinear system, the standard-form state equations for which are

(4.15a) $\dot{\mathbf{x}}(t) = \mathbf{f}(\mathbf{x}(t),\mathbf{u}(t),t)$

and

(4.15b) $\mathbf{y}(t) = \mathbf{g}(\mathbf{x}(t),\mathbf{u}(t),t)$

Now suppose we have the input-state-output solution $(\mathbf{u}_0,\mathbf{x}_0,\mathbf{y}_0)$, $t_0 \leq t \leq t_f$, of equation (4.15), that is,

$$\begin{aligned} \dot{\mathbf{x}}_0 &= \mathbf{f}(\mathbf{x}_0,\mathbf{u}_0,t) \\ \mathbf{y}_0 &= \mathbf{f}(\mathbf{x}_0,\mathbf{u}_0,t) \end{aligned} \qquad t_0 \leq t \leq t_f$$

We seek the perturbed input-state-output solution $(\mathbf{u}_1,\mathbf{x}_1,\mathbf{y})$, $t_0 \leq t \leq t_f$, where

$$\mathbf{n} = \mathbf{u}_1 - \mathbf{u}_0$$
$$\boldsymbol{\xi} = \mathbf{x}_1 - \mathbf{x}_0$$

and

$$\boldsymbol{\nu} = \mathbf{y}_1 - \mathbf{y}_0$$

Thus we have

$$\dot{\mathbf{x}}_0 + \dot{\boldsymbol{\xi}} = \mathbf{f}(\mathbf{x}_0 + \boldsymbol{\xi}, \mathbf{u}_0 + \mathbf{n}, t)$$

and

$$\mathbf{y}_0 + \boldsymbol{\nu} = \mathbf{g}(\mathbf{x}_0 + \boldsymbol{\xi}, \mathbf{u}_0 + \mathbf{n}, t)$$

Assume that **f** and **g** are twice differentiable (at least) in all arguments, except perhaps t, and make a Taylor series expansion (at each point in time) about the original solution:

$$\dot{\mathbf{x}}_0 + \dot{\boldsymbol{\xi}} = \mathbf{f}(\mathbf{x}_0,\mathbf{u}_0,t) + \left.\frac{\partial \mathbf{f}}{\partial \mathbf{x}}\right|_{\mathbf{x}_0,\mathbf{u}_0} \boldsymbol{\xi} + \left.\frac{\partial \mathbf{f}}{\partial \mathbf{u}}\right|_{\mathbf{x}_0,\mathbf{u}_0} \mathbf{n} + 0(\|\boldsymbol{\xi}\|^2, \|\mathbf{n}\|^2)$$

and

$$\mathbf{y}_0 + \boldsymbol{\nu} = \mathbf{g}(\mathbf{x}_0,\mathbf{u}_0,t) + \left.\frac{\partial \mathbf{g}}{\partial \mathbf{x}}\right|_{\mathbf{x}_0,\mathbf{u}_0} \boldsymbol{\xi} + \left.\frac{\partial \mathbf{g}}{\partial \mathbf{u}}\right|_{\mathbf{x}_0,\mathbf{u}_0} \mathbf{n} + 0(\|\boldsymbol{\xi}\|^2, \|\mathbf{n}\|^2)$$

where we have the jacobian matrices

$$\frac{\partial \mathbf{f}}{\partial \mathbf{x}} = \begin{bmatrix} \dfrac{\partial f_1}{\partial x_1} & \dfrac{\partial f_1}{\partial x_2} & \cdots & \dfrac{\partial f_1}{\partial x_n} \\ \dfrac{\partial f_2}{\partial x_1} & \dfrac{\partial f_2}{\partial x_2} & \cdots & \dfrac{\partial f_2}{\partial x_n} \\ \cdots & \cdots & \cdots & \cdots \\ \dfrac{\partial f_n}{\partial x_1} & \dfrac{\partial f_n}{\partial x_2} & \cdots & \dfrac{\partial f_n}{\partial x_n} \end{bmatrix}$$

$$\frac{\partial \mathbf{f}}{\partial \mathbf{u}} = \begin{bmatrix} \dfrac{\partial f_1}{\partial u_1} & \dfrac{\partial f_1}{\partial u_2} & \cdots & \dfrac{\partial f_1}{\partial u_r} \\ \dfrac{\partial f_2}{\partial u_1} & \dfrac{\partial f_2}{\partial u_2} & \cdots & \dfrac{\partial f_2}{\partial u_r} \\ \cdots & \cdots & \cdots & \cdots \\ \dfrac{\partial f_n}{\partial u_1} & \dfrac{\partial f_n}{\partial u_2} & \cdots & \dfrac{\partial f_n}{\partial u_r} \end{bmatrix}$$

$$\frac{\partial \mathbf{g}}{\partial \mathbf{x}} = \begin{bmatrix} \dfrac{\partial g_1}{\partial x_1} & \dfrac{\partial g_1}{\partial x_2} & \cdots & \dfrac{\partial g_1}{\partial x_n} \\ \dfrac{\partial g_2}{\partial x_1} & \dfrac{\partial g_2}{\partial x_2} & \cdots & \dfrac{\partial g_2}{\partial x_n} \\ \cdots & \cdots & \cdots & \cdots \\ \dfrac{\partial g_m}{\partial x_1} & \dfrac{\partial g_m}{\partial x_2} & \cdots & \dfrac{\partial g_m}{\partial x_n} \end{bmatrix}$$

and

$$\frac{\partial \mathbf{g}}{\partial \mathbf{u}} = \begin{bmatrix} \frac{\partial g_1}{\partial u_1} & \frac{\partial g_1}{\partial u_2} & \cdots & \frac{\partial g_1}{\partial u_r} \\ \frac{\partial g_2}{\partial u_1} & \frac{\partial g_2}{\partial u_2} & \cdots & \frac{\partial g_2}{\partial u_r} \\ \cdots & \cdots & \cdots & \cdots \\ \frac{\partial g_m}{\partial u_1} & \frac{\partial g_m}{\partial u_2} & \cdots & \frac{\partial g_m}{\partial u_r} \end{bmatrix}$$

If $\|\boldsymbol{\xi}\|^2$ and $\|\mathbf{n}\|^2$ are negligibly small, we obtain the approximate linear equations

$$\dot{\boldsymbol{\xi}} = \frac{\partial \mathbf{f}}{\partial \mathbf{x}}\bigg|_{\mathbf{x}_0,\mathbf{u}_0} \boldsymbol{\xi} + \frac{\partial \mathbf{f}}{\partial \mathbf{u}}\bigg|_{\mathbf{x}_0,\mathbf{u}_0} \mathbf{n}$$

and

$$\mathbf{v} = \frac{\partial \mathbf{g}}{\partial \mathbf{x}}\bigg|_{\mathbf{x}_0,\mathbf{u}_0} \boldsymbol{\xi} + \frac{\partial \mathbf{g}}{\partial \mathbf{u}}\bigg|_{\mathbf{x}_0,\mathbf{u}_0} \mathbf{n}$$

or

$$\dot{\boldsymbol{\xi}}(t) = \mathbf{A}(t)\boldsymbol{\xi}(t) + \mathbf{B}(t)\mathbf{n}(t)$$

and

$$\mathbf{v}(t) = \mathbf{C}(t)\boldsymbol{\xi}(t) + \mathbf{D}(t)\mathbf{n}(t)$$

where

$$\mathbf{A}(t) = \frac{\partial \mathbf{f}}{\partial \mathbf{x}}\bigg|_{\mathbf{x}_0,\mathbf{u}_0} \qquad \mathbf{B}(t) = \frac{\partial \mathbf{f}}{\partial \mathbf{u}}\bigg|_{\mathbf{x}_0,\mathbf{u}_0}$$

$$\mathbf{C}(t) = \frac{\partial \mathbf{g}}{\partial \mathbf{x}}\bigg|_{\mathbf{x}_0,\mathbf{u}_0} \qquad \text{and} \qquad \mathbf{D}(t) = \frac{\partial \mathbf{g}}{\partial \mathbf{u}}\bigg|_{\mathbf{x}_0,\mathbf{u}_0}$$

In other words,

$$\mathbf{A}(t) = [a_{kl}(t)] \Rightarrow a_{kl} \equiv \frac{\partial f_k}{\partial x_l}\bigg|_{\mathbf{x}_0,\mathbf{u}_0} \qquad \mathbf{B}(t) = [b_{kl}(t)] \Rightarrow b_{kl} \equiv \frac{\partial f_k}{\partial u_l}\bigg|_{\mathbf{x}_0,\mathbf{u}_0}$$

$$\mathbf{C}(t) = [c_{kl}(t)] \Rightarrow c_{kl} \equiv \frac{\partial g_k}{\partial x_l}\bigg|_{\mathbf{x}_0,\mathbf{u}_0} \qquad \mathbf{D}(t) = [d_{kl}(t)] \Rightarrow d_{kl} \equiv \frac{\partial g_k}{\partial u_l}\bigg|_{\mathbf{x}_0,\mathbf{u}_0}$$

The assumption that $\|\mathbf{n}\|^2$ is small can always be met, since it is an input (control) deviation. On the other hand, the assumption that $\|\boldsymbol{\xi}\|^2$ is small is dependent upon the system itself and may be violated. This problem is to be considered in a subsequent chapter on stability.

(4.16) Example
A third-order nonlinear system has the state representation

$$\begin{aligned}\dot{x}_1 &= x_2\\ \dot{x}_2 &= -2x_1 - 3x_3{}^2 + u_1\\ \dot{x}_3 &= -4x_1x_2 - x_3 + 2u_2\end{aligned}$$

For the inputs $u_1 = 3$ and $u_2 = \frac{1}{2}$, one equilibrium or quiescent point is

$$\mathbf{x}_0 = \begin{bmatrix} 0 \\ 0 \\ 1 \end{bmatrix}$$

Obviously an equilibrium point is a solution of the system. The linearized system about this equilibrium point is

$$\dot{\boldsymbol{\xi}} = \mathbf{A}\boldsymbol{\xi} + \mathbf{B}\mathbf{n}$$

where

$$\mathbf{A} = \begin{bmatrix} 0 & 1 & 0 \\ -2 & 0 & -6 \\ 0 & 0 & -1 \end{bmatrix}$$

and

$$\mathbf{B} = \begin{bmatrix} 0 \\ 1 \\ 2 \end{bmatrix}$$

4.5 THE HOMOGENEOUS EQUATION AND THE FUNDAMENTAL MATRIX

A large class of systems can be described by the linear, time-variable state equations

(4.17*a*) $\dot{\mathbf{x}}(t) = \mathbf{A}(t)\mathbf{x}(t) + \mathbf{B}(t)\mathbf{u}(t)$

and

(4.17*b*) $\mathbf{y}(t) = \mathbf{C}(t)\mathbf{x}(t) + \mathbf{D}(t)\mathbf{u}(t)$

Moreover, many other systems may be approximated by such equations for various ranges of operation. Therefore it is reasonable to concentrate on the solution of this class of equations first.

As has been the procedure for first- and second-order systems, we study the homogeneous equation

(4.18) $\dot{\mathbf{x}}(t) = \mathbf{A}(t)\mathbf{x}(t)$

first. One possible solution of this equation is the zero vector, i.e.,

$$\mathbf{x} = \mathbf{0}$$

since

$$\dot{\mathbf{0}} = \mathbf{A0}$$

Certainly, for nonzero initial conditions, there must be a nontrivial solution. We can establish the validity of this statement in terms of the following two theorems.

(4.19) Theorem

The solution to the homogeneous differential equation

$$\dot{\mathbf{x}}(t) = \mathbf{A}(t)\mathbf{x}(t)$$

for $\mathbf{x}(t_0) = \mathbf{x}_0$ is unique.

Proof

Suppose the hypothesis is false. Then there are at least two solutions, $\mathbf{x}_1(t)$ and $\mathbf{x}_2(t)$ such that

$$\mathbf{x}_1(t_0) = \mathbf{x}_2(t_0)$$

but

$$\mathbf{x}_1(t_1) \neq \mathbf{x}_2(t_1)$$

for at least one $t_1 > t_0$. Since

$$\dot{\mathbf{x}}_1(t) = \mathbf{A}(t)\mathbf{x}_1(t)$$

and

$$\dot{\mathbf{x}}_2(t) = \mathbf{A}(t)\mathbf{x}_2(t)$$

then

$$\|\dot{\mathbf{x}}_1(t) - \dot{\mathbf{x}}_2(t)\| = \|\mathbf{A}(t)(\mathbf{x}_1(t) - \mathbf{x}_2(t))\| \leq \|\mathbf{A}(t)\| \, \|\mathbf{x}_1(t) - \mathbf{x}_2(t)\|$$

or

$$(4.20) \quad \dot{w}(t) \leq k(t)w(t)$$

if for convenience, we let

$$w(t) = \|\mathbf{x}_1(t) - \mathbf{x}_2(t)\|$$

and

$$k(t) = \|A(t)\|$$

Observe that $w(t_0) = 0$, but $w(t_1) > 0$. If we multiply both sides of (4.20) by the positive quantity

$$\exp\left[-\int_{t_0}^{t} k(\tau)\,d\tau\right]$$

then we have, upon rearrangement of terms,

$$\exp\left[-\int_{t_0}^{t} k(\tau)\,d\tau\right]\dot{w}(t) - \exp\left[-\int_{t_0}^{t} k(\tau)\,d\tau\right]k(t)w(t) \le 0$$

The right-hand side is merely a total differential, so that

$$\frac{d}{dt}\left\{\exp\left[-\int_{t_0}^{t} k(\tau)\,d\tau\right]w(t)\right\} \le 0$$

Integration of this equation yields the inequality (Bellman-Gronwell)

$$w(t) \le w(t_0)\exp\left[\int_{t_0}^{t} k(\tau)\,d\tau\right]$$

or

$$\text{(4.21)}\quad \|\mathbf{x}_1(t) - \mathbf{x}_2(t)\| \le \|\mathbf{x}_1(t_0) - \mathbf{x}_2(t_0)\| \exp\left[\int_{t_0}^{t} \|\mathbf{A}(\tau)\|\,d\tau\right]$$

We assume that

$$\exp\left[\int_{t_0}^{t} \|\mathbf{A}(\tau)\|\,d\tau\right] < \infty$$

For all practical purposes, this relation will always hold, since it is a requirement for the system to be characterizable in state-variable form. Since $\|\mathbf{x}_1(t_0) - \mathbf{x}_2(t_0)\| = 0$ we have from (4.21) and the properties of norms

$$\|\mathbf{x}_1(t) - \mathbf{x}_2(t)\| = 0$$

for all time t. This contradiction establishes the theorem. ∎

(4.22) Theorem

Suppose that $\boldsymbol{\theta}$ is a solution which vanishes at some time t_1, $-\infty < t_1 < \infty$, $\boldsymbol{\theta}(t_1) = 0$, then $\boldsymbol{\theta}(t) = 0$ for all t such that $-\infty < t < \infty$, or $\boldsymbol{\theta} = 0$.

Proof

$\mathbf{0}$ is a solution which vanishes at t_1,

$$\mathbf{0} = \dot{\mathbf{0}} = \mathbf{A}(t)\mathbf{0} = \mathbf{0}$$

and from Theorem (4.19) the solution is unique, therefore, $\boldsymbol{\theta} \equiv 0$ for all time t. ∎

For motivational purposes consider the homogeneous second order system described by

$$\dot{x}_1 = -x_1 + x_2$$

and

$$\dot{x}_2 = -2x_2$$

discussed in Chap. 2. The solution to these equations was found to be (see Example 2.57)

$$x_1 = e^{-(t-t_0)}x_{10} + [e^{-(t-t_0)} - e^{-2(t-t_0)}]x_{20}$$

and

$$x_2 = e^{-2(t-t_0)}x_{20}$$

or, in matrix form

$$\begin{bmatrix} x_1 \\ x_2 \end{bmatrix} = \begin{bmatrix} e^{-(t-t_0)} & e^{-(t-t_0)} - e^{-2(t-t_0)} \\ 0 & e^{-2(t-t_0)} \end{bmatrix} \begin{bmatrix} x_{10} \\ x_{20} \end{bmatrix}$$

Observe that this solution, which includes the effects of initial conditions, is a combination of the two linearly independent "solutions"

$$\boldsymbol{\phi}_1(t) = \begin{bmatrix} e^{-t} \\ 0 \end{bmatrix}$$

and

$$\boldsymbol{\phi}_2(t) = \begin{bmatrix} e^{-t} - e^{-2t} \\ e^{-2t} \end{bmatrix}$$

that is, $x_1 = e^{-t}$ and $x_2 = 0$ is a solution of the homogeneous equations and so is $x_1 = e^{-t} - e^{-2t}$, and $x_2 = e^{-2t}$ as can be verified by direct substitution.

In general, we have the following:

(4.23) Theorem
If $\boldsymbol{\theta}_1, \boldsymbol{\theta}_2, \ldots, \boldsymbol{\theta}_k$ are solutions, so is

$$c_1\boldsymbol{\theta}_1 + c_2\boldsymbol{\theta}_2 + \cdots + c_k\boldsymbol{\theta}_k$$

for an arbitrary (even complex!) set of constants $\{c_1,c_2, \ldots, c_k\}$. ▌
This theorem is easily proven and left as an exercise for the reader.

We now show the eminently useful fact that if a set of solutions of an nth-order linear system are linearly dependent (independent) at any time, t, $-\infty < t < \infty$, then they are linearly dependent (independent) for all time.

(4.24) Theorem
A set of solutions $\boldsymbol{\theta}_1, \boldsymbol{\theta}_2, \ldots, \boldsymbol{\theta}_k$ is linearly dependent if for any time t, $-\infty < t < \infty$, the set of vectors $\{\boldsymbol{\theta}_1(t),\boldsymbol{\theta}_2(t), \ldots ,\boldsymbol{\theta}_k(t)\}$ is linearly dependent; similarly a set of solutions $\boldsymbol{\theta}_1, \boldsymbol{\theta}_2, \ldots, \boldsymbol{\theta}_k$ is linearly independent if for any time t, $-\infty < t < \infty$, the set of vectors $\{\boldsymbol{\theta}_1(t),\boldsymbol{\theta}_2(t), \ldots ,\boldsymbol{\theta}_k(t)\}$ is linearly independent.

Proof

$\boldsymbol{\theta} \equiv c_1\boldsymbol{\theta}_1 + c_2\boldsymbol{\theta}_2 + \cdots + c_k\boldsymbol{\theta}_k$ is a solution for any set of constants $\{c_1,c_2, \ldots ,c_k\}$; by uniqueness if a solution vanishes for one time, it vanishes for all time. ∎

Thus the test for linear dependence (or linear independence) simplifies considerably, since it may be made at any time (the initial time t_0 for example), rather than for all time. That is, we deal in finite-dimensional vector spaces rather than infinite-dimensional vector spaces (function spaces).

(4.25) Fundamental set of solutions

A set of n solutions $\{\boldsymbol{\theta}_1,\boldsymbol{\theta}_2, \ldots ,\boldsymbol{\theta}_n\}$, where n is the order of the system (dimensionality of the state vector x), is said to be a *fundamental set of solutions* if it is linearly independent. ∎

For instance, a fundamental set of solutions for the second-order system discussed earlier is

$$\boldsymbol{\theta}_1(t) = \begin{bmatrix} e^{-t} \\ 0 \end{bmatrix}$$

and

$$\boldsymbol{\theta}_2(t) = \begin{bmatrix} e^{-t} - e^{-2t} \\ e^{-2t} \end{bmatrix}$$

The usefulness of a fundamental set of solutions is embodied in the following.

(4.26) Theorem

Every solution $\boldsymbol{\theta}$ can be represented in the form

$$\boldsymbol{\theta} = c_1\boldsymbol{\theta}_1 + c_2\boldsymbol{\theta}_2 + \cdots + c_n\boldsymbol{\theta}_n$$

for some suitably chosen set of constants $\{c_1,c_2, \ldots ,c_n\}$, if

$$\{\boldsymbol{\theta}_1,\boldsymbol{\theta}_2, \ldots ,\boldsymbol{\theta}_n\}$$

is a fundamental set of solutions.

Proof

A solution $\boldsymbol{\theta}$ is defined uniquely by the requirement $\boldsymbol{\theta}(t_0) = x_0$. Now consider the set of vectors $\{\mathbf{a}_1,\mathbf{a}_2, \ldots ,\mathbf{a}_n\}$ defined by

$$\mathbf{a}_1 \equiv \boldsymbol{\theta}_1(t_0),\ \mathbf{a}_2 \equiv \boldsymbol{\theta}_2(t_0),\ \ldots ,\ \mathbf{a}_n \equiv \boldsymbol{\theta}_n(t_0)$$

The set of vectors $\{\mathbf{a}_1,\mathbf{a}_2, \ldots ,\mathbf{a}_n\}$ is linearly independent because the set of solutions $\{\boldsymbol{\theta}_1,\boldsymbol{\theta}_2, \ldots ,\boldsymbol{\theta}_n\}$ is fundamental and, hence, linearly independent at any time t_0, $-\infty < t_0 < \infty$. Since the space is n dimensional, the set of vectors $\{\mathbf{a}_1,\mathbf{a}_2, \ldots ,\mathbf{a}_n\}$ is a basis, and we can find a set of constants $\{c_1,c_2, \ldots ,c_n\}$ such that

$$\mathbf{x}_0 = c_1\mathbf{a}_1 + c_2\mathbf{a}_2 + \cdots + c_n\mathbf{a}_n$$

Hence, the two solutions $\boldsymbol{\theta}$ and $c_1\boldsymbol{\theta}_1 + c_2\boldsymbol{\theta}_2 + \cdots + c_n\boldsymbol{\theta}_n$ coincide at t_0 and, therefore, coincide everywhere by uniqueness. ∎

Note, we have not as yet found the homogeneous solution, but have merely been investigating properties of the solution. Temporarily we continue along these lines.

Given a set of solutions to the homogeneous equation,

$$\{\boldsymbol{\phi}_1,\boldsymbol{\phi}_2, \ldots ,\boldsymbol{\phi}_n\}$$

where

$$\boldsymbol{\phi}_k = \begin{bmatrix} \phi_{1k} \\ \phi_{2k} \\ \cdot \\ \cdot \\ \cdot \\ \phi_{nk} \end{bmatrix} \qquad (k = 1, 2, \ldots , n)$$

we can form the matrix

$$\mathbf{X} = [\phi_{lk}]$$

or more explicitly,

$$\mathbf{X}(t) = \begin{bmatrix} \phi_{11}(t) & \phi_{12}(t) & \cdots & \phi_{1n}(t) \\ \phi_{21}(t) & \phi_{22}(t) & \cdots & \phi_{2n}(t) \\ \cdots & \cdots & \cdots & \cdots \\ \phi_{n1}(t) & \phi_{n2}(t) & \cdots & \phi_{n2}(t) \end{bmatrix}$$

Sometimes we may write

$$\mathbf{X} = \begin{bmatrix} \boldsymbol{\phi}_1 & \boldsymbol{\phi}_2 & \cdots & \boldsymbol{\phi}_n \\ \downarrow & \downarrow & & \downarrow \end{bmatrix}$$

or

$$\mathbf{X}(t) = \begin{bmatrix} \boldsymbol{\phi}_1(t) & \boldsymbol{\phi}_2(t) & \cdots & \boldsymbol{\phi}_n(t) \\ \downarrow & \downarrow & & \downarrow \end{bmatrix}$$

to show explicitly how an $n \times n$ matrix is constructed of the $n \times n$ vectors (arrayed side by side).

Note that $\mathbf{X}$ satisfies the matrix-differential equation

$$\dot{\mathbf{X}}(t) = \mathbf{A}(t)\mathbf{X}(t)$$

(4.27) Fundamental matrix
If the set of solutions $\{\phi_1, \phi_2, \ldots, \phi_n\}$ is linearly independent, we have

$$\det(\mathbf{X}(t)) \neq 0$$

for all t such that $-\infty < t < \infty$, and $\mathbf{X}$ is said to be a *fundamental matrix.* ∎

It is interesting to note that given *any* $n \times n$ matrix $\mathbf{X}(t)$ such that

$$\det(\mathbf{X}(t)) \neq 0$$

and for which $\dot{\mathbf{X}}(t)$ exists for all t such that $t_0 \leq t \leq t_f$, then $\mathbf{X}$ defines a homogeneous set of linear, time-variable differential equations of the form

$$\dot{\mathbf{x}}(t) = \mathbf{A}(t)\mathbf{x}(t)$$

where

$$\mathbf{A}(t) = \dot{\mathbf{X}}(t)[\mathbf{X}(t)]^{-1}$$

Obviously a fundamental matrix is not unique, since any matrix formed from elementary column operations, e.g., addition of columns or multiplication by a constant, is also a fundamental matrix. This fact leads to the following:

(4.28) Theorem
If the $n \times n$ matrices $\mathbf{X}$ and $\hat{\mathbf{X}}$ are fundamental matrices associated with the homogeneous equation

$$\mathbf{x}(t) = \mathbf{A}(t)\mathbf{x}(t)$$

then

$$\hat{\mathbf{X}} = \mathbf{XC}$$

where $\mathbf{C}$ is some $n \times n$ constant nonsingular matrix.

Proof
First we show that $\mathbf{C}$ is nonsingular. Since $\mathbf{X}$ and $\mathbf{C}$ are both $n \times n$ matrices

$$\det(\hat{\mathbf{X}}(t)) = \det(\mathbf{X}(t)) \det(\mathbf{C})$$

but $\mathbf{X}$ and $\hat{\mathbf{X}}$ are fundamental matrices so that $\det(\mathbf{X}(t)) \neq 0$ and $\det(\hat{\mathbf{X}}(t)) \neq 0$; hence,

$$\det(\mathbf{C}) = \frac{\det(\hat{\mathbf{X}})}{\det(\mathbf{X})} \neq 0$$

To show that the matrix $\mathbf{C}$ is a constant matrix, we recognize that any column $\hat{\phi}_k$ of $\hat{\mathbf{X}}$ is a nontrivial solution of the homogeneous equation and the n columns of $\mathbf{X}$, $\{\boldsymbol{\phi}_1,\boldsymbol{\phi}_2, \ldots ,\boldsymbol{\phi}_n\}$, are a fundamental set of solutions and therefore linearly independent and a basis; hence we may always write

$$\hat{\boldsymbol{\phi}}_k = c_{1k}\boldsymbol{\phi}_1 + c_{2k}\boldsymbol{\phi}_2 + \cdots + c_{nk}\boldsymbol{\phi}_n$$

where $\{c_{1k},c_{2k}, \ldots ,c_{nk}\}$ is a nonzero set of constants. We recognize that the matrix $\mathbf{C}$ is given by

$$\mathbf{C} = [c_{lk}]$$ ∎

Note also that if $\mathbf{X}$ is a matrix solution (not necessarily fundamental) of the homogeneous equation, then for any $n \times n$ constant matrix $\mathbf{C}$ (not necessarily nonsingular) the matrix $\hat{\mathbf{X}} = \mathbf{XC}$ is also a matrix solution of the homogeneous equations, since by direct substitution, we have

$$\dot{\hat{\mathbf{X}}}(t) = \dot{\mathbf{X}}(t)\mathbf{C} = \mathbf{A}(t)\mathbf{X}(t)\mathbf{C} = \mathbf{A}(t)\hat{\mathbf{X}}(t)$$

We wish to show next that if $\mathbf{X}$ is any $n \times n$ matrix solution of the homogeneous equation such that

$$\det\,(\mathbf{X}(t_0)) \neq 0 \qquad \text{for some } -\infty < t_0 < \infty$$

then

$$\det\,(\mathbf{X}(t)) \neq 0 \qquad \text{for all } -\infty < t < \infty$$

i.e., that $\mathbf{X}$ is a fundamental matrix. The result is obvious since the columns of $\mathbf{X}$ must constitute a fundamental set of solutions under the two provisos that

$$\dot{\mathbf{X}}(t) = \mathbf{A}(t)\mathbf{X}(t)$$

(the relation must hold column-by-column) and

$$\det\,(\mathbf{X}(t_0)) \neq 0$$

which implies linear independence of the columns at some time, and, therefore, for all time from Theorem (4.24). It is instructive, however, to prove this result directly without recourse to properties of fundamental sets of solutions. To do so, we consider $d/dt(\mathbf{X}(t))$.

(4.29) Theorem
If

$$\mathbf{X}(t) = \begin{pmatrix} \phi_{11}(t) & \phi_{12}(t) & \cdots & \phi_{1n}(t) \\ \phi_{21}(t) & \phi_{22}(t) & \cdots & \phi_{2n}(t) \\ \cdots & \cdots & \cdots & \cdots \\ \phi_{n1}(t) & \phi_{n2}(t) & \cdots & \phi_{nn}(t) \end{pmatrix}$$

then

$$\frac{d}{dt}[\det\ (\mathbf{X}(t))] = \det \begin{pmatrix} \dot{\phi}_{11}(t) & \dot{\phi}_{12}(t) & \cdots & \dot{\phi}_{1n}(t) \\ \phi_{21}(t) & \phi_{22}(t) & \cdots & \phi_{2n}(t) \\ \cdots & \cdots & \cdots & \cdots \\ \phi_{n1}(t) & \phi_{n2}(t) & \cdots & \phi_{nn}(t) \end{pmatrix}$$

$$+ \det \begin{pmatrix} \phi_{11}(t) & \phi_{12}(t) & \cdots & \phi_{1n}(t) \\ \dot{\phi}_{21}(t) & \dot{\phi}_{22}(t) & \cdots & \dot{\phi}_{2n}(t) \\ \cdots & \cdots & \cdots & \cdots \\ \phi_{n1}(t) & \phi_{n2}(t) & \cdots & \phi_{nn}(t) \end{pmatrix} + \cdots$$

$$+ \det \begin{pmatrix} \phi_{11}(t) & \phi_{12}(t) & \cdots & \phi_{1n}(t) \\ \phi_{21}(t) & \phi_{22}(t) & \cdots & \phi_{2n}(t) \\ \cdots & \cdots & \cdots & \cdots \\ \dot{\phi}_{n1}(t) & \dot{\phi}_{n2}(t) & \cdots & \dot{\phi}_{nn}(t) \end{pmatrix}$$

This result (Liouville's formula) is most easily understood when stated in words: The derivative of the determinant of an $n \times n$ matrix may be expressed as the sum of n determinants, the kth of which is that of the original matrix with the kth row (or column) replaced term-by-term with the derivative of the kth row (or column) and all other rows (or columns) remaining as in the original. We may prove this result by induction.

Proof

Consider a 1×1 matrix

$$\mathbf{X} = \phi_{11}$$

then

$$\dot{\mathbf{X}}(t) = \dot{\phi}(t)$$

as expected. Next consider a 2×2 matrix

$$\mathbf{X}(t) = \begin{pmatrix} \phi_{11}(t) & \phi_{12}(t) \\ \phi_{21}(t) & \phi_{22}(t) \end{pmatrix}$$

the Laplace expansion yields

$$\det\ (\mathbf{X}(t)) = \phi_{11}(t)\phi_{22}(t) - \phi_{12}(t)\phi_{21}(t)$$

so that

$$\frac{d}{dt}[\det\ (\mathbf{X}(t)] = \dot{\phi}_{11}(t)\phi_{22}(t) - \dot{\phi}_{12}(t)\phi_{21}(t) + \phi_{11}(t)\dot{\phi}_{22}(t) - \phi_{12}(t)\dot{\phi}_{21}(t)$$

But

$$\dot{\phi}_{11}(t)\phi_{22}(t) - \dot{\phi}_{12}(t)\phi_{21}(t) = \det \begin{pmatrix} \dot{\phi}_{11}(t) & \dot{\phi}_{12}(t) \\ \phi_{21}(t) & \phi_{22}(t) \end{pmatrix}$$

and

$$\phi_{11}(t)\dot{\phi}_{22}(t) - \phi_{12}(t)\dot{\phi}_{21}(t) = \det \begin{pmatrix} \phi_{11}(t) & \phi_{12}(t) \\ \dot{\phi}_{21}(t) & \dot{\phi}_{22}(t) \end{pmatrix}$$

Now we assume the result to hold for $(n-1) \times (n-1)$ matrices and show that it holds for $n \times n$ matrices. By the Laplace expansion, we have

$$\det(\mathbf{X}(t)) = \phi_{11}(t)\mathbf{M}_{11}(t) + \phi_{12}(t)\mathbf{M}_{12}(t) + \cdots + \phi_{1n}(t)\mathbf{M}_{1n}(t)$$

where $\phi_{1k}(t)$ is the element in the first row and kth column of the matrix $\mathbf{X}(t)$ and $\mathbf{M}_{1k}(t)$ is its cofactor (signed minor). Hence,

$$\begin{aligned} \frac{d}{dt}[\det(\mathbf{X}(t))] = {} & \dot{\phi}_{11}(t)\mathbf{M}_{11}(t) + \dot{\phi}_{12}(t)\mathbf{M}_{12}(t) + \cdots \\ & + \dot{\phi}_{1n}(t)\mathbf{M}_{1n}(t) + \phi_{11}(t)\dot{\mathbf{M}}_{11}(t) + \phi_{12}(t)\dot{\mathbf{M}}_{12}(t) + \cdots \\ & + \phi_{1n}\dot{\mathbf{M}}_{1n}(t) \end{aligned}$$

The first line on the right here is obviously

$$\begin{vmatrix} \dot{\phi}_{11}(t) & \dot{\phi}_{12}(t) & \cdots & \dot{\phi}_{1n}(t) \\ \phi_{21}(t) & \phi_{22}(t) & \cdots & \phi_{2n}(t) \\ \cdots & \cdots & \cdots & \cdots \\ \phi_{n1}(t) & \phi_{n2}(t) & \cdots & \phi_{nn}(t) \end{vmatrix}$$

The formula is presumed to work for determinants of $(n-1) \times (n-1)$ matrices [which is what the cofactors $M_{1k}(t)$ are] so the second line may be written as

$$+ \det \begin{pmatrix} \phi_{11} & 0 & \cdots & 0 \\ 0 & \dot{\phi}_{22} & \cdots & \dot{\phi}_{2n} \\ \cdots & \cdots & \cdots & \cdots \\ 0 & \phi_{n2} & \cdots & \phi_{nn} \end{pmatrix} + \cdots + \det \begin{pmatrix} \phi_{11} & 0 & \cdots & 0 \\ 0 & \phi_{22} & \cdots & \phi_{2n} \\ \cdots & \cdots & \cdots & \cdots \\ 0 & \dot{\phi}_{n2} & \cdots & \dot{\phi}_{nn} \end{pmatrix}$$

$$+ \det \begin{pmatrix} 0 & \phi_{12} & \cdots & 0 \\ \dot{\phi}_{21} & 0 & \cdots & \dot{\phi}_{n2} \\ \cdots & \cdots & \cdots & \cdots \\ \phi_{n1} & 0 & \cdots & \phi_{nn} \end{pmatrix} + \cdots + \det \begin{pmatrix} 0 & \phi_{12} & \cdots & 0 \\ \phi_{21} & 0 & \cdots & \phi_{2n} \\ \cdots & \cdots & \cdots & \cdots \\ \dot{\phi}_{n1} & 0 & \cdots & \phi_{nn} \end{pmatrix}$$

$$+ \cdots + \det \begin{pmatrix} 0 & 0 & \cdots & \phi_{1n} \\ \dot{\phi}_{21} & \dot{\phi}_{22} & \cdots & 0 \\ \cdots & \cdots & \cdots & \cdots \\ \phi_{n1} & \phi_{n2} & \cdots & 0 \end{pmatrix} + \cdots$$

$$+ \det \begin{pmatrix} 0 & 0 & \cdots & \phi_{1n} \\ \phi_{21} & \phi_{22} & \cdots & 0 \\ \cdots & \cdots & \cdots & \cdots \\ \dot{\phi}_{n1} & \dot{\phi}_{n2} & \cdots & 0 \end{pmatrix}$$

An alternate form for writing the sum of the first column of determinants above, i.e., using an inverse Laplace expansion, is

$$\det \begin{pmatrix} \phi_{11} & \phi_{12} & \cdots & \phi_{1n} \\ \dot{\phi}_{21} & \dot{\phi}_{22} & \cdots & \dot{\phi}_{2n} \\ \cdots & \cdots & \cdots & \cdots \\ \phi_{n1} & \phi_{n2} & \cdots & \phi_{nn} \end{pmatrix}$$

Repeating this process for each column of determinants, we obtain the following expression

$$\frac{d}{dt}\{\det [x(t)]\} = \det \begin{pmatrix} \dot{\phi}_{11} & \dot{\phi}_{12} & \cdots & \dot{\phi}_{1n} \\ \phi_{21} & \phi_{22} & \cdots & \phi_{2n} \\ \cdots & \cdots & \cdots & \cdots \\ \phi_{n1} & \phi_{n2} & \cdots & \phi_{nn} \end{pmatrix}$$

$$+ \det \begin{pmatrix} \phi_{11} & \phi_{12} & \cdots & \phi_{1n} \\ \dot{\phi}_{21} & \dot{\phi}_{22} & \cdots & \dot{\phi}_{2n} \\ \cdots & \cdots & \cdots & \cdots \\ \phi_{n1} & \phi_{n2} & \cdots & \phi_{nn} \end{pmatrix} + \cdots$$

$$+ \det \begin{pmatrix} \phi_{11} & \phi_{12} & \cdots & \phi_{1n} \\ \phi_{21} & \phi_{22} & \cdots & \phi_{2n} \\ \cdots & \cdots & \cdots & \cdots \\ \dot{\phi}_{n1} & \dot{\phi}_{n2} & \cdots & \dot{\phi}_{nn} \end{pmatrix} \quad \blacksquare$$

Now suppose that $\mathbf{X}$ is a matrix which satisfies

$$\dot{\mathbf{X}}(t) = \mathbf{A}(t)\mathbf{X}(t)$$

or more explicitly, if $\mathbf{X}(t) = [x_{lk}(t)]$, then

$$\dot{x}_{lk} = \sum_{p=1}^{n} a_{lp}(t)x_{pk}(t) \qquad (l = 1, 2, \ldots, n)$$

but from the previous theorem

$$\frac{d}{dt}[\det \mathbf{X}(t)] = \det \begin{bmatrix} \dot{x}_{11} & \dot{x}_{12} & \cdots & \dot{x}_{1n} \\ x_{21} & x_{22} & \cdots & x_{21} \\ \cdots & \cdots & \cdots & \cdots \\ x_{n1} & x_{n2} & \cdots & x_{nn} \end{bmatrix}$$

$$+ \det \begin{bmatrix} x_{11} & x_{12} & \cdots & x_{1n} \\ \dot{x}_{21} & \dot{x}_{22} & \cdots & \dot{x}_{2n} \\ \cdots & \cdots & \cdots & \cdots \\ x_{n1} & x_{n2} & \cdots & x_{nn} \end{bmatrix} + \cdots + \det \begin{bmatrix} x_{11} & x_{12} & \cdots & x_{1n} \\ x_{21} & x_{22} & \cdots & x_{2n} \\ \cdots & \cdots & \cdots & \cdots \\ \dot{x}_{n1} & \dot{x}_{n2} & \cdots & \dot{x}_{nn} \end{bmatrix}$$

Substituting the above into the homogeneous equation and performing some elementary row operations that do not affect the determinant yield

$$\frac{d}{dt}[\det(X(t))] = \det\begin{pmatrix} a_{11}x_{11} & a_{11}x_{12} & \cdots & a_{11}x_{1n} \\ x_{21} & x_{22} & \cdots & x_{2n} \\ \cdots & \cdots & \cdots & \cdots \\ x_{n1} & x_{n2} & \cdots & x_{nn} \end{pmatrix}$$

$$+ \det\begin{pmatrix} x_{11} & x_{12} & \cdots & x_{1n} \\ a_{22}x_{21} & a_{22}x_{22} & \cdots & a_{22}x_{2n} \\ \cdots & \cdots & \cdots & \cdots \\ x_{n1} & x_{n2} & \cdots & x_{nn} \end{pmatrix} + \cdots$$

$$+ \det\begin{pmatrix} x_{11} & x_{12} & \cdots & x_{1n} \\ x_{21} & x_{22} & \cdots & x_{2n} \\ \cdots & \cdots & \cdots & \cdots \\ a_{nn}x_{n1} & a_{nn}x_{n2} & \cdots & a_{nn}x_{nn} \end{pmatrix}$$

In other words, the differentiation of the kth row ($k = 1, 2, \ldots, n$) amounts to multiplying it by $a_{kk}(t)$ and adding multiples (by $a_{k1}(t), a_{k2}(t), \ldots, a_{k,k-1}(t), a_{k,k+1}(t), \ldots, a_{kn}(t)$) of the other rows to it; the latter operations do not alter the value of the determinant. Hence,

$$\frac{d}{dt}[\det(\mathbf{X}(t))] = a_{11}(t)\det(\mathbf{X}(t)) + a_{22}(t)\det(\mathbf{X}(t)) + \cdots + a_{nn}(t)\det(\mathbf{X}(t))$$

or

$$\frac{d}{dt}[\det(\mathbf{X}(t))] = \operatorname{tr}(\mathbf{A}(t))\det(\mathbf{X}(t))$$

where the trace of the matrix $\mathbf{A}(t)$ is defined by

$$\operatorname{tr}(\mathbf{A}(t)) = \sum_{k=1}^{n} a_{kk}(t)$$

i.e., it is the sum of the elements on the diagonal. Therefore, any time-varying matrix $\mathbf{X}(t)$ which satisfies

$$\dot{\mathbf{X}}(t) = \mathbf{A}(t)\mathbf{X}(t)$$

and is nonsingular for some time, is nonsingular for all time; i.e., it is a fundamental matrix since

$$\det(\mathbf{X}(t)) = \det(\mathbf{X}(t_0))\exp\left[\int_{t_0}^{t}\operatorname{tr}(\mathbf{A}(\tau))\,d\tau\right]$$

so that

$$\det(\mathbf{X}(t_0)) \neq 0 \qquad \text{for some } -\infty < t_0 < \infty$$

implies

$$\det(\mathbf{X}(t)) \neq 0 \qquad \text{for all } -\infty < t_0 < \infty$$

4.6 THE STATE-TRANSITION MATRIX AND THE SOLUTION OF THE HOMOGENEOUS EQUATION

In general, it may be exceedingly difficult, or impossible, to find a closed-form solution to the linear, time-variable state equation (4.17). In Chap. 7 numerical methods suitable for the solution of these equations will be explored. But to carry our present studies a little further, we may discuss in the abstract a useful matrix known as the *state-transition matrix* $\mathbf{\Phi}(t,t_0)$. We assume that $\mathbf{\Phi}(t,t_0)$ has the following two properties:

(1) $d/dt\mathbf{\Phi}(t,t_0) = \mathbf{A}(t)\mathbf{\Phi}(t,t_0)$
(2) $\mathbf{\Phi}(t_0,t_0) = \mathbf{1}$

Initially we will be rather vague as to the form of $\mathbf{\Phi}(t,t_0)$, but we will formulate a general solution to linear-state equations in terms of it. Later, when studying certain classes of systems, we will find specific expressions for $\mathbf{\Phi}(t,t_0)$. $\mathbf{\Phi}(t,t_0)$ is a fundamental matrix for the homogeneous system of linear differential equations

$$\dot{\mathbf{x}}(t) = \mathbf{A}(t)\mathbf{x}(t)$$

Moreover, given the linear system of differential equations

$$\dot{\mathbf{x}}(t) = \mathbf{A}(t)\mathbf{x}(t)$$

with

$$\mathbf{x}(t_0) = \mathbf{x}_0$$

the *unique solution* is given by $\mathbf{x}$ in terms of $\mathbf{\Phi}(t,t_0)$:

$$\mathbf{x}(t) = \mathbf{\Phi}(t,t_0)\mathbf{x}_0$$

for all t such that $-\infty < t < \infty$, because

$$\mathbf{x}(t_0) = \mathbf{\Phi}(t_0,t_0)\mathbf{x}_0 = \mathbf{1}\mathbf{x}_0 = \mathbf{x}_0$$

and

$$\frac{d}{dt}[\mathbf{x}(t)] = \frac{d}{dt}[\mathbf{\Phi}(t,t_0)\mathbf{x}_0] = \frac{d}{dt}[\mathbf{\Phi}(t,t_0)]\mathbf{x}_0 = \mathbf{A}(t)\mathbf{\Phi}(t,t_0)\mathbf{x}_0 = \mathbf{A}(t)\mathbf{x}(t)$$

Hence, we see that the name *state-transition matrix* is appropriate for $\mathbf{\Phi}(t,t_0)$, since it maps the state at time t_0 into the state at time t via a linear transformation:

$$\mathbf{x}(t) = \mathbf{\Phi}(t,t_0)\mathbf{x}(t_0)$$

The initial time is arbitrary and may be taken to be a variable, so that we may write the state-transition matrix as $\mathbf{\Phi}(t,\tau)$ with the properties

(1) $\partial/\partial t[\mathbf{\Phi}(t,\tau)] = \mathbf{A}(t)\mathbf{\Phi}(t,\tau)$
(2) $\mathbf{\Phi}(t,\tau) = \mathbf{1} \qquad \text{for } t = \tau$

It is evident from the properties of fundamental matrices that

$$\det(\mathbf{\Phi}(t,\tau)) = \exp\left[\int_\tau^t \operatorname{tr}(\mathbf{A}(\xi))\,d\xi\right]$$

The state-transition matrix possesses some interesting properties. Suppose that the $n \times n$ matrix function $\mathbf{X}$ is a solution of the matrix-differential equation

$$\dot{\mathbf{X}}(t) = \mathbf{A}(t)\mathbf{X}(t)$$

such that

$$\mathbf{X}(t_0) = \mathbf{C}$$

where $\mathbf{C}$ is a constant matrix; then the solution can be written in terms of $\mathbf{\Phi}(t,t_0)$:

$$\mathbf{X}(t) = \mathbf{\Phi}(t,t_0)\mathbf{C}$$

Clearly

$$\mathbf{X}(t_0) = \mathbf{\Phi}(t_0,t_0)\mathbf{C} = \mathbf{1C} = \mathbf{C}$$

and

$$\dot{\mathbf{X}}(t) = \mathbf{\Phi}(t,t_0)\mathbf{C} = \mathbf{A}(t)\mathbf{\Phi}(t,t_0)\mathbf{C} = \mathbf{A}(t)\mathbf{X}(t)$$

By uniqueness, any solution can be put in this form.

(4.30) Theorem
The state-transition matrix $\mathbf{\Phi}(t,\tau)$ has the group property:

$$\mathbf{\Phi}(t_1,t_2)\mathbf{\Phi}(t_2,t_3) = \mathbf{\Phi}(t_1,t_3)$$

for all t_1, t_2, and t_3 such that $-\infty\ t_1 < \infty$, $-\infty < t_2 < \infty$, and $-\infty < t_3 < \infty$.

Proof
The solution of

$$\dot{\mathbf{X}}(t) = \mathbf{A}(t)\mathbf{X}(t) \qquad \text{with } \mathbf{X}(t_3) = \mathbf{1}$$

is

$$\mathbf{X}(t) = \mathbf{\Phi}(t,t_3)\mathbf{1} = \mathbf{\Phi}(t,t_3) \qquad -\infty < t < \infty$$

and the solution of

$$\dot{\mathbf{Y}}(t) = \mathbf{A}(t)\mathbf{Y}(t) \qquad \text{with } \mathbf{Y}(t_2) = \mathbf{\Phi}(t_2,t_3)$$

is

$$\mathbf{Y}(t) = \mathbf{\Phi}(t,t_2)\mathbf{\Phi}(t_2,t_3)$$

But these two solutions must coincide (by uniqueness of the solution for any initial-condition vector); therefore,

$$\mathbf{\Phi}(t,t_2)\mathbf{\Phi}(t_2,t_3) = \mathbf{\Phi}(t,t_2)$$

and a fortiori

$$\mathbf{\Phi}(t_1,t_2)\mathbf{\Phi}(t_2,t_3) = \mathbf{\Phi}(t_1,t_3)$$ ▮

We note that the order in which t_1, t_2, and t_3 occur is immaterial for this result. A particularly interesting consequence of the above general result is

$$\mathbf{\Phi}(t_1,t_2)\mathbf{\Phi}(t_2,t_1) = \mathbf{\Phi}(t_1,t_1) = \mathbf{1}$$

or

$$[\mathbf{\Phi}(t_1,t_2)]^{-1} = \mathbf{\Phi}(t_2,t_1)$$

We can establish a useful relationship between the state-transition matrix and any fundamental matrix. Suppose that $\mathbf{X}$ is any fundamental matrix, i.e.,

$$\dot{\mathbf{X}}(t) = \mathbf{A}(t)\mathbf{X}(t)$$

and $\mathbf{X}(t_0) = \mathbf{C}$ where t_0 is an arbitrary time and $\mathbf{C}$ is an $n \times n$ nonsingular matrix. Hence the solution is

$$\mathbf{X}(t) = \mathbf{\Phi}(t,t_0)\mathbf{C}$$

so that

$$\mathbf{\Phi}(t,t_0) = \mathbf{X}(t)\mathbf{C}^{-1} = \mathbf{X}(t)[\mathbf{X}(t_0)]^{-1} \tag{4.31}$$

(4.32) Example

Consider the time-varying homogeneous state equations

$$\dot{\mathbf{x}}(t) = \begin{bmatrix} \frac{1}{t} & 0 \\ \frac{-2}{t^2} & \frac{2}{t} \end{bmatrix} \mathbf{x}(t)$$

One possible fundamental matrix is

$$\mathbf{X}(t) = \begin{bmatrix} t & 0 \\ 1 & t^2 \end{bmatrix}$$

since

$$\dot{\mathbf{X}}(t) = \begin{bmatrix} 1 & 0 \\ 0 & 2t \end{bmatrix}$$

and

$$\mathbf{A}(t)\mathbf{X}(t) = \begin{bmatrix} \frac{1}{t} & 0 \\ \frac{-2}{t^2} & \frac{2}{t} \end{bmatrix} \begin{bmatrix} t & 0 \\ 1 & t^2 \end{bmatrix} = \begin{bmatrix} 1 & 0 \\ 0 & 2t \end{bmatrix}$$

that is,

$$\dot{\mathbf{X}}(t) = \mathbf{A}(t)\mathbf{X}(t)$$

The state-transition matrix can be found from (4.31):

$$\mathbf{\Phi}(t,t_0) = \mathbf{X}(t)\mathbf{X}^{-1}(t_0) = \begin{bmatrix} t & 0 \\ 1 & t^2 \end{bmatrix} \begin{bmatrix} \frac{1}{t_0} & 0 \\ -\frac{1}{t_0^3} & \frac{1}{t_0^2} \end{bmatrix} = \begin{bmatrix} \frac{t}{t_0} & 0 \\ \frac{1}{t_0} - \frac{t^2}{t_0^3} & \frac{t^2}{t_0^2} \end{bmatrix}$$

Note that $\mathbf{\Phi}(t_0,t_0) = \mathbf{1}$. Hence the solution of the homogeneous equation is

$$\mathbf{x}(t) = \begin{bmatrix} \frac{t}{t_0} & 0 \\ \frac{1}{t_0} - \frac{t^2}{t_0^3} & \frac{t^2}{t_0^2} \end{bmatrix} \mathbf{x}(t_0)$$

∎

4.7 THE COMPLETE SOLUTION OF LINEAR-STATE EQUATIONS

Let us now consider the solution to the differential-state equation

$$\dot{\mathbf{x}}(t) = \mathbf{A}(t)\mathbf{x}(t) + \mathbf{B}(t)\mathbf{u}(t) \qquad t_0 \le t < \infty$$

with the initial state $\mathbf{x}(t_0) = \mathbf{x}_0$. We have formulated the solution to the homogeneous equation

$$\dot{\mathbf{x}}(t) = \mathbf{A}(t)\mathbf{x}(t) \qquad \mathbf{x}(t_0) = \mathbf{x}_0$$

as

$$\mathbf{x}(t) = \mathbf{\Phi}(t,t_0)\mathbf{x}(t_0)$$

where the state-transition matrix $\mathbf{\Phi}(t,\tau)$ has the properties

(1) $\partial/\partial t[\mathbf{\Phi}(t,\tau)] = \mathbf{A}(t)\mathbf{\Phi}(t,\tau)$

(2) $\mathbf{\Phi}(t,\tau) = \mathbf{1}$ for $t = \tau$

To obtain the particular solution, we attempt once again to employ the method of "variation or parameters." Assume the particular solution is

$\mathbf{X}\mathbf{n}$ where $\mathbf{X}$ is a fundamental matrix and $\mathbf{n}$ an arbitrary vector, then

$$\frac{d}{dt}[\mathbf{X}(t)\mathbf{n}(t)] = \mathbf{A}(t)\mathbf{X}(t)\mathbf{n}(t) + \mathbf{B}(t)\mathbf{u}(t)$$

but

$$\frac{d}{dt}[\mathbf{X}(t)\mathbf{n}(t)] = \dot{\mathbf{X}}(t)\mathbf{n}(t) + \mathbf{X}(t)\dot{\mathbf{n}}(t) = \mathbf{A}(t)\mathbf{X}(t)\mathbf{n}(t) + \mathbf{X}(t)\dot{\mathbf{n}}(t)$$

hence, we obtain

$$\mathbf{X}(t)\dot{\mathbf{n}}(t) = \mathbf{B}(t)\mathbf{u}(t)$$

or

$$\mathbf{n}(t) = [\mathbf{X}(t)]^{-1}\mathbf{B}(t)\mathbf{u}(t) \tag{4.33}$$

Note that $[\mathbf{X}(t)]^{-1}$ exists for all time, because $\mathbf{X}$ is a fundamental matrix. Integration of (4.33) with $\mathbf{n}(t_0) = \mathbf{0}$ yields

$$\mathbf{n}(t) = \int_{t_0}^{t} [\mathbf{X}(\tau)]^{-1}\mathbf{B}(\tau)\mathbf{u}(\tau)\,d\tau$$

Therefore, the particular solution is

$$\begin{aligned}\mathbf{X}(t)\mathbf{n}(t) &= \int_{t_0}^{t} \mathbf{X}(t)[\mathbf{X}(\tau)]^{-1}\mathbf{B}(\tau)\mathbf{u}(\tau)\,d\tau \\ &= \int_{t_0}^{t} \mathbf{\Phi}(t,\tau)\mathbf{B}(\tau)\mathbf{u}(\tau)\,d\tau\end{aligned}$$

The complete solution is the sum of the homogeneous and particular solutions

$$\mathbf{x}(t) = \mathbf{\Phi}(t,t_0)\mathbf{x}_0 + \int_{t_0}^{t} \mathbf{\Phi}(t,\tau)\mathbf{B}(\tau)\mathbf{u}(\tau)\,d\tau \qquad t_0 \le t < \infty$$

which follows from uniqueness. An alternate form for the solution is

$$\mathbf{x}(t) = \mathbf{\Phi}(t,t_0)\left[\mathbf{x}_0 + \int_{t_0}^{t} \mathbf{\Phi}(t_0,\tau)\mathbf{B}(\tau)\mathbf{u}(\tau)\,d\tau\right]$$

To summarize briefly, the response of a lumped system characterized by linear-state equations

$$\begin{aligned}&(4.34a)\quad \dot{\mathbf{x}}(t) = \mathbf{A}(t)\mathbf{x}(t) + \mathbf{B}(t)\mathbf{u}(t) \\ &(4.34b)\quad \mathbf{y}(t) = \mathbf{C}(t)\mathbf{x}(t) + \mathbf{D}(t)\mathbf{u}(t)\end{aligned} \qquad t_0 \le t < \infty$$

is

$$\mathbf{y}(t) = \mathbf{C}(t)\mathbf{\Phi}(t,t_0)\mathbf{x} + \int_{t_0}^{t} \mathbf{C}(t)\mathbf{\Phi}(t,\tau)\mathbf{B}(\tau)\mathbf{u}(\tau)\,d\tau + \mathbf{D}(t)\mathbf{u}(t) \tag{4.35}$$

where

$$\frac{\partial}{\partial t}[\mathbf{\Phi}(t,\tau)] = \mathbf{A}(t)\mathbf{\Phi}(t,\tau)$$

and

$$\mathbf{\Phi}(t,\tau) = \mathbf{1} \qquad \text{for } t = \tau$$

Observe that the system response as given by (4.35) may be separated into two distinct parts: the *zero-input response*

$$(4.36) \quad \mathbf{y}_{0i}(t) = \mathbf{C}(t)\mathbf{\Phi}(t,t_0)\mathbf{x}(t_0)$$

and the *zero-state response*

$$(4.37) \quad \mathbf{y}_{0s}(t) = \int_{t_0}^{t} \mathbf{C}(t)\mathbf{\Phi}(t,\tau)\mathbf{B}(\tau)\mathbf{u}(\tau)\,d\tau + \mathbf{D}(t)\mathbf{u}(t)$$

We may rewrite (4.37) as

$$\mathbf{y}_{0s}(t) = \int_{t_0}^{t} [\mathbf{C}(t)\mathbf{\Phi}(t,\tau)\mathbf{B}(\tau)\mathbf{u}(\tau) + \mathbf{D}(\tau)\delta(t-\tau)]\mathbf{u}(\tau)\,d\tau$$

where the *delta function* $\delta(t)$ is defined by

$$f(t) = \int_{t_0}^{t_1} f(\tau)\delta(t-\tau)\,d\tau \qquad t_0 \leq t \leq t_1$$

where $f(t)$ is any ordinary function. The delta function will be discussed more thoroughly in Chap. 5. The zero-state response is a relation between the system's excitations and responses and as seen from (4.37) is independent of the state variables. The $m \times r$ matrix function

$$(4.38) \quad \mathbf{H}(t,\tau) \equiv \mathbf{C}(t)\mathbf{\Phi}(t,\tau)\mathbf{B}(\tau) + \mathbf{D}(t)\delta(t-\tau)$$

is called the "weighting pattern," "system kernal," "impulse response matrix," among other descriptive names. In Chap. 5 we will discuss the convolution integral and relate it to expression (4.38) in the time-invariant case.

The following relation is of fundamental importance.

(4.39) Theorem

An r input—m output linear system which is characterized by the weighting pattern $\mathbf{H}(t,\tau)$, that is,

$$\mathbf{y}(t) = \int_{-\infty}^{t} \mathbf{H}(t,\tau)\mathbf{u}(\tau)\,d\tau$$

is lumped (has a finite-dimensional state space) if and only if the pattern is separable; i.e., there exists an $m \times n$ matrix function $\boldsymbol{\theta}$ and a $n \times r$ matrix function $\boldsymbol{\psi}$ (where n is arbitrary, but finite) such that

$$\mathbf{H}(t,\tau) = \boldsymbol{\theta}(t)\boldsymbol{\psi}(\tau)$$

Proof

Sufficiency: Given

$$\mathbf{y}(t) = \int_{-\infty}^{t} \boldsymbol{\theta}(t)\boldsymbol{\psi}(t)\mathbf{u}(\tau)\,d\tau$$

this relation is equivalent to

$$\mathbf{x}(t) = \mathbf{0x}(t) + \boldsymbol{\psi}(t)\mathbf{u}(t)$$

and

$$\mathbf{y}(t) = \boldsymbol{\theta}(t)\mathbf{x}(t)$$

where $\mathbf{x}$ is an n-vector state variable since $\boldsymbol{\theta}$ is $m \times n$ and $\boldsymbol{\psi}$ is $n \times r$. (Note: This is not a "good" realization of the weighting pattern since $\mathbf{A} = \mathbf{0}$ would indicate a system prone to instabilities.)

Necessity: Given

$$\dot{\mathbf{x}}(t) = \mathbf{A}(t)\mathbf{x}(t) + \mathbf{B}(t)\mathbf{u}(t)$$

and

$$\mathbf{y}(t) = \mathbf{C}(t)\mathbf{x}(t)$$

where $\mathbf{x}$ is an n vector (the system is lumped), then the general solution is

$$\mathbf{y}(t) = \int_{-\infty}^{t} \mathbf{C}(t)\mathbf{X}(t)[\mathbf{X}(\tau)]^{-1}\mathbf{B}(\tau)\mathbf{u}(\tau)\, d\tau$$

where $\mathbf{X}$ is an $n \times n$ fundamental matrix. Take

$$\boldsymbol{\theta}(t) = \mathbf{C}(t)\mathbf{X}(t)$$

and

$$\boldsymbol{\psi}(\tau) = [\mathbf{X}(\tau)]^{-1}\mathbf{B}(\tau)$$

∎

4.8 LINEAR TIME-INVARIANT SYSTEMS

As opposed to the general case, it is possible to find closed-form solutions for state equations which describe linear, time-invariant, nth-order systems. Recall that the solution for the first-order, linear, time-invariant state equation

$$\dot{x}(t) = ax(t) + bu(t)$$

was

$$x(t) = e^{a(t-t_0)}x(t_0) + \int_{t_0}^{t} e^{a(t-t_0)}bu(\tau)\, d\tau$$

Thus the "state-transition matrix" of this first-order system is

$$\Phi(t,t_0) = e^{a(t-t_0)}$$

Moreover, we found that the matrix $e^{\mathbf{A}(t-t_0)}$ is present in the solution of the state equations for linear, time-invariant, second-order systems. Thus we are motivated to see if, indeed, $e^{\mathbf{A}(t-t_0)}$ is the state-transition matrix for a general, linear, time-invariant system, i.e.,

$$\boldsymbol{\Phi}(t,t_0) = e^{\mathbf{A}(t-t_0)}$$

If $\mathbf{X}(t)$ is a fundamental matrix, then we know that

$$\mathbf{\Phi}(t,t_0) = \mathbf{X}(t)\mathbf{X}^{-1}(t_0)$$

which would indicate that if $e^{\mathbf{A}(t-t_0)}$ is the state-transition matrix, then

$$\mathbf{X}(t) = e^{\mathbf{A}t}$$

must be a fundamental matrix. It is easily verified that $e^{\mathbf{A}t}$ is a fundamental matrix, since by definition

$$e^{\mathbf{A}t} = \mathbf{1} + \mathbf{A}t + \frac{1}{2!}\mathbf{A}^2t^2 + \cdots$$

and upon differentiation

$$\begin{aligned}\frac{d}{dt}(e^{\mathbf{A}t}) &= \mathbf{A} + \mathbf{A}^2t + \frac{1}{2}\mathbf{A}^3t^2 + \cdots \\ &= \mathbf{A}\left(\mathbf{1} + \mathbf{A}t + \frac{1}{2!}\mathbf{A}^2t^2 + \cdots\right) \\ &= \mathbf{A}e^{\mathbf{A}t} \qquad (= e^{\mathbf{A}t}\mathbf{A})\end{aligned}$$

We leave it as an exercise for the reader to show that $e^{\mathbf{A}(t-t_0)}$ has the necessary properties to be a state-transition matrix. Note, in the time-invariant case, we may simplify the state-transition matrix notation from $\mathbf{\Phi}(t,\tau)$ to $\mathbf{\Phi}(t-\tau)$. Therefore, the solution of the linear, time-invariant state equations

$$(4.40a)\quad \dot{\mathbf{x}}(t) = \mathbf{A}\mathbf{x}(t) + \mathbf{B}\mathbf{u}(t)$$

and

$$(4.40b)\quad \mathbf{y}(t) = \mathbf{C}\mathbf{x}(t) + \mathbf{D}\mathbf{u}(t)$$

is

$$(4.41)\quad \mathbf{y}(t) = \mathbf{C}e^{\mathbf{A}(t-t)}\mathbf{x}_0 + \int_{t_0}^{t} \mathbf{C}e^{\mathbf{A}(t-\tau)}\mathbf{B}\mathbf{u}(\tau)\,d\tau + \mathbf{D}\mathbf{u}(t)$$

(4.42) Example

In Example (4.14) we wrote the following state equations for the network of Fig. (4.12):

$$\dot{\mathbf{x}} = \begin{bmatrix} -2 & 1 & 0 \\ -1 & -1 & 0 \\ 0 & 2 & -1 \end{bmatrix}\mathbf{x} + \begin{bmatrix} 1 & 0 \\ 0 & 0 \\ 0 & 2 \end{bmatrix}\mathbf{u}$$

and

$$\mathbf{y} = \begin{bmatrix} 2 & 0 & 0 \\ 0 & 0 & \frac{1}{2} \end{bmatrix}\mathbf{x}$$

The solution to these equations can be easily found after calculating $e^{\mathbf{A}t}$. The eigenvalues of $\mathbf{A}$ are $\lambda_1 = -1$, $\lambda_2 = -\frac{3}{2} + j\frac{3}{2}$, $\lambda_3 = -\frac{3}{2} - j\frac{3}{2}$. A suitable set of eigenvectors is

$$\boldsymbol{\xi}_1 = \begin{bmatrix} 0 \\ 0 \\ 1 \end{bmatrix} \qquad \boldsymbol{\xi}_2 = \begin{bmatrix} -1 \\ \frac{1}{2} + j\frac{3}{2} \\ 0 \end{bmatrix} \qquad \boldsymbol{\xi}_3 = \begin{bmatrix} -1 \\ \frac{1}{2} - j\frac{3}{2} \\ 0 \end{bmatrix}$$

In Chap. 3 we found that

$$e^{\mathbf{A}t} = \mathbf{S}e^{\mathbf{\Lambda}t}\mathbf{S}^{-1}$$

where $\mathbf{\Lambda} = \text{diag}\,(e^{\lambda_1 t}, e^{\lambda_2 t}, e^{\lambda_3 t})$ and $\mathbf{S}$ is the modal matrix. Therefore,

$$e^{\mathbf{A}t} = \begin{bmatrix} 0 & -1 & -1 \\ 0 & \frac{1}{2} + j\frac{3}{2} & \frac{1}{2} - j\frac{3}{2} \\ 1 & 0 & 0 \end{bmatrix} \begin{bmatrix} e^{\lambda_1 t} & 0 & 0 \\ 0 & e^{\lambda_2 t} & 0 \\ 0 & 0 & e^{\lambda_3 t} \end{bmatrix} \begin{bmatrix} 0 & 0 & 1 \\ -\frac{1}{2} - j\frac{1}{6} & -j\frac{1}{3} & 0 \\ -\frac{1}{2} + j\frac{1}{6} & +j\frac{1}{3} & 0 \end{bmatrix}$$

$$= \begin{bmatrix} \left(\frac{1}{2} + j\frac{1}{2\sqrt{3}}\right) e^{\lambda_2 t} + \left(\frac{1}{2} - j\frac{1}{2\sqrt{3}}\right) e^{\lambda_3 t} & j\frac{1}{\sqrt{3}}(e^{\lambda_2 t} - e^{\lambda_3 t}) & 0 \\ j\frac{1}{2\sqrt{3}}[e^{\lambda_2 t} - e^{\lambda_3 t}] & \left(\frac{1}{2} - j\frac{1}{2\sqrt{3}}\right) e^{\lambda_2 t} + \left(\frac{1}{2} + j\frac{1}{2\sqrt{3}}\right) e^{\lambda_3 t} & 0 \\ 0 & 0 & e^{\lambda_1 t} \end{bmatrix}$$

From (4.41) we find that the system response is

$$\mathbf{y}(t) = \begin{bmatrix} \left(1 + j\frac{1}{\sqrt{3}}\right) e^{\lambda_2(t-t_0)} + \left(1 - j\frac{1}{\sqrt{3}}\right) e^{\lambda_3(t-t_0)} & j\frac{2}{\sqrt{3}}(e^{\lambda_2(t-t_0)} - e^{\lambda_3(t-t_0)}) & 0 \\ 0 & 0 & \frac{1}{2}e^{\lambda_1(t-t_0)} \end{bmatrix} \begin{bmatrix} x_{10} \\ x_{20} \\ x_{30} \end{bmatrix}$$

$$+ \int_{t_0}^{t} \begin{bmatrix} \left(1 + j\frac{1}{\sqrt{3}}\right) e^{\lambda_2(t-\tau)} + \left(1 - j\frac{1}{\sqrt{3}}\right) e^{\lambda_3(t-\tau)} & 0 \\ 0 & e^{\lambda_1(t-\tau)} \end{bmatrix} \begin{bmatrix} u_1(\tau) \\ u_2(\tau) \end{bmatrix} d\tau$$

We may rewrite this response as

$$\mathbf{y}(t) = \begin{bmatrix} 2e^{-\frac{3}{2}(t-t_0)}\left[\cos\frac{\sqrt{3}}{2}(t-t_0) - \frac{1}{\sqrt{3}}\sin\frac{\sqrt{3}}{2}(t-t_0)\right] & \frac{-4}{3}e^{-\frac{3}{2}(t-t_0)}\left[\frac{1}{\sqrt{3}}\cos\frac{\sqrt{3}}{2}(t-t_0) + \sin\frac{\sqrt{3}}{2}(t-t_0)\right] & 0 \\ 0 & 0 & \frac{1}{2}e^{-(t-t_0)} \end{bmatrix} \begin{bmatrix} x_{10} \\ x_{20} \\ x_{30} \end{bmatrix}$$

$$+ \int_{t_0}^{t} \begin{bmatrix} 2e^{-\frac{3}{2}(t-\tau)}\left[\cos\frac{\sqrt{3}}{2}(t-\tau) - \frac{1}{\sqrt{3}}\sin\frac{\sqrt{3}}{2}(t-\tau)\right] & 0 \\ 0 & e^{-(t-\tau)} \end{bmatrix} \begin{bmatrix} u_1(\tau) \\ u_2(\tau) \end{bmatrix} d\tau$$

Note that the response is real in spite of the intermediate appearance of complex eigenvalues. ∎

Let us study the zero-input response of linear time-invariant systems:

$$(4.43)\quad \mathbf{y}_{0i}(t) = \mathbf{C}e^{(\mathbf{A}t-t_0)}\mathbf{x}_0$$

Assume that $\mathbf{A}$ has n distinct eigenvalues $(\lambda_1,\lambda_2, \ldots ,\lambda_n)$, then we may rewrite (4.43) as

$$(4.44)\quad \mathbf{y}_{0i}(t) = \mathbf{C}\mathbf{S}e^{\mathbf{\Lambda}(t-t_0)}\mathbf{S}^{-1}\mathbf{x}_0$$

where $\mathbf{S}$ is the modal matrix and $\mathbf{\Lambda} = \text{diag}\,(\lambda_1,\lambda_2, \ldots ,\lambda_n)$. If $\boldsymbol{\xi}_1$, $\boldsymbol{\xi}_2$, $\ldots$, $\boldsymbol{\xi}_n$ denote the eigenvectors associated with the eigenvalues λ_1, λ_2, $\ldots$, λ_n, respectively, then by definition,

$$\mathbf{S} = \begin{bmatrix} \boldsymbol{\xi}_1 & \boldsymbol{\xi}_2 & \cdots & \boldsymbol{\xi}_n \\ \downarrow & \downarrow & & \downarrow \end{bmatrix}$$

and

$$\mathbf{S}^{-1} = \begin{bmatrix} \mathbf{n}_1 & \rightarrow \\ \mathbf{n}_2 & \rightarrow \\ \cdots & \cdots \\ \mathbf{n}_n & \rightarrow \end{bmatrix}$$

The vectors $\mathbf{n}_1$, $\mathbf{n}_2$, $\ldots$, $\mathbf{n}_n$ are called the reciprocal basis, and we have already shown that

$$\mathbf{n}_i'\boldsymbol{\xi}_j = \begin{cases} 1 & \text{if } i = j \\ 0 & \text{if } i \neq j \end{cases}$$

Since

$$e^{\mathbf{\Lambda}(t-t_0)} = \text{diag}\,(e^{\lambda_1(t-t_0)},e^{\lambda_2(t-t_0)}, \ldots e^{\lambda_n(t-t_0)})$$

(4.44) may be written as

$$\mathbf{y}_{0i}(t) = \mathbf{C}\begin{bmatrix} e^{\lambda_1(t-t_0)}\boldsymbol{\xi}_1 & e^{\lambda_2(t-t_0)}\boldsymbol{\xi}_2 & \cdots & e^{\lambda_n(t-t_0)}\boldsymbol{\xi}_n \\ \downarrow & \downarrow & & \downarrow \\ & & & \end{bmatrix}\begin{bmatrix} \mathbf{n}_1' \rightarrow \\ \mathbf{n}_2' \rightarrow \\ \mathbf{n}_n' \rightarrow \end{bmatrix}\mathbf{x}_0$$

Now let $\mathbf{x}_0$ be equal to some multiple of one of the eigenvectors, i.e.,

$$\mathbf{x}_0 = \alpha\boldsymbol{\xi}_k$$

where α is any constant. Then

$$\mathbf{y}_{0i}(t) = \mathbf{C}\begin{bmatrix} e^{\lambda_1(t-t_0)}\boldsymbol{\xi}_1 & e^{\lambda_2(t-t_0)}\boldsymbol{\xi}_2 & \cdots & e^{\lambda_n(t-t_0)}\boldsymbol{\xi}_n \\ \downarrow & \downarrow & & \downarrow \\ \downarrow & \downarrow & & \downarrow \\ \downarrow & \downarrow & & \downarrow \end{bmatrix}\begin{bmatrix} 0 \\ 0 \\ \cdot \\ \cdot \\ \cdot \\ \alpha \\ \cdot \\ \cdot \end{bmatrix} \begin{matrix} \\ \\ \\ \\ \\ (k\text{th row}) \\ \\ \\ \end{matrix}$$

or

$$\mathbf{y}_{0i}(t) = \alpha \mathbf{C} e^{\lambda_k(t-t_0)} \boldsymbol{\xi}$$

In other words, if the vector of initial conditions is "parallel" with any one of the eigenvectors, only the associated mode (eigenvalue, natural frequency) will be excited. Thus we see that the invariant subspaces of **A** are rightly termed the "preferred directions" of the system.

(4.45) Example

The zero-input response for the system discussed in Example (4.42) is

$$\mathbf{y}_{0i}(t) = \begin{bmatrix} \left(1 + j\frac{1}{\sqrt{3}}\right) e^{\lambda_2(t-t_0)} + \left(1 - j\frac{1}{\sqrt{3}}\right) e^{\lambda_3(t-t_0)} & j\frac{2}{\sqrt{3}}\left(e^{\lambda_2(t-t_0)} - e^{\lambda_3(t-t_0)}\right) & 0 \\ 0 & 0 & \frac{1}{2} e^{\lambda_1(t-t_0)} \end{bmatrix} \begin{bmatrix} x_{10} \\ x_{20} \\ x_{30} \end{bmatrix}$$

Let the initial-condition vector lie in the same direction as the eigenvector associated with eigenvalue $\lambda_1 = -1$, that is,

$$\mathbf{x}_0 = \alpha \begin{bmatrix} 0 \\ 0 \\ 1 \end{bmatrix}$$

Then for the zero-input response

$$\mathbf{y}_{0i}(t) = \begin{bmatrix} 0 \\ \frac{1}{2} \alpha e^{\lambda_1(t-t_0)} \end{bmatrix}$$

only the first mode is present. If the initial-condition vector lies in the same direction as the eigenvector associated with $\lambda_2 = -\frac{3}{2} + j\frac{3}{2}$, that is,

$$\mathbf{x}_0 = \alpha \begin{bmatrix} -1 \\ \frac{1}{2} - j\frac{\sqrt{3}}{2} \\ 0 \end{bmatrix}$$

then the zero-input response is

$$\mathbf{y}_{0i}(t) = \begin{bmatrix} -j\frac{2\alpha}{\sqrt{3}} e^{\lambda_2(t-t_0)} \\ 0 \end{bmatrix}$$

which involves only the mode λ_2. Note that although what we have done is mathematically correct, this situation is not physical since a complex initial condition and complex output is entailed. ∎

4.9 LINEAR TIME-VARIABLE SYSTEMS

The solution of the state equations for the first-order, linear, time-variable system

$$\dot{x}(t) = a(t)x(t) + b(t)u(t)$$

and

$$y(t) = c(t)x(t) + d(y)u(t)$$

was found to be

$$y(t) = c(t) \exp\left[\int_{t_0}^{t} a(\xi)\, d\xi\right] x_0 + \int_{t_0}^{t} c(t) \exp\left[\int_{\tau}^{t} a(\xi)\, d\xi\right] b(\tau)u(\tau)\, d\tau + d(t)u(t)$$

The question arises, "Does this form of solution extend to the general case?" If it did, then the state-transition matrix for the general linear, time-variable state equations

$$\text{(4.46}a\text{)} \quad \dot{\mathbf{x}}(t) = \mathbf{A}(t)\mathbf{x}(t) + \mathbf{B}(t)\mathbf{u}(t)$$
$$\text{(4.46}b\text{)} \quad \mathbf{y}(t) = \mathbf{C}(t)\mathbf{x}(t) + \mathbf{D}(t)\mathbf{u}(t)$$

would be

$$\mathbf{\Phi}(t,t_0) \stackrel{?}{=} \exp\left[\int_{t_0}^{t} \mathbf{A}(\xi)\, d\xi\right]$$

Therefore, we must determine if

$$\frac{d}{dt}\mathbf{\Phi}(t,t_0) \stackrel{?}{=} \mathbf{A}(t)\mathbf{\Phi}(t,t_0)$$

a required property of state-transition matrices. Observe that

$$\text{(4.47)} \quad \frac{d}{dt}\exp\left[\int_{t_0}^{t} \mathbf{A}(\xi)\, d\xi\right]$$
$$= \lim_{h\to 0} \frac{\exp\left[\int_{t_0}^{t+h} \mathbf{A}(\xi)\, d\xi\right] - \exp\left[\int_{t_0}^{t} \mathbf{A}(\xi)\, d\xi\right]}{h}$$
$$= \lim_{h\to 0} \frac{\exp\left[\int_{t_0}^{t} \mathbf{A}(\xi)\, d\xi + \int_{t}^{t+h} \mathbf{A}(\xi)\, d\xi\right] - \exp\left[\int_{t_0}^{t} \mathbf{A}(\xi)\, d\xi\right]}{h}$$
$$\simeq \lim_{h\to 0} \frac{\exp\left[\int_{t_0}^{t} \mathbf{A}(\xi)\, d\xi + \mathbf{A}(t)h\right] - \exp\left[\int_{t_0}^{t} \mathbf{A}(\xi)\, d\xi\right]}{h}$$

To proceed further we must determine *under what circumstances*

$$\text{(4.48)} \quad e^{\mathbf{F}+\mathbf{G}} \stackrel{?}{=} e^{\mathbf{F}}e^{\mathbf{G}}$$

where $\mathbf{F}$ and $\mathbf{G}$ are $n \times n$ matrices. Consider the expression

$$(4.49)\quad e^{\mathbf{F}+\mathbf{G}} - e^{\mathbf{F}}e^{\mathbf{G}}$$

Expansion of (4.49) in a power series yields

$$(4.50)\quad \mathbf{1} + (\mathbf{F} + \mathbf{G}) + \frac{(\mathbf{F} + \mathbf{G})^2}{2!} + \cdots - \left(\mathbf{1} + \mathbf{F} + \frac{\mathbf{F}^2}{2!} + \cdots\right)\left(\mathbf{1} + \mathbf{G} + \frac{\mathbf{G}^2}{2!} + \cdots\right)$$

If and only if

$$\mathbf{FG} = \mathbf{GF}$$

that is, $\mathbf{F}$ and $\mathbf{G}$ commute, does expression (4.50) equal zero and expression (4.48) remain valid. Hence, under the assumption that $\int_{t_0}^{t} \mathbf{A}(\xi)\, d\xi$ and $\mathbf{A}(t)$ commute, (4.47) becomes

$$\frac{d}{dt}\exp\left[\int_{t_0}^{t} \mathbf{A}(\xi)\, d\xi\right] = \lim_{h\to 0} \frac{(e^{\mathbf{A}(t)h} - \mathbf{1})\exp\left[\int_{t_0}^{t} \mathbf{A}(\xi)\, d\xi\right]}{h}$$
$$= \mathbf{A}(t)\exp\left[\int_{t_0}^{t} \mathbf{A}(\xi)\, d\xi\right]$$

This circumstance is extremely unlikely. Observe that for a constant $\mathbf{A}$, that is, a time-invariant system,

$$\int_{t_0}^{t} \mathbf{A}\, d\xi = \mathbf{A}(t - t_0)$$

so that

$$\mathbf{A}[\mathbf{A}(t - t_0)] = \mathbf{A}^2(t - t_0) = [\mathbf{A}(t - t_0)]\mathbf{A}$$

so that the state-transition matrix may be $e^{\mathbf{A}(t-t_0)}$, as has been already shown.

Thus given a general nth-order, linear, time-variable system, we will be at a loss to find a closed-form solution unless the $\mathbf{A}$ matrix has the special property indicated above. Numerical techniques must be employed, some of these are discussed in Chap. 7.

There is an important subclass of time-variable systems for which we can extract much more information. Before proceeding with this discussion, we first digress to investigate system equivalence and transformation of state variables.

4.10 TRANSFORMATIONS OF THE STATE VARIABLES

Suppose that $\mathbf{x}(t)$ is an n-dimensional state vector in the n-dimensional, linear-vector space X, the state space. Suppose further that $\mathbf{W}$ is an $n \times n$

constant nonsingular matrix; then

$$\boldsymbol{\xi}(t) \equiv \mathbf{W}^{-1}\mathbf{x}(t) \qquad (\text{so } \mathbf{x}(t) = \mathbf{W}\boldsymbol{\xi}(t))$$

also qualifies to be a state vector. Hence, if we are given a set of linear, time-invariant state equations

$$(4.51a)\quad \dot{\mathbf{x}} = \mathbf{A}\mathbf{x} + \mathbf{B}\mathbf{u}$$

and

$$(4.51b)\quad \mathbf{y} = \mathbf{C}\mathbf{x} + \mathbf{D}\mathbf{u}$$

then, since

$$\dot{\mathbf{x}} = \mathbf{W}\dot{\boldsymbol{\xi}}$$

we have

$$(4.52a)\quad \dot{\boldsymbol{\xi}} = \mathbf{W}^{-1}\mathbf{A}\mathbf{W}\boldsymbol{\xi} + \mathbf{W}^{-1}\mathbf{B}\mathbf{u}$$

and

$$(4.52b)\quad \hat{\mathbf{y}} = \mathbf{C}\mathbf{W}\boldsymbol{\xi} + \mathbf{D}\mathbf{u}$$

The motivation behind considering such a transformation of the state vector is that the solution may be simpler in terms of the transformed state equations which represent a system equivalent to the original. In other words, the system described by the state equations (4.51) and the system described by the state equations (4.52) cannot be distinguished by external measurements under multiple experiments. To see that this statement is true, note that the solution of (4.51) is

$$(4.53)\quad \mathbf{y}(t) = \mathbf{C}e^{\mathbf{A}(t-t_0)}\mathbf{x}_0 + \int_{t_0}^{t} \mathbf{C}e^{\mathbf{A}(t-\tau)}\mathbf{B}\mathbf{u}(\tau)\,d\tau + \mathbf{D}\mathbf{u}(t)$$

and the solution of (4.52) is

$$(4.54)\quad \hat{\mathbf{y}}(t) = \mathbf{C}\mathbf{W}e^{\mathbf{W}^{-1}\mathbf{A}\mathbf{W}(t-t_0)}\boldsymbol{\xi}_0 + \int_{t_0}^{t} \mathbf{C}\mathbf{W}e^{\mathbf{W}^{-1}\mathbf{A}\mathbf{W}(t-t_0)}\mathbf{B}\mathbf{u}(\tau)\,d\tau + \mathbf{D}\mathbf{u}(t)$$

But, recall that for any function of a matrix $f(\mathbf{A})$ and any nonsingular matrix $\mathbf{W}$,

$$f(\mathbf{W}\mathbf{A}\mathbf{W}^{-1}) = \mathbf{W}f(\mathbf{A})\mathbf{W}^{-1}$$

Furthermore

$$\mathbf{W}\boldsymbol{\xi}_0 = \mathbf{x}_0$$

so that (4.54) becomes

$$\hat{\mathbf{y}}(t) = \mathbf{C}e^{\mathbf{A}(t-t_0)}\mathbf{x}_0 + \int_{t_0}^{t} \mathbf{C}e^{\mathbf{A}(t-\tau)}\mathbf{B}\mathbf{u}(\tau)\,d\tau + \mathbf{D}\mathbf{u}(t)$$

or, in other words

$$\mathbf{y}(t) \equiv \hat{\mathbf{y}}(t)$$

regardless of the choice of input functions $\mathbf{u}$.

The obvious choice for $\mathbf{W}$ is, of course, a modal matrix $\mathbf{S}$, so that

$$\mathbf{S}^{-1}\mathbf{A}\mathbf{S} = \mathbf{J}$$

the Jordan canonical form of $\mathbf{A}$. The transformed state equations are

$$\dot{\boldsymbol{\xi}}(t) = \mathbf{J}\boldsymbol{\xi}(t) + \mathbf{S}^{-1}\mathbf{B}\mathbf{u}(t)$$

and

$$\mathbf{y}(t) = \mathbf{C}\mathbf{S}\boldsymbol{\xi}(t) + \mathbf{D}\mathbf{u}(t)$$

The state-transition matrix for this system,

$$\boldsymbol{\Phi}(t,t_0) = e^{\mathbf{J}(t-t_0)}$$

can be written by inspection.

(4.55) Example

Consider a system described by the state equations

$$\dot{\mathbf{x}} = \mathbf{A}\mathbf{x} + \mathbf{B}\mathbf{u}$$

and

$$\mathbf{y} = \mathbf{C}\mathbf{x}$$

where

$$\mathbf{A} = \begin{bmatrix} 2 & -2 & 3 \\ 1 & 1 & 1 \\ 1 & 3 & -1 \end{bmatrix}$$

$$\mathbf{B} = \begin{bmatrix} 0 \\ 2 \\ 0 \end{bmatrix} \qquad \mathbf{C} = [1 \quad 2 \quad 0]$$

The eigenvalues associated with the matrix $\mathbf{A}$ are $\lambda_1 = 1$, $\lambda_2 = -2$, $\lambda_3 = 3$ and a suitable modal matrix is

$$\mathbf{S} = \begin{bmatrix} 0 & 11 & 1 \\ 1 & 1 & 1 \\ 1 & -14 & 1 \end{bmatrix}$$

Then the transformed state equations are

$$\begin{bmatrix} \dot{\xi}_1 \\ \dot{\xi}_2 \\ \dot{\xi}_3 \end{bmatrix} = \begin{bmatrix} 1 & 0 & 0 \\ 0 & -2 & 0 \\ 0 & 0 & 3 \end{bmatrix} \begin{bmatrix} \xi_1 \\ \xi_2 \\ \xi_3 \end{bmatrix} + \begin{bmatrix} \frac{50}{15} \\ \frac{2}{15} \\ -\frac{22}{15} \end{bmatrix} u$$

and

$$y = [2 \quad 13 \quad 3]\begin{bmatrix} \xi_1 \\ \xi_2 \\ \xi_3 \end{bmatrix}$$

and the state-transition matrix for this system is

$$\mathbf{\Phi}(t,t_0) = \begin{bmatrix} e^{(t-t_0)} & 0 & 0 \\ 0 & e^{-2(t-t_0)} & 0 \\ 0 & 0 & e^{3(t-t_0)} \end{bmatrix}$$

▮

The transformation matrix $\mathbf{W}$ need not be time invariant so long as it is nonsingular for all time. Thus, consider

$$\boldsymbol{\xi}(t) \equiv [\mathbf{W}(t)]^{-1}\mathbf{x}(t) \qquad (\text{so } \mathbf{x}(t) = \mathbf{W}(t)\boldsymbol{\xi}(t))$$

which also qualifies to be a state vector. Then

$$\dot{\mathbf{x}}(t) = \dot{\mathbf{W}}(t)\boldsymbol{\xi}(t) + \mathbf{W}(t)\dot{\boldsymbol{\xi}}(t) = \mathbf{AW}(t)\boldsymbol{\xi}(t) + \mathbf{Bu}(t)$$

so that the equivalent set of state equations becomes

$$\dot{\boldsymbol{\xi}}(t) = [\mathbf{W}^{-1}(t)\mathbf{AW}(t) - \mathbf{W}^{-1}(t)\dot{\mathbf{W}}(t)]\boldsymbol{\xi}(t) + \mathbf{W}^{-1}(t)\mathbf{Bu}(t)$$

and

$$\mathbf{y}(t) = \mathbf{CW}(t)\boldsymbol{\xi}(t) + \mathbf{Du}(t)$$

Hence, we may effect a transformation from a system *characterization* which is time invariant to one which is not; clearly, what is desired is the reverse of this procedure.

Suppose we are given the set of state equations

$$\dot{\mathbf{x}}(t) = \mathbf{A}(t)\mathbf{x}(t) + \mathbf{B}(t)\mathbf{u}(t)$$

and

$$\mathbf{y}(t) = \mathbf{C}(t)\mathbf{x}(t) + \mathbf{D}(t)\mathbf{u}(t)$$

for a linear, time-variable system. Consider the transformation of state variables

$$\boldsymbol{\xi}(t) \equiv \mathbf{W}^{-1}(t)\mathbf{x}(t)$$

so that the equivalent system is

$$(4.56a) \quad \dot{\boldsymbol{\xi}}(t) = [\mathbf{W}^{-1}(t)\mathbf{A}(t)\mathbf{W}(t) - \mathbf{W}^{-1}(t)\dot{\mathbf{W}}(t)]\boldsymbol{\xi}(t) + \mathbf{W}^{-1}(t)\mathbf{B}(t)\mathbf{u}(t)$$

and

$$(4.56b) \quad \mathbf{y}(t) = \mathbf{C}(t)\mathbf{W}(t)\boldsymbol{\xi}(t) + \mathbf{D}(t)\mathbf{u}(t)$$

We can effect a simple solution if we can render the transformed matrix

$$\hat{\mathbf{A}}(t) \equiv \mathbf{W}^{-1}(t)\mathbf{A}(t)\mathbf{W}(t) - \mathbf{W}^{-1}(t)\dot{\mathbf{W}}(t)$$

time invariant or, at least in (time-variable) Jordan form. Unfortunately, finding the appropriate transformation is tantamount to solution of the original equations, since, even if we could make

$$\mathbf{W}^{-1}(t)\mathbf{A}(t)\mathbf{W}(t) = \mathbf{J}(t)$$

a time-variable Jordan form, the additive term $-\mathbf{W}^{-1}(t)\dot{\mathbf{W}}(t)$ could be virtually anything. In fact, suppose that $\mathbf{X}(t)$ is a fundamental matrix and take

$$\mathbf{W}(t) = \mathbf{X}(t)$$

then

$$\boldsymbol{\xi}(t) \equiv [\mathbf{X}(t)]^{-1}\mathbf{x}(t)$$

yields

$$\dot{\boldsymbol{\xi}}(t) = \mathbf{X}^{-1}(t)\mathbf{B}(t)\mathbf{u}(t)$$

and

$$\mathbf{y}(t) = \mathbf{C}(t)\mathbf{X}(t)\boldsymbol{\xi}(t) + \mathbf{D}(t)\mathbf{u}(t)$$

an equivalent-system characterization which is easily solved.

(4.57) Example

Consider the seemingly time-variable system described by

$$\dot{x}(t) = \left(a - \frac{2t}{t^2 + 1}\right) x(t) + b(t^2 + 1)u(t)$$

and

$$y(t) = \frac{1}{t^2 + 1}\, x(t) + du(t)$$

If we choose the transformation

$$w(t) = t^2 + 1$$

that is,

$$\xi(t) = \frac{1}{t^2 + 1}\, x(t)$$

then from (4.56) the system is seen to be characterized by the linear, *time-invariant* state equations

$$\dot{\xi}(t) = a\xi(t) + bu(t)$$

and

$$y(t) = c\xi(t) + du(t)$$

This example illustrates the fact that *time-invariant systems* may be characterized by *time-variable* state *equations*. ∎

4.11 PERIODICALLY VARIABLE SYSTEMS

Although we cannot find a closed-form solution to the general linear, time-variable state equations (4.46), we can derive some interesting properties for *periodically variable systems.* Periodically variable systems may also be described by the state equations (4.46) with the additional property that the matrix function $\mathbf{A}$ is periodic with period T, that is,

$$\mathbf{A}(t + T) = \mathbf{A}(t) \qquad -\infty < t < \infty$$

It is not uncommon for such systems to arise as the result of linearizing nonlinear-state equations operating in the steady state with periodic input functions.

(4.58) Example

The operation of a parametric amplifier is most easily illustrated in terms of the simple network shown in Fig. 4.16 which consists of a fixed inductor and a periodically varying capacitor. In actuality, the time-varying capacitor is realized by applying a sinusoidal "pump" signal to a fixed nonlinear capacitor (varactor). The linear, time-varying network described here is a linearized approximation.

A second-order equation which describes the linear network may be written in terms of the capacitance charge q:

$$L\ddot{q} + \frac{1}{C(t)} q = 0$$

Choosing $\dot{q}$ and q as state variables, we have the state-equation description

$$\dot{\mathbf{x}} = \begin{bmatrix} 0 & 1 \\ \dfrac{-1}{LC(t)} & 0 \end{bmatrix} \mathbf{x}$$

Under the assumption that $L = 1$, C varies sinusoidally with period $T = 2\pi$, and that the time origin is chosen properly, we can write the state equations as

$$\dot{\mathbf{x}} = \begin{bmatrix} 0 & 1 \\ \dfrac{-1}{\alpha + \beta \cos t} & 0 \end{bmatrix} \mathbf{x}$$

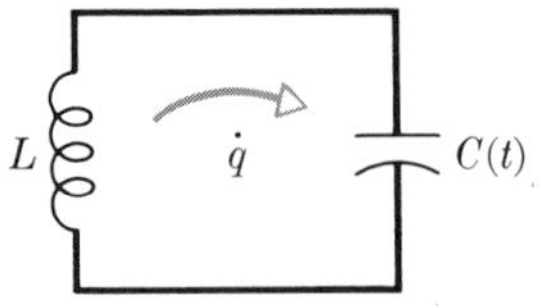

FIG. 4.16 A crude model of a parametric amplifier.

Observe that, for this example,

$$\mathbf{A}(t + T) = \mathbf{A}(t)$$

where $T = 2\pi$. ▮

Consider now a fundamental matrix $\mathbf{X}$ which is a solution of the homogeneous matrix-differential equation

$$\dot{\mathbf{X}}(t) = \mathbf{A}(t)\mathbf{X}(t) \tag{4.59}$$

Merely by a change of variables $t \rightarrow t + T$, we have

$$\dot{\mathbf{X}}(t + T) = \mathbf{A}(t + T)\mathbf{X}(t + T) \tag{4.60}$$

Because $\mathbf{A}(t + T) = \mathbf{A}(t)$, (4.60) becomes

$$\dot{\mathbf{X}}(t + T) = \mathbf{A}(t)\mathbf{X}(t + T)$$

which demonstrates that $\mathbf{X}(t + T)$ is also a fundamental matrix. Recall that since the solution of the homogeneous differential equation

$$\dot{\mathbf{x}}(t) = \mathbf{A}(t)\mathbf{x}(t)$$

with $\mathbf{x}(t_0) = \mathbf{x}_0$ is unique, any pair of fundamental matrices $\hat{\mathbf{X}}$ and $\mathbf{X}$ are related by a constant $n \times n$ nonsingular transformation matrix $\mathbf{C}$:

$$\hat{\mathbf{X}}(t) = \mathbf{X}(t)C$$

Consequently, for a periodic $\mathbf{A}$ with period T

$$\hat{\mathbf{X}}(t + T) = \mathbf{X}(t)\mathbf{C} \tag{4.61}$$

where $\mathbf{C}$ is a constant $n \times n$ nonsingular matrix. This result has far-reaching consequences.

We now demonstrate that the eigenvalues of the matrix $\mathbf{C}$ in expression (4.61) are invariant quantities directly related to the system. To see this let $\mathbf{X}$ and $\hat{\mathbf{X}}$ be any two fundamental matrices for the homogeneous system, so, from (4.61)

$$\mathbf{X}(t + T) = \mathbf{X}(t)\mathbf{C} \tag{4.62}$$

and

$$\hat{\mathbf{X}}(t + T) = \hat{\mathbf{X}}(t)\hat{\mathbf{C}} \tag{4.63}$$

Moreover, from the properties of fundamental matrices,

$$\hat{\mathbf{X}}(t) = \mathbf{X}(t)\mathbf{P} \tag{4.64}$$

where $\mathbf{P}$ is a constant $n \times n$ nonsingular matrix. After a change of variables (4.64) may be written as

$$\hat{\mathbf{X}}(t+T) = \mathbf{X}(t+T)\mathbf{P} \tag{4.65}$$

Combination of (4.62) with (4.65) yields

$$\hat{\mathbf{X}}(t)\hat{\mathbf{C}} = \mathbf{X}(t)\mathbf{C}\mathbf{P} = \hat{\mathbf{X}}(t)\mathbf{P}^{-1}\mathbf{C}\mathbf{P}$$

so that

$$\hat{\mathbf{C}} = \mathbf{P}^{-1}\mathbf{C}\mathbf{P}$$

The transformation which relates $\hat{\mathbf{C}}$ to $\mathbf{C}$ is recognized to be a *similarity transformation,* which indicates that the eigenvalues of the matrix $\mathbf{C}$ are invariant quantities. That is,

$$\begin{aligned}\det(\hat{\mathbf{C}} - \lambda\mathbf{1}) &= \det(\mathbf{P}^{-1}\mathbf{C}\mathbf{P} - \lambda\mathbf{1})\\ &= \det(\mathbf{P}^{-1}\mathbf{C}\mathbf{P} - \lambda\mathbf{P}^{-1}\mathbf{P})\\ &= \det(\mathbf{P}^{-1}(\mathbf{C} - \lambda\mathbf{1})\mathbf{P})\\ &= \det(\mathbf{P}^{-1})\det(\mathbf{C} - \lambda\mathbf{1})\det(\mathbf{P})\\ &= \det(\mathbf{C} - \lambda\mathbf{1})\end{aligned}$$

Let us now introduce the concept of periodic equivalence.

(4.66) Periodic equivalence

Two periodic, linear, time-variable homogeneous systems

$$\dot{\mathbf{x}}(t) = \mathbf{A}(t)\mathbf{x}(t)$$

and

$$\dot{\boldsymbol{\xi}}(t) = \hat{\mathbf{A}}(t)\boldsymbol{\xi}(t)$$

where both $\mathbf{A}$ and $\hat{\mathbf{A}}$ are periodic with period T,

$$\mathbf{A}(t+T) = \mathbf{A}(t)$$

and

$$\hat{\mathbf{A}}(t+T) = \hat{\mathbf{A}}(t)$$

are said to be *periodically equivalent* if there exists a periodic matrix $\mathbf{W}$ of period T,

$$\mathbf{W}(t+T) = \mathbf{W}(t)$$

such that the fundamental matrices are related by

$$\hat{\mathbf{X}}(t) = \mathbf{W}(t)\mathbf{X}(t)$$

where

$$\dot{\mathbf{X}}(t) = \mathbf{A}(t)\mathbf{X}(t)$$

and

$$\dot{\hat{\mathbf{X}}}(t) = \hat{\mathbf{A}}(t)\hat{\mathbf{X}}(t)$$ ∎

Given the two periodically equivalent systems

$$\dot{\mathbf{x}}(t) = \mathbf{A}(t)\mathbf{x}(t)$$

and

$$\dot{\boldsymbol{\xi}}(t) = \hat{\mathbf{A}}(t)\boldsymbol{\xi}(t)$$

with fundamental matrices $\mathbf{X}(t)$ and $\hat{\mathbf{X}}(t)$, respectively, we can establish a relationship between $\mathbf{A}(t)$ and $\hat{\mathbf{A}}(t)$ as follows. First note that

$$\text{(4.67)} \quad \hat{\mathbf{A}}(t) = (\dot{\hat{\mathbf{X}}}t)(\hat{\mathbf{X}}(t))^{-1}$$

and

$$\text{(4.68)} \quad \hat{\mathbf{X}}(t) = \mathbf{W}(t)\mathbf{X}(t)$$

where $\mathbf{W}(t)$ is periodic with period T. Substituting (4.68) into (4.67) yields

$$\hat{\mathbf{A}}(t) = [\dot{\mathbf{W}}(t)\mathbf{X}(t) + \mathbf{W}(t)\dot{\mathbf{X}}(t)][\mathbf{X}(t)]^{-1}[\mathbf{W}(t)]^{-1}$$

But

$$\dot{\mathbf{X}}(t) = \mathbf{A}(t)\mathbf{X}(t)$$

so the last expression becomes

$$\hat{\mathbf{A}}(t) = [\dot{\mathbf{W}}(t) + \mathbf{W}(t)\mathbf{A}(t)][\mathbf{W}(t)]^{-1}$$

Alternatively, we have

$$\mathbf{A}(t) = [\mathbf{W}(t)]^{-1}\hat{\mathbf{A}}(t)\mathbf{W}(t) - [\mathbf{W}(t)]^{-1}\dot{\mathbf{W}}(t)$$

(4.69) Theorem

Two periodic systems of period T,

$$\dot{\mathbf{x}}(t) = \mathbf{A}(t)\mathbf{x}(t)$$

and

$$\dot{\boldsymbol{\xi}}(t) = \hat{\mathbf{A}}(t)\boldsymbol{\xi}(t)$$

are *periodically equivalent* if and only if there exist fundamental matrices $\mathbf{X}$ and $\hat{\mathbf{X}}$, solutions of

$$\dot{\mathbf{X}}(t) = \mathbf{A}(t)\mathbf{X}(t)$$

and

$$\dot{\hat{\mathbf{X}}}(t) = \hat{\mathbf{A}}(t)\hat{\mathbf{X}}(t)$$

where

$$\mathbf{X}(t + T) = \mathbf{X}(t)\mathbf{C}$$

and

$$\mathbf{X}(t + T) = \mathbf{X}(t)\hat{\mathbf{C}}$$

such that

$$\mathbf{C} = \hat{\mathbf{C}}$$

Proof

Necessity: Let **X** be a fundamental matrix for the homogeneous system

$$\dot{\mathbf{x}}(t) = \mathbf{A}(t)\mathbf{x}(t)$$

such that

$$\mathbf{X}(t + T) = \mathbf{X}(t)\mathbf{C}$$

and let $\hat{\mathbf{X}}$ be a fundamental matrix for the homogeneous system

$$\dot{\boldsymbol{\xi}}(t) = \hat{\mathbf{A}}(t)\boldsymbol{\xi}(t)$$

such that

$$\hat{\mathbf{X}}(t + T) = \hat{\mathbf{X}}(t)\hat{\mathbf{C}}$$

Assume these systems are periodically equivalent, then by definition

$$\hat{\mathbf{X}}(t) = \mathbf{W}(t)\mathbf{X}(t) \tag{4.66}$$

for some periodic matrix $\mathbf{W}(t)$. But

$$\begin{aligned}\hat{\mathbf{X}}(t + T) &= \mathbf{W}(t + T)\mathbf{X}(t + T)\\ &= \mathbf{W}(t)\mathbf{X}(t)\mathbf{C}\\ &= \hat{\mathbf{X}}(t)\mathbf{C}\end{aligned}$$

which shows that $\hat{\mathbf{C}} = \mathbf{C}$.

Sufficiency: Now suppose that $\hat{\mathbf{C}} = \mathbf{C}$. We have that

$$\dot{\mathbf{X}}(t) = \mathbf{A}(t)\mathbf{X}(t)$$

where

$$\mathbf{X}(t + T) = \mathbf{X}(t)\mathbf{C}$$

and

$$\dot{\hat{\mathbf{X}}}(t) = \hat{\mathbf{A}}(t)\hat{\mathbf{X}}(t)$$

where

$$\hat{\mathbf{X}}(t + T) = \hat{\mathbf{X}}(t)\hat{\mathbf{C}}$$

Hence

$$\begin{aligned}\hat{\mathbf{X}}(t + T)[\mathbf{X}(t + T)]^{-1} &= \hat{\mathbf{X}}(t)\hat{\mathbf{C}}\mathbf{C}^{-1}[\mathbf{X}(t)]^{-1}\\ &= \hat{\mathbf{X}}(t)[X(t)]^{-1}\end{aligned}$$

Thus,

$$\begin{aligned}\mathbf{W}(t) &= \hat{\mathbf{X}}(t)[\mathbf{X}(t)]^{-1} \\ &= \hat{\mathbf{X}}(t+T)[\mathbf{X}(t+T)]^{-1} \\ &= \mathbf{W}(t+T)\end{aligned}$$

which shows that $\mathbf{W}$ is periodic with period T. ∎

Periodic equivalence is most useful if a given periodic system can be found to be equivalent to one for which the solution, or qualitative aspects thereof, is known. The following theorem, then, is of considerable significance.

(4.70) Theorem

Any periodic, linear, time-variable homogeneous differential equation of the form

$$\dot{\mathbf{x}}(t) = \mathbf{A}(t)\mathbf{x}(t)$$

where $\mathbf{A}$ is periodic, is equivalent to a linear, time-invariant homogeneous differential equation of the form

$$\dot{\boldsymbol{\xi}}(t) = \hat{\mathbf{A}}\boldsymbol{\xi}(t)$$

where $\hat{\mathbf{A}}$ is a constant (perhaps complex) $n \times n$ matrix.

Proof

The associated state-transition matrix for

$$\dot{\boldsymbol{\xi}}(t) = \hat{\mathbf{A}}\boldsymbol{\xi}(t)$$

is

$$\boldsymbol{\Phi}(t,\tau) = e^{\hat{\mathbf{A}}(t-\tau)}$$

and therefore a fundamental matrix is

$$\hat{\mathbf{X}}(t) = e^{\hat{\mathbf{A}}t}$$

This system is (trivially) periodic with period T, so

$$\hat{\mathbf{X}}(t+T) = e^{\hat{\mathbf{A}}(t+T)} = e^{\hat{\mathbf{A}}t}e^{\hat{\mathbf{A}}T} = \hat{\mathbf{X}}(t)\hat{\mathbf{C}}$$

where

$$\hat{\mathbf{C}} = e^{\hat{\mathbf{A}}t}$$

Now consider the periodic system

$$\dot{\mathbf{x}}(t) = \mathbf{A}(t)\mathbf{x}(t)$$

for which we know that

$$\mathbf{X}(t+T) = \mathbf{X}(t)\mathbf{C}$$

for some $\mathbf{C}$. We need only take

$$\mathbf{C} = \hat{\mathbf{C}}$$

for equivalence, or

$$e^{\hat{\mathbf{A}}t} = \mathbf{C}$$

hence

$$\hat{\mathbf{A}} = \frac{1}{T} \ln (\mathbf{C})$$

gives a coincident set of $\mathbf{C}$ matrices. Since $\mathbf{C} = \hat{\mathbf{C}}$, the immediately preceding theorem indicates periodic equivalence. ∎

Finally, we translate the derived results into the nomenclature of the state-transition matrix.

(4.71) Theorem (Floquet)

If $\mathbf{A}$ is periodic with period T,

$$\mathbf{A}(t + T) = \mathbf{A}(t) \qquad \text{for all } t$$

the periodic, linear, time-variable homogeneous system

$$\dot{\mathbf{x}}(t) = \mathbf{A}(t)\mathbf{x}(t)$$

has a state-transition matrix $\mathbf{\Phi}(t,t_0)$ which can be factored as

$$\mathbf{\Phi}(t,t_0) = \mathbf{P}(t,t_0)e^{\mathbf{F}(t-t_0)}$$

where

$$\mathbf{P}(t_0,t_0) = \mathbf{1}$$
$$\mathbf{P}(t,t_0) \text{ is periodic with period } T$$

and $\mathbf{F}$ is an $n \times n$ constant matrix.

Proof

Since $\mathbf{A}$ is periodic with period T it follows that

$$\mathbf{\Phi}(t + T, t_0) = \mathbf{\Phi}(t,t_0)\mathbf{C} = \mathbf{\Phi}(t,t_0)e^{\mathbf{F}T}$$

where

$$\mathbf{F} = \frac{1}{T} \ln (\mathbf{C})$$

since $\mathbf{\Phi}(t,t_0)$ is a fundamental matrix. We can then define

$$\mathbf{P}(t,t_0) = \mathbf{\Phi}(t,t_0)e^{-\mathbf{F}(t-t_0)}$$

$\mathbf{P}(t,t_0)$ is therefore nonsingular. $\mathbf{P}(t,t_0)$ is periodic with period T since

$$\begin{aligned}\mathbf{P}(t+T,\ t_0) &= \mathbf{\Phi}(t+T,\ t_0)e^{-\mathbf{F}(t+T-t_0)} \\ &= \mathbf{\Phi}(t,t_0)\mathbf{C}e^{-\mathbf{F}T}e^{-\mathbf{F}(t-t_0)} \\ &= \mathbf{P}(t,t_0)\end{aligned}$$

because

$$e^{-\mathbf{F}T} = \mathbf{C}^{-1}$$

▮

(4.72) Example

Consider the linear, periodic system (period $T = 2\pi$) described by the homogeneous-state equations

$$\dot{\mathbf{x}} = \begin{bmatrix} 1 & 0 \\ \cos t & 1 \end{bmatrix} \mathbf{x}$$

A fundamental matrix is

$$\mathbf{X}(t) = \begin{bmatrix} e^t & 0 \\ \sin te^t & e^t \end{bmatrix}$$

Note that

$$\mathbf{X}(t+T) = \begin{bmatrix} e^{t+T} & 0 \\ \sin\,(t+T)e^{(t+T)} & e^{t+T} \end{bmatrix}$$

where $T = 2\pi$ is also a fundamental matrix. Moreover

$$\mathbf{X}(t+T) = \mathbf{X}(t)\mathbf{C}$$

where the constant matrix $\mathbf{C}$ is given by

$$\mathbf{C} = \begin{bmatrix} e^T & 0 \\ 0 & e^T \end{bmatrix}$$

The state-transition matrix is easily found:

$$\begin{aligned}\mathbf{\Phi}(t,t_0) &= \mathbf{X}(t)\mathbf{X}^{-1}(t_0) \\ &= \begin{bmatrix} e^{(t-t_0)} & 0 \\ (\sin t - \sin t_0)e^{(t-t_0)} & e^{(t-t_0)} \end{bmatrix}\end{aligned}$$

We can write $\mathbf{\Phi}(t,t_0)$ as

$$\mathbf{\Phi}(t,t_0) = \mathbf{P}(t,t_0)e^{-\mathbf{F}(t-t_0)}$$

where

$$\mathbf{P}(t,t_0) = \begin{bmatrix} 1 & 0 \\ \sin t - \sin t_0 & 1 \end{bmatrix}$$

and

$$\mathbf{F} = \begin{bmatrix} -1 & 0 \\ 0 & -1 \end{bmatrix}$$

▮

4.12 DISCRETE-TIME SYSTEMS

We now turn our attention to discrete-time systems and generalize the concepts introduced in Chaps. 1 and 2.

In general any nth-order, linear, discrete-time system can be modeled by the nth-order difference equation

$$\begin{aligned} &a_n y(k+n) + a_{n-1} y(k+n-1) + \cdots + a_1 y(k+1) + a_0 y(k) \\ &= b_m u(k+m) + b_{m-1} u(k+m-1) + \cdots + b_1 u(k+1) + b_0 \end{aligned}$$

or by the n first-order state-difference equation

$$\mathbf{x}(k+1) = \mathbf{A}(k)\mathbf{x}(k) + \mathbf{B}(k)\mathbf{u}(k)$$

and the input-state-output equation

$$\mathbf{y}(k) = \mathbf{C}(k)\mathbf{x}(k) + \mathbf{D}(k)\mathbf{u}(k)$$

where $\{\mathbf{u}(k)\}$ is the input r-vector sequence, $\{\mathbf{y}(k)\}$ is the output m-vector sequence, and $\{\mathbf{x}(k)\}$ the state n-vector sequence.

The $n \times n$ matrix sequence $\{\mathbf{A}(k)\}$, $n \times r$ matrix sequence $\{\mathbf{B}(k)\}$, $m \times n$ matrix sequence $\{\mathbf{C}(k)\}$, and the $m \times r$ matrix sequence $\{\mathbf{D}(k)\}$ indicate that the system is time varying. If the system is time invariant, these matrices are independent of k and the state equations become

$$\mathbf{x}(k+1) = \mathbf{A}\mathbf{x}(k) + \mathbf{B}\mathbf{u}(k)$$

and

$$\mathbf{y}(k) = \mathbf{C}\mathbf{x}(k) + \mathbf{D}\mathbf{u}(k)$$

Consider the homogeneous, time-varying, discrete-state difference equation

$$\mathbf{x}(k+1) = \mathbf{A}(k)\mathbf{x}(k) \tag{4.73}$$

If the initial conditions $\mathbf{x}_0$ are given, we have

$$\begin{aligned} \mathbf{x}(1) &= \mathbf{A}(0)\mathbf{x}_0 \\ \mathbf{x}(2) &= \mathbf{A}(1)\mathbf{x}(1) = \mathbf{A}(1)\mathbf{A}(0)\mathbf{x}_0 \end{aligned}$$

or, in general

$$\mathbf{x}(k) = \prod_{i=1}^{k-1} \mathbf{A}(i)\mathbf{x}_0 \qquad k > 0$$

We now define the *discrete-state-transition* matrix $\mathbf{\Phi}(k,m)$ by the relations

(1) $\mathbf{x}(k) = \mathbf{\Phi}(k,m)\mathbf{x}(m)$

(2) $\mathbf{\Phi}(k,k) = \mathbf{1}$

In other words, the state transition matrix describes the motion of the states of the system and is analogous to the state-transition matrix defined for continuous systems.

From the definition of the state-transition matrix, we have

$$\mathbf{x}(k) = \mathbf{\Phi}(k,0)\mathbf{x}_0 \tag{4.74}$$

Comparing (4.73) and (4.74) yields

$$\mathbf{\Phi}(k,0) = \prod_{i=0}^{k-1} \mathbf{A}(i) \qquad k > 0$$

When $\mathbf{A}(k)$ is a constant matrix,

$$\mathbf{\Phi}(k,0) = \mathbf{\Phi}(k) = \mathbf{A}^k$$

It is easy to show that the state-transition matrix $\mathbf{\Phi}(k,m)$ has the following properties:

(1) $\mathbf{\Phi}(k_3,k_2) \cdot \mathbf{\Phi}(k_2,k_1) = \mathbf{\Phi}(k_3,k_1)$

(2) $\mathbf{\Phi}(k_1,k_2) = [\mathbf{\Phi}(k_2,k_1)]^{-1}$

For the time-invariant case, we can use the Cayley-Hamilton theorem as a means of calculating the state-transition matrix.

(4.75) Example

Consider a discrete-time system described by

$$\mathbf{x}(k+1) = \begin{bmatrix} 0 & 1 \\ -4 & -5 \end{bmatrix} \mathbf{x}(k)$$

Then

$$\mathbf{\Phi}(k) = \mathbf{A}^k = \alpha_0\mathbf{1} + \alpha_1\mathbf{A}$$

a result which we have already proven. The eigenvalues of $\mathbf{A}$ are $\lambda_1 = -1$ and $\lambda_2 = -4$. Hence the eigenvalues of $\mathbf{A}^k$ are

$$(\lambda_1)^k = (-1)^k \qquad \text{and} \qquad (\lambda_2)^k = (-4)^k$$

Therefore

$$(\lambda_1)^k = (-1)^k = \alpha_0 + \alpha_1\lambda_1 = \alpha_0 - \alpha_1$$
$$(\lambda_2)^k = (-4)^k = \alpha_0 + \alpha_1\lambda_2 = \alpha_0 - 4\alpha_1$$

These equations can be solved to yield

$$\alpha_0 = \tfrac{4}{3}(-1)^k - \tfrac{1}{3}(-4)^k$$

and

$$\alpha_1 = \tfrac{1}{3}(-1)^k - \tfrac{1}{3}(-4)^k$$

so that

$$\mathbf{\Phi}(k) = \begin{bmatrix} \frac{4}{3}(-1)^k - \frac{1}{3}(-4)^k & \frac{1}{3}(-1)^k - \frac{1}{3}(-4)^k \\ -\frac{4}{3}(-1)^k + \frac{4}{3}(-4)^k & -\frac{1}{3}(-1)^k + \frac{4}{3}(-4)^k \end{bmatrix} \qquad \blacksquare$$

We now find the complete solution of the discrete-time state equations. Given the initial state $\mathbf{x}_0$, we have successively

$$\begin{aligned} \mathbf{x}(1) &= \mathbf{A}(0)\mathbf{x}_0 + \mathbf{B}(0)\mathbf{u}(0) \\ \mathbf{x}(2) &= \mathbf{A}(1)\mathbf{x}(1) + \mathbf{B}(1)\mathbf{u}(1) \\ &= \mathbf{A}(1)\mathbf{A}(0)\mathbf{x}_0 + \mathbf{A}(1)\mathbf{B}(0)u(0) + \mathbf{B}(1)\mathbf{u}(1) \\ &\cdots\cdots\cdots\cdots\cdots\cdots\cdots \\ \mathbf{x}(k) &= \prod_{i=0}^{k-1} \mathbf{A}(i)\mathbf{x}_0 + \sum_{i=0}^{k-1} \left[\prod_{j=i+1}^{k-1} \mathbf{A}(j) \right] \mathbf{B}(i)\mathbf{u}(i) \qquad k = 1, 2, \ldots \end{aligned}$$

Using the definition of the state-transition matrix:

$$\mathbf{x}(k) = \mathbf{\Phi}(k)\mathbf{x}_0 + \sum_{i=0}^{k-1} \mathbf{\Phi}(k - i - 1)\mathbf{B}(i)\mathbf{u}(i)$$

and

$$\mathbf{y}(k) = \mathbf{C}(k)\mathbf{\Phi}(k)\mathbf{x}_0 + \sum_{i=0}^{k-1} \mathbf{C}(k)\mathbf{\Phi}(k - i - 1)\mathbf{B}(i)\mathbf{u}(i) + \mathbf{D}(k)\mathbf{u}(k)$$

When the system is time invariant, these equations become

$$\mathbf{x}(k) = \mathbf{\Phi}(k)\mathbf{x}_0 + \sum_{i=0}^{k-1} \mathbf{\Phi}(k - i - 1)\mathbf{B}\mathbf{u}(i)$$

and

$$\mathbf{y}(k) = \mathbf{C}\mathbf{\Phi}(k)\mathbf{x}_0 + \mathbf{C} \sum_{i=0}^{k-1} \mathbf{\Phi}(k - i - 1)\mathbf{B}\mathbf{u}(i) + \mathbf{D}\mathbf{u}(k)$$

Consider a linear, time-invariant, discrete-time system in which $\mathbf{D} \equiv \mathbf{0}$ and $\mathbf{x}_0 = \mathbf{0}$. Then

$$\mathbf{y}(k) = \sum_{i=0}^{k-1} \mathbf{C}\mathbf{\Phi}(k - i - 1)\mathbf{B}\mathbf{u}(i)$$

If we define

$$\mathbf{H}(k) = \mathbf{C}\mathbf{\Phi}(k - 1)\mathbf{B}$$

then

$$\mathbf{y}(k) = \sum_{i=0}^{k-1} \mathbf{H}(k - i)\mathbf{u}(i)$$

or alternatively, if we let $j = k - i$

$$\mathbf{y}(k) = \sum_{j=1}^{k} \mathbf{H}(j)\mathbf{u}(k-j)$$

This expression is known as the *convolution summation* of the system. It is the discrete-time counterpart of the convolution integral for continuous systems. Observe that the $\mathbf{H}(k-i)$ determine the *weights* with which the input values $\mathbf{u}(i)$, $i = 0, 1, \ldots, k-1$, contribute to the output $\mathbf{y}(k)$ at time k. Hence we refer to the sequence $\{\mathbf{H}(k)\}$ as the *weighting sequence* of the system.

We will now discuss discretization of continuous systems. This approach, as will be seen in Chap. 7, has great utility in the solution of state equations on a digital computer.

Suppose we are given the continuous-time, time-invariant system shown in Fig. 4.17*a* described by the standard-form state equations

$$\dot{\mathbf{x}}(t) = \mathbf{A}\mathbf{x}(t) + \mathbf{B}\mathbf{u}(t)$$

and

$$\mathbf{y}(t) = \mathbf{C}\mathbf{x}(t) + \mathbf{D}\mathbf{u}(t)$$

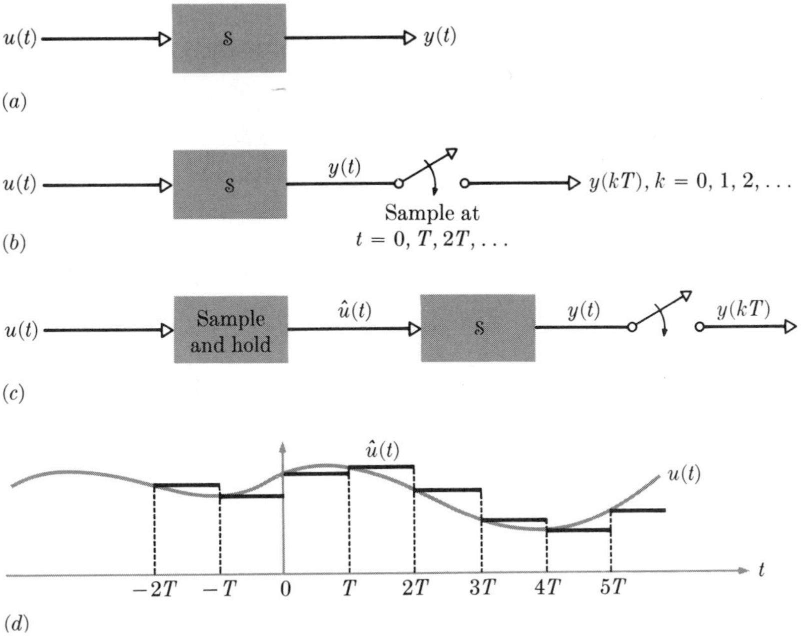

FIG. 4.17 (*a*) A linear time-invariant network, (*b*) the linear time-invariant network with a sample output, (*c*) the discretized version of the system, (*d*) sample and hold-device operation, $u(t)$ input, $\hat{u}(t)$ output.

We know from our previous work that the solution to the differential-state equations is

$$\mathbf{x}(t) = e^{\mathbf{A}(t-t_0)}\mathbf{x}(t_0) + \int_{t_0}^{t} e^{\mathbf{A}(t-\tau)}\mathbf{Bu}(\tau)\,d\tau$$

where $\mathbf{x}(t_0)$ is a given initial state. For convenience let $t_0 = 0$.

Now suppose that we are interested only in observing the output $\mathbf{y}(t)$ at fixed intervals of time $0, T, 2T, \ldots$, that is, we wish to *sample* the output at time $t = 0, T, 2T, \ldots$. This situation is shown in Fig. 4.17*b*. From the input-state-output equation we have

$$\mathbf{y}(kT) = \mathbf{Cx}(kT) + \mathbf{Du}(kT) \qquad k = 0, 1, 2, \ldots \tag{4.76}$$

and so we must determine the state $\mathbf{x}(t)$ at the times $0, T, 2T, \ldots$. From the solution of the differential-state equation, we have

$$\begin{aligned}
\mathbf{x}(0) &= \mathbf{x}(0)\\
\mathbf{x}(T) &= e^{\mathbf{A}t}\left[\mathbf{x}(0) + \int_0^T e^{-\mathbf{A}\tau}\mathbf{Bu}(\tau)\,d\tau\right]\\
\mathbf{x}(2T) &= e^{\mathbf{A}2T}\left[\mathbf{x}(0) + \int_0^{2T} e^{-\mathbf{A}\tau}\mathbf{Bu}(\tau)\,d\tau\right]\\
&= e^{\mathbf{A}T}\left\{e^{\mathbf{A}T}\left[\mathbf{x}(0) + \int_0^T e^{-\mathbf{A}\tau}\mathbf{Bu}(\tau)\,d\tau\right]\right.\\
&\qquad\left. + e^{\mathbf{A}T}\int_T^{2T} e^{-\mathbf{A}\tau}\mathbf{Bu}(\tau)\,d\tau\right\}\\
&= e^{\mathbf{A}T}\left[\mathbf{x}(T) + e^{\mathbf{A}T}\int_T^{2T} e^{-\mathbf{A}\tau}\mathbf{Bu}(\tau)\,d\tau\right]\\
&\cdots\cdots\cdots\cdots\cdots\cdots\\
\mathbf{x}(kT) &= e^{\mathbf{A}T}\left[\mathbf{x}((k-1)T) + e^{\mathbf{A}(k-1)T}\int_{(k-1)T}^{kT} e^{-\mathbf{A}\tau}\mathbf{Bu}(\tau)\,d\tau\right]
\end{aligned} \tag{4.77}$$

By combination of (4.76) and (4.77), the samples $\mathbf{y}(0), \mathbf{y}(T), \mathbf{y}(2T), \ldots$ can be determined.

Let us further assume that before applying the input $\mathbf{u}(t)$ to the system we pass it through a *sample and hold* device as shown in Fig. 4.17*c*. Operation of the sample and hold device is as follows: If $\mathbf{u}(t)$ is its input, then its output is the piecewise-constant function $\mathbf{u}(t)$ where

$$\hat{\mathbf{u}}(t) = \mathbf{u}(kT) \qquad kT < t \leq (k+1)T$$

and where k is any integer ($k = (\ldots, -2, -1, 0, 1, 2, \ldots)$). Figure 4.17*d* pictorially describes the operation of the sample and hold device. Note that as T becomes smaller, $\hat{\mathbf{u}}(t)$ becomes a much better approximation of $\mathbf{u}(t)$.

At this juncture, it becomes convenient to introduce the following notation. Since we are ultimately only concerned with $\mathbf{y}(t)$, $\mathbf{u}(t)$, and $\mathbf{x}(t)$ at certain fixed times, for example, $\mathbf{y}(kT)$, $\mathbf{u}(kT)$, and $\mathbf{x}(kT)$, where k is an integer, and since T is fixed, we abuse our notation and let

$$\mathbf{y}(k) \equiv \mathbf{y}(kT)$$
$$\mathbf{x}(k) \equiv \mathbf{x}(kT)$$

and

$$\mathbf{u}(k) \equiv \mathbf{u}(kT)$$

Using the above notation, we see that the output of the system shown in Fig. 4.17c is

$$\mathbf{y}(k) = \mathbf{Cx}(k) + \mathbf{Du}(k)$$

where, from (4.77)

$$\mathbf{x}(k) = e^{\mathbf{A}T}\mathbf{x}(k - 1) + \left[e^{\mathbf{A}kT} \int_{(k-1)T}^{kT} e^{-\mathbf{A}\tau} B \, d\tau \right] u(k - 1) \qquad k = 1, 2, \ldots$$

Consider the term

$$e^{\mathbf{A}kT} \int_{(k-1)T}^{kT} e^{-\mathbf{A}T}\mathbf{B} \, d\tau \tag{4.78}$$

We can rewrite (4.78) as

$$\int_{(k-1)T}^{kT} e^{\mathbf{A}(kT-\tau)}\mathbf{B} \, d\tau \tag{4.79}$$

Upon a change of variables ($\sigma = kT - \tau$), (4.79) becomes

$$\int_0^T e^{\mathbf{A}\sigma}\mathbf{B} \, d\sigma \qquad \text{a constant matrix}$$

Therefore, expression (4.77) becomes

$$\mathbf{x}(k) = e^{\mathbf{A}T}\mathbf{x}(k - 1) + \mathbf{u}(k - 1) \int_0^T e^{\mathbf{A}\sigma}\mathbf{B} \, d\sigma$$

We define the fundamental matrix $\mathbf{F}$ by

$$\mathbf{F} \equiv e^{\mathbf{A}T}$$

and let

$$\mathbf{G} \equiv \int_0^T e^{A\sigma}\mathbf{B} \, d\sigma$$

so that the equations describing the system shown in Fig. 4.17c are

$$\mathbf{x}(k + 1) = \mathbf{Fx}(k) + \mathbf{Gu}(k)$$

and

$$\mathbf{y}(k) = \mathbf{Cx}(k) + \mathbf{Du}(k)$$

In summary, we have shown that by suitable sampling, a continuous, linear, time-invariant system described by the standard-form state equations

$$\dot{\mathbf{x}}(t) = \mathbf{Ax}(t) + \mathbf{Bu}(t)$$

and

$$\mathbf{y}(t) = \mathbf{Cx}(t) + \mathbf{Du}(t)$$

may be transformed into a discrete-time system described by the "discrete-state equations"

$$\mathbf{x}(k+1) = \mathbf{Fx}(k) + \mathbf{Gu}(k)$$

and

$$\mathbf{y}(k) = \mathbf{Cx}(k) + \mathbf{Du}(k)$$

where $\mathbf{F} \equiv e^{\mathbf{A}T}$ and $\mathbf{G} \equiv \int_0^T e^{\mathbf{A}\tau}\mathbf{B}\,d\tau$

and T is the sampling interval.

(4.80) Example

Consider the continuous system described by

$$\begin{bmatrix} \dot{x}_1 \\ \dot{x}_2 \end{bmatrix} = \begin{bmatrix} -1 & 1 \\ 0 & -2 \end{bmatrix} \begin{bmatrix} x_1 \\ x_2 \end{bmatrix} + \begin{bmatrix} 0 \\ 1 \end{bmatrix} u$$

and

$$y = [1 \quad 1] \begin{bmatrix} x_1 \\ x_2 \end{bmatrix}$$

It is easy to show that

$$e^{\mathbf{A}t} = \begin{bmatrix} e^{-t} & e^{-t} - e^{-2t} \\ 0 & e^{-2t} \end{bmatrix}$$

Now let us find the associated discrete system. We have that

$$\mathbf{F} = e^{\mathbf{A}T} = \begin{bmatrix} e^{-T} & e^{-T} - e^{-2T} \\ 0 & e^{-2T} \end{bmatrix}$$

and

$$\begin{aligned} G &= \int_0^T e^{\mathbf{A}\tau}\mathbf{B}\,d\tau \\ &= \begin{bmatrix} \frac{1}{2} - e^{-T} + \frac{1}{2}e^{-2T} \\ \frac{1}{2}(1 - e^{-2T}) \end{bmatrix} \end{aligned}$$

so that the discrete-state equations are

$$\mathbf{x}(k-1) = \begin{bmatrix} e^{-T} & e^{-T} - e^{-2T} \\ 0 & e^{-2T} \end{bmatrix} \mathbf{x}(k) + \begin{bmatrix} e^{-T} - 1 \\ e^{-2T} - 1 \end{bmatrix} u(k)$$

and

$$y(k) = [1 \quad 1]\,\mathbf{x}(k)$$

∎

4.13 SUMMARY

All the concepts we have encountered previously in conjunction with first- and second-order systems apply (with more effort, perhaps) to higher-order systems. Quantitatively, we may usually only study linear, time-invariant, nth-order systems, where the solution for the state-transition matrix

$$\mathbf{\Phi}(t,\tau) = e^{\mathbf{A}(t-\tau)}$$

is of primary importance. However, in general studies, a number of qualitative properties emerge as useful extensions of those encountered in the linear, time-invariant case.

Specifically, we found it convenient to reduce nth-order differential equations to n first-order, *standard-form state equations.* The choice of state variables is not unique, and it is possible to "overstate" the description. Thus *state equivalence* and *system equivalence* arise. It is desirable in general to study the *reduced* set of state equations.

Solution of linear-state equations was carried out in terms of the *state-transition matrix,* which for time-invariant systems had a specific form. Matrix techniques were used to find the solution explicitly.

nth-order, discrete-time systems proved to be no more difficult to study than the simpler second-order, discrete-time systems.

4.14 PROBLEMS

(4.1) Write differential-state equations which describe the system of two identical pendulums coupled via a spring shown in Fig. 4.18. The rest length of the spring is x_0. Assume the values

$$l = k = \frac{mg}{10} = 1$$

and find the normal modes for small vibrations about the equilibrium

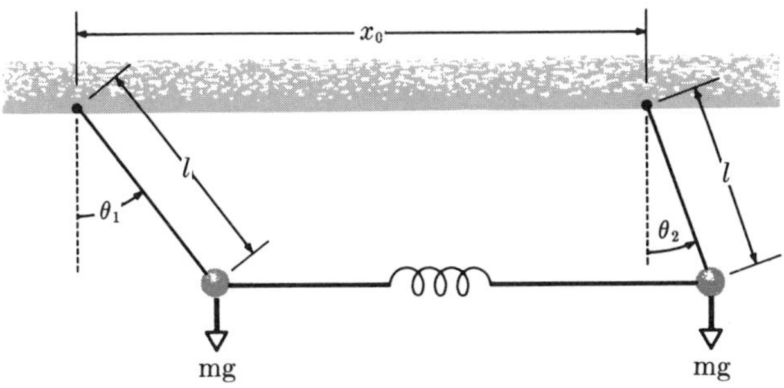

FIG. 4.18 Prob. 4.1.

point $\theta_1 = \theta_2 = 0$. What are the eigenvectors and what is their significance?

(4.2) Write the state equations for the mechanical system of Fig. 4.19; the cart is massless and rolls without friction on the plane, the stick has uniform density, and the pivot where the stick is attached to the cart is frictionless. Consider two situations, one in which the input u is force, and the other in which the input u is velocity. Show that $\theta = 0$ is an equilibrium position. Linearize the state equations about the equilibrium solution and consider the "small signal" input function

$$u(t) = A \sin \omega t$$

(for both the force and the velocity case). Is it possible to find *sufficient* conditions on A and ω so that the equilibrium position $\theta = 0$ is stable, asymptotically stable? Note $\theta = 0$ is an unstable equilibrium for $A = 0$.

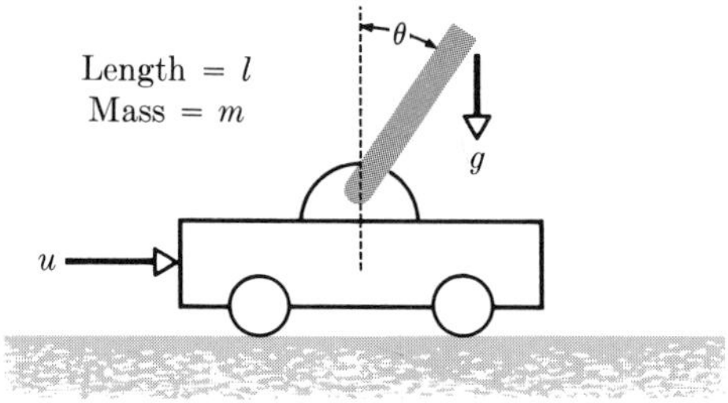

FIG. 4.19 Prob. 4.2.

(4.3) Write the differential-state equations and the input-state-output equations for the network of Fig. 4.20.

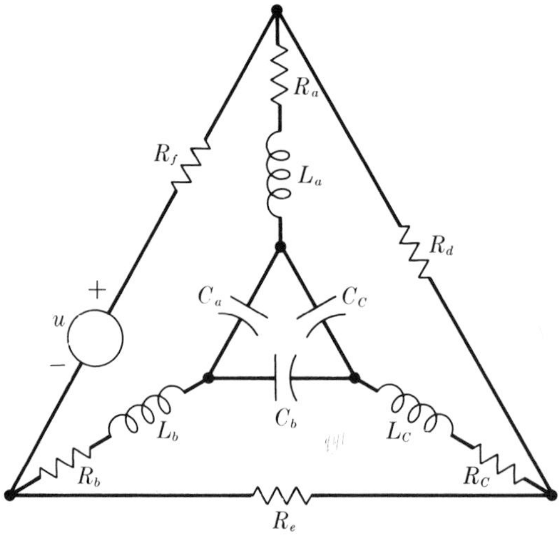

FIG. 4.20 Prob. 4.3.

(4.4) Consider the differential-state equations for a particle in a central force field,

$$u(r) = -\frac{k}{r^2}$$

$$\dot{\theta} = -\frac{1}{mr^2} p_\theta$$

$$\dot{p}_\theta = 0$$

$$\dot{r} = \frac{1}{m} p_r$$

and

$$\dot{p}_r = \frac{1}{mr} p_\theta^2 - \frac{k}{r^2}$$

Suppose that the zero-order solution is a circular orbit:

$$p_\theta = l$$

$$r = \frac{mk}{l^2} \qquad \text{a constant}$$

$$\theta = \theta(t_0) + \frac{l^3}{m^3 k} (t - t_0)$$

Find linearized equations describing perturbations about this orbit.

(4.5) Given the set of linear homogeneous differential equations

$$\dot{x}_1(t) = x_2(t)$$

and

$$\dot{x}_2(t) = -x_1(t)$$

what are the conditions on the amplitudes (a, b, c, and d) and the phases (μ, ν, γ, and λ) under which the matrix

$$\begin{bmatrix} a \sin (t + \mu) & b \sin (t + \nu) \\ c \sin (t + \gamma) & d \sin (t + \lambda) \end{bmatrix}$$

is fundamental?

(4.6) A real, linear homogeneous system characterized by

$$\dot{\mathbf{x}}(t) = \mathbf{A}(t)\mathbf{x}(t)$$

is said to be *self-adjoint* if the state-transition matrix has the following property:

$$\mathbf{\Phi}(t,\tau) = \mathbf{\Phi}'(\tau,t)$$

What is the equivalent self-adjoint property directly in terms of the matrix $\mathbf{A}(t)$?

(4.7) Consider the network shown in Fig. 4.21.

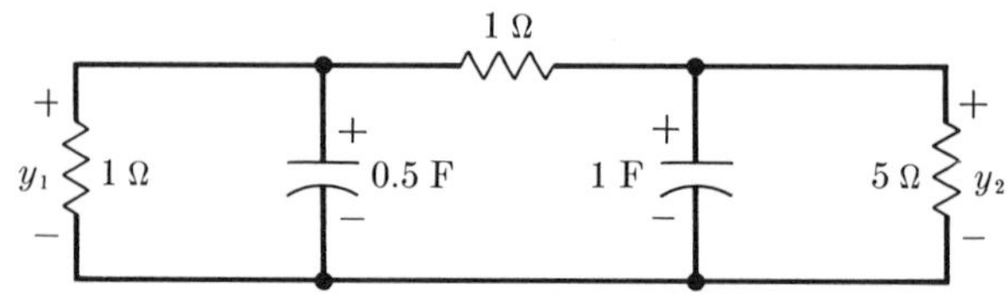

FIG. 4.21 Prob. 4.7.

(*a*) Write the standard-form state equations for this network where the outputs are $y_1(t)$, and $y_2(t)$.

(*b*) Solve these equations for the outputs in terms of the initial conditions.

(*c*) Can you pick the initial conditions in such a way so as to excite each mode independently of the others? What are these?

(*d*) What conclusions, if any, can you draw from your answer to part (*c*) in connection with something you know about the $\mathbf{A}$ matrix, i.e., give a physical interpretation to your answer in (*c*)?

(4.8) Show that if a system is zero-state additive, then if y is the zero-state response to an input u_1, the output due to cu_1 is cy_1, where c is any finite integer (including negative numbers).

(4.9) Repeat Prob. 4.8 for c equal to a finite rational number (finite ratio of two integers). Note that since any irrational number may be approximated arbitrarily closely by a rational number, zero-state additivity *almost* implies zero-state linearity.

(4.10) What is the most general form the standard-form state equation

$$\dot{\mathbf{x}}(t) = \mathbf{f}(\mathbf{x}(t), \mathbf{u}(t), t)$$

can have and still be linear?

(4.11) Consider a linear, time-invariant system of which the differential-state equation is in companion form:

$$\dot{\mathbf{x}} = \begin{bmatrix} 0 & 1 & 0 & \cdots & 0 \\ 0 & 0 & 1 & \cdots & 0 \\ \cdots & \cdots & \cdots & \cdots & \cdots \\ 0 & 0 & 0 & \cdots & 1 \\ \dfrac{-a_0}{a_n} & \dfrac{-a_1}{a_n} & \cdot & \cdots & \dfrac{-a_{n-1}}{a_n} \end{bmatrix} \mathbf{x} + \begin{bmatrix} 0 \\ 0 \\ \cdot \\ \cdot \\ \cdot \\ \dfrac{1}{a_n} \end{bmatrix} u$$

which is equivalent to

$$a_n y^{(n)} + a_{n-1} y^{(n-1)} + \cdots + a_1 \dot{y} + a_0 y = u.$$

(*a*) Show that if λ_k is an eigenvalue of $\mathbf{A}$, then the corresponding eigenvector is

$$\boldsymbol{\xi}_k = \begin{bmatrix} 1 \\ \lambda_{k_2} \\ \lambda_k \\ \cdot \\ \cdot \\ \cdot \\ \lambda_k^{n-1} \end{bmatrix}$$

Hence, if the eigenvalues are distinct the Vandermonde matrix is a modal matrix, and one may easily obtain the corresponding Jordan canonical form.

(*b*) Suppose the eigenvalues are not distinct and attempt to find explicit forms for the generalized eigenvectors which may correspond to λ_k.

(4.12) Find the values of $\mathbf{u}(0)$ and $\mathbf{u}(1)$ which take the system

$$\begin{bmatrix} x_1(k+1) \\ x_2(k+1) \end{bmatrix} = \begin{bmatrix} 0 & 1 \\ -2 & -3 \end{bmatrix} \begin{bmatrix} x_1(k) \\ x_2(k) \end{bmatrix} + \begin{bmatrix} 0 \\ 1 \end{bmatrix} u(k)$$

$$\mathbf{x}(0) = \begin{bmatrix} 1 \\ 0 \end{bmatrix}$$

to the origin at $k = 2$.

(4.13) Consider the homogeneous equation

$$\dot{\mathbf{x}}(t) = \mathbf{A}\mathbf{x}(t)$$

Using the fact that for a small enough time interval, T

$$\dot{\mathbf{x}}(t) \simeq \frac{\mathbf{x}(t+T) - \mathbf{x}(t)}{T}$$

find a numerical method to determine $\mathbf{x}(t)$. Compare your results with those derived in the text by discretizing the solution

$$\mathbf{x}(t) = e^{\mathbf{A}(t-t_0)}\mathbf{x}(t_0)$$

5 MACROSCOPIC SYSTEM THEORY AND TRANSFORM ANALYSIS

To this juncture, we have stressed the state-space approach to system studies. The objective has been to choose as state variables a set of system parameters which can relate all possible system signals to the inputs. The state-variable characterization of a system is aptly termed *microscopic,* because of its necessary attention to internal-system structure.

An alternative to the state-space approach is to consider the system under study to be a black box and to characterize it solely in terms of its output response to various excitations. In this chapter, we are to explore this input-output or *macroscopic* approach to system analysis. Many of the related concepts which arise here are also applicable to state-variable studies, as we will observe in the course of the study.

5.1 DELTA FUNCTION AND DISTRIBUTION THEORY

In Chap. 2 we discussed the solution of second-order differential equations. We found that second-order, differential-equation solution is significantly more complicated than the first-order case. The general solution of an nth-order differential equation would be quite tedious if the methods described in Chaps. 1 and 2 were to be employed. In this chapter, we consider more convenient methods for dealing with higher-order systems. It turns out that a linear system is most conveniently specified on an input-output basis in the time domain in terms of its impulse response. The impulse-input "function" is a convenient idealization which possesses many useful mathematical properties. To lend credence to the use of impulse and related "functions" in linear-system theory, we must digress briefly to discuss the entire class of generalized "functions."

The Dirac *delta function* $\delta(t)$, also known as the *impulse function*, is often described as follows:

$$\delta(t) = 0 \qquad \text{for } t \neq 0$$

and

$$\int_{-\infty}^{\infty} \delta(t)\, dt = 1$$

Note that $\delta(t)$ is *not* defined for the point $t = 0$. Obviously no such function exists in the sense of ordinary functions, for a function which is nonzero only on a set of measure zero (in this case the single point $t = 0$) cannot have a nonzero (Lebesgue) integral. We are loath not to discuss the delta "function," however, since it is a convenient fiction which approximately, but adequately, describes many physical phenomena.

As an example of the usefulness of the delta function, consider the ordinary differential equation

$$\frac{d}{dt}[mv(t)] = f(t)$$

which describes Newton's second law of motion. We may attribute an instantaneous change of momentum

$$mv(t_0^+) - mv(t_0^-) = \Delta p$$

to a "delta-function" force $\Delta p \delta(t - t_0)$ occurring at time t_0. Of course, there cannot be an instantaneous change of momentum for a nonzero mass, since the required power (force times velocity) would be infinite; however, there are many instances in which it is not worthwhile to transcend this assumption. For example, if we consider a particle in a box as shown in Fig. 5.1 (under the assumption of perfectly elastic collisions) the force supplied on the particle by a wall of the box is impulsive when the particle hits it.

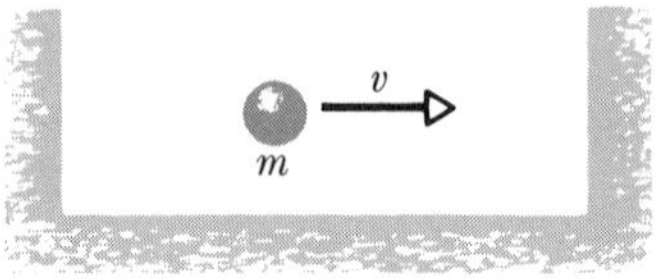

FIG. 5.1 A particle in a box. When the particle hits the rigid walls, an impulsive force that instantaneously alters the momentum of the particle is exerted by the walls.

Another convenient use for the impulse "function" is in the replacement of the initial conditions of a differential equation. For example, the causal solutions of

$$\dot{x}(t) = ax(t) + bu(t) \qquad \text{with } x(t_0) = x_0$$

and

$$\dot{x}(t) = ax(t) + bu(t) + x_0\delta(t - t_0) \qquad \text{with } x(t_0-) = 0$$

are identical for $t \geq t_0$. We may verify this equivalence by noting that upon integration the second equation yields

$$x(t_0^+) - x(t_0^-) = \int_{t_0^-}^{t_0^+} [ax(t) + bu(t)]\, dt + x_0 \int_{t_0^-}^{t_0^+} \delta(t - t_0)\, dt$$

Since the first integral on the right-hand side is of ordinary functions over an infinitesimal interval, it vanishes while the second integral on the right-hand side becomes x_0; hence,

$$x(t_0^+) = x_0$$

as is required. *The desired effect of the delta "function" emerges upon integration.* Thus we are not really interested in the delta "function" per se, but rather in how it performs upon integration. The concept of functionals will aid in our discussion.

(5.1) Function

A *single-valued function* f is a collection of ordered pairs (x,y) such that no two pairs have identical first members. The first member of a pair is called the *argument* of the function and the second member the *value* at that argument. ∎

We often write

$$y = f(x)$$

The collection of arguments of a function $\{x \in X\}$ is called the *domain* of that function, and the set of values $\{y \in Y\}$, when the argument runs over its entire domain, is called the *range* of the function. Ordinarily, the domain and range of a function are taken to be subsets of the real line. Thus we can think of a function as being a mapping which associates a unique number in the range of the function with every number in the domain of the function. A simple example of such a mapping is

$$y = \sin x$$

where $X = \{x: -\infty < x < \infty\}$ and $Y = \{y: -1 \leq y \leq 1\}$.

(5.2) Functional
A (single-valued) *functional* is a mapping which associates a unique *number in the range* of the functional with every *function* in the domain of the functional

$$z = F[f(x)] \qquad f(x) \in \mathfrak{F} \qquad z \in Z \qquad \blacksquare$$

A simple example of such a mapping is

$$z = c_k = \frac{1}{2\pi} \int_{-\pi}^{\pi} f(x)\, e^{jkx}\, dx$$

where the function $f(x)$ is such that

$$\int_{-n}^{\pi} |f(x)|^2\, dx < \infty$$

The range of this function is $-\infty < c_k < \infty$. Another example of a functional is

$$z = f(x_0)$$

where the domain is $L_\infty(-\infty, \infty)$ and the range is $-\infty < z < \infty$. The relation between functions, which map numbers into numbers, and functionals, which map functions into numbers, is demonstrated in Fig. 5.2. The latter example leads us to recognize that we may study the delta "function" as a functional operator if we consider the defining relation

$$(5.3) \qquad \int_{-\infty}^{\infty} f(x)\delta(x - x_0)\, dx \equiv f(x_0)$$

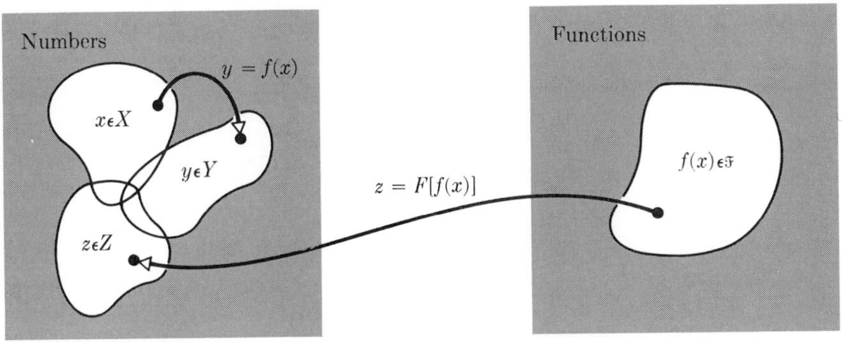

FIG. 5.2 A function maps numbers into numbers; a functional maps functions into numbers.

an integral which may only be interpreted *symbolically;* i.e., we do not formally integrate $f(x)\delta(x - x_0)$, but merely follow the "rule" defined by (5.3) for "integration." Hence, we are ultimately led to describe more accurately the so-called delta function as the delta functional. First, however, we must ensure that functional relationships, such as those describing the delta functional, make physical and mathematical sense.

Let us give physical interpretation to the description of a function by means of a functional relationship such as (5.3). Suppose that we have a "slow" meter (a dc meter, for example) with which we wish to measure the signal $f(t)$. By the time we turn the meter on and off (or consider the dynamics), we may obtain only the averaging effect indicated in Fig. 5.3. That is, a more accurate representation of what the meter shows may be

$$\hat{f}(t) \equiv \frac{1}{\Delta} \int_{t-\Delta/2}^{t+\Delta/2} f(\xi)\, d\xi$$

where $\Delta > 0$ is some small, but finite, number. If we know $\hat{f}(t)$, we may almost recover $f(t)$ mathematically since

$$\frac{d}{dt}[\hat{f}(t)] \simeq \frac{1}{\Delta}[f(t) - f(t - \Delta)]$$

a sequence of such measurements, i.e.

$$\frac{d}{dt}[\hat{f}(t - \Delta)] \simeq \frac{1}{\Delta}[f(t - \Delta) - f(t - 2\Delta)]$$

$$\frac{d}{dt}[\hat{f}(t - 2\Delta)] \simeq \frac{1}{\Delta}[f(t - 2\Delta) - f(t - 3\Delta)]$$

$$\cdots\cdots\cdots\cdots\cdots\cdots\cdots\cdots$$

yields

$$f(t) \simeq \lim_{n\to\infty} \left\{[\hat{f}(t - (n + 1)\Delta)] + \sum_{k=0}^{n} \frac{d}{dt}[\hat{f}(t - k\Delta)]\right\}$$

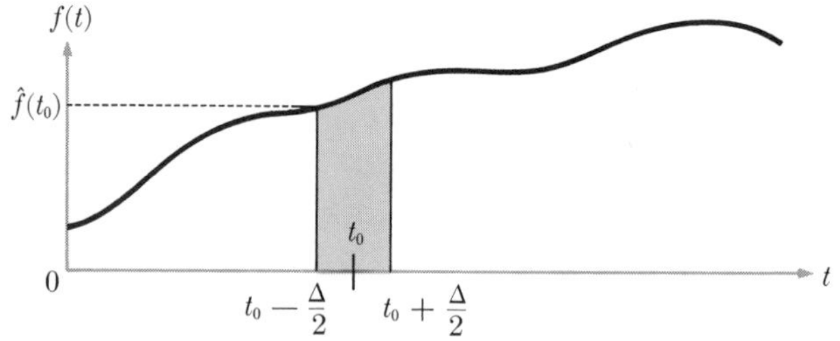

FIG. 5.3 A gating meter might indicate the average of $f(t)$ as $\hat{f}(t_0)$ at each point t_0.

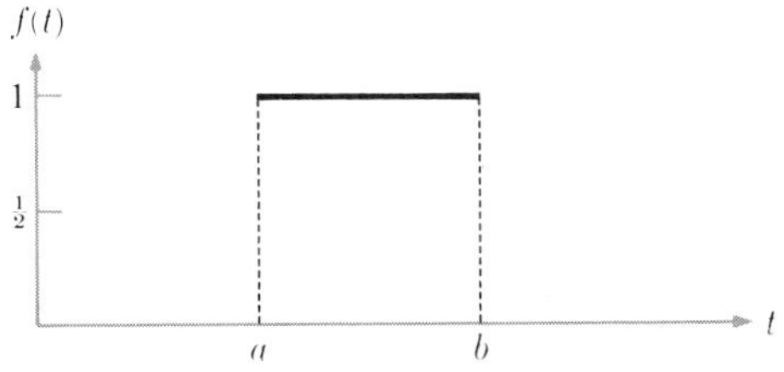

FIG. 5.4 A rectangular-gating function.

Thus $f(t)$ is "defined" in terms of samples, or "tested" segments of itself. For most signals, the first term within the brackets may be assumed to converge to zero or a known initial quantity, while the second results from presumably known measurements. It turns out that the "gating" function indicated in this example and illustrated in Fig. 5.4 has severe disadvantages. Alternatively, we can use the gating function illustrated in Fig. 5.5 which is assumed to be nonzero only over a finite time interval and to be, moreover, infinitely differentiable everywhere. Thus, we consider meters which turn on and off smoothly and stay on only for finite intervals. This class of gating or "testing" functions is sufficiently mathematically rich that we may clearly distinguish any practical or theoretical signal encountered in system analysis. Let us define the *set of all testing functions* $\mathfrak{D}$ to be that which contains all functions $\phi(t)$ such that:

$$\begin{aligned} &\phi(t) = 0 \qquad t \leq a \\ &\phi(t) = 0 \qquad t \geq b \\ &0 \leq b - a \end{aligned}$$

and

$$\frac{d^k}{dt^k}[\phi(t)] \qquad \text{exists everywhere for } k = 1, 2, \ldots$$

We see that the set of testing functions $\mathfrak{D}$ contains all infinitely differentiable functions which are nonzero only over finite intervals of their argu-

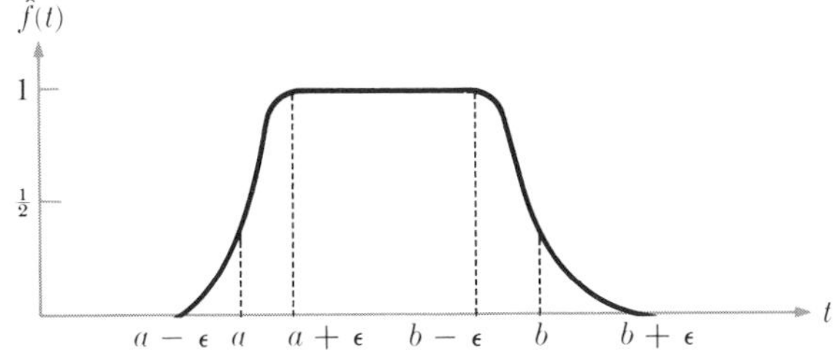

FIG. 5.5 A smooth replacement for the gating function of Fig. 5.4.

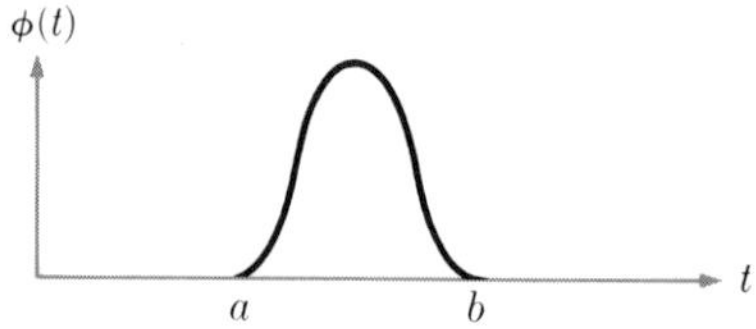

FIG. 5.6 A testing function.

ments. For example the functions shown in Figs. 5.6 and 5.7 are testing functions. We leave it as an exercise for the reader to show that

$$\phi(t) = \begin{cases} 0 & t < a \\ \exp\left\{-\dfrac{1}{(t-a)(t-b)}\right\} & a \leq t \leq b \\ 0 & t > b \end{cases}$$

is a testing function, for example.

We choose to characterize functions solely by their *distribution* on the space of testing functions. That is, given any function f, or $f(t)$, $-\infty < t < \infty$, the set of all numbers

$$\{f_\phi\} = \left\{\int_{-\infty}^{\infty} f(t)\phi(t)\,dt\text{: for all } \phi \in \mathfrak{D}\right\} \tag{5.4}$$

completely characterizes it in the sense of distributions. In other words, we can find no meter of the type we are employing which further distinguishes f. With the aid of distributional relations, we may characterize a given function f with an uncountable set of numbers. Although the set of complex functions $e^{jn\omega_0 t}$ ($n = 0, \pm 1, \pm 2, \ldots$) does not qualify as testing functions (nonzero in infinite interval), we recognize an affinity between the distributional representation of a function and the Fourier series representation of a suitably restricted periodic function by the sequence of Fourier coefficients

$$c_k \equiv \frac{1}{T}\int_{-T/2}^{T/2} f(t)e^{-jk\omega_0 t}\,dt \qquad (k = 0, \pm 1, \pm 2, \ldots)$$

where $f(t)$ is of period T with $T = 2\pi/\omega_0$. Hence, the Fourier series coefficients are a countable set of complex numbers which represent a suitably restricted periodic function. Similarly, when we consider the

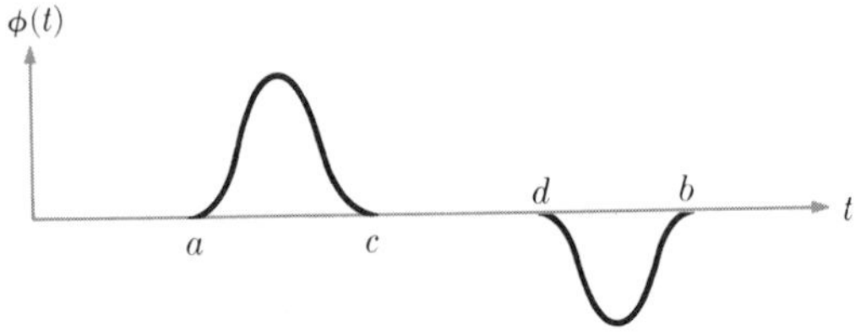

FIG. 5.7 A testing function.

Fourier transform in a subsequent section

$$\hat{f}(\omega) \equiv \int_{-\infty}^{\infty} f(t)e^{-j\omega t}\, dt$$

where $f(t)$ must be such that

$$\int_{-\infty}^{\infty} |f(t)|^2\, dt < \infty$$

we will find that the role of testing functions is being assumed by the uncountable set $\{e^{-j\omega t}: -\infty < \omega < \infty\}$, even though these again are nonzero over an infinite interval. The use of testing functions which are nonzero over infinite intervals may be justified generally in terms of distributions, but a great deal of mathematical sophistication is entailed to do so rigorously.

In order for this characterization to be useful, we must be able to discuss properties of functions in terms of their distributions. One important property is equality.

(5.5) Equality

The two functions f and g are said to be *equal in the sense of distributions* if

$$\int_{-\infty}^{\infty} f(t)\phi(t)\, dt = \int_{-\infty}^{\infty} g(t)\phi(t)\, dt$$

for all $\phi \in \mathfrak{D}$. ∎

Equivalently, we can say that f and g are equal (in the sense of distributions) if

$$\int_{-\infty}^{\infty} [f(t) - g(t)]\phi(t)\, dt = 0$$

for all $\phi \in \mathfrak{D}$.

Suppose f and g are continuous functions and that $f = g$ in the sense of distributions. Let us investigate the possibility of finding a t_0 such that

$$f(t_0) \neq g(t_0)$$

There are two possibilities,

$$f(t_0) - g(t_0) < 0$$

or

$$f(t_0) - g(t_0) > 0$$

Consider the first possibility; if we use the testing function

$$\phi(t) = \begin{cases} 0 & t - t_0 > \varepsilon \\ \exp \dfrac{\varepsilon^2}{-\varepsilon^2 - (t - t_0)^2} & |t - t_0| \leq \varepsilon \end{cases}$$

then

$$\int_{-\infty}^{\infty} [f(t) - g(t)]\phi(t)\, dt = \int_{t_0-}^{t_0+} [f(t) - g(t)]\phi(t)\, dt < 0$$

which contradicts the hypothesis that f and g are equal in the sense of distributions. A similar contradiction may be obtained when $f(t_0) - g(t_0) > 0$. Hence, two continuous functions are equal everywhere when their distributions are the same. Moreover, it has required only a small subset of all possible testing functions to obtain this result; since the space of all testing functions $\mathfrak{D}$ is much greater, we expect equality in the distributional sense to be of much greater consequence than mere equality of continuous functions.

(5.6) Regulated Functions
A function is said to be a *regulated function* if it is continuous everywhere except at a countable set of discontinuities where it possesses unique right- and left-hand limits. ∎

By the above, we can show that two regulated functions that are equal in the distributional sense are equal everywhere where both are continuous. However, there is no way to ensure their equality at points of discontinuity; since if h is a function which is nonzero only on a countable set of points, the theory of (Lebesgue) integration yields

$$\int_{-\infty}^{\infty} h(t)\phi(t)\, dt = 0 \qquad \text{for all } \phi \in \mathfrak{D}$$

Thus we say that two regulated functions which are equal in the sense of distributions are equal *almost everywhere* (i.e., equal except in a subset of the real line of measure zero—a countable set of points). From the physical standpoint, it does not matter what value a function takes at these isolated points. For consistency, and because it fits in with later developments, we will (usually) set the value of a regulated function to the mean value of the two adjacent segments at a point of discontinuity, i.e.,

$$f(t) = \tfrac{1}{2}[f(t+) + f(t-)]$$

as is illustrated in Fig. 5.8; moreover, this expression is valid at points of continuity as well.

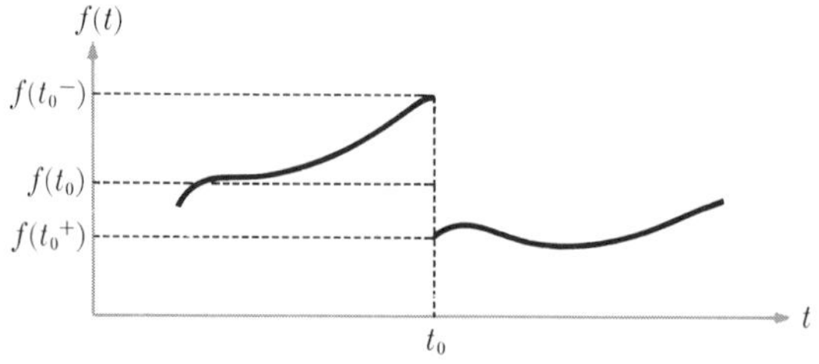

FIG. 5.8 To avoid ambiguity, the value of a regulated function at a point of discontinuity is taken to be the mean of the values on either side of it, that is, $f(t_0) = \frac{1}{2}[f(t_0-) + f(t_0+)]$.

Because we wish to consider derivatives of discontinuous functions, and these derivatives do not exist in the ordinary sense, we must expand our attention to beyond the realm of regulated functions to the so-called generalized functions (functional operators, in reality). We may define a symbolic function according to its projection on the space of testing functions. For example, we define the unit-impulse functional as a generalized function with the property

$$\int_{-\infty}^{\infty} \delta(t)\phi(t)\,dt \equiv \phi(0) \qquad \text{for all } \phi \in \mathfrak{D}$$

Hence, given any functional operator f such that

$$\int_{-\infty}^{\infty} f(t)\phi(t)\,dt = \phi(0)$$

we say that

$$f = \delta \qquad \text{or} \qquad f(t) = \delta(t)$$

in the sense of distributions. Of course, these integrals cannot be strictly interpreted since δ is not a function in the ordinary sense. Hence, we interpret the integrals strictly when they exist, or we revert to definitional properties when generalized functions are involved. We note in passing that the class of generalized functions includes that of ordinary (regulated) functions as well.

To study further the attributes of the delta functional, we consider the meaning of the convergence of a sequence of (symbolic) functions in the sense of distributions.

(5.7) Convergence

A sequence of (generalized) functions f_n is said to *converge* to the (generalized) function f *in the sense of distributions* if

$$\lim_{n\to\infty} \int_{-\infty}^{\infty} f_n(t)\phi(t)\,dt = \int_{-\infty}^{\infty} f(t)\phi(t)\,dt \qquad \text{for all } \phi \in \mathfrak{D}$$ ∎

(5.8) Example

It is often said that the delta function is the idealization of a narrow pulse of infinite height. To be precise, the delta function is taken to be the limit of the following functions

$$f_n(t) = \begin{cases} \dfrac{n}{2} & \text{for } |t| < n^{-1} \\ 0 & \text{for } |t| \geq n^{-1} \end{cases}$$

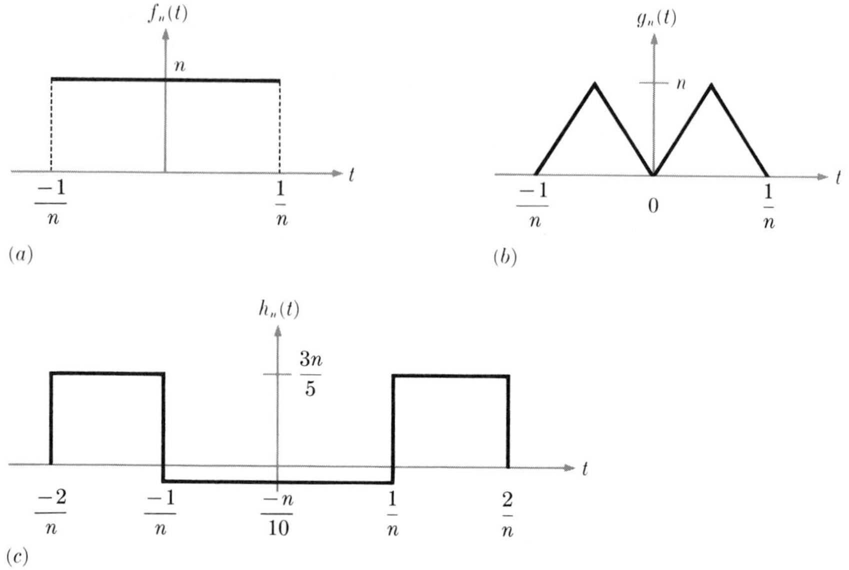

FIG. 5.9 Representatives from each of three sequences of functions that converge to delta functionals in the limit as $n \to \infty$.

which are shown in Fig. 5.9*a*. Let us check to determine if the sequence of pulses $f_n(t)$ indeed converges to a delta function. Observe that for all $\phi \in \mathfrak{D}$

$$F_n(\phi) = \int_{-\infty}^{\infty} f_n(t)\phi(t)\,dt = \frac{n}{2}\int_{-1/n}^{1/n} \phi(t)\,dt$$

$$= \phi(0) + \frac{n}{2}\int_{-1/n}^{1/n} [\phi(t) - \phi(0)]\,dt$$

or

$$F_n(\phi) - \phi(0) = \frac{n}{2}\int_{-1/n}^{1/n} [\phi(t) - \phi(0)]\,dt$$

Now consider

$$(5.9)\qquad |F_n(\phi) - \phi(0)| = \frac{n}{2}\int_{-1/n}^{1/n} [\phi(t) - \phi(0)]\,dt$$

$$\leq \frac{n}{2}\int_{-1/n}^{1/n} |\phi(t) - \phi(0)|\,dt$$

Expanding $\phi(t)$ in a Taylor series about zero yields

$$\phi(t) = \phi(0) + \phi'(t)\big|_{t=0}\, t + 0(t^2)$$

Therefore

(5.10) $\phi(t) - \phi(0) \simeq \phi'(0)t$

Combining (5.10) with (5.9) yields

$$|F_n(\phi) - \phi(0)| \le \frac{n}{2}\int_{-1/n}^{1/n} |\phi'(0)|(t)\, dt$$

or

$$|F_n(\phi) - \phi(0)| \le |\phi'(0)|\,\frac{1}{2n}$$

so that by letting $n \to \infty$ $F_n(\phi) \to \phi(0)$, that is,

$$\phi(0) = \lim_{n\to\infty} \int_{-\infty}^{\infty} f_n(t)\phi(t)\, dt$$

which is just the definition of the delta function. (Note: The higher-order terms, $\frac{1}{2}\phi''(0)t^2$, etc., provide integrals which go to zero even faster as $n \to \infty$ than the one we have retained.) ▮

Similarly we can show that the sequence of functions defined by

$$g_n(t) = \begin{Bmatrix} 2n^2t & \text{for } 0 \le t < \dfrac{1}{2n} \\ 2n^2(n^{-1} - t) & \text{for } \dfrac{1}{2n} < t < \dfrac{1}{n} \\ 0 & \text{for } t > \dfrac{1}{n} \end{Bmatrix} \qquad \text{and } g_n(-t) = g_n(t)$$

shown in Fig. 5.9*b*, and the sequence of functions defined by

$$h_n(t) = \begin{Bmatrix} -\dfrac{n}{10} & \text{for } t < \dfrac{1}{n} \\ \dfrac{3n}{5} & \text{for } \dfrac{1}{n} < t < \dfrac{2}{n} \\ 0 & \text{for } t \ge \dfrac{2}{n} \end{Bmatrix}$$

shown in Fig. 5.9*c*, also converge to the delta functional. It is interesting to note that

$$\lim_{n\to\infty} [f_n(0)] = \infty$$
$$\lim_{n\to\infty} [g_n(0)] = 0$$

and

$$\lim_{n\to\infty} [h_n(0)] = -\infty$$

so it is indeed folly to speak of the value assumed by $\delta(t)$ at $t = 0$.

An interesting, and useful, property of the delta function is the so-called *sifting property:*

$$\int_{-\infty}^{\infty} f(t)\,\delta(t-\tau)\,d\tau = f(\tau)$$

To see that this equality is valid, we must investigate the distributions of both the left- and right-hand sides on the space of testing functions $\mathfrak{D}$. Let ϕ be any testing function in the domain of f. Then

$$\int_{-\infty}^{\infty} \left[\int_{-\infty}^{\infty} f(t)\,\delta(t-\tau)\,dt\right] \phi(\tau)\,d\tau = \int_{-\infty}^{\infty} f(t) \int_{-\infty}^{\infty} \delta(t-\tau)\phi(\tau)\,d\tau\,dt$$

But

$$\int_{-\infty}^{\infty} \delta(t-\tau)\phi(\tau)\,d\tau = \int_{-\infty}^{\infty} \delta(\tau)\phi(t-\tau)\,d\tau = \phi(t)$$

after a change of variables. Hence

$$\begin{aligned}\int_{-\infty}^{\infty} \left[\int_{-\infty}^{\infty} f(t)\,\delta(t-\tau)\,dt\right] \phi(\tau)\,d\tau &= \int_{-\infty}^{\infty} f(t)\phi(t)\,dt \\ &= \int_{-\infty}^{\infty} f(\tau)\phi(\tau)\,d\tau\end{aligned}$$

since t and τ are just dummy variables. Thus we have shown that

$$\int_{-\infty}^{\infty} f(t)\,\delta(t-\tau)\,dt = f(\tau)$$

in the sense of distributions.

The question of whether the delta function is even (that is, $\delta(t-t_0) = \delta(t_0-t)$) or odd (that is, $\delta(t-t_0) = -\delta(t_0-t)$) often arises. We can determine the answer to this question as follows. Let $\phi(t) \in \mathfrak{D}$, then

$$\int_{-\infty}^{\infty} \phi(t)\,\delta(t-t_0)\,dt = \phi(t_0)$$

and

$$\int_{-\infty}^{\infty} \phi(t)\,\delta(t_0-t)\,dt = \int_{-\infty}^{\infty} \phi(t_0-s)\,\delta(s)\,ds = \phi(t_0)$$

Therefore

$$\int_{-\infty}^{\infty} \phi(t)\,\delta(t-t_0)\,dt = \int_{-\infty}^{\infty} \phi(t)\,\delta(t_0-t)\,dt$$

in the sense of distributions, and the delta function is even.

There is much confusion concerning the interpretations of the time-scaled function $\delta(\alpha t)$, where α is a nonzero real constant. Consider the distribution of $\delta(\alpha t)$ on $\mathfrak{D}$

$$\int_{-\infty}^{\infty} \delta(\alpha t)\phi(t)\,dt = \begin{cases} \displaystyle\int_{-\infty}^{\infty} \delta(x)\phi\left(\frac{x}{\alpha}\right)\frac{dx}{\alpha} & \text{if } \alpha > 0 \\ \displaystyle\int_{-\infty}^{\infty} \delta(x)\phi\left(\frac{x}{\alpha}\right)\frac{dx}{\alpha} & \text{if } \alpha > 0 \end{cases}$$

in either case

$$\int_{-\infty}^{\infty} \delta(\alpha t)\phi(t)\,dt = \int_{-\infty}^{\infty} \delta(x)\frac{1}{|\alpha|}\phi\left(\frac{x}{\alpha}\right)dx = \frac{1}{|\alpha|}\phi(0)$$

Hence,

$$\delta(\alpha t) = \frac{1}{|\alpha|}\delta(t) \qquad \alpha \neq 0$$

If f is a differentiable function, we may consider the distribution of its derivative on the space of testing functions as being given by

$$\int_{-\infty}^{\infty} \frac{d}{dt}[f(t)]\delta(t)\,dt = [f(t)\phi(t)]_{-\infty}^{\infty} - \int_{-\infty}^{\infty} f(t)\frac{d}{dt}[\phi(t)]\,dt$$

where the first term on the right-hand side vanishes, since

$$\phi(-\infty) = \phi(\infty) = 0$$

for all $\phi \in \mathfrak{D}$. Now since $d\phi/dt \in \mathfrak{D}$ for all $\phi \in \mathfrak{D}$, we recognize that we need never differentiate f to characterize its derivative by means of a distributional relation. An identical maneuver may be employed in the case of the derivative of a generalized function, which is not necessarily differentiable in the ordinary sense. That is, we characterize the first derivative of a generalized function f by the uncountable set of numbers

$$\{f_{\phi'}\} = \left\{-\int_{-\infty}^{\infty} f(t)\phi'(t)\,dt,\ \phi \in \mathfrak{D}\right\}$$

since

$$\int_{-\infty}^{\infty} \frac{d}{dt}[f(t)]\phi(t)\,dt = -\int_{-\infty}^{\infty} f(t)\frac{d}{dt}[\phi(t)]\,dt$$

Similarly, we characterize the kth derivative of a symbolic function f by the uncountable set of numbers

$$\{f_{\phi^{(k)}}\} = \left\{(-1)^k\int_{-\infty}^{\infty} f(t)\phi^{(k)}(t)\,dt,\ \phi \in \mathfrak{D}\right\}$$

since

$$\int_{-\infty}^{\infty} \frac{d^k}{dt^k}[f(t)]\phi(t)\,dt = (-1)^k\int_{-\infty}^{\infty} f(t)\frac{d^k}{dt^k}[\phi(t)]\,dt$$

Since the testing functions are infinitely differentiable, we may take derivatives of generalized functions of all orders in the sense of distributions. For example,

$$\delta(t) = \frac{d}{dt}[1(t)]$$

where $1(t)$ is the unit-step function defined by

$$1(t) = \begin{cases} 0 & \text{for } t < 0 \\ 1 & \text{for } t > 0 \end{cases}$$

To obtain this result, we consider

$$\int_{-\infty}^{\infty} \frac{d}{dt}[1(t)]\phi(t)\,dt = -\int_{-\infty}^{\infty} 1(t)\frac{d}{dt}[\phi(t)]\,dt$$
$$= -\int_{0}^{\infty} \frac{d}{dt}[\phi(t)]\,dt$$
$$= \phi(0)$$

The unit-doublet function is the symbolic function $\delta^{(1)}(t)$ described by the relation

$$\int_{-\infty}^{\infty} \delta^{(1)}(t)\phi(t)\,dt = -\phi'(0) \qquad \text{for all } \phi \in \mathfrak{D}$$

it is the first derivative in the sense of distributions of the delta functional. Similarly, the generalized function $\delta^{(k)}(t)$, described by the relation

$$\int_{-\infty}^{\infty} \delta^{(k)}(t)\phi(t)\,dt = (-1)^k\phi^{(k)}(0) \qquad \phi \in \mathfrak{D}$$

is the kth derivative in the sense of distributions of the delta functional.

5.2 REPRESENTATION OF SIGNALS IN TERMS OF IMPULSES—THE CONVOLUTION INTEGRAL

The central problem in system analysis is the determination of the response of a system to any given excitation. The philosophy behind the approach we are about to introduce is that if we know the response of a linear system to a relatively simple input, then we can find the response to any other input if the second input can be represented appropriately in terms of the first. For example, we may consider the unit pulse shown in Fig. 5.10*a*. We can describe the pulse by

$$p_k(t) = \begin{cases} 1 & \text{for } \left(k - \frac{1}{2}\right)\Delta T \le t \le \left(k + \frac{1}{2}\right)\Delta T \\ 0 & \text{elsewhere} \end{cases}$$

or by

$$p_k(t) = 1\left(t - \left(k - \frac{1}{2}\right)\Delta T\right) - 1\left(t - \left(k + \frac{1}{2}\right)\Delta T\right)$$

Assume that the response of the system at time t due to the pulse applied at time $\tau = (k - \frac{1}{2})\,\Delta T$ is $\eta(t,\tau)$. Since $\eta(t, (k - \frac{1}{2})\,\Delta T)$ is the response due to $p_k(t)$, we may think of the system, which will be denoted by $\mathcal{S}$, as operating on $p_k(t)$ to produce $\eta(t, (k - \frac{1}{2})\,\Delta T)$; symbolically we can write

$$\eta\left(t, \left(k - \frac{1}{2}\right)\Delta T\right) = \mathcal{S}[p_k(t)]$$

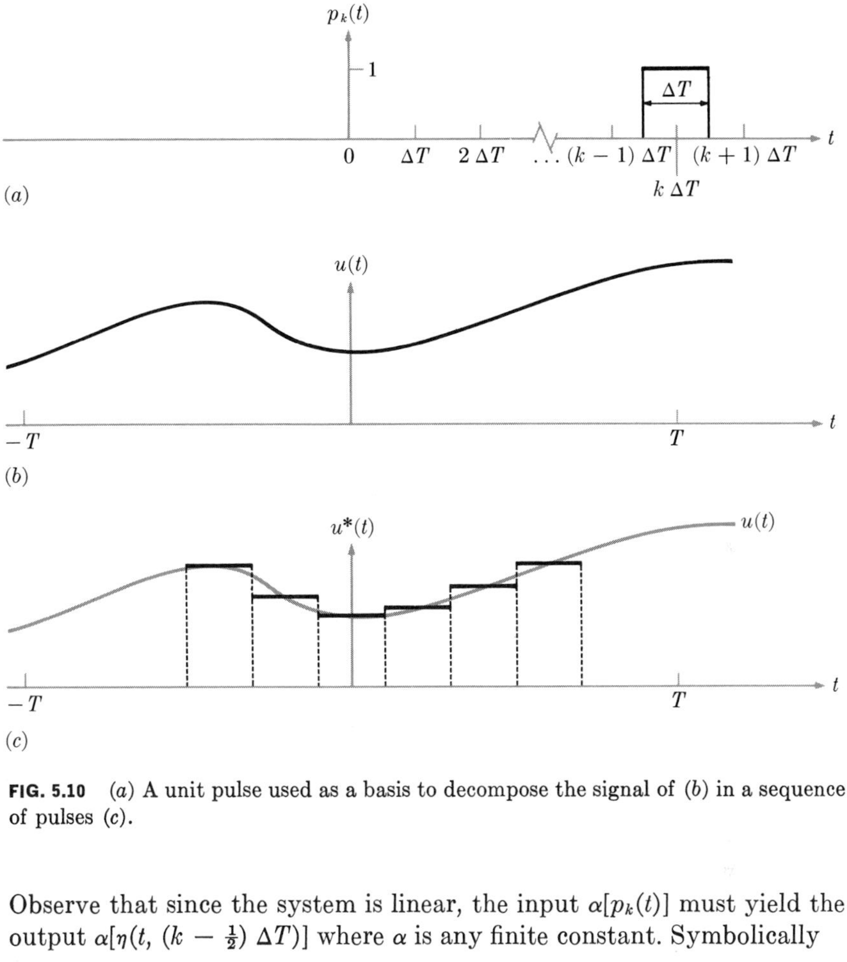

FIG. 5.10 (a) A unit pulse used as a basis to decompose the signal of (b) in a sequence of pulses (c).

Observe that since the system is linear, the input $\alpha[p_k(t)]$ must yield the output $\alpha[\eta(t, (k - \frac{1}{2})\,\Delta T)]$ where α is any finite constant. Symbolically

$$\mathcal{S}[\alpha p_k(t)] = \alpha\eta\left(t, \left(k - \frac{1}{2}\right)\Delta T\right) = \alpha\mathcal{S}[p_k(t)]$$

Moreover, also by linearity

$$\begin{aligned}\mathcal{S}[p_k(t) + p_j(t)] &= \eta\left(t, \left(k - \frac{1}{2}\right)\Delta T\right) + \eta\left(t, \left(j - \frac{1}{2}\right)\Delta T\right) \\ &= \mathcal{S}[p_k(t)] + \mathcal{S}[p_j(t)]\end{aligned}$$

Now consider the input shown in Fig. 5.10b. We can approximate this arbitrary signal by a sequence of pulses $u^*(t)$ as shown in Fig. 5.10c. The height of the pulse is the value of $u(t)$ at the center of each of the time intervals. The smaller the time interval ΔT, the better the set $\{u^*(t)\}$

approximates $u(t)$. We can express $u^*(t)$ in terms of our unit pulse:

$$u^*(t) = \sum_{k=-N}^{N} u(k\,\Delta T)\left[1\left(t - \left(k - \frac{1}{2}\right)\Delta T\right) - 1\left(t - \left(k + \frac{1}{2}\right)\Delta T\right)\right]$$

By linearity, the response to $u^*(t)$ is easily obtained in terms of the response to a single pulse:

$$(5.11)\quad \mathcal{S}[u^*(t)] = \mathcal{S}\left[\sum_{k=-N}^{N} u(k\,\Delta T)\left[1\left(t - \left(k - \frac{1}{2}\right)\Delta T\right) - 1\left(t - \left(k + \frac{1}{2}\right)\Delta T\right)\right]\right]$$

$$= \sum_{k=-N}^{N} u(k\,\Delta T)\mathcal{S}[p_k(t)]$$

$$= \sum_{k=-N}^{N} u(k\,\Delta T)\eta\left(t, \left(k - \frac{1}{2}\right)\Delta T\right)$$

Thus we can easily find an approximation to the response of the system for any signal which can be decomposed into a sequence of pulses if we know the response to the pulse shown in Fig. 5.10*a*. As ΔT gets smaller, the approximation improves. Let us consider the limiting case of (5.11); multiply and divide the right-hand side of (5.11) by ΔT and take the limit as ΔT approaches zero (observe N must approach infinity):

$$(5.12)\quad y(t) = \mathcal{S}[u(t)]$$

$$= \lim_{\Delta T \to 0} \mathcal{S}[u^*(t)]$$

$$= \lim_{\substack{\Delta T \to 0 \\ N \to \infty}} \mathcal{S}\left[\sum_{k=-N}^{N} u(k\,\Delta T)\,\frac{1(t - (k - \frac{1}{2})\,\Delta T) - 1(t - (k + \frac{1}{2})\,\Delta T)}{\Delta T}\,\Delta T\right]$$

$$= \lim_{\substack{\Delta T \to 0 \\ N \to \infty}} \sum_{k=-N}^{N} u(k\,\Delta T)\,\mathcal{S}\left[\frac{1(t - (k - \frac{1}{2})\,\Delta T) - 1(t - (k + \frac{1}{2})\,\Delta T)}{\Delta T}\right]\Delta T$$

$$= -\int_{-T}^{T} u(\tau)\left[\frac{d1(t - \tau)}{d\tau}\right] d\tau$$

if $\tau = k\,\Delta T$ in the limit. Recall that the derivative of step function is the delta function so that

$$\frac{d1(t - \tau)}{d\tau} = -\delta(t - \tau)$$

and we have, upon letting $T \to \infty$,

$$(5.13)\quad y(t) = \int_{-\infty}^{\infty} u(\tau)\mathcal{S}[\delta(t - \tau)]\,d\tau$$

If we denote the response of the system at time t to an impulse applied at time τ by $h(t,\tau)$, then (5.13) becomes

$$(5.14)\quad y(t) = \int_{-\infty}^{\infty} u(\tau)h(t,\tau)\,d\tau$$

Inherent in the above discussion is the fact that $u(t)$ can be represented by a continuum of impulses, i.e.,

$$(5.15)\quad u(t) = \int_{\infty-}^{\infty} u(\tau)\delta(t-\tau)\,d\tau$$

which we also know to be true from our discussion of distribution theory.

If the linear system is time invariant, then the form of response of the system is not dependent upon the time of application of the input pulse, but only depends on the difference in time between application and observation. Hence, the response may be more simply characterized as a function of $t - \tau$ [recall $\mathbf{\Phi}(t,\tau) = e^{\mathbf{A}(t-\tau)}$ for a lumped, linear *time-invariant* system], and we allow the abuse of notation

$$h(t,\tau) = h(t-\tau, 0) \text{ “=” } h(t-\tau)$$

More conveniently yet, we need only consider $\eta(t)$, the response to a pulse applied at $t = 0$, since τ may be set arbitrarily to zero without loss of information. Therefore, for time-invariant systems, the impulse response would depend only on the length of time after the application of the impulse and not on the time of application. Hence (5.14) becomes

$$(5.16)\quad y(t) = \int_{-\infty}^{\infty} u(\tau)h(t-\tau)\,d\tau$$

Expression (5.16) is known as the *convolution integral.* We introduce the following convenient shorthand notation to denote convolution:

$$[f_1 * f_2](t) \equiv \int_{\infty}^{\infty} f_1(\tau)f_2(t-\tau)\,d\tau$$

We leave it as an exercise for the reader to show that the convolution integral has the following properties:

(1) Commutivity:

$$[f_1 * f_2] = [f_2 * f_1]$$

(2) Distributivity:

$$[f_1 * (f_2 + f_3)] = [f_1 * f_2] + [f_1 * f_3]$$

(3) Associativity:

$$[f_1 * (f_2 * f_3)] = [(f_1 * f_2) * f_3]$$

If the linear, time-invariant system is *causal*, i.e., if a given cause (input) uniquely determines a specified effect (output), it cannot have a response before application of the excitation. Therefore we must have

$$h(t-\tau) = 0 \qquad \text{for } t < \tau$$

or

$$h(t) = 0 \qquad \text{for } t < 0$$

and the convolution integral becomes

$$y(t) = \int_{-\infty}^{t} u(t)h(t-\tau)\,d\tau$$

Upon a change of variables, the result may also be written as

$$y(t) = \int_{0}^{\infty} u(t-\tau)h(\tau)\,d\tau$$

(5.17) Example

Consider the network of Fig. 5.11. The following input-output description is easily derived,

$$\dot{y}(t) = -\frac{1}{RC}\,v(t) + \frac{1}{RC}\,u(t)$$

To find the impulse response, we must first solve the first-order differential equation with the assumption that all initial conditions are zero:

$$y(t) = \frac{1}{RC}\int_{0}^{t} \exp\left[-\frac{1}{RC}(t-\tau)\right] u(\tau)\,d\tau$$

Then for $u(t) = \delta(t)$, we have

$$\begin{aligned} h(t) &= \frac{1}{RC}\int_{0}^{t} \exp\left[-\frac{1}{RC}(t-\tau)\right] \delta(\tau)\,d\tau \\ &= \frac{1}{RC}\exp\left[-\frac{1}{RC}t\right] \end{aligned}$$

Note that we actually had $h(t-\tau)$ in

$$y(t) = \int_{0}^{t} \left\{\frac{1}{RC}\exp\left[-\frac{1}{RC}(t-\tau)\right]\right\} u(\tau)\,d\tau$$

above. ∎

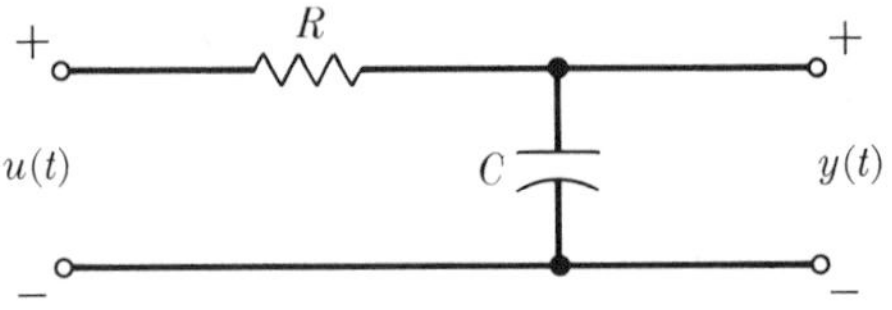

FIG. 5.11 A network whose impulse responses are $h(t) = \dfrac{1}{RC}\,e^{-(1/RC)e}$.

Observe that to find the impulse response, we had to solve the differential equation. Thus the convolution integral is really only useful in practice, provided that the impulse response is known.

Recall that if a linear, single input—single output system admits a state-space description, it can be described by the standard-form state equations

$$\dot{\mathbf{x}}(t) = \mathbf{A}(t)\mathbf{x}(t) + \mathbf{b}(t)u(t)$$

and

$$y(t) = \mathbf{c}'\mathbf{x}(t) + d(t)u(t)$$

For a delta-function input, the zero-state causal solution of these equations is

$$y(t) = \int_0^t [\mathbf{c}'(t)\mathbf{\Phi}(t,\tau)\mathbf{b}(\tau) + d(\tau)\delta(t-\tau)]u(\tau)\,d\tau$$

where the state-transition matrix $\mathbf{\Phi}(t,\tau)$ has the properties

$$\frac{\partial}{\partial t}\mathbf{\Phi}(t,\tau) = \mathbf{A}(t)\mathbf{\Phi}(t,\tau)$$

and

$$\mathbf{\Phi}(t,t) = \mathbf{1}$$

Hence, the impulse response is related to the state-variable system characterization and the state-transition matrix as

$$h(t,\tau) = \mathbf{c}'(t)\mathbf{\Phi}(t,\tau)\mathbf{b}(\tau) + d(t)\delta(t-\tau)$$

or for time-invariant linear systems

$$h(t-\tau) = \mathbf{c}'e^{\mathbf{A}(t-\tau)}\mathbf{b} - d\delta(t-\tau)$$

If we were to try to measure the impulse response in the laboratory, we might find it more convenient to use a unit step as the input and measure the step response, because step functions are easy to come by. We can easily relate the step response and impulse response as follows. Let $w(t)$ denote the step response, then

$$w(t) = [1 * h](t) = \int_0^t h(t-\lambda)\,d\lambda$$
$$= \int_0^t h(\tau)\,d\tau$$

where the system is assumed to be causal since it is physical. Now observe that

$$\frac{d}{dt}w(t) = \frac{d}{dt}\int_0^t h(\tau)\,d\tau = h(t)$$

In other words, the derivative of the step response is the impulse response. Recall that this property depends on the system being initially in the zero state in both instances.

5.3 FOURIER SERIES

In the preceding section, we have found it convenient to represent functions in terms of a continuum of impulses. If we know the zero-state response of a linear system to an impulse excitation, we can ascertain its response to any other input. Let us entertain the possibility of representing functions in terms of other "elemental" functions.

Let the function $f(t)$ be periodic with a finite period T, that is, $f(t + T) = f(t)$ for all t, $-\infty < t < \infty$. Consider representing the time function $f(t)$ on the interval $-T/2 \leq t \leq T/2$ in terms of a set of N function $\theta_k(t)$, $k = 1, 2, \ldots, N$. In other words, consider the series expansion

$$(5.18) \quad \hat{f}(t) = \sum_{k=1}^{N} f_k\theta_k(t) \qquad -\frac{T}{2} \leq t \leq \frac{T}{2}$$

where f_k are coefficients which depend on $f(t)$ and the N functions $\theta_k(t)$. It is our hope that $\hat{f}(t)$ is a good approximation to $f(t)$, and as N becomes large, the approximation improves. In general we will allow each $\theta_k(t)$ to be a complex-valued function, i.e., each $\theta_k(t)$ is composed of two real-valued time functions $\xi_k(t)$ and $\eta_k(t)$ such that

$$\theta_k(t) = \xi_k(t) + j\eta_k(t)$$

The functions $\theta_k(t)$, $k = 1, 2, \ldots, N$, are said to be an *orthogonal* set over the interval $-T/2 \leq t \leq T/2$ if

$$\int_{-T/2}^{T/2} \theta_k(t)\theta_l{}^*(t)\,dt = 0$$

for all $k, l = 1, 2, \ldots, N$ such that $k \neq l$. The asterisk denotes complex conjugate

$$\theta_k{}^*(t) = \xi_k(t) - j\eta_k(t)$$

The functions $\theta_k(t)$ are said to be *normalized* if

$$\int_{-T/2}^{T/2} \theta_k(t)\theta_k{}^*(t)\,dt = \int_{-T/2}^{T/2} |\theta_k(t)|^2\,dt = 1$$

If the set of $\theta_k(t)$'s are orthogonal and normalized, they are said to be *orthonormal.*

We introduce the following notation for convenience. The *inner product* of two complex time functions $f(t)$ and $g(t)$ on the interval

$-T/2 \leq t \leq T/2$ is given by

$$(5.19) \quad \langle f,g \rangle \equiv \int_{-T/2}^{T/2} f(t)g^*(t)\,dt$$

The square root of the inner product of a complex time function $f(t)$ with itself is called the *norm* of $f(t)$ and is denoted by $\|f\|$, that is,

$$(5.20) \quad \|f\|^2 = \langle f,f \rangle = \int_{-T/2}^{T/2} |f(t)|^2\,dt$$

Observe that the norm of a function defined here is analogous to the L_2 norm of a vector defined in Chap. 4.

We are now in a position to measure the accuracy with which the series expansion (5.18) approximates $f(t)$. The error in this approximation is given by

$$\begin{aligned}(5.21) \quad \varepsilon_N &\equiv \|f - \hat{f}\|^2 = \int_{-T/2}^{T/2} |f(t) - \hat{f}(t)|^2\,dt \\ &= \|f(t)\|^2 - 2\,\text{Re}\,\{\langle f,\hat{f} \rangle\} + \|\hat{f}(t)\|^2 \\ &= \|f(t)\|^2 - 2\,\text{Re}\,\{\sum_{k=1}^{N} f_k^* \langle f,\theta_k \rangle\} + \sum_{k=1}^{N} |f_k|^2\end{aligned}$$

if we assume the θ_k are orthogonal. Let us choose the coefficients f_k in such a way so as to minimize this error. If we add and subtract the term

$$\sum_{k=1}^{N} \langle f,\theta_k \rangle^2$$

from the right-hand side of (5.21), it may be written as

$$(5.22) \quad \varepsilon_N = \|f\|^2 - \sum_{k=1}^{N} |\langle f,\theta_k \rangle|^2 + \sum_{k=1}^{N} |f_k - \langle f,\theta_k \rangle|^2$$

Observe that the first two terms on the right-hand side of (5.22) are independent of f_k, and the third term is minimized if we choose

$$f_k = \langle f,\theta_k \rangle = \int_{-T/2}^{T/2} f(t)\theta_k^*(t)\,dt$$

These mininum-error coefficients are referred to as the *Fourier coefficients*.

Now consider the situation in which N is arbitrarily large so that we wish to express $f(t)$ in terms of the infinite set of functions

$$\theta_k(t) \qquad k = 1, 2, 3, \ldots$$

A natural question to ask is under what conditions does the series expansion

$$\sum_{k=1}^{\infty} f_k \theta_k(t)$$

equal $f(t)$ exactly? Assuming the f_k are Fourier coefficients, then from (5.22) we have

$$\varepsilon_N = \|f\| - \sum_{k=1}^{N} |f_k|^2$$

Hence we wish to determine the conditions under which

$$\lim_{N \to \infty} \varepsilon_N = 0$$

A detailed derivation of these conditions is beyond the scope of this text. Suffice it to say that if we choose the set of functions

$$\theta_k(t) = \begin{cases} \cos\left(\dfrac{(k-1)\pi}{T} t\right) & k \text{ odd} \\ \sin\left(\dfrac{k\pi}{T} t\right) & k \text{ even} \end{cases} \tag{5.23}$$

$k = 1, 2, \ldots$, a real periodic $f(t)$ is described exactly by the infinite series if it satisfies the *Dirichlet conditions:*

(1) $f(t)$ is single valued for $|t| \leq T/2$.
(2) $f(t)$ may have only a finite number of maxima and minima for any finite time interval.
(3) $f(t)$ may have only a finite number of finite discontinuities for $|t| \leq T/2$.
(4) $f(t) \in L_1(-T/2,T/2)$, that is,

$$\int_{T/2}^{T/2} |f(t)|\, dt < \infty$$

For all practical purposes, most real, periodic physical signals satisfy these conditions. We leave it as an exercise for the reader to show that the set of functions (5.23) is orthogonal.

Our series expansion becomes

$$f(t) = \sum_{k=0}^{\infty} a_k \cos\left(\frac{2\pi kt}{T}\right) + \sum_{k=0}^{\infty} b_k \sin\left(\frac{2\pi kt}{T}\right) \tag{5.24}$$

for $-T/2 \leq t \leq T/2$ where

$$a_k = \frac{1}{T} \int_{-T/2}^{T/2} f(t) \cos\left(\frac{2\pi kt}{T}\right) dt$$

and

$$b_k = \frac{1}{T} \int_{-T/2}^{T/2} f(t) \sin\left(\frac{2\pi kt}{T}\right) dt$$

Expression (5.24) gives the *Fourier series* representation for $f(t)$. Since

$$\cos \theta = \tfrac{1}{2}[e^{j\theta} + e^{-j\theta}]$$

and

$$\sin \theta = \frac{1}{2j} [e^{j\theta} - e^{-j\theta}]$$

we can rewrite (5.24) as

$$f(t) = \sum_{k=-\infty}^{\infty} c_k e^{jk\Omega t} \tag{5.25}$$

for $-T/2 \leq t \leq T/2$, where $\Omega = 2\pi/T$ and

$$c_k = \frac{1}{T} \int_{-T/2}^{T/2} f(t) e^{-jk\Omega t} \, dt$$

Expression (5.25) is called the *complex Fourier series*. If $f(t)$ is periodic with period T and satisfies the Dirichlet conditions, then $f(t)$ is equal to its Fourier series representation for all time t.

Now consider the nth-order differential equation

$$\alpha_n y^{(n)}(t) + \alpha_{n-1} y^{(n-1)}(t) + \cdots + \alpha_0 y(t) = \beta_0 u(t) + \beta_1 u^{(1)}(t) + \cdots + \beta_n u^{(n)}(t) \tag{5.26}$$

which describes a linear time-invariant system that has an asymptotically stable-equilibrium state. Assume that the system is in the zero state at time $t = 0$. Let the input $u(t)$ be periodic with period T; it has the Fourier series representation

$$u(t) = \sum_{k=-\infty}^{\infty} u_k e^{jk\Omega t} \tag{5.27}$$

Since the system is linear and time invariant, the zero-state or steady-state output $y(t)$ must also be periodic with period T. This result is easily seen upon considering the convolution integral:

$$y(t) = \int_{-\infty}^{t} h(t - \tau) u(\tau) \, d\tau$$

then

$$y(t + T) = \int_{-\infty}^{t+T} h(t + T - \tau) u(\tau) \, d\tau$$

The change of variables $\sigma = \tau - T$ yields

$$y(t + T) = \int_{-\infty}^{t} h(t - \sigma) u(\sigma + T) \, d\sigma$$

But $u(t)$ is periodic with period T, so $u(\sigma + T) = u(\sigma)$, and therefore, $y(t + T) = y(t)$. Hence $y(t)$ may also be expanded in a Fourier series:

$$(5.28) \quad y(t) = \sum_{k=-\infty}^{\infty} y_k e^{jk\Omega t}$$

Upon substitution of (5.27) and (5.28) into (5.26), we find that

$$\sum_{k=-\infty}^{\infty} y_k e^{jk\Omega t} \sum_{i=0}^{n} \alpha_i (j\Omega k)^i = \sum_{k=-\infty}^{\infty} e^{jk\Omega t} u_k \sum_{i=0}^{n} \beta_i (j\Omega k)^i$$

or

$$\sum_{k=-\infty}^{\infty} \left[y_k \sum_{i=0}^{n} \alpha_i (j\Omega k)^i - u_k \sum_{i=0}^{n} \beta_i (j\Omega k)^i \right] e^{jk\Omega t} = 0$$

Since the set of function $\{e^{jk\Omega t}\}$ is orthogonal, and therefore, linearly independent for all k, we must have

$$(5.29) \quad y_k = \frac{\sum_{i=0}^{n} \beta_i (j\Omega k)^i}{\sum_{i=0}^{n} \alpha_i (j\Omega k)^i} u_k$$

Thus the Fourier coefficients of the output may be determined algebraically in terms of the Fourier coefficients of the input.

(5.30) Example

Consider a system described by

$$\ddot{y} + 5\dot{y} + 6y = u + \dot{u}$$

and let us find the steady-state response for the complex input

$$u(t) = e^{j\omega_0 t}$$

The Fourier coefficients of the input function are

$$u_k = \begin{cases} 0 & \text{for all } k \neq 1 \\ 1 & \text{if } k = 1 \end{cases}$$

and $\Omega = \omega_0$. Therefore, the only nonzero Fourier coefficient of the output signal is found from (5.29) to be

$$y_1 = \frac{(j\omega_0)^2 + 5(j\omega_0) + 6}{j\omega_0 + 1}$$

and the steady-state response is

$$y(t) = \frac{(j\omega_0)^2 + 5(j\omega_0) + 6}{j\omega_0 + 1} e^{j\omega_0 t}$$ ∎

It becomes apparent that the steady-state response of a linear system to the exponential input $e^{j\omega t}$ will be merely the exponential $e^{j\omega t}$ multiplied by some constant. This *preservation of form* makes exponential signals especially convenient for the analysis of linear systems.

So far, we have limited ourselves to periodic signals or to the time interval $-T/2 \leq t \leq T/2$. We now expand our discussion to include arbitrary signals over all time.

5.4 THE FOURIER TRANSFORM

Let $f(t)$ be an arbitrary function as shown in Fig. 5.12*a*. Consider only that portion of the signal for which $-T/2 \leq t \leq T/2$. We artificially create a periodic signal $\hat{f}(t)$ by repeating the portion of $f(t)$ for which $-T/2 \leq t \leq T/2$ as shown in Fig. 5.12*b*. Observe that

$$f(t) = \hat{f}(t) \qquad \text{for } -\frac{T}{2} \leq t \leq \frac{T}{2}$$

The periodic function $\hat{f}(t)$ can be expanded in a Fourier series of period T:

$$\hat{f}(t) = \sum_{k=-\infty}^{\infty} c_k \exp \frac{j2\pi nt}{T} \tag{5.31}$$

where

$$c_k = \frac{1}{T} \int_{-T/2}^{T/2} f(t) \exp\left(-j\frac{2\pi nt}{T}\right) dt \tag{5.32}$$

We define

$$\Delta\omega \equiv \frac{2\pi}{T} = \Omega$$

and $\omega \equiv k\,\Delta\omega = k\Omega$. Then (5.31) and (5.32) become

$$\hat{f}(t) = \sum_{\substack{\omega = k\Delta\omega \\ k=-\infty}}^{\infty} c_\omega e^{j\omega t} \tag{5.33}$$

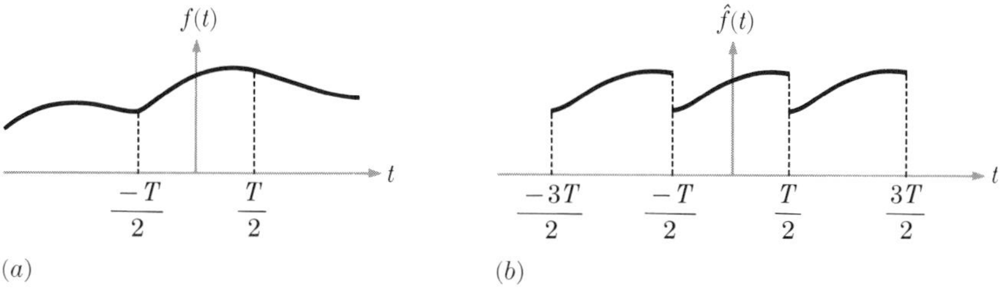

FIG. 5.12 (*a*) An arbitrary signal $f(t)$, (*b*) periodic representation of the signal.

and

$$(5.34)\quad c_\omega = \frac{1}{T}\int_{-T/2}^{T/2} f(t)e^{-j\omega t}\,dt$$

Now let

$$F(\omega) = Tc_\omega$$

so that

$$(5.35)\quad \hat{f}(\omega) = \sum_{\substack{\omega = k\Delta\omega \\ k=-\infty}}^{\infty} \frac{1}{2\pi} F(\omega)e^{j\omega t}\,\Delta\omega$$

and

$$(5.36)\quad F(\omega) = \int_{-T/2}^{T/2} f(t)e^{-j\omega t}\,dt$$

Now if we let $T \to \infty$, $f(t) = \hat{f}(t)$ for all time, $\Delta\omega$ be infinitesimal and the summation (5.35) becomes an integral:

$$(5.37a)\quad f(t) = \frac{1}{2\pi}\int_{-\infty}^{\infty} F(\omega)e^{j\omega t}\,d\omega$$

and expression (5.36) becomes

$$(5.37b)\quad F(\omega) = \int_{-\infty}^{\infty} f(t)e^{-j\omega t}\,dt$$

Expression (5.37*b*) is known as the *Fourier integral*, and $F(\omega)$ is called the Fourier transform of $f(t)$. Expression (5.37*a*) is known as the *inverse Fourier transform*. We sometimes write

$$F(\omega) = \mathfrak{F}[f(t)]$$

and

$$f(t) = \mathfrak{F}^{-1}[F(\omega)]$$

Our derivation of the Fourier transform was formal, and the validity of it remains to be shown.[1]

Before investigating the properties of the Fourier transform, we demonstrate why it is useful in system analysis. To this end we must con-

[1] It is proved by A. A. Papoulis ("The Fourier Integral and Its Applications," McGraw-Hill, New York, 1962) that $f(t)$ is *Fourier transformable*, i.e., the Fourier transform of $f(t)$ exists, and the inverse Fourier transform equals $f(t)$, if $f(t)$ is absolutely integrable

$$\int_{-\infty}^{\infty} |f(t)|\,dt < \infty$$

and if $f(t)$ is continuous for all t. These are sufficient, but not necessary conditions.

sider the Fourier transform of the derivative of a function. Therefore

$$f(t) = \frac{1}{2\pi} \int_{-\infty}^{\infty} F(\omega) e^{j\omega t}\, d\omega$$

Upon differentiation, we have

$$\begin{aligned} \frac{df(t)}{dt} &= \frac{1}{2\pi} \int_{-\infty}^{\infty} j\omega F(\omega) e^{j\omega t}\, d\omega \\ &= \mathfrak{F}^{-1}[j\omega F(\omega)] \end{aligned}$$

We conclude then that

(5.38) $\mathfrak{F}[\dot{f}(t)] = j\omega F(\omega)$

It is left as an exercise to show that

(5.39) $\mathfrak{F}[f^{(n)}(t)] = (j\omega)^n F(\omega)$

Consider again the nth-order differential equation (5.26). Assume that the input $u(t)$ is zero for all $t \leq 0$. Furthermore, assume that the system is causal so that $y(t) = 0$ for $t \leq 0$. Finally assume that the system is in the zero state. Then if $U(\omega) = \mathfrak{F}[u(t)]$ and $Y(\omega) = \mathfrak{F}[y(t)]$, we have

$$\begin{aligned} &[\alpha_n(j\omega)^n + \alpha_{n-1}(j\omega)^{n-1} + \cdots + \alpha_0]Y(\omega) \\ &\qquad = [\beta_0 + \beta_1(j\omega) + \cdots + \beta_n(j\omega)^n]U(\omega) \end{aligned}$$

or that

$$Y(\omega) = H(\omega)u(\omega)$$

where

$$H(\omega) \equiv \frac{\beta_0 + \beta_1(j\omega) + \cdots + \beta_n(j\omega)^n}{\alpha_0 + \alpha_1(j\omega) + \cdots + \alpha_n(j\omega)^n}$$

Thus we have transformed the nth-order differential equation into an algebraic equation which can be solved easily. The term $H(\omega)$ is referred to as the system's *transfer function*, and we will show that it is intimately related to the impulse response. Once we find $Y(\omega)$, we take the inverse Fourier transform to find $y(t)$.

We now compute the Fourier transform of some common functions.

(5.40) Example

Consider the function e^{st}, where s is a complex constant. This function is not absolutely integrable, and therefore, not Fourier transformable. On the other hand, the function $1(t)e^{st}$ is absolutely integrable if s has a negative real part. We find the Fourier transform as follows:

$$\mathfrak{F}[1(t)e^{st}] = \int_{-\infty}^{\infty} [1(t)e^{st}]e^{-j\omega t}\, dt$$

$$= \int_{0}^{\infty} e^{(s-j\omega)t}\, dt = \frac{1}{s-j\omega}\, e^{(s-j\omega)t}\Big]_{0}^{\infty}$$

$$= \frac{1}{j\omega - s}\ \text{if Re}\ \{s\} < 0 \qquad\blacksquare$$

(5.41) Example
A unit pulse is defined by

$$P_T(t) = \begin{cases} 1 & 0 \le t \le T \\ 0 & \text{elsewhere} \end{cases}$$

The Fourier transform of $P_T(t)$ is

$$\mathfrak{F}[P_T(t)] = \int_{-\infty}^{\infty} P_T(t)e^{-j\omega t}\, dt = \int_{0}^{T} e^{-j\omega t}\, dt$$

$$= -\frac{1}{j\omega}[e^{-j\omega T} - 1]$$

$$= Te^{-j\omega T/2}\left\{\frac{\sin \omega T/2}{\omega T/2}\right\} \qquad\blacksquare$$

(5.42) Example
The Fourier transform of $f(t) = e^{-\alpha|t|}$, where α is a real positive number, is found by considering $f(t)$ over two separate intervals:

$$f(t) = \begin{cases} e^{\alpha t} & t < 0 \\ e^{-\alpha t} & t > 0 \end{cases}$$

Then

$$F(\omega) = \int_{-\infty}^{0} e^{\alpha t}e^{-j\omega t}\, d\omega + \int_{0}^{\infty} e^{-\alpha t}e^{-j\omega t}\, d\omega$$

$$= \frac{2\alpha}{\alpha^2 + \omega^2} \qquad\blacksquare$$

Unfortunately there are many useful functions such as the delta function, unit step, and even the simple sinusoids $\cos t$ and $\sin t$ which do not possess Fourier transforms in the usual sense. It is convenient to generalize the Fourier transform techniques to include these functions. First consider the delta function. Using definition (5.3), we have

$$(5.43)\quad \mathfrak{F}[\delta(t)] = \int_{-\infty}^{\infty} \delta(t)e^{-j\omega t}\, dt = 1$$

Now note that if

$$F(\omega) = \mathfrak{F}[f(t)]$$

then

(5.44) $F(t) = 2\pi\mathfrak{F}^{-1}[f(-\omega)]$

because

$$\begin{aligned} F(t) &= \int_{-\infty}^{\infty} f(\sigma)e^{-j\sigma t}\,d\sigma \\ &= \int_{-\infty}^{\infty} f(-\omega)e^{-j\omega t}\,d\omega \\ &= 2\pi\left[\frac{1}{2\pi}\int_{-\infty}^{\infty} f(-\omega)e^{j\omega t}\,d\omega\right] \end{aligned}$$

Therefore, since $\mathfrak{F}[\delta(t)] = 1$ we conclude that

(5.45) $\mathfrak{F}[1] = 2\pi\delta(\omega)$

Expression (5.45) is known as the *Riemann-Lebesgue lemma.* Although we have found this expression rather informally, rigorous proof of it does exist. In fact since the validity of (5.45) can be established independently of Fourier transforms, it is possible to derive the Fourier transform from it. It is instructive to digress briefly here and present a plausibility argument for (5.45), since this result will be quite important when we discuss the fast Fourier transform in Chap. 7. Expression (5.45) must hold in the sense of distributions since a delta functional appears, but first we must interpret the infinite integral as a limit (as is always the case); i.e.,

$$2\pi\delta(\omega) = \lim_{n\to\infty}\int_{-n}^{n} e^{j\omega t}\,dt$$

In other words,

$$\int_{-\infty}^{\infty} 2\pi\delta(\omega)\phi(\omega)\,d\omega = \int_{-\infty}^{\infty}\left[\lim_{n\to\infty}\int_{-n}^{n} e^{j\omega t}\,dt\right]\phi(\omega)\,d\omega \qquad \text{for all } \phi \in \mathfrak{D}$$

What we wish, then, is to investigate the sequence

$$g_n(\phi) = \int_{-\infty}^{\infty}\int_{-n}^{n} e^{j\omega t}\,dt\,\phi(\omega)\,d\omega = \int_{-\infty}^{\infty}\frac{2\sin n\omega}{\omega}\phi(\omega)\,d\omega$$

to show that

$$\lim_{n\to\infty} g_n(\omega) = 2\pi\phi(0) \qquad \text{for all } \phi \in \mathfrak{D}$$

We effect the change of variable

$$\xi = n\omega$$

so that

$$g_n(\phi) = \int_{-\infty}^{\infty} \frac{2 \sin \xi}{\xi} \phi\left(\frac{\xi}{n}\right) d\xi$$

Now,

$$\lim_{n\to\infty} \phi\left(\frac{\xi}{n}\right) = \phi(0)$$

and by continuity (and other justifications) we take

$$\lim_{n\to\infty} g_n(\phi) = \int_{-\infty}^{\infty} \frac{2 \sin \xi}{\xi} \phi(0)\, d\xi$$
$$= 2\phi(0) \int_{-\infty}^{\infty} \frac{\sin \xi}{\xi}\, d\xi$$

But, it is easily verified that

$$\int_{-\infty}^{\infty} \frac{\sin \xi}{\xi}\, d\xi = \pi$$

so

$$\lim_{n\to\infty} g_n(\phi) = 2\pi\phi(0) \qquad \text{for all } \phi \in \mathfrak{D}$$

Hence, we accept the formula (5.45) independent of the Fourier transform development.

We can now find the Fourier transform of $e^{j\omega_0 t}$:

$$\begin{aligned} \mathfrak{F}[e^{j\omega_0 t}] &= \int_{-\infty}^{\infty} e^{j\omega_0 t} e^{-j\omega t}\, dt \\ &= \int_{-\infty}^{\infty} e^{j(\omega-\omega_0)t}\, dt \\ &= 2\pi\delta(\omega - \omega_0) \end{aligned} \tag{5.46}$$

from which we can conclude that

$$\mathfrak{F}[\cos \omega_0 t] = \pi[\delta(\omega - \omega_0) + \delta(\omega + \omega_0)] \tag{5.47}$$

and

$$\mathfrak{F}[\sin \omega_0 t] = j\pi[\delta(\omega + \omega_0) - \delta(\omega - \omega_0)] \tag{5.48}$$

Before attempting to find the Fourier transform for a unit-step function, we must point out a subtlety which arises in conjunction with generalized functions which may not be Fourier transformable in the ordinary sense, because they are not absolutely integrable. First consider

$$f_\alpha(t) = \begin{cases} 0 & t < 0 \\ e^{-\alpha t} & t > 0 \end{cases}$$

where α is a real nonnegative number. We recognize that we may obtain the unit-step function from

$$1(t) = \lim_{\alpha \to 0} [f_\alpha(t)]$$

For nonzero α the functions $f_\alpha(t)$ are Fourier transformable, the result being

$$\begin{aligned} F_\alpha(\omega) &= \int_0^\infty e^{-(\alpha + j\omega)t}\, dt \\ &= \frac{1}{-(\alpha + j\omega)} e^{-(\alpha+j\omega)t} \Big|_0^\infty \\ &= \frac{1}{\alpha + j\omega} \end{aligned}$$

So long as $\omega \neq 0$, we may take the limit[1]

$$F(\omega) = \lim_{\alpha \to 0} [F_\alpha(\omega)] = \frac{1}{j\omega} \qquad \omega \neq 0$$

To attempt to find out what may be happening for $\omega = 0$, we expand $F_\alpha(\omega)$ into its real and imaginary parts:

$$F_\alpha(\omega) = \frac{\alpha}{\alpha^2 + \omega^2} + \frac{-j\omega}{\alpha^2 + \omega^2}$$

In the limit as $\alpha \to 0$, the second term becomes $1/j\omega$, as we have shown before, and the first term is zero; but the first term is indeterminant for $\alpha = 0$ and $\omega = 0$. Recall that the delta function is zero for nonzero argument and indeterminant for zero argument. To see that in the limit the first term may become a delta function, we recognize that

$$\int_{-\infty}^{\infty} \frac{\alpha}{\alpha^2 + \omega^2}\, d\omega = \pi$$

independent of α. Consequently, we postulate that the unit-step function should have the Fourier transform

$$\mathfrak{F}[1(t)] = \frac{1}{j\omega} + \pi\delta(\omega)$$

We note that

$$\mathfrak{F}^{-1}[\pi\delta(\omega)] = \frac{1}{2\pi} \int_{-\infty}^{\infty} \pi\delta(\omega) e^{j\omega t}\, d\omega = \tfrac{1}{2}$$

[1] Interchanging the limit with the Fourier integral may be justified rigorously only by means of sophisticated arguments in distribution theory (A. Papoulis, "The Fourier Integral and Its Applications," McGraw-Hill, New York, 1962). For present purposes, suffice it to say that we may obtain an unambiguous and convenient result.

a constant which is not Fourier transformable in the ordinary sense. Apparently, we require the impulse-frequency function to distinguish between the unit-step function and the odd function

$$f(t) = \begin{cases} -\frac{1}{2} & t < 0 \\ +\frac{1}{2} & t > 0 \end{cases}$$

which does have the purely imaginary Fourier transform $1/j\omega$. The unit-impulse function is also the derivative of this function. Alternatively, we may attempt to justify the above arguments in terms of distribution theory. If we have the expression

$$1 = j\omega F(\omega) \tag{5.49}$$

then

$$F(\omega) = \frac{1}{j\omega} + k\delta(\omega) \tag{5.50}$$

not

$$F(\omega) = \frac{1}{j\omega}$$

as we would first expect. To see this, observe that upon multiplication of (5.50) by $j\omega$, we have

$$j\omega F(\omega) = 1 + j\omega k\delta(\omega) \tag{5.51}$$

Expression (5.51) must be interpreted in the sense of distributions. Hence, if $\phi(\omega)$ is a testing function, then (5.51) must be considered as follows

$$\int_{-\infty}^{\infty} j\omega F(\omega)\phi(\omega)\,d\omega = \int_{-\infty}^{\infty} \phi(\omega)\,d\omega + \int_{-\infty}^{\infty} j\omega k\delta(\omega)\phi(\omega)\,d\omega \tag{5.52}$$

But from definition (5.3),

$$\int_{-\infty}^{\infty} j\omega k\delta(\omega)\phi(\omega)\,d\omega = 0$$

so that (5.52) becomes

$$\int_{-\infty}^{\infty} j\omega F(\omega)\phi(\omega)\,d\omega = \int_{-\infty}^{\infty} \phi(\omega)\,d\omega$$

which indicates that

$$j\omega F(\omega) = 1$$

in the sense of distributions. Thus we conclude that (5.51) and (5.49) are equivalent expressions in the sense of distributions. We now find the Fourier transform of the unit step. Since we have already seen that

$$\delta(t) = \frac{d}{dt}1(t)$$

if $I(\omega)$ is the Fourier transform of $1(t)$, then from (5.38)

$$\mathfrak{F}[\delta(t)] = j\omega I(\omega) \tag{5.53}$$

so that

$$1 = j\omega I(\omega)$$

From the discussion above, we conclude that

$$I(\omega) = \frac{1}{j\omega} + k\delta(\omega) \tag{5.54}$$

It remains to evaluate the constant k. We first show that if $F(\omega) = \mathfrak{F}[f(t)]$ and $G(\omega) = \mathfrak{F}[g(t)]$, then

$$\int_{-\infty}^{\infty} f(t)G(t)\,dt = \int_{-\infty}^{\infty} F(\omega)g(\omega)\,d\omega \tag{5.55}$$

The validity of (5.55) is easily demonstrated:

$$\begin{aligned}\int_{-\infty}^{\infty} f(t)G(t)\,dt &= \int_{-\infty}^{\infty} dt\,f(t)\int_{-\infty}^{\infty} g(\omega)e^{-j\omega t}\,d\omega \\ &= \int_{-\infty}^{\infty} d\omega\,g(\omega)\int_{-\infty}^{\infty} f(t)e^{-j\omega t}\,dt \\ &= \int_{-\infty}^{\infty} F(\omega)g(\omega)\,d\omega\end{aligned}$$

We have neglected questions concerning the above change in order of integration. Suffice it to say, that for all cases in which we are interested, the change in order of integration may be justified.

Using (5.55) we may write

$$\int_{-\infty}^{\infty} 1(t)\Phi(t)\,dt = \int_{-\infty}^{\infty} I(\omega)\phi(\omega)\,d\omega \tag{5.56}$$

where $\phi(t) = \mathfrak{F}^{-1}[\Phi(\omega)]$ is a testing function. Let $\phi(t) = e^{-\frac{1}{2}t^2}$. Although $\phi(t)$ is not zero outside some finite interval of time and therefore not a testing function as described earlier, it can be used as a testing function for the present purpose. (This function is called a *tempered* testing function and has the property that

$$\lim_{t\to\pm\infty} t^r e^{-\frac{1}{2}t^2} = 0$$

for all finite values of r.) Then

$$\Phi(\omega) = \sqrt{2\pi}\,e^{-\frac{1}{2}\omega^2}$$

and

$$\int_{-\infty}^{\infty} 1(t)\Phi(t)\,dt = \int_0^{\infty} \sqrt{2\pi}\,e^{-\frac{1}{2}t^2}\,dt = \pi$$

But

$$\int_{-\infty}^{\infty} I(\omega)\phi(\omega)\,d\omega = \int_{-\infty}^{\infty}\left[\frac{1}{j\omega} + k\delta(\omega)\right]\phi(\omega)\,d\omega$$
$$= k\phi(0) + \int_{-\infty}^{\infty}\frac{1}{j\omega}\,\phi(\omega)\,d\omega$$

Special consideration must be given to the principle-value integral

$$\int_{-\infty}^{\infty}\frac{1}{j\omega}\,\phi(\omega)\,d\omega$$

since the integrand is undefined for $\omega = 0$. We proceed as follows:

$$\int_{-\infty}^{\infty}\frac{1}{j\omega}\,\phi(\omega)\,d\omega = \lim_{\varepsilon\to 0}\left[\int_{-\infty}^{-\varepsilon}\frac{1}{j\omega}\,\phi(\omega)\,d\omega + \int_{+\varepsilon}^{\infty}\frac{1}{j\omega}\,\phi(\omega)\,d\omega\right]$$
$$= \lim_{\varepsilon\to 0}\int_{\varepsilon}^{\infty}\frac{1}{j\omega}\,[\phi(\omega) - \phi(-\omega)]\,d\omega$$

Now observe that

$$\phi(\omega) - \phi(-\omega) = 0$$

and

$$\phi(0) = 1$$

for our choice of testing function so that (5.56) becomes

$$\pi = k$$

Thus, the Fourier transform of the unit step is

$$\text{(5.57)}\quad \mathfrak{F}[1(t)] = \pi\delta(\omega) + \frac{1}{j\omega}$$

5.5 GRAPHICAL REPRESENTATION OF THE FOURIER TRANSFORM

The Fourier transform of a function of time is itself a function of the variable ω. It is physically meaningful to consider ω to be radian frequency. Therefore $F(\omega)$ may be thought of as the *spectral representation* of the time function $f(t)$. Analysis carried out in terms of Fourier transforms is called *frequency domain analysis*. To justify these statements and gain insight into the Fourier transform, we can consider the plot of $F(\omega)$ as a function of ω. In general $F(\omega)$ is a complex function, and we have two options. Either the real and imaginary parts of $F(\omega)$ may be plotted separately, or else the magnitude and phase components of $F(\omega)$ may be plotted separately, as a function of ω. The latter proves to be the most convenient. We may rewrite $F(\omega)$ as

(5.58) $F(\omega) = A(\omega)e^{\theta(\omega)}$

where $A(\omega)$ is a real nonnegative function of ω representing the amplitude of $F(\omega)$:

(5.59) $A(\omega) = |F(\omega)| = \sqrt{\{\text{Re}\,[F(\omega)]\}^2 + \{\text{Im}\,[F(\omega)]\}^2}$

and $\theta(\omega)$ is a real function of ω representing the phase of $F(\omega)$:

(5.60) $\theta(\omega) = \arctan \dfrac{\text{Im}\,\{F(\omega)\}}{\text{Re}\,\{F(\omega)\}}$

Knowledge of $A(\omega)$ and $\theta(\omega)$ allows us to determine $F(\omega)$. Both the amplitude and phase can be plotted conveniently as functions of frequency. Usually the magnitude is plotted in decibels, that is, $20 \log A(\omega)$, and frequency (in radians) is plotted on a log scale. The resulting plot (also known as a *Bode plot*) completely characterizes the transform $F(\omega)$.

(5.61) Example

Consider the transform

$$F(\omega) = \frac{1}{1 + \alpha j\omega}$$

then

$$A(\omega) = \frac{1}{(1 + (\alpha\omega)^2)^{\frac{1}{2}}}$$

and

$$\theta(\omega) = \tan^{-1}(-\alpha\omega)$$

Plots of $A(\omega)$ and $\theta(\omega)$ are shown in Fig. 5.13. ∎

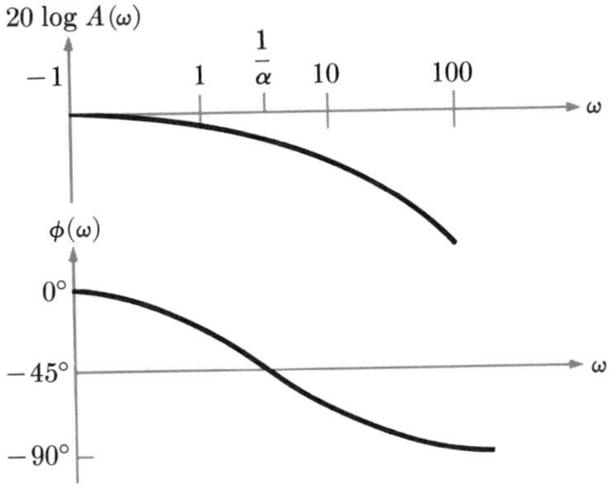

FIG. 5.13 Bode plot of $F(\omega) = \dfrac{1}{1 + \alpha j\omega}$.

Bode plots are rather easy to construct by inspection for multipoled functions such as

$$A(\omega) = \prod_{i=1}^{n} \frac{k_i}{[(j\omega - s_i)(-j\omega - s_i)]^{\frac{1}{2}}}$$

The interested reader should consult the literature for a more detailed discussion.[1]

For the most part, when studying physical systems, only real-time functions are of interest. Let $f(t)$ be a real-time function, that is, $f^*(t) = f(t)$, and consider the following:

$$\begin{aligned} (5.62) \qquad F^*(\omega) &= \int_{-\infty}^{\infty} f^*(t)e^{-j\omega t}\,dt \\ &= \left[\int_{-\infty}^{\infty} f(t)e^{j\omega t}\,dt\right]^* = \int_{-\infty}^{\infty} f(t)e^{-j(-\omega)t}\,dt \\ &= F(-\omega) \end{aligned}$$

The inverse formula takes on a special form when $f(t)$ is a real-time function:

$$\begin{aligned} f(t) &= \frac{1}{2\pi}\int_{-\infty}^{\infty} F(\omega)e^{j\omega t}\,d\omega \\ &= \frac{1}{2\pi}\int_{-\infty}^{0} F(\omega)e^{j\omega t}\,d\omega + \frac{1}{2\pi}\int_{0}^{\infty} F(\omega)e^{j\omega t}\,d\omega \\ &= \frac{1}{2\pi}\int_{0}^{\infty} F(\omega)e^{-j\omega t}\,d\omega + \frac{1}{2\pi}\int_{0}^{\infty} F(\omega)e^{j\omega t}\,d\omega \end{aligned}$$

after a change of variables. But from (5.62) we have

$$\begin{aligned} (5.63) \qquad f(t) &= \left[\frac{1}{2\pi}\int_{0}^{\infty} F(\omega)e^{j\omega t}\,d\omega\right]^* + \frac{1}{2\pi}\int_{0}^{\infty} F(\omega)e^{j\omega t}\,d\omega \\ &= \frac{1}{\pi}\,\mathrm{Re}\left\{\int_{0}^{\infty} F(\omega)e^{j\omega t}\,d\omega\right\} \end{aligned}$$

The magnitude plot associated with the transform of a real-time function is seen to be symmetrical since

$$|F(-\omega)| = |F^*(\omega)| = |F(\omega)|$$

To see why associating ω with radian frequency is meaningful, consider the transform of a sinusoid of frequency ω_0,

$$F(\omega) = \mathfrak{F}[\sin \omega_0 t] = j\pi[\delta(\omega + \omega_0) - \delta(\omega - \omega_0)]$$

[1] See, for example, J. L. Melsa and D. G. Schultz, "Linear Control Systems," chap. 5, McGraw-Hill, New York, 1969.

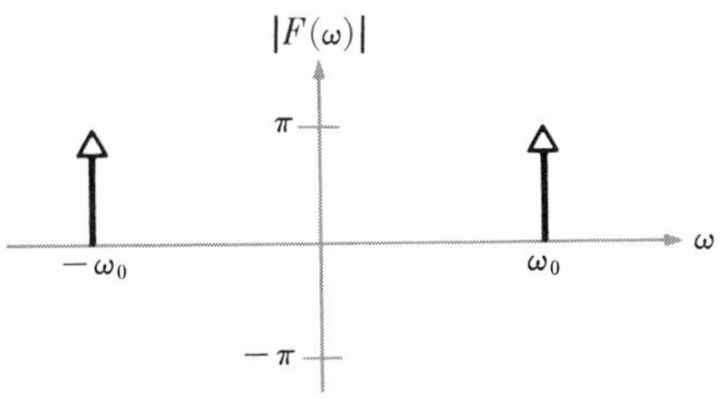

FIG. 5.14 Magnitude plots of $\mathfrak{F}[\sin \omega_0 t]$.

Therefore,

$$|F(\omega)| = \pi\delta(\omega + \omega_0) + \pi\delta(\omega - \omega_0)$$

and is plotted in Fig. 5.14. Thus the signal is concentrated at the frequency ω_0 which bears out our intuitive feeling.

Recall that the introduction of the Fourier transform was necessitated by the fact that only periodic signals could be expanded into a Fourier series. Therefore, we would expect that the Fourier transform of a periodic signal would consist of discrete components at various multiples of a fundamental frequency, i.e., a discrete spectrum. We leave it to the problems for the reader to show that the above is true in general.

5.6 THE FOURIER TRANSFORM IN SYSTEM ANALYSIS

Let us now return to the use of the Fourier transform to study system behavior. Recall that if $u(t)$ is the input to a linear time-invariant system in the zero state and $h(t)$ its impulse response, the output $y(t)$ may be ascertained from the convolution integral

$$y(t) = \int_{-\infty}^{\infty} h(t - \tau)u(\tau)\, d\tau$$

Assume that $u(t)$, $h(t)$, and $y(t)$ are Fourier transformable with Fourier transforms $U(\omega)$, $H(\omega)$, and $Y(\omega)$, respectively. Then

$$Y(\omega) = \int_{-\infty}^{\infty} d\omega\, e^{j\omega t} \int_{-\infty}^{\infty} h(t - \tau)u(\tau)\, d\tau$$

Upon interchanging the order of integration and a change in variables, we find that

$$(5.64) \quad \begin{aligned} Y(\omega) &= \int_{-\infty}^{\infty} u(\tau)e^{j\omega\tau}\, d\tau \int_{-\infty}^{\infty} h(\sigma)e^{j\omega\sigma}\, d\sigma \\ &= U(\omega)H(\omega) \end{aligned}$$

In other words, the Fourier transform of the convolution of two functions is equal to the product of the transforms of the functions. Put in another way, convolution in the time domain becomes multiplication in the frequency domain (the converse is also true!).

We have already seen that if the system is characterized by the differential equation

$$\alpha_n y^{(n)}(t) + \alpha_{n-1} y^{(n-1)}(t) + \cdots + \alpha_0 y(t) = \beta_0 u(t) + \beta_1 u^{(1)}(t) + \cdots + \beta_n u^{(n)}(t)$$

then

$$Y(\omega) = H(\omega)U(\omega)$$

where

$$(5.65) \quad H(\omega) = \frac{\beta_n(j\omega)^n + \beta_{n-1}(j\omega)^{n-1} + \cdots + \beta_0}{\alpha_n(j\omega)^n + \alpha_{n-1}(j\omega)^{n-1} + \cdots + \alpha_0}$$

So we conclude that the system-transfer function $H(\omega)$ is merely the Fourier transform of the impulse response $h(t)$. This fact is further substantiated since, if $u(t) = \delta(t)$, then

$$U(\omega) = 1$$

and

$$Y(\omega) = H(\omega)$$

or

$$y(t) = h(t)$$

(5.66) Example
Consider again the network discussed in Example (5.17) which is described by the differential equation

$$\dot{y}(t) + \frac{1}{RC} y(t) = \frac{1}{RC} u(t)$$

The transfer function is found from (5.65) to be

$$H(\omega) = \frac{1}{j\omega + (1/RC)}$$

From Example (5.40) we see that

$$h(t) = \begin{cases} \dfrac{1}{RC} \exp\left(-\dfrac{1}{RC} t\right) & t > 0 \\ 0 & t < 0 \end{cases}$$

which agrees with our former result. ∎

We have limited the use of the Fourier transform to linear time-invariant systems. The reason for the restriction to linear systems should be obvious. The reason for the time-invariance restriction becomes clear if we consider the time-variable, linear differential equation

$$\dot{y}(t) + ty(t) = u(t)$$

Let us take the Fourier transform of $ty(t)$:

$$\text{(5.67)}\quad \mathfrak{F}[ty(t)] = \int_{-\infty}^{\infty} ty(t)e^{-j\omega t}\,dt$$
$$= j\frac{d}{d\omega}\int_{\infty}^{\infty} y(t)e^{-j\omega t}\,dt$$
$$= j\frac{d}{d\omega}Y(\omega)$$

Therefore the transformed differential equation becomes

$$j\omega\, Y(\omega) + j\frac{d}{d\omega}Y(\omega) = U(\omega)$$

a differential equation itself. Hence, *nothing has been gained.*

There are many properties of the Fourier transform that we have not discussed. For the most part, these properties are the same as those to be presented for the Laplace transform in the next section. We summarize some of these properties in Table 5.1. In Table 5.2 we list some common functions and their transforms.

TABLE 5.1 Properties of Fourier transforms

Linearity:

$$\mathfrak{F}[\alpha f_1(t) + \beta f_2(t)] = \alpha F_1(\omega) + \beta F_2(\omega)$$

Time differentiation:

$$\left[\frac{d}{dt}f(t)\right] = j\omega F(\omega) \qquad \mathfrak{F}\left[\frac{d^n}{dt^n}f(t)\right] = (j\omega)^n F(\omega)$$

Multiplication by time:

$$\mathfrak{F}[tf(t)] = -j\frac{d}{d\omega}F(\omega)$$

Multiplication by an exponential:

$$\mathfrak{F}[e^{-\omega_0 t}f(t)] = F(\omega + \omega_0)$$

Time convolution:

$$\mathfrak{F}\left[\int_0^t f_1(t-\lambda)\,f_2(\lambda)\,d\lambda\right] = F_1(\omega)F_2(\omega)$$

Miscellaneous:

$$F(t) = 2\pi\mathfrak{F}^{-1}[f(-\omega)]$$

$F^*(\omega) = F(-\omega)$	for real $f(t)$
$f(t)$ even $\Rightarrow F(\omega)$	real
$f(t)$ odd $\Rightarrow F(\omega)$	imaginary

TABLE 5.2 Fourier transforms of some common functions

$f(t)$	$F(\omega)$
e^{st}, Re $\{s\} < 0$	$\dfrac{1}{j\omega - s}$
$p_T(t) = \begin{cases} 1 & 0 \le t \le T \\ 0 & \text{elsewhere} \end{cases}$	$Te^{-j\omega T/2}\left[\dfrac{\sin \omega T/2}{\omega T/2}\right]$
$e^{-\alpha t}$, $\alpha > 0$	$\dfrac{2\alpha}{\alpha^2 + \omega^2}$
$\delta(t)$	1
1	$2\pi\delta(\omega)$
$e^{j\omega_0 t}$	$2\pi\delta(\omega - \omega_0)$
$\cos \omega_0 t$	$\pi[\delta(\omega - \omega_0) + \delta(\omega + \omega_0)]$
$\sin \omega_0$	$j\pi[\delta(\omega + \omega_0) - \delta(\omega - \omega_0)]$
$1(t)$	$\dfrac{1}{j\omega} + \pi\delta(\omega)$

We now present a theorem which will play an important role in Chap. 7 when we investigate numerical techniques of systems analysis.

(5.68) Sampling theorem
If the Fourier transform of a function $f(t)$ is zero outside of some frequency range, i.e.,

$$F(\omega) = 0 \qquad \text{for } |\omega| > \omega_c$$

then $f(t)$ can be uniquely determined by its values

$$f_n = f\left(\frac{n\pi}{\omega_c}\right)$$

at a sequence of equidistant points, in particular, points which are π/ω_c apart. In fact

$$f(t) = \sum_{n=-\infty}^{\infty} f\left(\frac{n\pi}{\omega_c}\right) \frac{\sin(\omega_c t - n\pi)}{\omega_c t - n\pi}$$

Proof
The inverse Fourier transform of the bandlimited function $F(\omega)$ is

$$f(t) = \frac{1}{2\pi}\int_{-\omega_c}^{\omega_c} F(\omega)e^{j\omega t}\, d\omega$$

so that

$$f_n = f\left(\frac{n\pi}{\omega_c}\right) = \frac{1}{2\pi}\int_{-\omega_c}^{\omega_c} F(\omega)e^{jn\pi\omega/\omega_c}\,d\omega$$

Since $F(\omega)$ is bandlimited, we can create an artificially periodic signal $\hat{F}(\omega)$ such that

$$\hat{F}(\omega) = F(\omega) \qquad \text{for } -\omega_c < \omega < \omega_c$$

and

$$\hat{F}(\omega + 2\omega_c) = \hat{F}(\omega)$$

Expanding $\hat{F}(\omega)$ in a Fourier series yields

$$\hat{F}(\omega) = \sum_{k=-\infty}^{\infty} F_k e^{-jk2\pi\omega/2\omega_c}$$

where

$$F_k = \frac{1}{2\omega_c}\int_{-\omega_c}^{\omega_c} F(\omega)e^{jk\pi\omega/\omega_c}\,d\omega$$

Therefore

$$F_k = \frac{\pi}{\omega_c} f_k$$

and

$$\hat{F}(\omega) = \sum_{k=-\infty}^{\infty} \frac{\pi}{\omega_c} f_k e^{-jk\pi\omega/\omega_c}$$

for all ω. We now define the pulse $p_\omega(\omega)$ by

$$p_{\omega_c}(\omega) = \begin{cases} 1 & |\omega| < \omega_c \\ 0 & |\omega| > \omega_c \end{cases}$$

then

$$\begin{aligned} F(\omega) &= p_{\omega_c}(\omega)\hat{F}(\omega) \\ &= p_{\omega_c}(\omega) \sum_{k=-\infty}^{\infty} \frac{\pi}{\omega_c} f_k e^{-jk\pi\omega/\omega_c} \end{aligned}$$

We leave it as an exercise to show that

$$\mathfrak{F}^{-1}[p_{\omega_c}(\omega)e^{-jk\pi\omega/\omega_c}] = \frac{\omega_c}{\pi}\frac{\sin(\omega_c t - n\pi)}{\omega_c t - n\pi}$$

Therefore

$$f(t) = \sum_{k=-\infty}^{\infty} f_k \frac{\sin(\omega_c t - n\pi)}{\omega_c t - n\pi}$$

∎

There are several limitations of Fourier transforms that restrict their use. First, many functions such as e^t are not Fourier transformable. Second, Fourier transform analysis yields information only about the zero-state response. Zero-input response cannot be ascertained, because there is no mechanism to account for initial conditions. These problems are alleviated by using the Laplace transform.

5.7 THE LAPLACE TRANSFORM

Many functions that are not otherwise Fourier transformable are Fourier transformable when multiplied by the exponential $e^{-\sigma t}$, for certain values of the real number σ. As an example, consider the function

$$f(t) = \begin{cases} 0 & \text{for } t \leq 0 \\ e^t & \text{for } t > 0 \end{cases}$$

The Fourier transform of $f(t)$ does not exist. Now consider

$$\hat{f}(t) = e^{-\sigma t} f(t) = \begin{cases} 0 & \text{for } t \leq 0 \\ e^{(1-\sigma)t} & \text{for } t > 0 \end{cases}$$

$$\begin{aligned} \hat{F}(\omega) &= \mathfrak{F}[\hat{f}(t)] \\ &= \int_0^\infty e^{(1-\sigma)t} e^{-j\omega t}\, dt = \frac{1}{j\omega - (1-\sigma)} \end{aligned}$$

if $\sigma > 1$. In other words, the Fourier transform of $\hat{f}(t)$ exists only for those values of σ such that $\sigma > 1$.

Although at this point the use of the function $e^{\sigma t}$ may seem somewhat unmotivated, let us continue along these lines. Consider an arbitrary $f(t)$ and let us find the Fourier transform of $e^{-\sigma t} f(t)$:

$$\begin{aligned} \mathfrak{F}[e^{-\sigma t} f(t)] &= \int_{-\infty}^{\infty} f(t) e^{-\sigma t} e^{-j\omega t}\, dt \\ &= \int_{-\infty}^{\infty} f(t) e^{-(\sigma + j\omega)t}\, dt \\ &= F(\sigma + j\omega) \end{aligned}$$

By defining the complex variable s as

$$s \equiv \sigma + j\omega$$

we have

$$\begin{aligned} \mathfrak{F}[e^{-\sigma t} f(t)] &= \int_{-\infty}^{\infty} f(t) e^{-st}\, dt \\ &= F(s) \end{aligned}$$

under the assumption that the integral exists for some set of values of σ. We can also derive an inverse relation. We have

$$e^{-\sigma t}f(t) = \mathfrak{F}^{-1}[F(\sigma + j\omega)] = \frac{1}{2\pi}\int_{-\infty}^{\infty} F(\sigma + j\omega)e^{j\omega t}\, d\omega$$

Multiplication by $e^{\sigma t}$ and substitution of the complex variable $s = \sigma + j\omega$ yields

$$f(t) = \frac{1}{2\pi j}\int_{\sigma - j\infty}^{\sigma + j\infty} F(s)e^{st}\, ds$$

where the path of complex integration is the vertical straight line from $\sigma - j\infty$ to $\sigma + j\infty$.

In summary, the direct and inverse transforms are given by the relations

$$(5.69)\quad F(s) = \int_{-\infty}^{\infty} f(t)e^{-st}\, dt$$

and

$$(5.70)\quad f(t) = \frac{1}{2\pi j}\int_{-\infty}^{\infty} F(s)e^{st}\, ds$$

respectively, for the set of values of σ for which $F(s)$ exists. $F(s)$ is called the *two-sided*, or *bilateral, Laplace transform* of $f(t)$. We denote this relationship by

$$F(s) = \mathfrak{L}_{\text{II}}\,[f(t)]$$

and

$$f(t) = \mathfrak{L}_{\text{II}}^{-1}\,[F(s)]$$

$F(s)$ and $f(t)$ are sometimes called Laplace transform pairs, denoted by

$$f(t) \leftrightarrow F(s)$$

The value of σ in the inverse Laplace transform integral (5.70) is assumed to be in the range of values for which (5.69) converges. Observe that if (5.69) exists for $\sigma = 0$, then the Fourier and Laplace transforms are essentially the same. The range of values of σ for which (5.69) exists is called the strip of convergence, since it is represented by a "strip" in the complex plane defined by the two axes Re $\{s\} = \sigma$ and Im $\{s\} = \omega$.

(5.71) Example

Let us try to find the Laplace transform of the function

$$f(t) = e^{-a|t|} \qquad a > 0$$

We have that

$$\begin{aligned} F(s) &= \int_{-\infty}^{\infty} e^{-a|t|}e^{-st}\,dt \\ &= \int_{\infty}^{0} e^{(a-s)t}\,dt + \int_{0}^{\infty} e^{-(a+s)t}\,dt \\ &= \frac{1}{a-s}\,e^{(a-s)t}\Big]_{-\infty}^{0} + \frac{-1}{a+s}\,e^{-(a+s)t}\Big]_{0}^{\infty} \end{aligned}$$

The above integral converges if we restrict Re $\{s\} = \sigma$ to lie in the interval $-a < \sigma < a$, then

$$F(s) = \frac{1}{a-s} + \frac{1}{a+s} = \frac{2a}{a^2+s^2} \qquad -a < \sigma < a$$

Observe that since the strip of convergence contains the "$j\omega$" axis, that is, Re $\{s\} = \sigma = 0$ is allowable, the Fourier transform exists and can be found from $F(s)$ by letting $\sigma = 0$, or $s = j\omega$, therefore

$$F(\omega) = \frac{2a}{a^2 - \omega^2}$$

which agrees with the results obtained in Example (5.42). The strip of convergence is shown in Fig. 5.15. ▮

We must not underestimate the importance of the strip of convergence, as the following example illustrates.

(5.72) Example
Given the time function

$$f(t) = \begin{cases} 0 & \text{for } t < 0 \\ e^{at} & \text{for } t \geq 0,\ a \text{ is real} \end{cases}$$

shown in Fig. 5.16*a*. We find the Laplace transform from

$$F(s) = \int_{0}^{\infty} e^{at}e^{-st}\,dt = \frac{-1}{a-s}\,e^{(a-s)t}\Big]_{0}^{\infty}$$

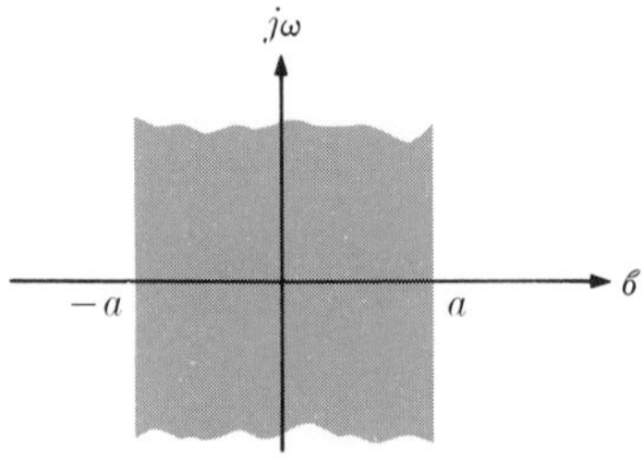

FIG. 5.15 The strip of convergence for $\mathcal{L}_{II}[e^{-a|t|}]$.

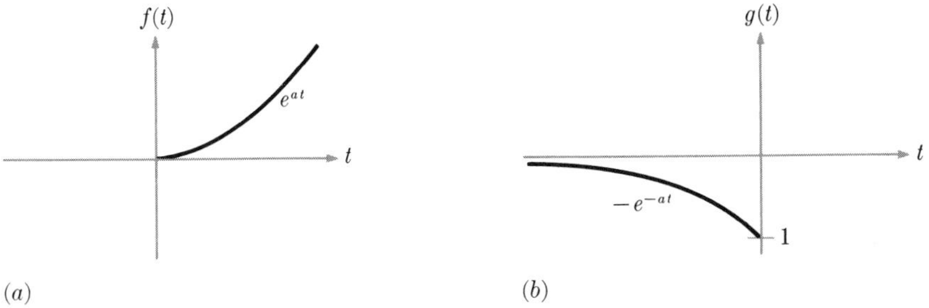

FIG. 5.16 Two different time functions which have the same Laplace transform but different regions of convergence.

which converges to

$$F(s) = \frac{1}{s-a}$$

for all $\sigma > a$. Now consider the time function

$$g(t) = \begin{cases} -e^{at} & \text{for } t \leq 0 \qquad a \text{ is real} \\ 0 & \text{for } t > 0 \end{cases}$$

shown in Fig. 5.16*b*. The Laplace transform is

$$G(s) = \int_{-\infty}^{0} -e^{at}e^{-st}\,dt = \frac{-1}{a-s}\,e^{(a-s)t}\Big]_{-\infty}^{0}$$

which converges to

$$G(s) = \frac{1}{s-a}$$

for $\sigma < a$. Thus we see that two quite different time functions have the same Laplace transform, and only the strip of convergence, or in this case the *region of convergence*, distinguishes between them. Observe that the regions of convergence for these two identically Laplace transformed functions do not overlap. ∎

For the most part, we are interested in system behavior from some initial time t_0 onward. The initial conditions are specified at time t_0. When studying time-invariant systems, without loss of generality, we can assume $t_0 = 0$. (Note that for the same reasons expressed in the section on Fourier transforms, we limit the use of Laplace transform analysis to linear time-invariant systems.) The past history of the system is adequately described by the initial state of the system. Therefore, time signals of interest may be assumed to be zero for $t < 0$. For this class of signals, the *one-sided,* or *unilateral, Laplace transform* is used

$$(5.73)\quad F(s) = \int_0^\infty f(t)e^{-st}\,dt = \mathcal{L}[f(t)]$$

The subscript I is not used since, henceforth, all Laplace transforms are assumed to be one sided, unless otherwise stated.

The strip of convergence is really a *region of convergence* for the one-sided Laplace transform. The smallest σ_a for which $F(s)$ exists is called the *abscissa of convergence.*

The expression for the inverse transform is the same whether the one-sided or the two-sided transform is used, so

$$(5.74)\quad f(t) = \frac{1}{2\pi j}\int_{\sigma-j\infty}^{\sigma+j\infty} F(s)e^{st}\,ds = \mathcal{L}^{-1}[F(s)]$$

The integration must be carried out with σ within the interval that ensures convergence of (5.73).

There are several rigorous theorems which are concerned with the existence and uniqueness of the Laplace transform. We omit these theorems here and refer the interested reader to the myriad of pertinent books on the subject. Suffice it to say that any function $f(t)$ which is defined for all t, except possibly at a countable set of points, which is piecewise continuous, and of exponential order, i.e.,

$$\lim_{t\to\infty} f(t)e^{kt} = 0$$

for some real number k, has a Laplace transform. Note that a function that is not of exponential order may or may not have a Laplace transform.

We leave it as an exercise for the reader to show that the functions e^{t^2} and t^t are not Laplace transformable.

The Laplace transforms of some common functions are given in Table 5.3.

5.8 PROPERTIES OF THE LAPLACE TRANSFORM

The Laplace transform has some properties that increase its usefulness for system studies. Many of these properties can be specialized to Fourier transforms. Table 5.4 lists these properties. It is left as an exercise to demonstrate their validity.

5.9 THE LAPLACE TRANSFORM IN SYSTEM ANALYSIS

Let us now turn to the use of the Laplace transform in system analysis. Any linear, time-invariant, lumped, nth-order system may be described

TABLE 5.3 Laplace transforms of some common functions

$f(t),\ t \geq 0$	$F(s)$ *(One-sided Laplace transform)*	*Region of convergence*
$\delta(t)$	1	$\sigma > -\infty$
$1(t)$	$\frac{1}{s}$	$\sigma > 0$
t	$\frac{1}{s^2}$	$\sigma > 0$
e^{-at}	$\frac{1}{s+a}$	$\sigma > -a$
$\sin \omega_0 t$	$\frac{\omega_0}{s^2 + \omega_0^2}$	$\sigma > 0$
$\cos \omega_0 t$	$\frac{s}{s^2 + \omega_0^2}$	$\sigma > 0$
$e^{-at} \sin \omega_0 t$	$\frac{\omega_0}{(s+a)^2 + \omega_0^2}$	$\sigma > -a$
$e^{-at} \cos \omega_0 t$	$\frac{s+a}{(s+a)^2 + \omega_0^2}$	$\sigma > -a$
$\frac{e^{-at} t^{n-1}}{(n-1)!}$	$\frac{1}{(s+a)^n}$	$\sigma > -a$

by the differential equation

$$(a_n D^n + a_{n-1} D^{n-1} + \cdots + a_0) y(t) = (b_n D^n + b_{n-1} D^{n-1} + \cdots + b_0) u(t) \tag{5.75}$$

where D is the differential operator $D \equiv d/dt$. The Laplace transform of both sides of (5.75) gives

$$\begin{aligned}[a_n s^n + a_{n-1} s^{n-1} + \cdots + a_0] Y(s) &= [b_n s^n + b_{n-1} s^{n-1} + \cdots \\ &+ b_0] U(s) - \{b_n u^{(n-1)}(0) + (b_n s + b_{n-1}) u^{(n-2)}(0) \cdots \\ &+ (b_n s^{n-1} + b_{n-1} s^{n-2} + \cdots + b_1) u(0)\} \\ &+ \{a_n y^{(n-1)}(0) + (a_n s + a_{n-1}) y^{(n-2)}(0) \\ &+ (a_n s^{n-1} + a_{n-1} s^{n-2} + \cdots + a_1) Y(0)\}\end{aligned} \tag{5.76}$$

We can rewrite (5.76) as

$$Y(s) = H(s) U(s) + E(s) \tag{5.77}$$

TABLE 5.4

Property

Linearity:

$$\mathcal{L}[\alpha f_1(t) + \beta f_2(t)] = \alpha F_1(s) + \beta F_2(s)$$

Time differentiation:

$$\mathcal{L}\left[\frac{d}{dt} f(t)\right] = sF(s) - f(0)$$

$$\mathcal{L}\left[\frac{d}{dt^n} f(t)\right] = s^n F(s) - s^{n-1} f(0) - s^{n-2} \frac{df(0)}{dt} - \cdots - \frac{d^{n-1}}{dt^{n-1}} f(0)$$

Time integration:

$$\mathcal{L}\left[\int_0^t f(\tau)\right] = \frac{F(s)}{s}$$

Multiplication by time:

$$\mathcal{L}[tf(t)] = -\frac{d}{ds} F(s)$$

Division by time:

$$\mathcal{L}\left[\frac{f(t)}{t}\right] = \int_s^\infty F(\lambda)\, d\lambda$$

Multiplication by an exponent:

$$\mathcal{L}[e^{-at} f(t)] = F(s + a)$$

Time shift:

$$\mathcal{L}[f(t - t_0)1(t - t_0)] = e^{-t_0 s} F(s)$$

Scale change:

$$\mathcal{L}\left[f\left(\frac{t}{a}\right)\right] = aF\left(\frac{s}{a}\right)$$

Time convolution:

$$\mathcal{L}\left[\int_0^t f_1(t - \lambda) f_2(\lambda)\, d\lambda\right] = F_1(s) F_2(s)$$

Multiplication in time domain:

$$\mathcal{L}[f_1(t) f_2(t)] = \frac{1}{2\pi j} \int_{\xi - j\infty}^{\xi + j\infty} F_1(\eta) F_2(s - \eta)\, d\eta$$

where $\eta = \xi + j\omega$ and ξ must be greater than the abscissa of absolute convergence for $f_1(t)$ and $f_2(t)$ over the path of integration

Initial value:

$$\lim_{t \to 0} f(t) = \lim_{s \to \infty} sF(s)$$ provided that the limit exists

Final value:

$$\lim_{t \to \infty} f(t) = \lim_{s \to 0} sF(s)$$ provided that $sF(s)$ is analytic on the $j\omega$ axis and in the right half of the s plane.

where

$$(5.78) \quad H(s) = \frac{b_n s^n + b_{n-1}s^{n-1} + \cdots + b_0}{a_n s^n + a_{n-1}s^{n-1} + \cdots + a_0}$$

and $E(s)$ is a rational function which involves the initial value of $y(t)$ and its $(n - 1)$st derivatives. If all the initial conditions are zero, and if $u(t) = 0$ for $t \leq 0$, then $E(s) = 0$, the zero-state situation, and (5.77) reduces to

$$(5.79) \quad Y(s) = H(s)U(s)$$

(5.80) Example

Consider the second-order differential equation

$$(D^2 + 5D + 6)y(t) = (4D + 1)u(t)$$

The Laplace transformed equation is

$$(s^2 + 5s + 6)Y(s) = (4s + 1)U(s) - 4u(0) + (s + 5)y(0) + y(0)$$

or

$$Y(s) = \frac{4s + 1}{s^2 + 5s + 6}U(s) - \frac{4u(0) + (s + 5)y(0) - \dot{y}(0)}{s^2 + 5s + 6}$$

If $y(0) = \dot{y}(0) = u(0) = 0$ then

$$Y(s) = \frac{4s + 1}{s^2 + 5s + 6}U(s)$$

∎

Returning to (5.79), if $u(t) = \delta(t)$, then $U(s) = 1$ and $Y(s) = H(s)$ so that $H(s)$, the system's transfer function, is the Laplace transform of the impulse response $h(t)$.

For arbitrary inputs, expression (5.77) may be used to find the transform of the corresponding response. The actual response may be found, using Table 5.1, or other methods still to be discussed. In summary, the Laplace transform transforms an nth-order differential equation into an algebraic equation. The algebraic equation is easier to manipulate, although difficulties may arise in the attempt to find the inverse transform. As can be seen from (5.77), the major difference between Fourier and Laplace transform analysis is that the latter accounts for initial conditions. Since Laplace transform analysis is carried out in terms of the complex variable s, we sometimes call it s-plane or s-domain analysis.

(5.81) Example

We wish to find the voltage response $v(t)$ of the network shown in Fig. 5.17 to the current excitation $i(t)$. We write the single-node equation

$$i(t) = i_L(0)1(t) - \int_0^t 12v(\tau)\,d\tau + \dot{v}(t) + 7v(t)$$

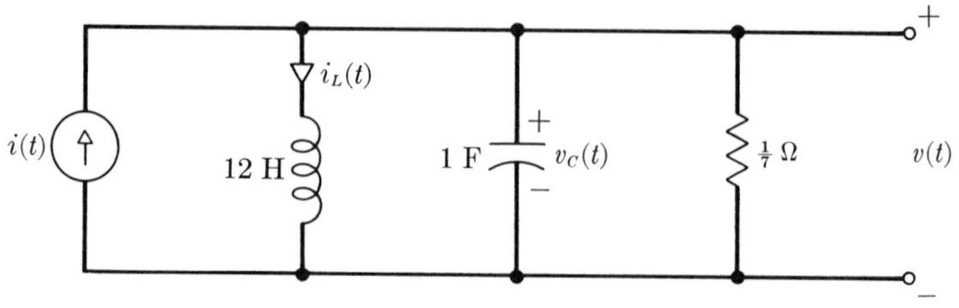

FIG. 5.17 Example (5.80).

(Note that $i_L(0)1(t) = 0$ for $t < 0$.) The Laplace transform of this expression is

$$I(s) = \frac{i_L(0)}{s} + \left(\frac{12}{s} + s + 7\right) V(s) - v(0)$$

Recognizing that $v(0) = v_c(0)$, we have

$$V(s) = \frac{s}{s^2 + 7s + 12} I(s) + \frac{sv_c(0) - i_L(0)}{s^2 + 7s + 12}$$

Comparison of the above expression with (5.77) indicates that the system's transfer function is

$$H(s) = \frac{s}{s^2 + 7s + 12}$$

We recognize $H(s)$ to be the input impedance of the network. Let the input be the unit step, $i_L(0) = 4$, and $v_c(0) = -1$. Then the response is

$$V(s) = \frac{1}{s^2 + 7s + 12} - \frac{1}{s + 3} = -\frac{1}{s + 4}$$

Using Table 5.3, we find that

$$v(t) = -e^{-4t} \qquad t \geq 0$$

Observe that we can find the impulse response of this network from $H(s)$:

$$\begin{aligned} h(t) &= \mathfrak{L}^{-1}[H(s)] \\ &= \mathfrak{L}^{-1}\left[\frac{s}{s^2 + 7s + 12}\right] = \mathfrak{L}^{-1}\left[\frac{4}{s + 4} - \frac{3}{s + 3}\right] \\ &= 4e^{-4t} - 3e^{-3t} \end{aligned}$$

∎

Once the transform of a system's response is found, we are usually interested in finding the inverse transform, or the time response. The easiest approach, if applicable, is to perform a partial fraction expansion on the transform and then use Tables 5.3 and 5.4 to find the inverse transform.

(5.82) Example
Consider the transform

$$F(s) = \frac{s^3 + 5s^2 + 7s + 5}{s^4 + 2s^3 + 5s^2}$$

We can factor the denominator as

$$(s^4 + 2s^3 + 5s^2) = s^2[(s + 1)^2 + 4]$$

Therefore it remains to determine the constants A, B, and C such that

$$F(s) = \frac{A}{s} + \frac{B}{s^2} + \frac{C}{(s^2 + 1) + 4}$$

The reader should verify that

$$F(s) = \frac{1}{s} + \frac{1}{s^2} + \frac{2}{(s + 1)^2 + 4}$$

From Table 5.3 we find that

$$\mathcal{L}^{-1}\left[\frac{2}{(s + 1)^2 + 4}\right] = e^{-t} \sin 2t, \ \mathcal{L}^{-1}\left[\frac{1}{s}\right] = 1(t)$$

and

$$\mathcal{L}^{-1}\left[\frac{1}{s^2}\right] = t$$

Hence, by linearity of the Laplace transform

$$f(t) = 1(t)[1 + t + e^{-t} \sin 2t]$$ ∎

In many instances it is not possible to use the procedure outlined above to find the inverse Laplace transform. For these cases, we must resort to the inversion integral

$$f(t) = \frac{1}{2\pi j} \int_{\sigma - j\infty}^{\sigma + j\infty} F(s)e^{st}\, ds \tag{5.83}$$

The above integral involves contour integration in the complex plane. It is not our intent to delve into a detailed study of complex-variable theory. The interested reader will find numerous texts that cover this topic thoroughly.[1] Rather, we will cite some of the more relevant theorems and demonstrate how they aid in evaluation of the inversion integral (5.83).

[1] R. V. Churchill, "Complex Variables and Applications," 2d ed., McGraw-Hill, New York, 1960.

5.10 ELEMENTS OF COMPLEX-VARIABLE THEORY

Functions of a single complex variable z can be thought of as being a function of the two real variables x and y where

$$z \equiv x + jy$$

Thus we are motivated to extend various properties that are attributed to functions of a real variable to functions of a complex variable. Analyticity of complex functions, which is comparable to differentiability of ordinary functions, is an extremely important property. Before defining analyticity, we present some useful nomenclature.

A complex number may be thought to be made up of a real and an imaginary part. It is therefore convenient to envision a complex number as a *point* in a two-dimensional cartesian coordinate system (the complex plane) where the real part is plotted on the abscissa and the imaginary part is plotted on the ordinate.

The complex number z may be characterized in two convenient ways; it may be expressed in terms of real and imaginary parts

$$z = x + jy$$

or in terms of magnitude and phase

$$z = |z|e^{j\theta}$$

where $|z|$ is known as the magnitude of z and θ the phase. The following relationships exist between these two characterizations:

$$|z| = (zz^*)^{\frac{1}{2}} = \sqrt{x^2 + y^2}$$

and

$$\theta = \arctan \frac{y}{x}$$

where * denotes complex conjugate, i.e.,

$$z^* = x - jy$$

An ε (epsilon), *neighborhood* of a point (complex number) z_0, is the set of all points (complex numbers) for which

$$|z - z_0| < \varepsilon$$

where ε is a positive number. In other words an ε neighborhood of the point z_0 is all the points (or the region) in the *interior* of a circle of radius ε centered at z_0. Observe that the boundary of this circle, i.e., the points for which $|z - z_0| = \varepsilon$, are not included in the neighborhood.

(5.84) Continuity

A (single-valued) function of the complex variable z, $f(z)$, is *continuous* at a point z_0 if and only if all three of the following conditions are satisfied.

(1) $f(z_0)$ exists

(2) $\lim_{z \to z_0} f(z)$ exists

(3) $\lim_{z \to z_0} f(z) = f(z_0)$

The limit in (3) must approach $f(z_0)$ no matter how (in which direction) z approaches z_0. ▮

If a function f is continuous at every point in a region R, we say f is *continuous in* R.

(5.85) Differentiability

If $f(z)$ is single valued and continuous for every z in some neighborhood of z_0, then we say that $f(z)$ is differentiable at z_0 if

$$(5.86) \quad \lim_{\Delta z \to 0} \left[\frac{f(z_0 + \Delta z) - f(z_0)}{\Delta z} \right]$$

exists as a finite number and is independent of how the increment Δz tends to zero. This limit is called the *derivative* of f at z_0 and is denoted by $f'(z_0)$ or $\left.\frac{df}{dz}\right|_{z_0}$. ▮

We say that $f(z)$ is *not differentiable* at z_0 if the limit (5.86) does not exist or if it depends on how Δz approaches zero.

(5.87) Example

Consider the function

$$f(z) = z^2 + z + 1$$

We calculate the derivative for this function at any point z as follows

$$\begin{aligned} f'(z) &= \lim_{\Delta z \to 0} \frac{[(z + \Delta z)^2 + (z + \Delta z) + 1] - [z^2 + z + 1]}{\Delta z} \\ &= \lim_{\Delta z \to 0} \frac{[z\,\Delta z + \Delta z + \Delta z^2]}{\Delta z} \\ &= z + 1 \end{aligned}$$

independent of the way Δz approaches zero. ▮

We leave it as an exercise for the reader to show that the function

$$f(z) = |z|^2$$

is not differentiable at the point $z = 0$.

(5.88) Analyticity

We say that a function f is *analytic at a point* z_0 if it is differentiable in some ε neighborhood containing z_0. The function f is said to be an *analytic function* in a region R if it is differentiable at every point in R. ∎

In the sequel, we will be very interested in whether or not complex functions are analytic in certain regions of the complex plane. Thus we wish to have some convenient means for determining the analyticity of a function. For manipulative ease, we introduce the following notation. The complex variable z may be written as

$$z = x + jy$$

where x and y are real variables. Similarly, the complex function f may be written as

$$f(z) = u(z) + jv(z)$$

where u and v are real functions. We may consider u and v as functions of x and y, that is,

$$u(z) = u(x,y) \qquad \text{and } v(z) = v(x,y)$$

The necessary and sufficient condition we seek for functions to be analytic is given by the following theorem.

(5.89) Theorem

A necessary and sufficient condition for $f(z) = u(x,y) + jv(x,y)$ to be analytic at the point $z_0 = x_0 + jy_0$ is that $u(x,y)$ and $v(x,y)$ together with their partial derivatives be continuous and satisfy the *Cauchy-Riemann* conditions

$$\frac{\partial u(x,y)}{\partial x} = \frac{\partial v(x,y)}{\partial y}$$

$$\frac{\partial u(x,y)}{\partial y} = -\frac{\partial v(x,y)}{\partial x}$$

in the neighborhood of (x_0,y_0).

(5.90) Example

Again consider the complex function

$$\begin{aligned} f(z) &= z^2 + z + 1 \\ &= (x^2 - y^2 + x + 1) + j(2xy + y) \end{aligned}$$

Then

$$\frac{\partial u}{\partial x} = 2x + 1 = \frac{\partial v}{\partial y}$$

and

$$\frac{\partial u}{\partial y} = -2y = -\frac{\partial v}{\partial x}$$

Hence $f(z)$ is analytic as indicated by Example (5.87).

Now consider the complex function

$$f(z) = |z|^2 = x^2 + y^2$$

We have

$$\frac{\partial u}{\partial x} = 2x \qquad \frac{\partial v}{\partial y} = 0$$

$$\frac{\partial u}{\partial y} = 2y \qquad \frac{\partial v}{\partial x} = 0$$

so that the Cauchy-Riemann conditions are not satisfied, which implies that $f'(z)$ does not exist at $z = 0$. ▮

(5.91) Corollary

A function f is analytic in a region R if and only if the Cauchy-Riemann conditions are satisfied at every point in R. ▮

We leave it as an exercise for the reader to show that the familiar rules for differentiating sums, products, and quotients of real functions remain valid for analytic functions. The complex function

$$f(z) = z$$

is analytic everywhere. Thus, it follows that any polynomial in z,

$$P(z) = p_0 + p_1 z + \cdots + p_n z^n$$

is analytic and the ratio of polynomials

$$f(z) = \frac{P(z)}{Q(z)}$$

is analytic except possibly at those values of z for which $Q(z) = 0$. These values of z are called *zeros* of the polynomial $Q(z)$. A function which is the ratio of two polynomials is called a *rational function*. Therefore rational functions are analytic except possibly at the *zeros of the denominator*, which are also termed *poles of the function*.

The points of a region R where $f(z)$ ceases to be analytic are called *singular points*, and $f(z)$ is said to be *singular* at these points. Singular points are further classified as follows:

(1) If $f(z)$ is singular at z_0, but

$$\hat{f}(z) = f(z)(z - z_0)^n$$

is analytic and nonzero at $z = z_0$ for some finite integer n, then z_0 is called a *nonessential* or *removable* singularity. We also call z_0 a *pole* of order n.

(2) A singular point which is not removable is called an *essential* singularity.

(5.92) Example
The complex function

$$f(z) = \frac{z + 2}{z(z + 1)^2}$$

has a first-order pole at $z = 0$ and a second-order pole at $z = -1$. The complex function

$$f(z) = e^{1/z} = 1 + \frac{1}{z} + \frac{1}{2!z^2} + \cdots$$

has an essential singularity at $z = 0$. ∎

Finally if z is a singular point of an analytic function $f(z)$ and the ε neighborhood of this point contains no other singular points of $f(z)$, the singularity z is said to be *isolated.*

The definite integral of a real function f with respect to a real variable x,

$$\int_a^b f(x)\,dx$$

is a number that is determined by the values of the function $f(x)$ at the points along the segment of the x axis between the points a and b. The definite integral of a complex function f with respect to the complex variable z,

$$(5.93) \quad \int_\alpha^\beta f(z)\,dz$$

between the points represented by the complex numbers α and β, is defined in terms of the values of $f(z)$ at the points *along some curve from* α *to* β. This type of integration is called *contour integration*, and the value of the integral may depend on the curve selected. We sometimes write (5.93) as

$$(5.94) \quad \int_C f(z)\,dz$$

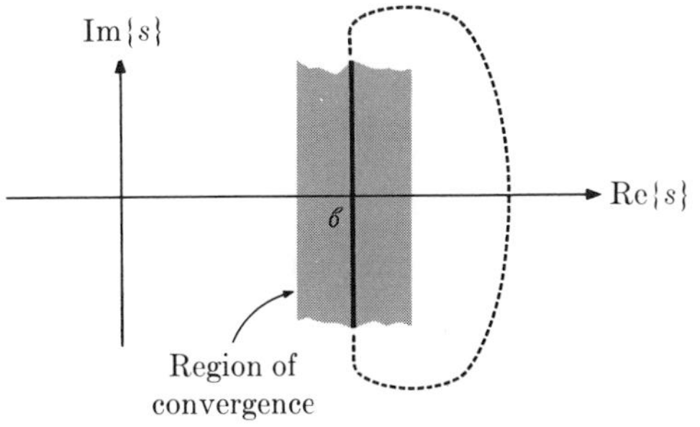

FIG. 5.18 Possible contour for Laplace inversion integral.

where C is some curve of finite length joining α and β. Recall the Laplace inversion integral,

$$\frac{1}{2\pi j}\int_{\sigma-j\infty}^{\sigma+j\infty} F(s)e^{st}\,ds$$

The contour of integration is the infinite vertical line passing through σ on the real axis (see Fig. 5.18). We now seek a convenient method for evaluation of integrals such as (5.94). Recall that we have defined the complex variable z as

$$z = x + jy$$

where x and y are real variables, and the complex function $f(z)$ is

$$f(z) = u(x,y) + jv(x,y)$$

where u and v are real functions. Therefore,

$$dz = dx + j\,dy$$

and the contour integral (5.94) may be written as

$$(5.95)\quad \begin{aligned}\int_C f(z)\,dz &= \int_C [u(x,y) + jv(x,y)][dx + j\,dy]\\ &= \int_C [u(x,y)\,dx - v(x,y)\,dy]\\ &\qquad + j\int_C [u(x,y)\,dy + v(x,y)\,dx]\end{aligned}$$

Let the curve C be defined parametrically by the parameter t, that is, the curve C is the locus of points defined by the function $z(t)$ such that $t_0 \le t \le t_f$. Now

$$z(t) = x(t) + jy(t)$$

and

$$dz = \dot{z}(t)\,dt = [\dot{x}(t) + j\dot{y}(t)]\,dt$$

Expression (5.95) can now be written as

$$(5.96)\quad \int_C f(z)\,dz = \int_{t_0}^{t_1} \{u[x(t),y(t)]\dot{x}(t) - v[x(t),y(t)]\dot{y}(t)\}\,dt + j\int_{t_0}^{t_1} \{u[x(t),y(t)]\dot{y}(t) + v[x(t),y(t)]\dot{x}(t)\}\,dt$$

Thus the complex contour integral is reduced to integrals of functions of a single real variable, and therefore has the same properties of real integrals, e.g., linearity.

If the curve C contains a finite number of arcs, $C_1, C_2, \ldots, C_n$, each of which has the parametric representation described above, the contour integral (5.94) can be written as the sum of the integrals along these arcs:

$$\int_C f(z)\,dz = \int_{C_1} f(z)\,dz + \int_{C_2} f(z)\,dz + \cdots + \int_{C_n} f(z)\,dz$$

Let $f(z)$ be an analytic function in a region containing C for which

$$\frac{dF}{dz} = f(z)$$

then

$$(5.97)\quad \int_a^b f(z)\,dz = \int_{t_0}^{t_1} \frac{dF(z)}{dz}\frac{dz}{dt}\,dt = \int_{t_0}^{t_1} \frac{dF[z(t)]}{dz}\,dz = F[z(t_1)] - F[z(t_0)] = F[b] - F[a]$$

Thus we see that if $f(z)$ is the derivative of an analytic function in a region containing the curve C, the integral depends only on the endpoints and not on the particular curve C chosen.

(5.98) Example

Consider the function

$$f(z) = z^n$$

Then

$$f(z) = \frac{d}{dz}\left[\frac{1}{n+1} z^{n+1}\right] = \frac{d}{dz} F(z)$$

for all $n \neq -1$. Hence

$$\int_{z_1}^{z_2} z^n\,dz = \frac{1}{n+1} z^{n+1}\Big]_{z_1}^{z_2} = \frac{1}{n+1}[z_2^{n+1} - z_1^{n+1}] \quad \blacksquare$$

Note that in the above example, if $n < 0$, $n \neq -1$, then the contour of integration may not pass through the origin, since the derivative does not exist there. It is interesting to note that if $z_1 = z_2$, that is, C is a closed curve, then

$$\int_C z^n \, dz = 0 \qquad n \neq -1 \qquad \blacksquare$$

and C does not pass through the origin for $n < 0$. Similarly we can show

$$\int_C (z - a)^n \, dz = 0 \qquad n \neq -1$$

for any closed path C which does not pass through the point $z = a$ if $n < 0$. This result will be generalized by the Cauchy integral theorem. Note first that a function that is analytic in a region containing a path C is *analytic on a path* C. The following theorem is fundamental to complex variable theory.

(5.99) Theorem (Cauchy Integral Theorem)
If a function $f(z)$ is single valued and analytic within and on a closed curve C, then

$$\int_C f(z) \, dz = 0 \qquad \blacksquare$$

There are some important corollaries which can be easily proved by application of Theorem (5.99).

(5.100) Corollary
If C_1 and C_2 are two simple curves with the same end points (so $C_1 - C_2$ is a closed curve), and if $f(z)$ is analytic on and within $C_1 - C_2$, then

$$\int_{C_1} f(z) \, dz = \int_{C_2} f(z) \, dz \qquad \blacksquare$$

(5.101) Corollary
Let C_1 and C_2 be two simple closed curves lying within a region R, so that C_1 and C_2 enclose exactly the same points not in R, as shown in Fig. 5.19*a*. Let $f(z)$ be analytic in R (but not necessarily within C_1 or C_2). Then

$$\oint_{C_1} f(z) \, dz = \oint_{C_2} f(z) \, dz$$

Note that we denote integration about a closed contour by a circle through the integral sign.

Proof
Consider the closed path

$$C = C_1 + C_2 + I_1 + I_2$$

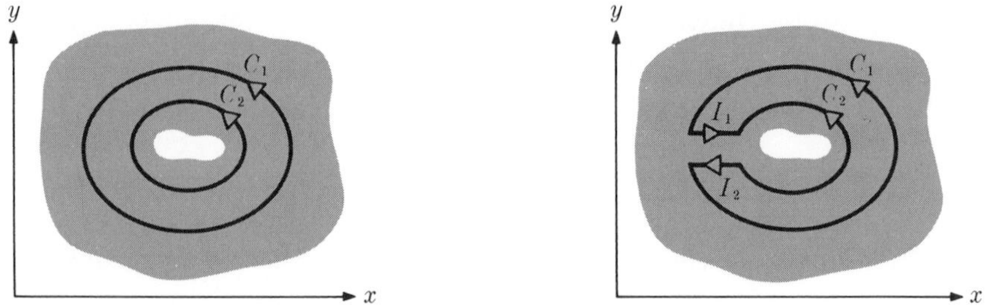

(a) (b)

FIG. 5.19 Contours of integration.

as shown in Fig. 5.19*b*. Observe that the pieces I_1 and I_2 result from an infinitesimal break in the curves, so that

$$I_2 = -I_1$$

C is a simple closed curve. Since C lies entirely in R, $f(z)$ is analytic in and on C. Therefore, by the Cauchy integral theorem,

$$0 = \oint_C f(z)\,dz = \int_{C_1} f(z)\,dz + \int_{C_2} f(z)\,dz + \int_{I_1} f(z)\,dz + \int_{I_2} f(z)\,dz$$

The last two terms cancel because $I_1 = -I_2$, so we have

$$\int_{C_1} f(z)\,dz = \int_{C_2} f(z)\,dz \qquad \blacksquare$$

which was to be proven.

(5.102) Example

We have already seen that

$$\oint_C (z-a)^n\,dz = 0 \qquad \text{any path, } n \geq 0$$

and

$$\oint_C (z-a)^n\,dz = 0 \qquad n < 0,\ n \neq -1$$

for any path not passing through $z = a$. Now consider

$$\oint \frac{dz}{z-a}$$

for a simple closed path C not passing through $z = a$. If C does not enclose $z = a$, $1/(z - a)$ is analytic on and within C, since $f(z) = 1/(z - a)$ is analytic everywhere except $z = a$. Hence

$$\oint \frac{dz}{z-a} = 0 \qquad C \text{ simple closed path not enclosing } a$$

If C encloses $z = a$, consider a new curve C_1 defined by

$$C_1 : z = a + re^{j2\pi t} \qquad 0 \leq t \leq 1$$

or

$$z - a = re^{j2\pi t}$$

This is a circle of radius r around the point a. The region R may be considered to be the entire plane except $z = a$. Since C and C_1 both enclose $z = a$, Corollary (5.101) implies that

$$\oint_C \frac{dz}{z - a} = \oint_{C_1} \frac{dz}{z - a} = \int_0^1 \frac{1}{z(t) - a} z'(t)\, dt$$
$$= \int_0^1 \frac{jr2\pi e^{j2\pi t}}{re^{j2\pi t}} = j2\pi \int_0^1 dt = 2\pi j$$

Corollary (5.101) says that in evaluating the integral of a function around a closed path C, the important thing is the points enclosed by C where the function is *not analytic*. Any two closed curves containing the same singular points will have the same integrals.

(5.103) Theorem (Cauchy Integral Formula)
Let $f(x)$ be analytic on and within a simple closed curve C. Let z_0 be an arbitrary point inside C. Then

$$(5.104) \quad f(z_0) = \frac{1}{2\pi j} \oint_C \frac{f(z)}{z - z_0}\, dz$$

∎

It is interesting to observe (5.104) upon differentiation:

$$\frac{d}{dz_0} f(z_0) = \frac{1}{2\pi j} \oint_C \frac{d}{dz} \left[\frac{f(z)}{z - z_0} \right] dz$$
$$= \frac{1}{2\pi j} \oint_C \frac{f(z)}{(z - z_0)^2}\, dz$$

Furthermore, upon repetitive differentiation (5.104) becomes

$$(5.105) \quad \frac{d^n}{dz_0{}^n} f(z_0) = \frac{n!}{2\pi j} \oint_C \frac{f(z)}{(z - z_0)^{n+1}}\, dz$$

Two rather interesting properties of analytic functions emerge. First, since the right-hand side of (5.105) is well defined for all n, an analytic function has derivatives of all orders. In other words, even though the definition of analyticity only required the first derivative to exist, the condition is so strong that all derivatives then exist. Note therefore, that all derivatives of an analytic function are also analytic functions. Second, all these derivatives are determined by $f(z)$ along any closed path C.

If we know the values of $f(z)$ on such a path, we can use Eq. (5.105) to determine the function and all its derivatives at any point enclosed by the path. Further, if two analytic functions agree along a simple closed contour, they must agree inside the contour.

From corollary (5.101) we see that when integrating around a closed path the singularities enclosed by the path are of prime importance. If no singularities are enclosed, the integral is zero by the Cauchy integral theorem. The simplest case is a path which encloses one singularity. Let $f(z)$ have a singularity at $z = z_0$, and let C be a simple counterclockwise closed path which encloses z_0, but no other singularities. The *residue* of $f(z)$ at $z = a_0$ is defined as

$$\text{(5.106)} \quad \operatorname*{Res}_{z=z_0} f(z) = \frac{1}{2\pi j} \oint_C f(z)\, dz$$

Note that by corollary (5.101) this integral has the same value for all such paths C. When the singularity of $f(z)$ at z_0 is a pole of order n, we can write

$$f(z) = \frac{f_1(z)}{(z - z_0)^n}$$

in which $f_1(z)$ is analytic about z_0. The Cauchy integral formula then gives for a pole of order n,

$$\begin{aligned}\text{(5.107)} \quad \operatorname*{Res}_{z=z_0} f(z) &= \frac{1}{2\pi j} \oint \frac{f_1(z)}{(z - z_0)^n}\, dz \\ &= \frac{1}{(n-1)!} \frac{d^{n-1}}{dz^{n-1}} f_1(z) \bigg|_{z=z_0} \\ &= \frac{1}{(n-1)!} \frac{d^{n-1}}{dz^{n-1}} [(z - z_0)^n f(z)] \bigg|_{z=z_0}\end{aligned}$$

(5.108) Example

Consider the complex function

$$f(z) = \frac{z^2}{(z-1)(z-2)(z-3)}$$

This function is rational with poles of order 1 at $z_1 = 1 + j0$, $z_2 = 2 + j0$, and $z_3 = 3 + j0$. From (5.107), with $n = 1$, we have

$$\operatorname*{Res}_{z=z_1} f(z) = \frac{z^2}{(2-2)(z-3)} \bigg|_{z=1} = \frac{1}{2}$$

Similarly, we find

$$\operatorname*{Res}_{z=z_2} f(z) = -4$$

and

$$\operatorname*{Res}_{z=z_3} f(z) = \frac{9}{2}$$

Thus if we have a path C that encircles z_2 in a counterclockwise manner and does not encircle z_1 or z_3

$$\int_C f(z)\, dz = -4 \cdot 2\pi j = -8\pi j$$ ▮

If we are given an arbitrary (not necessarily simple) closed curve, it may encircle a point more than once. We denote by $n(C,z_0)$ the number of times the curve C encircles the point z_0. To find $n(C,z_0)$ we need only draw a radial line from z_0 to ∞ in any direction. If n_+ is the number of times C crosses the line in the counterclockwise direction, and n_- is the number of crossings in the clockwise direction, we have

$$n(C,z_0) = n_+ - n_-$$

If we know $n(C,z_0)$ for each singularity, and if we know all the residues, the following theorem gives the integral along C.

(5.109) Theorem (Cauchy Residue Theorem)
Let $f(z)$ be analytic in a region R, except at the singularities $z_1, z_2, \ldots,$ z_n. Let C be a closed path in R which does not pass through any of the points z_1, $i = 1, 2, \ldots, n$. Then

$$\oint_C f(z)\, dz = 2\pi j \sum_{i=1}^{n} n(C,z_i) \operatorname*{Res}_{z=z_i} f(z)$$

5.11 THE LAPLACE INVERSION INTEGRAL

Let us now turn to the solution of the inverse Laplace transform integral

$$(5.110)\quad f(z) = \frac{1}{2\pi j} \int_{\sigma-j\infty}^{\sigma+j\infty} F(s)e^{st}\, ds$$

Since the form of the inverse Laplace transform integral is identical for both the one- and two-sided Laplace transform, let us consider both cases simultaneously. Our intent is to use the Cauchy residue theorem (5.109) to evaluate (5.110). Observe that the Cauchy residue theorem assumes that the integration is carried out over a closed path C and that the

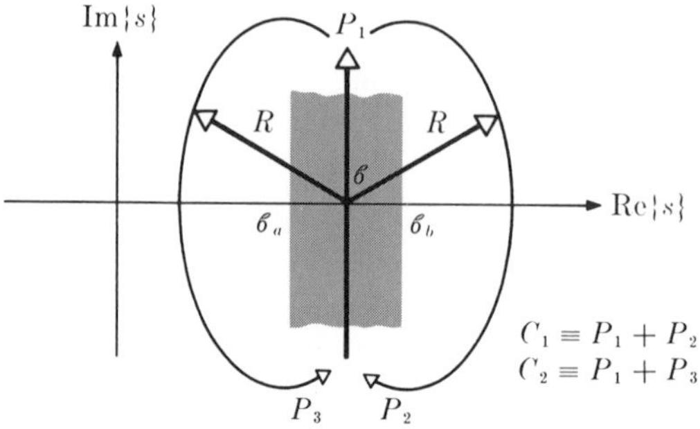

FIG. 5.20 Contours of integration for the Laplace inversion integral.

integrand, in our case $F(s)e^{st}$, is analytic within C except at a finite number of singularities. Moreover, the curve C must not pass through these singularities. Since the contour associated with the inversion integral is merely a vertical line defined by $-\infty < \text{Im}\ \{s\} \leq \infty$ for $\sigma_a \leq \text{Re}\ \{s\} \leq \sigma_b$, we must find an addition to the curve such that together with the original line it forms a closed contour, but which does not affect the value of the integral.

Consider the closed paths C_1 and C_2 indicated in Fig. 5.20. We know that $F(s)e^{st}$ is analytic in the region of convergence defined by $\sigma_a \leq \text{Re}\ \{s\} \leq \sigma_b$, and therefore, analytic on curve P_1. But $F(s)e^{st}$ has an essential singularity at $s = \infty$. If the semicircular curves P_2 and P_3 are assumed to have radii approaching infinity, then we can essentially consider that the singularity at infinity is excluded from the interior of the contour, and thereby, the conditions of Theorem (5.109) are satisfied. In other words we have made a detour about the singularity at infinity and have included within the closed contours C_1 or C_2 only the singularities of $F(s)$. This may be visualized by considering the complex plane as being the surface of a sphere of infinite radius. At this point, it is important to observe that if $t > 0$, $F(s)e^{st}$ cannot have any singularities on the right-hand side of the region of convergence shown in Fig. 5.20. Similarly for $t < 0$, $F(s)e^{st}$ cannot have any singularities to the left of the region of convergence. Now if we can show that

$$\lim_{R\to\infty} \int_{P_2} F(s)e^{st}\, ds = 0$$

then

$$\int_{C_1} F(s)e^{st}\, ds = \int_{\sigma-j\infty}^{\sigma+j\infty} F(s)e^{st}\, ds$$

for $t > 0$ and if

$$\lim_{R\to\infty} \int_{P_3} F(s)e^{st}\, ds = 0$$

then

$$\int_{C_2} F(s)e^{st}\,ds = \int_{\sigma-j\infty}^{\sigma+j\infty} F(s)e^{st}\,ds$$

for $t < 0$, and thereby apply the Cauchy residue theorem directly to find the inverse transform using the closed contours C_1 and C_2. The following lemma is an aid to this end.

(5.111) Jordan's lemma

Let $G(z)$ be a function of $z = Re^{j\theta}$ such that

$$\lim_{R\to\infty} G(Re^{j\theta}) = 0$$

uniformly in θ for $\pi/2 \leq \theta \leq 3\pi/2$ such that $G(Re^{j\theta})$ is analytic when both $R > C$ (a constant) and $\pi/2 \leq \theta \leq 3\pi/2$. Then if b is real and positive

$$\lim_{R\to\infty} \int_{C_l} G(z)e^{bz}\,dz = 0$$

where C_l is a semicircle of radius R in the left half plane about the origin. Similarly, if

$$\lim_{R\to\infty} G(Re^{j\theta}) = 0$$

uniformly in θ for $-\pi/2 \leq \theta \leq \pi/2$ such that $G(Re^{j\theta})$ is analytic when both $R > C$ and $-\pi/2 \leq \theta \leq \pi/2$, then if b is real and negative

$$\lim_{R\to\infty} \int_{C_r} G(z)e^{bz}\,dz = 0$$

where C_r is a semicircle of radius R in the right half plane about the origin. ▮

Consider again Fig. 5.20. For $t > 0$, $F(s)e^{st}$ cannot have singularities to the right of P_1. Similarly for $t < 0$, $F(s)e^{st}$ cannot have singularities to the left of P_1. Let us make the change of variables

$$z = s - \sigma$$

so that in the "z plane," the semicircles P_2 and P_3 have their centers at the origin. For $t > 0$, $F(z + \sigma)e^{(z+\sigma)t}$ has no poles in the left half plane and

$$\lim_{R\to\infty} F(Re_j^{\theta} + \sigma) \to 0$$

so that from Jordan's lemma

$$\int_{P_3} F(s)e^{st}\,ds = 0$$

Similarly for $t < 0$

$$\int_{P_2} F(s)e^{st}\,ds = 0$$

Combining these results with the Cauchy residue theorem we have the following result

$$(5.112)\quad f(t) = \frac{1}{2\pi j}\int_{\sigma-j\infty}^{\sigma+j\infty} F(s)e^{st}\,ds$$

$$= \begin{cases} \Sigma \text{ residues of } F(s)e^{st} \text{ at the singularities to the left of } P_1 \text{ for } t > 0 \\ -\Sigma \text{ residues of } F(s)e^{st} \text{ at the singularities to the right of } P_1 \text{ for } t < 0. \end{cases}$$

(5.113) Example

Consider the Laplace transform

$$F(s) = \frac{1}{s-a}$$

with the region of convergence Re $\{s\} > a$. This function has a single pole at $s = a$. Since the singularity is to the left of the region of convergence,

$$f(t) = 0$$

for $t < 0$. To find the inverse transform for $t \geq 0$, we use (5.105) for $t > 0$:

$$f(t) = \operatorname*{Res}_{s=a} \frac{1}{s-a} e^{st} = e^{at}$$

Therefore

$$f(t) = \begin{cases} 0 & t < 0 \\ e^{at} & t > 0 \end{cases}$$

Now consider the same transform with the region of convergence Re $\{s\} < a$. Since the singularity at $s = a$ is to the right of the region of convergence

$$f(t) = 0$$

for $t > 0$. The reader should verify that

$$f(t) = e^{-at}$$

for $t < 0$. This example illustrates again the importance of knowing the region of convergence [see Example (5.72)]. ∎

(5.114) Example
Find the inverse Laplace transform of

$$F(s) = \frac{2s^2 + 2s + 5}{s^4 + 2s^3 + 5s^2}$$

where the region of convergence is Re $\{s\} > 0$. There is a second-order pole of $F(s)$ at $s = 0$ and first-order poles at $s = -1 + j2$ and $s = -1 - j2$. Since all singularities lie to the left of the region of convergence, $f(t) = 0$ for $t < 0$. From (5.112) and (5.107), we have that

$$\operatorname*{Res}_{s=0} F(s)e^{st} = \frac{d}{ds}\left(\frac{2s^2 + 2s + 5}{s^2 + 2s + 5} e^{st}\right)\bigg|_{s=0} = t$$

$$\operatorname*{Res}_{s=-1+j2} F(s)e^{st} = e^{-t} \sin 2t$$

so that

$$F(s) = t + e^{-t} \sin 2t \qquad \text{for } t > 0$$

5.12 STATE EQUATIONS AND THE LAPLACE TRANSFORM

We have seen how the Laplace transform can be used to solve for a linear time-invariant system's response when given the nth-order differential-equation description. The Laplace transform may also be used to solve state equations for linear time-invariant systems. Our discussion will continue to be limited to single input—single output systems. This restriction is merely for convenience and in no way affects the generality of the results. The reader is urged to extend previous and further results to multiple input-output systems.

Consider the state-equation description for a single input—single output, linear, time-invariant system:

(5.115*a*) $\dot{\mathbf{x}}(t) = \mathbf{A}\mathbf{x}(t) + \mathbf{b}u(t)$

and

(5.115*b*) $y(t) = \mathbf{c}'\mathbf{x}(t) + du(t)$

where $\mathbf{A}$ is an $n \times n$ constant matrix, $\mathbf{b}$ and $\mathbf{c}$ are n vectors, and d is a scalar constant. Let the initial state at time 0 be $\mathbf{x}(0) = \mathbf{x}_0$. Application of the Laplace transform yields the pair of matrix equations

$$X(s) = (s\mathbf{1} - \mathbf{A})^{-1}[\mathbf{b}U(s) + \mathbf{x}_0]$$

and

$$Y(s) = \mathbf{c}'\mathbf{X}(s) + dU(s)$$

or, upon combination of these equations,

(5.116) $Y(s) = \mathbf{c}'(s\mathbf{1} - \mathbf{A})^{-1}\mathbf{x}_0 + [\mathbf{c}'(s\mathbf{1} + \mathbf{A})^{-1}\mathbf{b} + d]U(s)$

Let

$$\mathbf{G}(s) = (s\mathbf{1} - \mathbf{A})^{-1}$$

and

$$g(t) = \mathcal{L}^{-1}[G(s)]$$

then taking the inverse Laplace transform of (5.116) yields

$$y(t) = \mathbf{c}'\mathbf{g}(t)\mathbf{x}_0 + \int_0^t \mathbf{c}'\mathbf{g}(t - \tau)\mathbf{b}u(\tau)\, d\tau + du(t)$$

Recall the time domain solution of (5.115)

$$y(t) = \mathbf{c}'e^{\mathbf{A}t}\mathbf{x}_0 + \int_0^t \mathbf{c}'e^{\mathbf{A}(t-\tau)}\mathbf{b}u(\tau)\, d\tau + du(t)$$

Therefore, we conclude that

$$\mathbf{g}(t) = e^{\mathbf{A}t}$$

and, more importantly,

(5.117) $e^{\mathbf{A}t} = \mathcal{L}^{-1}[(s\mathbf{1} - \mathbf{A})^{-1}]$

Hence, we have found an alternative method for evaluating $e^{\mathbf{A}t}$.

(5.118) Example

Find $e^{\mathbf{A}t}$ by the Laplace transform method where

$$\mathbf{A} = \begin{bmatrix} 2 & 1 & 0 \\ 0 & 2 & 0 \\ 0 & 0 & 2 \end{bmatrix}$$

We first find that

$$(s\mathbf{1} - \mathbf{A})^{-1} = \begin{bmatrix} \frac{1}{s-2} & \frac{1}{(s-2)^2} & 0 \\ 0 & \frac{1}{(s-2)} & 0 \\ 0 & 0 & \frac{1}{(s-2)} \end{bmatrix}$$

Taking the inverse Laplace transform, term by term, yields

$$e^{\mathbf{A}t} = \mathcal{L}^{-1}[(s\mathbf{1} - \mathbf{A})^{-1}]$$
$$= \begin{bmatrix} e^{2t} & te^{2t} & 0 \\ 0 & e^{2t} & 0 \\ 0 & 0 & e^{2t} \end{bmatrix}$$

which agrees with the results found in Example (3.88). ∎

The Laplace transform approach is especially convenient in cases where $\mathbf{A}$ has multiple eigenvalues.

(5.119) Example

Find $e^{\mathbf{A}t}$ where

$$\mathbf{A} = \begin{bmatrix} 0 & 1 \\ -2 & -3 \end{bmatrix}$$

First we find $(s\mathbf{1} - \mathbf{A})^{-1}$:

$$(s\mathbf{1} - \mathbf{A})^{-1} = \frac{1}{s^2 + 3s + 2} \begin{bmatrix} s + 3 & 1 \\ -2 & s \end{bmatrix}$$

The inverse Laplace transform is

$$e^{\mathbf{A}t} = \begin{bmatrix} 2e^{-t} - e^{-2t} & e^{-t} - e^{-2t} \\ -2e^{-t} + 2e^{-2t} & -e^{-t} + 2e^{-t} \end{bmatrix}$$

which agrees with the results found in Example (3.77). ▮

5.13 THE z TRANSFORM

The Laplace transform has proved successful for the study of continuous-time, linear, time-invariant systems, since it transforms differential equations into algebraic equations. Similarly, the analysis of linear, time-invariant, discrete-time systems is greatly simplified by introduction of the z transform: Under this transformation, the difference equations which describe system behavior become linear algebraic equations which are often much simpler to solve than the original difference equations. Because we may extract a discrete-time signal from a continuous-time signal by sampling, we will derive the z transform from the Laplace transform.

Let $f(t)$ denote a continuous-time signal and $\hat{f}(t)$ a discrete-time signal obtained from $f(t)$ by sampling it every T seconds and multiplying it by an impulse. This situation is illustrated in Fig. 5.21. Then

$$\hat{f}(t) = \sum_{k=-\infty}^{\infty} f(t)\,\delta(t - kT)$$

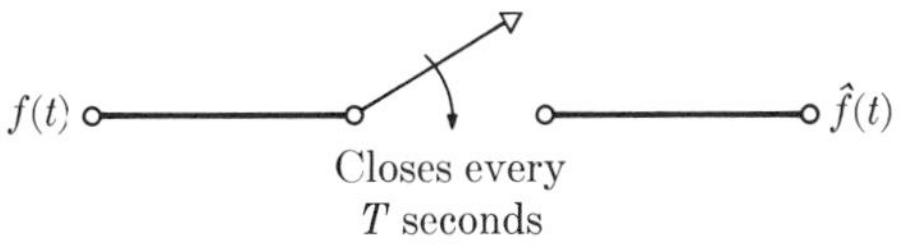

FIG. 5.21 Obtaining a discrete-time signal from a continuous-time signal by sampling.

or

$$(5.120)\quad \hat{f}(t) = \sum_{k=-\infty}^{\infty} f(kT)\delta(t - kT)$$

If

$$f(t) = 0 \qquad \text{for } t < 0$$

then

$$(5.121)\quad \hat{f}(t) = \sum_{n=0}^{\infty} f(kT)\delta(t - kT)$$

The two-sided Laplace transform of (5.120) is

$$\hat{F}_{II}(s) = \sum_{k=-\infty}^{\infty} f(kT)e^{-kTs}$$

and the one-sided Laplace transform of (5.120) is

$$\hat{F}_{I}(s) = \sum_{k=0}^{\infty} f(kT)e^{-kTs}$$

The term e^{sT} is prevalent throughout our discussion so that it is convenient to define a new variable

$$z = e^{sT}$$

then, allowing an abuse of notation

$$(5.122)\quad \hat{F}_{II}(z) = \sum_{k=-\infty}^{\infty} f(kT)z^{-n}$$

and

$$(5.123)\quad \hat{F}_{I}(z) = \sum_{k=0}^{\infty} f(kT)z^{-n}$$

The variable z can be thought of as a delay operator, that is, z^{-k} denotes a delay of kT seconds. Expressions (5.122) and (5.123) are known as the two- and one-sided z transforms of $\hat{f}(t)$, respectively. Formally we have the following definitions:

(5.124) Two-sided z transform

The two-sided z transform of the discrete-time signal

$$\{f(kT)\} = (\ldots, f(-2T), f(-T), f(0), f(T), f(2T), \ldots)$$

is

$$F_{II}(z) = Z[f(kT)] = \sum_{k=-\infty}^{\infty} f(kT)z^{-k}$$ ∎

(5.125) One-sided z transform
The one-sided z transform of the discrete-time signal

$$f\{(kT)\} = (f(0), f(T), \ldots)$$

is

$$F_{\mathrm{I}}(z) = \mathcal{Z}[f(kT)] = \sum_{n=0}^{\infty} f(kT)z^{-k}$$ ▮

Before proceeding with our discussion, we present the following simple example which indicates the usefulness of this transformation.

(5.126) Example
A first-order, linear, time-invariant, discrete-time system is characterized by the difference equation

$$y((k+1)T) = y(kT) + u(kT)$$

where $y(0) = 0$. Now let

$$\mathcal{Z}[y(kT)] = Y(z)$$

and

$$\mathcal{Z}[u(kT)] = U(z)$$

Observe that

$$\begin{aligned}\mathcal{Z}[y((k+1)T)] &= \sum_{k=0}^{\infty} y((k+1)T)z^{-k}\\ &= y(T) + y(2t)z^{-1} + y(3T)z^{-2} + \cdots\\ &= z[y(T)z^{-1} + y(2T)z^{-2} + y(3T)z^{-3} + \cdots]\\ &= z\left[\sum_{k=0}^{\infty} y(kT)z^{-k}\right]\end{aligned}$$

since $y(0) = 0$. Hence

$$[y((k+1)T)] = zY(z)$$

and the difference equation above transforms to the algebraic (in z) equation

$$zY(z) = Y(z) + U(z)$$

or

$$Y(z) = \frac{1}{z-1}U(z)$$ ▮

To be useful in the analysis of discrete-time systems, it is desirable to be able to express the infinite series given by the z transform in closed form. Since the coefficients of z^{-k} in the series expansion is $f(kT)$, we can "generate" the discrete signal $\{f(kT)\}$ by expanding the closed form of the transform into a power series in z^{-k}.

At this point it is convenient and necessary to introduce and discuss the properties of complex power series.

(5.127) Theorem

Let the complex function $f(z)$ be analytic at all points within a circle C_0 of radius r_0 centered at z_0. Then at each point z inside C_0, the *Taylor series*

$$(5.128)\quad f(z) = f(z_0) + \sum_{n=1}^{\infty} \frac{f^{(n)}(z_0)}{n!}(z - z_0)^n$$

converges to $f(z)$. ∎

A test for convergence is not necessary for all points within C_0. The maximum radius of C_0 is the distance from the point z_0 to the singular point of $f(z)$ nearest to z_0, since the function is to be analytic at all points inside C_0. It can be shown that the series (5.128) diverges at all points outside the circle of maximum radius. Thus the circle of maximum radius is called the *circle of convergence* of the series.

(5.129) Example

Let us find the Taylor series expansion for the function

$$f(z) = e^z$$

about the point $z = 0$. Since e^z is analytic everywhere, we have

$$e^z = 1 + \sum_{n=1}^{\infty} \frac{z^n}{n!} = \sum_{n=0}^{\infty} \frac{z^n}{n!}$$

when $|z| < \infty$. Now consider the function

$$f(z) = \frac{1}{1+z}$$

Since there is a singularity at the point $z = -1$, the radius of the circle of convergence must be less than 1, and the Taylor series expansion about $z = 0$ is

$$\frac{1}{1+z} = \sum_{n=0}^{\infty} (-1)^n z^n$$

when $|z| < 1$. ∎

Let C_1 and C_2 be two concentric circles of radii r_1 and r_2, $r_1 > r_2$, about z_0 in the complex plane. We then have the following theorem.

(5.130) Theorem
If $f(z)$ is analytic on C_1 and C_2 and throughout the region between those two circles (the annulus), then at each point z between them, $f(z)$ is represented by a convergent series of positive and negative powers of $(z - z_0)$,

$$(5.131)\quad f(z) = \sum_{n=0}^{\infty} a_n(z - z_0)^n + \sum_{n=1}^{\infty} \frac{b_n}{(z - z_0)^n}$$

where

$$(5.132)\quad a_n = \frac{1}{2\pi j} \oint_{C_1} \frac{f(z)\, dz}{(z - z_0)^{n+1}} \qquad (n = 0, 1, 2, \ldots)$$

and

$$(5.133)\quad b_n = \frac{1}{2\pi j} \oint_{C_2} \frac{f(z)\, dz}{(z - z_0)^{n+1}} \qquad (n = 1, 2, \ldots)$$

This series is called the *Laurent series* of $f(z)$ about z_0. ∎

The Taylor series is a special case of the Laurent series when $f(z)$ is analytic at every point on and in C_1, except the point z_0 itself, and the radius r_2 may be taken arbitrarily small.

Since the integrands in the integrals (5.132) and (5.133) are analytic functions of z throughout the region between C_1 and C_2, any closed curve C enclosing the point z_0 in this region can be used as the path of integration. Thus the Laurent series can be written as

$$(5.134)\quad f(z) = \sum_{n=-\infty}^{\infty} A_n(z - z_0)^n \qquad (r_2 < |z - z_0| < r_1)$$

where

$$(5.135)\quad A_n = \frac{1}{2\pi j} \oint_{C} \frac{f(z)\, dz}{(z - z_0)^{n+1}} \qquad (n = 0, 1, 2, \ldots)$$

Thus the one-sided z transform

$$F_{\mathrm{I}}(z) = f(0) + f(T)z^{-1} + f(2T)z^{-2} + \cdots$$

is the principal part of a Laurent series about the point $z = 0$, plus the added constant $f(0)$. We conclude that the one-sided z transform converges outside of a circle centered at the origin as shown in Fig. 5.22*a*. The two-sided z transform

$$F_{\mathrm{II}}(z) = \cdots + f(-2T)z^2 + f(-T)z^1 + f(0) + f(T)z^{-1} + f(2T)z^{-2} + \cdots$$

also defines a Laurent series about $z = 0$. Thus the two-sided z transform converges in an annulus centered at the origin as shown in Fig. 5.22*b*.

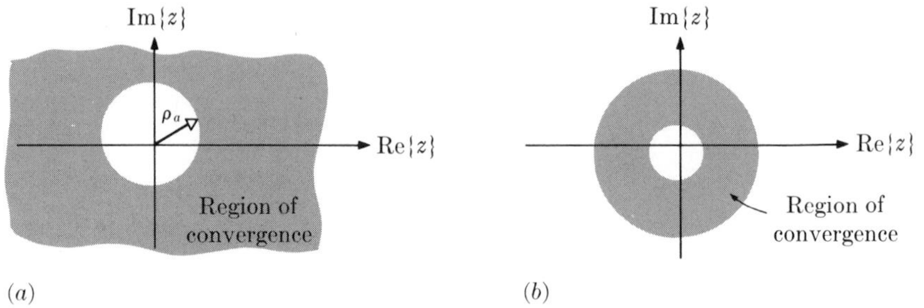

FIG. 5.22 The region of convergence for the (*a*) one-sided z transform, (*b*) two-sided z transform.

In the sequel, we will mostly be concerned with the one-sided z transform, and so we will drop the subscript I from the transform; no confusion should arise. The following examples illustrate how to find the z transform of some common functions.

(5.136) Example

Consider the discrete-time function $\{a, a^2, a^3, \ldots\}$. The (one-sided) z transform of this function is

$$F(z) = 1 + az^{-1} + a^2z^{-2} + \cdots$$

or

$$(5.137)\quad \mathcal{Z}[a^k] = F(z) = \sum_{k=0}^{\infty} a^k z^{-k}$$

We can rewrite (5.137) in closed form if we recognize that it is the sum of a geometric series. Thus

$$(5.138)\quad \mathcal{Z}[a^k] = \frac{1}{1 - az^{-1}}$$

for $|z| > |a|$.

Since the series (5.137) converges for all z such that $|z| > |a|$, the radius of absolute convergence, denoted by ρ_a, is $\rho_a = |a|$. ▮

(5.139) Example

The unit step can be represented by the sequence $\{1, 1, 1, \ldots\}$ for all $t > 0$. Thus the z transform of the unit step can be obtained from (5.138) with $a = 1$:

$$\mathcal{Z}[1] = \frac{1}{1 - z^{-1}}$$

The radius of absolute convergence is $\rho_a = 1$. ▮

Since the z transform is a power series, it can be shown to converge uniformly within the region of absolute convergence and may be differentiated or integrated an arbitrary number of times. As a result we have the following useful property. Let $\{f(nT)\}$ be a discrete-time signal whose z transform is $F(z)$, then

$$(5.140)\quad F(z) = \mathcal{Z}[f(kT)] = \sum_{k=0}^{\infty} f(kT)z^{-k}$$

for $|z| > \rho_a$. Observe that upon differentiation (5.140) becomes

$$\frac{d}{dz}F(z) = -\sum_{k=0}^{\infty} kf(kT)z^{-k-1}$$

or

$$-z\frac{d}{dz}F(z) = \sum_{k=0}^{\infty} kf(kT)z^{-k}$$

or

$$(5.141)\quad \mathcal{Z}[kf(kT)] = -z\frac{d}{dz}F(z) \qquad \text{for } |z| > \rho_a$$

In general, it can be shown that

$$(5.142)\quad \mathcal{Z}[k^{\nu}f(kT)] = \left(-z\frac{d}{dz}\right)^{\nu} F(z) \qquad \text{for } |z| > \rho_a$$

where the operation $(-zd/dz)^{\nu}$ is to be interpreted as ν-fold iteration of the operation $-zd/dz$. The following example illustrates the use of this property.

(5.143) Example

We wish to find the z transform of the unit-ramp sequence $\{k\} = (0, 1, 2, 3, \ldots)$. Using (5.142) with $\{f(kT)\} = \{1\}$, the unit-step sequence, we have

$$\mathcal{Z}[k] = -z\frac{d}{dz}\mathcal{Z}[1] = -z\frac{d}{dz}\left(\frac{1}{1 - z^{-1}}\right) = \frac{z}{(z-1)^2} \qquad ▮$$

In Table 5.5 we have listed the z transforms of some common discrete-time functions.

TABLE 5.5 Some z transforms of common functions

$\{f_K\}$	$F(z)$	*Region of convergence*
$\{1\}$	$\dfrac{1}{1 - z^{-1}}$	$\lvert z\rvert > 1$
$\{k\}$	$\dfrac{z}{(z - 1)^2}$	$\lvert z\rvert > 1$
$\{k^2\}$	$\dfrac{z(z + 1)}{(z - 1)^3}$	$\lvert z\rvert > 1$
$\left\{\dfrac{k^n}{(n)}\right\}$	$\lim\limits_{a\to 0} \dfrac{(-1)^{n+1}}{(n)!}\left[\dfrac{\partial^{n+1}}{\partial a^{n+1}}\left(\dfrac{z}{z - e^{-aT}}\right)\right]$	$\lvert z\rvert > 1$
$\{a^k\}$	$\dfrac{z}{z - a}$	$\lvert z\rvert > \lvert a\rvert$
$\lvert e^{\alpha k}\rvert$	$\dfrac{z}{z - e^{\alpha}}$	$\lvert z\rvert > e^{\alpha}$
$\{\sin \omega k\}$	$\dfrac{z \sin \omega}{z^2 - 2z \cos \omega + 1}$	$\lvert z\rvert > 1$
$\{\cos \omega k\}$	$\dfrac{z(z - \cos \omega)}{z^2 - 2z \cos \omega + 1}$	$\lvert z\rvert > 1$

5.14 THE INVERSE z TRANSFORM

Consider the difference equation description of an nth-order, linear, time-invariant, discrete-time system:

$$(5.144)\quad a_n y(k + n) + a_{n-1} y(k + n - 1) + \cdots a_1 y(k + 1) + a_0 y(k) = b_n u(k + n) + b_{n-1} u(k + n - 1) + \cdots + b_1 u(k + 1) + b_0 u(k)$$

Let $Y(z)$ denote the z transform of

$$\{y(k)\} = (y(0), y(1), \ldots)$$

that is,

$$\mathrm{Z}[y(k)] = Y(z) = y(0) + y(1)z^{-1} + y(2)z^{-2} + \cdots$$

Now let us find the z transform of the same sequence shifted by m units:

$$
\begin{aligned}
(5.145)\quad \{y(k+m)\} &= (y(m), y(m+1), \ldots) \\
\mathbf{Z}[y(k+m) &= y(m) + y(m+1)z^{-1} + y(m+2)z^{-2} + \cdots \\
&= z^m[y(m)z^{-m} + y(m+1)z^{-(m+1)} \\
&\qquad + y(m+2)z^{-(m+2)} + \cdots] \\
&= z^m \left[\sum_{k=0}^{\infty} y(k)z^{-k} - \sum_{k=0}^{m-1} y(k)z^{-k} \right] \\
&= z^m Y(z) - y(0)z^m - y(1)z^{m-1} - \cdots \\
&\qquad - y(m-1)z
\end{aligned}
$$

Expression (5.145) is useful in taking the z transform of (5.144):

$$
\begin{aligned}
(5.146)\quad & a_n[z^nY(z) - y(0)z^n - y(1)z^{n-1} - \cdots - y(n-1)z] \\
& + a_{n-1}[z^{n-1}Y(z) - y(0)z^{n-1} - y(1)z^{n-2} - \cdots \\
& - y(n+2)z] + \cdots + a_1[zY(z) - y(0)z] + a_0Y(z) \\
& = b_n[z^nU(z) - u(0)z^n - u(1)z^{n-1} - \cdots - u(m-1)z] \\
& + b_{n-1}[z^{n-1}U(z) - u(0)z^{n-1} - u(1)z^{n-2} - \cdots \\
& \qquad - u(m-2)z] + \cdots + b_1[zU(z) - zu(0)] + b_0U(z)
\end{aligned}
$$

an algebraic equation which can be written as

$$(5.147)\quad Y(z) = H(z)u(z) + E(z)$$

where

$$H(z) = \frac{b_nz^n + b_{n-1}z^{n-1} + \cdots + b_0}{a_nz^n + a_{n-1}z^{n-1} + \cdots + a_0}$$

and $E(z)$ is a rational polynomial which is a function of the initial conditions and inputs at times $k = 0, 1, 2, \ldots, n-1$.

To find the system's response, we need only find the discrete-time signal the z transform of which is $Y(z)$. In other words, we need to determine the inverse z transform.

Given the z transform $F(z)$ and the absolute radius of convergence ρ_a, we can find the original discrete-time function $\{f(k)\}$ by various methods. The most direct method results from realizing that the z transform is just the principal part of a Laurent series about the origin and a constant term. Thus the $f(k)$ can be determined by expanding $F(z)$ in a Laurent series. The coefficients of the powers of z^{-1} are determined by [see (5.133)]

$$(5.148)\quad f(k) = \frac{1}{2\pi j} \oint_C F(z)z^{k-1}\,dz$$

where C is a circle of radius $r > \rho_\alpha$, that is, a circle which encloses all the singularities of $z^{k-1}F(z)$. Recall that the integral (5.148) is most easily evaluated in terms of residues, i.e.,

$$f(k) = \sum_{\text{all residues}} \text{Res}\,(z^{k-1}F(z))$$

where the summation is taken over all the residues within the circle defined by ρ_a.

(5.149) Example
Consider the z transform

$$(5.150)\quad F(z) = \frac{1}{1 - z^{-1}} = \frac{z}{z - 1}$$

with $\rho_a = 1$. Obviously the function $z^{k-1}F(z)$ has singularities at $z = 1$ for all k. From (5.107)

$$f(0) = \text{Res}\left(\frac{1}{z - 1}\right) = 1$$

and

$$f(k) = \text{Res}\,\frac{z^k}{z - 1} = 1 \qquad \text{for all } k \geq 1$$

so that the discrete-time function whose z transform is given by (5.150) is (1, 1, 1, . . .), the unit step [see Example (5.139)]. ▮

Alternatively, if a table of z transforms is available, then we can simply find the inverse transform by consulting the table. A partial fraction expansion of the given function may be necessary so as to identify terms in the table.

(5.151) Example
Find the inverse transform of

$$F(z) = \frac{2z^2 - (e^3 - 2)z}{z^2 - (2 + e^3)z - 2e^3z}$$

A partial fraction expansion yields

$$F(z) = \frac{z}{z - 2} + \frac{z}{z - e^{-3}}$$

From Table 5.5 we have

$$f(k) = 2^k + e^{3k}$$ ▮

Another useful method of determining the value of $f(k)$ when $F(z)$ is a rational function is to express both the numerator and denominator of $F(z)$ in polynomials of z^{-1}. A power series in terms of z^{-1} can then be obtained by carrying out the indicated division.

We are now ready to study the use of the z transform in discrete-system analysis.

5.15 THE z TRANSFORM IN SYSTEM ANALYSIS

Recall the z transform of the nth-order difference equation (5.146). We are usually interested in causal systems so that $y(k)$ and $u(k)$ are zero for $k < 0$. Then from (5.146) for $k = -n, -n + 1, -n + 2, \ldots, -1$ we have

$$
\begin{aligned}
&a_n y(0) = b_n u(0) \\
&a_n y(1) + a_{n-1} y(0) = b_n u(1) + b_{n-1} u(0) \\
&\cdots\cdots\cdots\cdots\cdots\cdots\cdots\cdots \\
&a_n y(n-1) + a_{n-1} y(n-2) + \cdots + a_1 y(0) = b_n u(n-1) \\
&\qquad\qquad + b_{n-1} u(n-2) + \cdots + b_1 u(0)
\end{aligned}
$$

If the system is initially relaxed

$$y(0) = y(1) = y(2) = \cdots = y(n-1) = 0$$

so that the transformed equation becomes

$$Y(z) = H(z)U(z) \tag{5.152}$$

where

$$H(z) \equiv \frac{b_n z^n + b_{n-1} z^{n-1} + \cdots + b_0}{a_n z^n + a_{n-1} z^{n-1} + \cdots + a_0}$$

is called the *discrete transfer function.* Observe that the discrete transfer function can be written directly from the difference equation which describes the system.

We can define the discrete version of the delta function to be $\{\delta(k)\}$ where

$$\delta(k) = \begin{cases} 1 & \text{for } k = 0 \\ 0 & \text{for } k \neq 0 \end{cases} \tag{5.153}$$

The z transform of the discrete delta function is

$$\mathcal{Z}[\delta(k)] = 1$$

Consider again (5.152)

$$Y(z) = H(z)U(z)$$

Hence we can think of $H(z)$ as being the transformed response of a linear system when the input is the discrete delta function.

The following example demonstrates the use of the z transform.

(5.154) Example

A linear, time-invariant, discrete-time system is characterized by the difference equation

$$y(k+2) + y(k+1) - 6y(k) = 3u(k-1) - 2u(k)$$

Find the output when the system is initially relaxed and the input is

$$u(k) = \begin{cases} k & \text{for } k \geq 0 \\ 0 & \text{for } k < 0 \end{cases}$$

From (5.152)

$$Y(z) = \frac{3z-3}{z^2+z-6}\,U(z) = \frac{3(z-1)}{(z+3)(z-2)}\,U(z)$$

and from Table 5.5

$$U(z) = \mathcal{Z}[k] = \frac{z}{(z-1)^2}$$

so that

$$Y(z) = \frac{3z}{(z+3)(z-2)(z-1)}$$

We can easily find the inverse transform by the method of residues. $Y(z)$ has simple poles at $z = -3$, $z = 2$, and $z = 1$, therefore

$$y(k) = \sum \text{Res } z^{k-1}Y(z) = \sum \text{Res } \frac{3z^k}{(z+3)(z-2)(z-1)}$$

The residue of $z^{k-1}Y(z)$ at $z = -3$ is

$$\left[\frac{3z^k}{(z-2)(z-1)}\right]_{z=-3} = \frac{-(-3)^{k+1}}{20}$$

the residue of $z^{k-1}Y(z)$ at $z = 2$ is

$$\left[\frac{3z^k}{(z+3)(z-1)}\right]_{z=2} = \frac{3(2)^k}{5}$$

and the residue of $z^{k-1}Y(z)$ at $z = 1$ is

$$\left[\frac{3z^k}{(z+3)(z-2)}\right]_{z=1} = -\frac{3}{4}$$

Thus,

$$y(k) = -\frac{(-3)^{k+1}}{20} + \frac{3}{5}(2)^k - \frac{3}{4} \qquad k \geq 0$$ ∎

We may also use the z transform to find the solution of the discrete-state equations for linear time-invariant systems. For manipulative convenience, we limit our interest to the single input—single output description

(5.155a) $\mathbf{x}(k+1) = \mathbf{A}\mathbf{x}(k) + \mathbf{b}u(k)$

and

(5.155b) $y(k) = \mathbf{c}'\mathbf{x}(k) + du(k)$

Under the assumption that the system is causal, the transformed version of these equations is

$$\mathbf{X}(z) = (z\mathbf{1} - \mathbf{A})^{-1}z\mathbf{x}_0 + (z\mathbf{1} - \mathbf{A})^{-1}\mathbf{b}U(z)$$

and

$$Y(z) = \mathbf{c}'\mathbf{X}(z) + dU(z)$$

so that

(5.156) $Y(z) = \mathbf{c}(z\mathbf{1} - \mathbf{A})^{-1}z\mathbf{x}_0 + [\mathbf{c}'(z\mathbf{1} - \mathbf{A})^{-1}\mathbf{b} + d]U(z)$

Comparison of this expression with (5.147) indicates that

$$E(z) = \mathbf{c}(z\mathbf{1} - \mathbf{A})^{-1}z\mathbf{x}_0$$

and

$$H(z) = \mathbf{c}'(z\mathbf{1} - \mathbf{A})^{-1}\mathbf{b} + d$$

In Chap. 4 we found the solution to the discrete-state equations (5.155) to be

(5.157) $y(k) = \mathbf{c}'\boldsymbol{\Phi}(k)\mathbf{x}_0 + \mathbf{c}' \sum_{i=0}^{k-1} \boldsymbol{\Phi}(k-i-1)\mathbf{b}u(i) + du(k)$

The z transform of (5.157) is

(5.158) $Y(z) = \mathbf{c}'\mathrm{Z}[\boldsymbol{\Phi}(k)]\mathbf{x}_0 + [\mathbf{c}'\mathrm{Z}[\boldsymbol{\Phi}(k)]z^{-1}\mathbf{b} + d]U(z)$

We leave it as an exercise for the reader to show that

$$\mathrm{Z}\left[\sum_{i=0}^{k-1} \boldsymbol{\Phi}(k-i-1)u(i)\right] = [\boldsymbol{\Phi}(k)]U(z)z^{-1}$$

Comparison of (5.158) and (5.156) indicates that

$$\mathcal{Z}[\mathbf{\Phi}(k)] = (z\mathbf{1} - \mathbf{A})^{-1}z$$

or that

$$\mathbf{\Phi}(k) = \mathcal{Z}^{-1}[(z\mathbf{1} - \mathbf{A})^{-1}z]$$

So we have found an alternative means to determine the discrete state-transition matrix.

(5.159) Example

In Example (4.75) we found the state-transition matrix for the second-order system

$$\mathbf{x}(k+1) = \begin{bmatrix} 0 & 1 \\ -4 & -5 \end{bmatrix} \mathbf{x}(k)$$

Let us now find the state-transition matrix by the method of z transforms: We have

$$\mathcal{Z}[\mathbf{\Phi}(k)] = (z\mathbf{1} - \mathbf{A})^{-1}z = \frac{z}{z^2 + 5z - 4} \begin{bmatrix} z+5 & 1 \\ -4 & z \end{bmatrix}$$

To find the inverse transform, we use the method of residues:

$$\sum \operatorname{Res} \frac{z^{k-1}(z+5)z}{z^2+5z+4} = \operatorname*{Res}_{z=-1} \left(\frac{z^k(z+5)}{z^2+5z+4} \right) + \operatorname*{Res}_{z=-4} \left(\frac{z^k(z+5)}{z^2+5z+4} \right) = \tfrac{4}{3}(-1)^k - \tfrac{1}{3}(-4)^k$$

$$\sum \operatorname{Res} \frac{z^{k-1}z}{z^2+5z+4} = \operatorname*{Res}_{z=-1} \left(\frac{z^k}{z^2+5z+4} \right) + \operatorname*{Res}_{z=-4} \left(\frac{z^k}{z^2+5z+4} \right) = \tfrac{1}{3}(-1)^k - \tfrac{1}{3}(-4)^k$$

$$\sum \operatorname{Res} \frac{z^{k-1}(-4)z}{z^2+5z+4} = \operatorname*{Res}_{z=-1} \left(\frac{-4z^k}{z^2+5z+4} \right) + \operatorname*{Res}_{z=-4} \left(\frac{-4z^k}{z^2+5z+4} \right) = -\tfrac{4}{3}(-1)^k + \tfrac{4}{3}(-4)^k$$

and

$$\sum \operatorname{Res} \frac{z^{k-1}z^2}{z^2+5z+4} = \operatorname*{Res}_{z=-1} \left(\frac{z^{k+1}}{z^2+5z+4} \right) + \operatorname*{Res}_{z=-4} \left(\frac{z^{k+1}}{z^2+5z+4} \right) = -\tfrac{1}{3}(-1)^k + \tfrac{4}{3}(-4)^k$$

Hence

$$\mathbf{\Phi}(k) = \mathcal{Z}^{-1}[(z\mathbf{1} - \mathbf{A})^{-1}z] = \begin{bmatrix} \tfrac{4}{3}(-1)^k - \tfrac{1}{3}(-4)^k & \tfrac{1}{3}(-1)^k - \tfrac{1}{3}(-4)^k \\ -\tfrac{4}{3}(-1)^k + \tfrac{4}{3}(-4)^k & -\tfrac{1}{3}(-1)^k + \tfrac{4}{3}(-4)^k \end{bmatrix}$$

which agrees with our previous result. ▮

5.16 SUMMARY

For linear time-invariant systems (either continuous or discrete), transform techniques provide a means for obtaining the system response algebraically. The transform approach is especially convenient in studies of steady-state or zero-state response, because then a single input—single output system is completely characterized by a scalar algebraic entity.

5.17 PROBLEMS

(5.1) Prove that

$$\int_{-\infty}^{\infty} \delta(k)(t - \tau)\delta^{(l)}(\tau)\, d\tau = \delta^{(k+l)}(\tau)$$

where

$$\delta^{(k)}(t) \equiv \frac{d^k\delta(t)}{dt^k}$$

(5.2) Prove that

$$\int_{-\infty}^{\infty} \delta^{(k)}(t - \tau)g(\tau)\, d\tau = \int_{-\infty}^{\infty} g(t - \tau)\delta^{(k)}(\tau)\, d\tau$$
$$= g^{(k)}(t)$$

(5.3) Prove the following identities:

(a) $f(t)\delta(t) = f(0)\delta(t)$;
(b) $f(t)\delta^{(1)}(t) = -f^{(1)}(0)\delta(t) + f(0)\delta^{(1)}(t)$;
(c) $f(t)\delta^{(k)}(t) = \sum_{l=0}^{k} (-1)^l \binom{k}{l} f^{(l)}(0)\delta^{(k-l)}(t)$

(Assume f to have derivatives of all orders in the ordinary sense.)

(5.4) Given a system whose impulse response is

$$h(t) = e^{-3|t|}$$

find the response due to the input

$$u(t) = \begin{cases} 1 & t < 0 \\ e^t & t \geq 0 \end{cases}$$

(5.5) Show that if $f(t)$ is a real-valued periodic function of time, the coefficients of the complex Fourier series satisfy

$$c_{-k} = c_k^*$$

(5.6) Express the exponential Fourier coefficients c_k in terms of the sine and cosine Fourier coefficients a_k and b_k.

(5.7) Show that $e^{jn\omega_0 t}$ and $e^{jm\omega_0 t}$ are orthogonal, i.e.,

$$\langle e^{jn\omega_0 t}, e^{jm\omega_0 t}\rangle = 0 \qquad m \neq n$$

(5.8) Let $f(t)$ be a Fourier transformable time function and $F(\omega)$ its Fourier transform. For each of the cases below, determine if $F(\omega)$ is real, imaginary, complex, even $(F(-\omega) = F(\omega))$, and/or odd $(F(-\omega) = -F(\omega))$.

(*a*) $f(t)$ is even;
(*b*) $f(t)$ is odd;
(*c*) $f(t)$ is real;
(*d*) $f(t)$ is imaginary;
(*e*) $f(t)$ is real and even;
(*f*) $f(t)$ is real and odd;
(*g*) $f(t)$ is imaginary and even;
(*h*) $f(t)$ is imaginary and odd.

(5.9) Find the Fourier transform of each of the following functions if it exists.

(*a*) $f(t) = t1(-t)$

(*b*) $f(t) = \dfrac{1}{t-1}1(t-2)1(t-1)$

(*c*) $f(t) = e^{-3t}\cos 2t \qquad t > 0.$

(5.10) Let $f(t)$ be a bandlimited function, that is, $F(\omega) = 0$ for $|\omega| > r$. Consider the function

$$g(t) = f(t)\cos\omega_c t$$

where $\omega_c \gg r$. Find and sketch $G(\omega)$.

(5.11) Show that if $f(t)$ is a periodic function of time with period T, its Fourier transform consists of discrete components at multiples of some fundamental frequency.

(5.12) Find the Laplace transforms and regions of convergence for the following functions:

(*a*) $1(t)e^{-t}$
(*b*) $1(t)e^{t}$
(*c*) $1(-t)e^{-t}$
(*d*) $1(-t)e^{t}$

(5.13) Find the Laplace transform and region of convergence for the function

$$f(t) = \begin{cases} \dfrac{1}{T} & \dfrac{-T}{2} \leq t \leq \dfrac{T}{2} \\ 0 & \text{elsewhere} \end{cases}$$

(5.14) Using the results of 5.12, find the inverse Laplace transform of $1/(s^2 - 1)$ when the region of convergence is

(*a*) $\text{Re}\{s\} < -1$
(*b*) $-1 < \text{Re}\{s\} < 1$
(*c*) $\text{Re}\{s\} > 1$.

(5.15) Given a first-order, linear, time-invariant system with an a priori specified unknown initial state. Two experiments are performed (starting in the same initial state at $t = 0$):

Experiment 1
Input:

$$u(t) = \begin{cases} 1 & t \geq 0 \\ 0 & t < 0 \end{cases}$$

Output:

$$y_1(t) = \tfrac{1}{3} + \tfrac{11}{3}e^{-3t} \qquad t > 0$$

Experiment 2
Input:

$$u(t) = \text{impulse function } \delta(t)$$

Output:

$$y_2(t) = 5e^{-3t} \qquad t \geq 0$$

Using Laplace transforms determine:

(*a*) The zero-input response for the given initial state;
(*b*) The zero-state step response;
(*c*) The zero-state impulse response.

(5.16) Using the method of residues, find the inverse Laplace transform of the following functions

(*a*) $\dfrac{1}{s^2 - 1}$ (*b*) $\dfrac{1}{(s-1)^2}$ (*c*) $\dfrac{s^5}{s^6 - 1}$

(*d*) $\dfrac{s}{(s+1)(s+3)}$ (*e*) $\dfrac{s^3}{(s^2 - 1)^3}$

(5.17) How can the Fourier transform

$$F(\omega) = \int_{-\infty}^{\infty} f(t)e^{-j\omega t}\, dt$$

of the time function $f(t)$, $-\infty < t < \infty$, be found from a table of *one-sided* Laplace transforms?

(5.18) Consider a system whose discrete-time transfer function is

$$H(z) = \frac{4}{z^2 + 2}$$

(*a*) Find the difference equation governing this system.
(*b*) Find a block diagram representation for this system.
(*c*) Indicate on the block diagram the "states" of the system, i.e., at what points in the system would initial conditions be necessary for unique determination of the output? Write the discrete-time state equations for this system.
(*d*) What is the complete solution of these state equations? (Carry out as many of the details as you can.)

(5.19) If $f(t)$ is a continuous-time function the area under $f(t)$ is defined by

$$\text{Area}\,[f(t)] = \int_{-\infty}^{\infty} f(t)\, dt$$

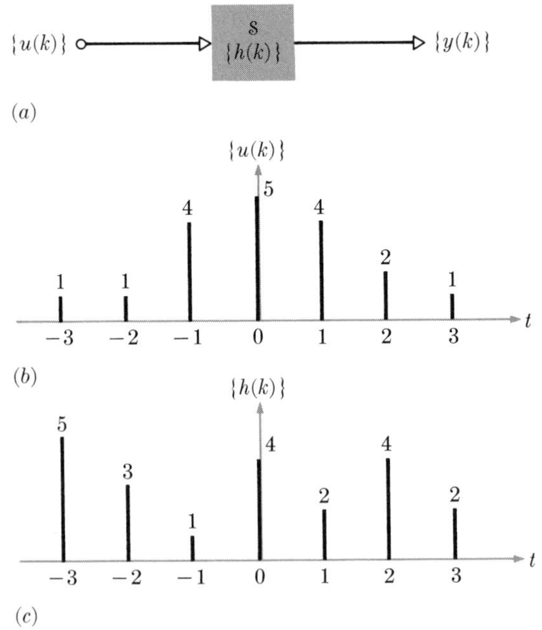

FIG. 5.23 Prob. 5.19.

In an analogous fashion, we can define the area "under" a discrete-time signal $\{f(k)\}$ by

$$\text{Area}\,[f(k)] = \sum_{k=-\infty}^{\infty} f(k)$$

Consider the situation shown in Fig. 5.23*a* where

$\{u(k)\}$ is the system-input sequence
$\{y(k)\}$ the system-output sequence
$\{h(k)\}$ the impulse-response sequence

of the time-invariant (fixed) discrete-time system. Given the input sequence shown in Fig. 5.23*b* [$u(k)$ is assumed to be equal to zero for all $|k| > 3$] and the impulse response sequence shown in Fig. 5.23*c* [$h(k)$ is assumed to be equal to zero for all $|k| > 3$], find the area "under" the discrete-time signal $\{y(k)\}$.

(5.20) Consider the discrete-time system of Fig. 5.24.

(*a*) What is the discrete transfer function of this system?
(*b*) Express the output in terms of the input by means of the convolution summation.

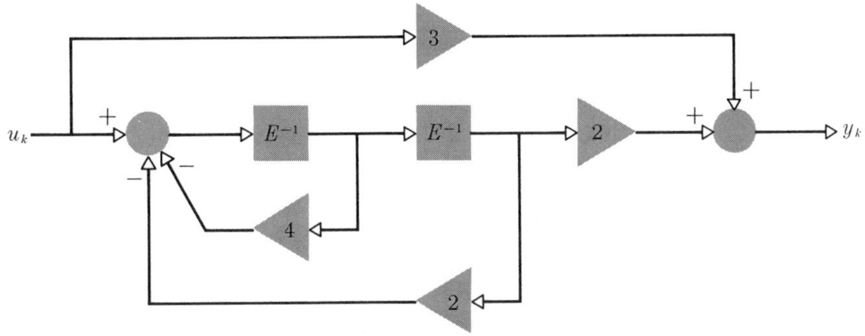

FIG. 5.24 Prob. 5.20.

6 STABILITY

In our studies of first- and second-order systems, we discussed briefly the concepts of stability of solutions and stability of equilibrium states. With the background gained since then, we are in a position to formalize these ideas. We start by presenting a physical basis for stability.

6.1 PHYSICAL BASIS FOR STABILITY

Let $\mathcal{E}$ denote the energy of an isolated system. If the rate of change of energy $\dot{\mathcal{E}}(t)$ is negative for every possible state $\mathbf{x}$, except for a single equilibrium state $\mathbf{x}_e$, then the energy will decrease until it reaches its minimum value, when the system attains the equilibrium state $\mathbf{x}_e$.

Consider for example the so-called linear oscillator, physical representations of which are the LC network or the mass-spring mechanical systems shown in Fig. 6.1. The electrical network is described by linear, time-invariant, differential-state equations

$$\begin{bmatrix} \dot{x}_1(t) \\ \dot{x}_2(t) \end{bmatrix} = \begin{bmatrix} 0 & -\dfrac{1}{C} \\ \dfrac{1}{L} & 0 \end{bmatrix} \begin{bmatrix} x_1(t) \\ x_2(t) \end{bmatrix}$$

and the mechanical system is described by an analogous pair of differential-state equations. We need consider only the electrical system, for which the stored energy is

$$\mathcal{E}(t) = \frac{1}{2} C[x_1(t)]^2 + \frac{1}{2} L[x_2(t)]^2$$

The time derivative of the stored energy is

$$\dot{\mathcal{E}}(t) = Cx_1(t)\dot{x}_1(t) + Lx_2(t)\dot{x}_2(t)$$

which, upon substitution of the differential-state equations, becomes

$$\dot{\mathcal{E}}(t) = x_1(t)x_2(t) - x_2(t)x_1(t) = 0$$

The system is said to be *conservative*, because the stored energy does not change (in the absence of an external input). An oscillator always conserves something, but it need not be the stored energy. We recognize, then, that for this example, the motion takes place on ellipses in the state space:

$$\frac{1}{2} C[x_1(t)]^2 + \frac{1}{2} L[x_2(t)]^2 = \mathcal{E}_k \qquad \text{a constant}$$

The constant (stored energy) $\mathcal{E}_k$ depends on the initial conditions,

$$\frac{1}{2} C[x_1(t)]^2 + \frac{1}{2} L[x_2(t)]^2 = \frac{1}{2} C[x_1(t_0)]^2 + \frac{1}{2} L[x_2(t_0)]^2$$

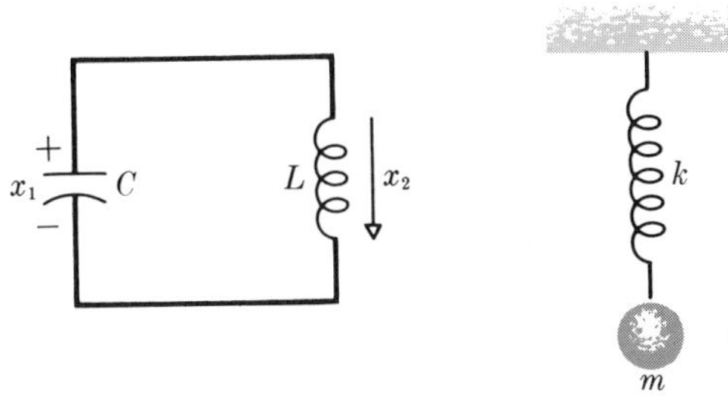

FIG. 6.1 Physical representations of the linear oscillator.

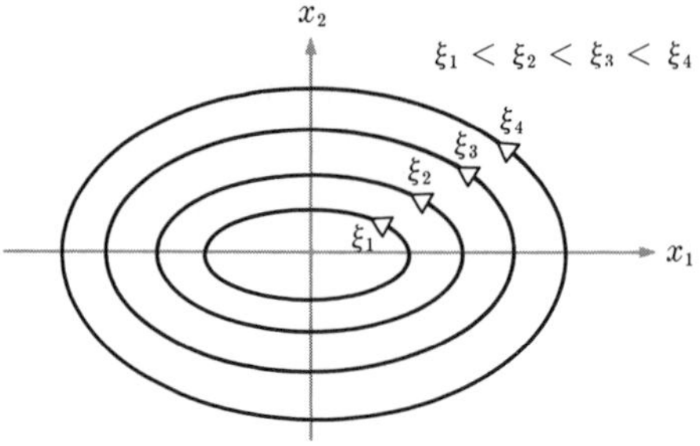

FIG. 6.2 Phase-plane plot of the response of the electrical system of Fig. 6.1.

while the size of the semiminor and semimajor axes of the ellipses depend on the values of C and L. Figure 6.2 shows the relation between the surfaces on which the motion takes place and the value of the stored energy; increased energy storage corresponds to increased area in the set of concentric ellipses. Note that the motion takes place in the counterclockwise direction in the phase plane.

We consider next the same network with the addition of series resistance, shown in Fig. 6.3. The differential-state equations which describe the system are

$$\begin{bmatrix} \dot{x}_1(t) \\ \dot{x}_2(t) \end{bmatrix} = \begin{bmatrix} 0 & -\frac{1}{C} \\ -\frac{1}{L} & -\frac{R}{L} \end{bmatrix} \begin{bmatrix} x_1(t) \\ x_2(t) \end{bmatrix}$$

The stored energy remains

$$\mathcal{E}(t) = \frac{1}{2} C[x_1(t)]^2 + \frac{1}{2} L[x_2(t)]^2$$

but its time derivative becomes

$$\dot{\mathcal{E}}(t) = -R[x_2(t)]^2$$

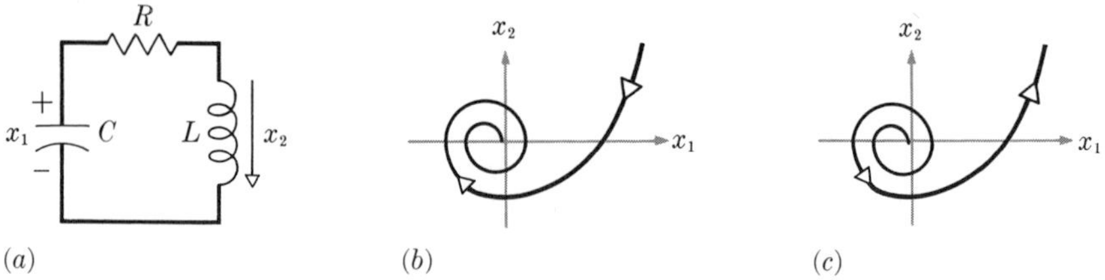

FIG. 6.3 (a) An RLC network and possible phase-plane trajectories for (b) $R > 0$; (c) $R < 0$.

This quantity is zero (and stays zero) only under the condition

$$x_1 \equiv 0 \qquad \text{and} \qquad x_2 \equiv 0$$

[Lest we hastily assume $x_2 \equiv 0$ and x_1 constant is a possibility, we recognize that $\dot{x}_2(t) = -(1/C)x_1(t)$ dictates that such a point is not an equilibrium state.] Consequently, $R > 0$ implies that $\mathcal{E}$ is a monotone-decreasing function which approaches zero and that all solutions tend to the equilibrium state $\mathbf{x}_e = (0,0)'$. Similarly, $R < 0$ implies that $\mathcal{E}$ is a monotone-increasing function which approaches infinity and that all solutions, except possibly those emanating from $\mathbf{x}_e = (0,0)'$, are unbounded. Figure 6.3*b* and *c* shows possible phase-plane trajectories for the situations $R > 0$ and $R < 0$, respectively. Intuitively, we call the case $R > 0$ *asymptotically stable*, the case $R = 0$ *stable*, and the case $R < 0$ *unstable;* in each situation we speak of the stability of the equilibrium state $\mathbf{x}_e = (0,0)'$.

Suppose that in the preceding example, the resistance *only* may be time variable; then

$$\dot{\mathcal{E}}(t) = -R(t)[x_2(t)]^2$$

Therefore,

$$R(t) \geq 0 \Rightarrow \dot{\mathcal{E}}(t) \leq 0$$

and

$$R(t) \leq 0 \Rightarrow \dot{\mathcal{E}}(t) \geq 0$$

In the preceding example, we had the stable situation in which the energy is monotone decreasing depicted in Fig. 6.4*a* for a time-invariant resistance $R > 0$. However, for a time-variable resistance, we may have a stable situation in which the energy only decreases "on the average," Fig. 6.4*b*. Thus, relating stability solely to instantaneous-energy considerations may be unnecessarily restrictive. In fact there are two objections to employing exclusively the energy approach to stability:

(1) The energy may decrease on the average, but not continuously (a function with the former quality may be preferable in some instances, though).
(2) It may be difficult or impossible to associate energy with an abstracted set of coupled, first-order, differential (state) equations.

Before launching into a general discussion of stability, we introduce some convenient terminology for the discussion of lumped systems.

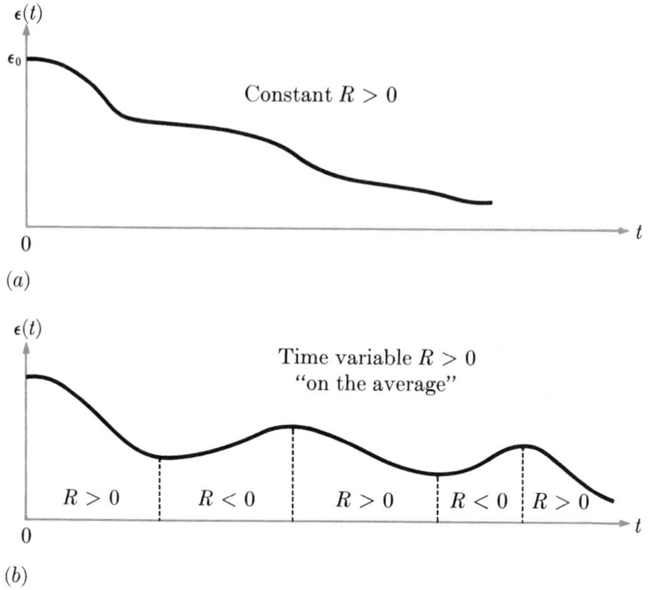

FIG. 6.4 Energy plots for the network of Fig. 6.3 with (*a*) a time-invariant R; (*b*) a time-variable R.

6.2 GENERAL PROPERTIES OF THE SOLUTIONS OF DIFFERENTIAL-STATE EQUATIONS

Consider an nth-order, nonlinear, time-variable system which is characterized by the differential-state equations

$$\dot{\mathbf{x}}(t) = \mathbf{f}(\mathbf{x}(t),\mathbf{u}(t),t) \qquad -\infty < t < \infty$$

If the input vector $\mathbf{u}(t)$ (sometimes called a forcing function or control) is zero, i.e.,

$$\mathbf{u} \equiv \mathbf{0}$$

the system is said to be *free* (or unforced) and is characterized by the differential-state equations

$$\dot{\mathbf{x}}(t) = \mathbf{f}(\mathbf{x}(t),t) \tag{6.1}$$

Since the solution of (6.1) is uniquely determined by the initial state x_0, we characterize it by $\boldsymbol{\phi}(t;\mathbf{x}_0,t_0)$. In other words

$$\frac{d}{dt}[\boldsymbol{\phi}(t;\mathbf{x}_0,t_0)] = \mathbf{f}(\boldsymbol{\phi}(t;\mathbf{x}_0,t_0),t)$$

and

$$\boldsymbol{\phi}(t_0;\mathbf{x}_0,t_0) = \mathbf{x}_0$$

Note that any system may be considered to be a free system for a *fixed* choice of input function. We call $\phi(t;x_0,t_0)$ the *state-transition function;* it is the generalization (to the nonlinear case) of the state-transition matrix of the linear case. Hence, we consider the mapping

$$\mathbf{x}_0 \xrightarrow{\phi(t;\mathbf{x}_0,t_0)} \mathbf{x}(t)$$

and we may call $\mathbf{f}(\mathbf{x}(t),t)$ the infinitesimal transition function since

$$\mathbf{x}(t) \xrightarrow{\mathbf{f}(\mathbf{x}(t),t)} \mathbf{x}(t) + d\mathbf{x}(t)$$

The following *axioms* are satisfied by the state-transition function $\phi(t;\mathbf{x}_0,t_0)$:

(1) $\phi(t_0;x_0,t_0) = \mathbf{x}_0$;
(2) $\phi(t_2;\phi(t_1;\mathbf{x}_0,t_0),t_1) = \phi(t_2;\mathbf{x}_0,t_0),\ t_2 \geq t_1$;
(3) $\phi(t;x_0,t_0)$ is *continuous* and *differentiable* with respect to *all* arguments;
(4) $\phi(t;\mathbf{x}_0,t_0)$ is *defined* for all t, $\mathbf{x}_0$, t_0 (no finite escape time).

Perhaps the most important concept in the discussion of stability is that of an equilibrium state.

(6.2) Equilibrium state
Given a free differential-state equation

$$\dot{\mathbf{x}}(t) = \mathbf{f}(\mathbf{x}(t),t)$$

the state $\mathbf{x}_e$ is said to be an *equilibrium state* if

$$\mathbf{f}(\mathbf{x}_e;t) \equiv \mathbf{0}$$

or, equivalently, if

$$\phi(t;\mathbf{x}_e,t_0) = \mathbf{x}_e \qquad \text{for all } t > t_0.$$ ∎

Time invariance of the differential-state equations, when applicable, will be important in our studies.

(6.3) Time invariance
The differential-state equations

$$\dot{\mathbf{x}} = \mathbf{f}(\mathbf{x}(t),\mathbf{u}(t),t)$$

are said to be time invariant if

$$\mathbf{f}(\mathbf{x}(t),\mathbf{u}(t),t) \equiv f(\mathbf{x}(t),\mathbf{u}(t))$$

for all $\mathbf{x}$ and $\mathbf{u}$, or equivalently, if

$$\phi(t;\mathbf{x}_0,t_0) = \phi(t + h;\cdot\mathbf{x}_0,\ t_0 + h)$$

for all t, $\mathbf{x}_0$, t_0, and finite real constants h. ∎

A time-invariant, differential-state equation is one for which the time dependence on the right-hand side enters only via the input function $\mathbf{u}$. We note that a system characterized by time-invariant differential-state equations need not be time invariant itself; to be so, $\mathbf{g}$ must be explicitly independent of time in the relation

$$\mathbf{y}(t) = \mathbf{g}(\mathbf{x}(t),\mathbf{u}(t),t)$$

that is,

$$y(t) = \mathbf{g}(\mathbf{x}(t),\mathbf{u}(t))$$

A system which is free and has time-invariant differential-state equations is said to be *autonomous*. Linearity, as usual, is an accessible special case.

(6.4) Linearity
A differential-state equation,

$$\dot{\mathbf{x}}(t) = \mathbf{f}(\mathbf{x}(t),\mathbf{u}(t),t)$$

is said to be linear if $\mathbf{f}$ is a linear function of $(\mathbf{x},\mathbf{u})$, that is,

$$\mathbf{f}(\alpha\mathbf{x}_1(t) + \beta\mathbf{x}_2(t),\ \alpha\mathbf{u}_1(t) + \beta\mathbf{u}_2(t),\ t) = \alpha\mathbf{f}(\mathbf{x}_1(t),\mathbf{u}_1(t),t) + \beta\mathbf{f}(\mathbf{x}_2(t),\mathbf{u}_2(t),t)$$

for all $\mathbf{x}_1$, $\mathbf{x}_2$, $\mathbf{u}$, and finite constants α and β. ∎

6.3 STABILITY IN TERMS OF FREE SYSTEMS

We have already seen in Chap. 1 that stability studies for first-order systems may be carried out in terms of a free system with an equilibrium state at the origin. We now show that stability studies of a general nth-order system may always be discussed in terms of a free system with an equilibrium state at the origin. Suppose that $\mathbf{x}$ or $\mathbf{x}(t)$ is a known solution of the differential-state equation

$$\dot{\mathbf{x}}(t) = \mathbf{f}(\mathbf{x}(t),\mathbf{u}(t),t),\ \mathbf{x}(t_0) = \mathbf{x}_0$$

and consider arbitrary deviations from the solution. That is, suppose that $\mathbf{v}$ or $\mathbf{v}(t)$ is another solution so that

$$\dot{\mathbf{v}}(t) = \mathbf{f}(\mathbf{v}(t),\mathbf{u}(t),t),\ \mathbf{v}(t_0) = \mathbf{v}_0$$

Let the deviation of $\mathbf{v}(t)$ from $\mathbf{x}(t)$ be denoted by $\boldsymbol{\xi}(t)$, that is,

$$\boldsymbol{\xi}(t) \equiv \mathbf{v}(t) - \mathbf{x}(t) \qquad \boldsymbol{\xi}(t_0) \equiv \boldsymbol{\xi}_0 = \mathbf{v}_0 - \mathbf{x}_0$$

moreover,

$$\boldsymbol{\xi}_0 = \mathbf{0} \Rightarrow \boldsymbol{\xi}(t) \equiv \mathbf{0} \qquad \text{for all } t$$

by uniqueness. We may write

$$\dot{\boldsymbol{\xi}}(t) = \mathbf{f}(\mathbf{x}(t) + \boldsymbol{\xi}(t), \mathbf{u}(t), t) - \mathbf{f}(\mathbf{x}(t),\mathbf{u}(t),t)$$

Since $\mathbf{u}$, the input function, is known and $\mathbf{x}$, the original unique solution, is presumed known, we may define

$$\mathbf{h}(\boldsymbol{\xi}(t),t) \equiv \mathbf{f}(\mathbf{x}(t) + \boldsymbol{\xi}(t), \mathbf{u}(t), t) - \mathbf{f}(\mathbf{x}(t),\mathbf{u}(t),t)$$

Hence, deviations from a *known solution* of the differential-state equations, when the *input is known*, form a free system,

$$\dot{\boldsymbol{\xi}}(t) = \mathbf{h}(\boldsymbol{\xi}(t),t) \qquad \boldsymbol{\xi}(t_0) = \boldsymbol{\xi}_0$$

moreover, the origin is an equilibrium state for this free system:

$$\mathbf{h}(\mathbf{0},t) = \mathbf{f}(\mathbf{x}(t),\mathbf{u}(t),t) - \mathbf{f}(\mathbf{x}(t),\mathbf{u}(t),t) \equiv \mathbf{0}$$

Hence, we may study the stability of a solution in terms of the stability of the origin of a free system.

Now suppose we are given the free system

$$\dot{\mathbf{x}}(t) = \mathbf{f}(\mathbf{x}(t),t) \qquad \mathbf{x}(t_0) = \mathbf{x}_0$$

with the equilibrium states $\mathbf{x}_{e1}, \mathbf{x}_{e2}, \ldots$, that is,

$$\mathbf{f}(\mathbf{x}_{e1},t) \equiv 0 \qquad \mathbf{f}(\mathbf{x}_{e2},t) \equiv 0, \ldots$$

Define

$$\boldsymbol{\xi}_1(t) \equiv \mathbf{x}(t) - \mathbf{x}_{e1}$$

so that

$$\dot{\boldsymbol{\xi}}_1(t) = \mathbf{f}(\boldsymbol{\xi}_1(t) + \mathbf{x}_{e1}, t) = \mathbf{h}_1(\boldsymbol{\xi}_1(t),t)$$

Similarly, define $\boldsymbol{\xi}_2(t) \equiv \mathbf{x}(t) - \mathbf{x}_{e2}$ so that

$$\dot{\boldsymbol{\xi}}_2(t) = \mathbf{f}(\boldsymbol{\xi}_2(t) + \mathbf{x}_{e2}, t) = \mathbf{h}_2(\boldsymbol{\xi}_2(t),t) \cdots$$

These transformations correspond to a simple fixed translation of the origin of coordinates with no rotation, as is shown in Fig. 6.5. The stability of each equilibrium state is then considered separately. Once again we see that we may study the stability of an equilibrium state in terms of the stability of the origin of a related free system.

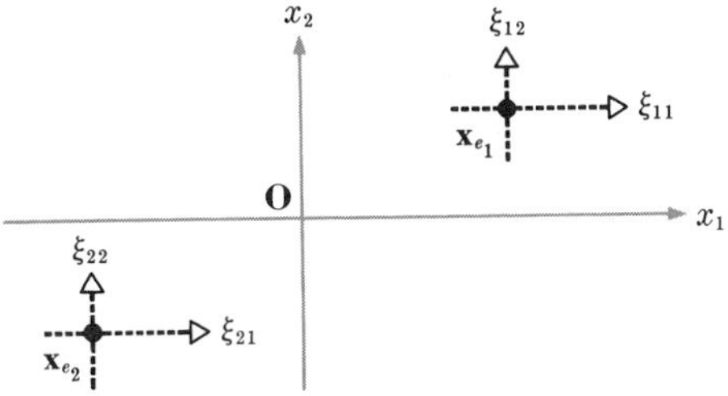

FIG. 6.5 Fixed translations of the origin to the equilibrium states.

(6.5) Example

A second-order nonlinear system is described by the differential-state equations

$$\dot{x}_1 = -x_1 + 2x_2 - 2$$

and

$$\dot{x}_2 = -3x_1 - x_2 + x_2^3$$

There are three equilibrium states

$$\mathbf{x}_{e1} = \begin{bmatrix} 0 \\ 1 \end{bmatrix} \qquad \mathbf{x}_{e2} = \begin{bmatrix} 2 \\ 2 \end{bmatrix} \qquad \mathbf{x}_{e3} = \begin{bmatrix} -8 \\ -3 \end{bmatrix}$$

Consider $\mathbf{x}_{e1}$. We wish to make the transformation

$$\boldsymbol{\xi} = \mathbf{x} - \mathbf{x}_{e1}$$

so that

$$x_1 = \xi_1 \qquad \text{and} \qquad x_2 = \xi_2 + 1$$

The transformed state equations are

$$\dot{\xi}_1 = -\xi_1 + 2\xi_2$$

and

$$\dot{\xi}_2 = -2\xi_1 + \xi_2^3 + 3\xi_2^2 + 2\xi_2$$

which has an equilibrium state at the origin. Next consider $\mathbf{x}_{e2}$. The transformation to be effected is

$$\boldsymbol{\xi} = \mathbf{x} - \mathbf{x}_{e2}$$

so that

$$x_1 = \xi_1 + 2 \qquad \text{and} \qquad x_2 = \xi_2 + 2$$

The transformed state equations are

$$\dot{\xi}_1 = -\xi_1 + 2\xi_2$$

and

$$\dot{\xi}_2 = -3\xi_1 + \xi_2^3 + 6\xi_2^2 + 11\xi_2$$

which has an equilibrium state at the origin. Finally, consider $\mathbf{x}_{e3}$. The desired transformation is

$$\boldsymbol{\xi} = \mathbf{x} - \mathbf{x}_{e3}$$

so that

$$x_1 = \xi_1 - 8 \qquad \text{and} \qquad x_2 = \xi_2 - 3$$

The transformed state equations are

$$\dot{\xi}_1 = -\xi_1 + 2\xi_2$$

and

$$\dot{\xi}_2 = -3\xi_1 + \xi_2^3 - 9\xi_2^2 - 26\xi_2$$

which has an equilibrium state at the origin.

6.4 FORMAL STABILITY DEFINITIONS

Let us first consider the qualitative aspects of the behavior of free systems in terms of a simple example. Suppose that a bead slides with friction under the influence of gravity on a wire bent to form any (differentiable) curve in a vertical plane; the situation is illustrated in Fig. 6.6*a*. This mechanical system is described by the following pair of nonlinear differential-state equations:

$$\dot{x}(t) = \frac{p(t)}{m\sqrt{1 + [\xi'(x(t))]^2}}$$

and

$$\dot{p}(t) = -\frac{mg\xi'(x(t))}{\sqrt{1 + [\xi'(x(t))]^2}} - \frac{\mu p(t)}{m}$$

where x is the horizontal displacement, p is the momentum of the bead (directed along the wire), m is the mass of the bead, g is the acceleration due to gravity, μ is the coefficient of (viscous) friction which results when the bead slides on the wire, and $\xi(x)$ describes the shape of the wire with $\xi'(x)$ as its derivative. The system is free (for given fixed g); in fact, the differential-state equations are autonomous. There may be a number of equilibrium states; any state $\mathbf{q}(t) = (x(t),p(t))'$ is an equilibrium state provided $\xi'(x) = 0$ and $p = 0$; so the equilibrium states have the form

$$\mathbf{q}_e = \begin{pmatrix} k \\ 0 \end{pmatrix} \qquad \text{such that } \xi'(k) = 0$$

We may now undertake a qualitative discussion of the stability of the equilibrium states for this example based on the shape of the wire in the immediate neighborhood of the points for which $\xi'(x) = 0$.

If the wire is horizontal in the immediate neighborhood of a possible equilibrium point (i.e., if there is a continuum of possible equilibrium points), then for a small displacement of the bead from such a point, it will remain where put. This, the *stable* situation, is illustrated in Fig. 6.6*b*.

If the wire curves up on either side of a possible equilibrium point

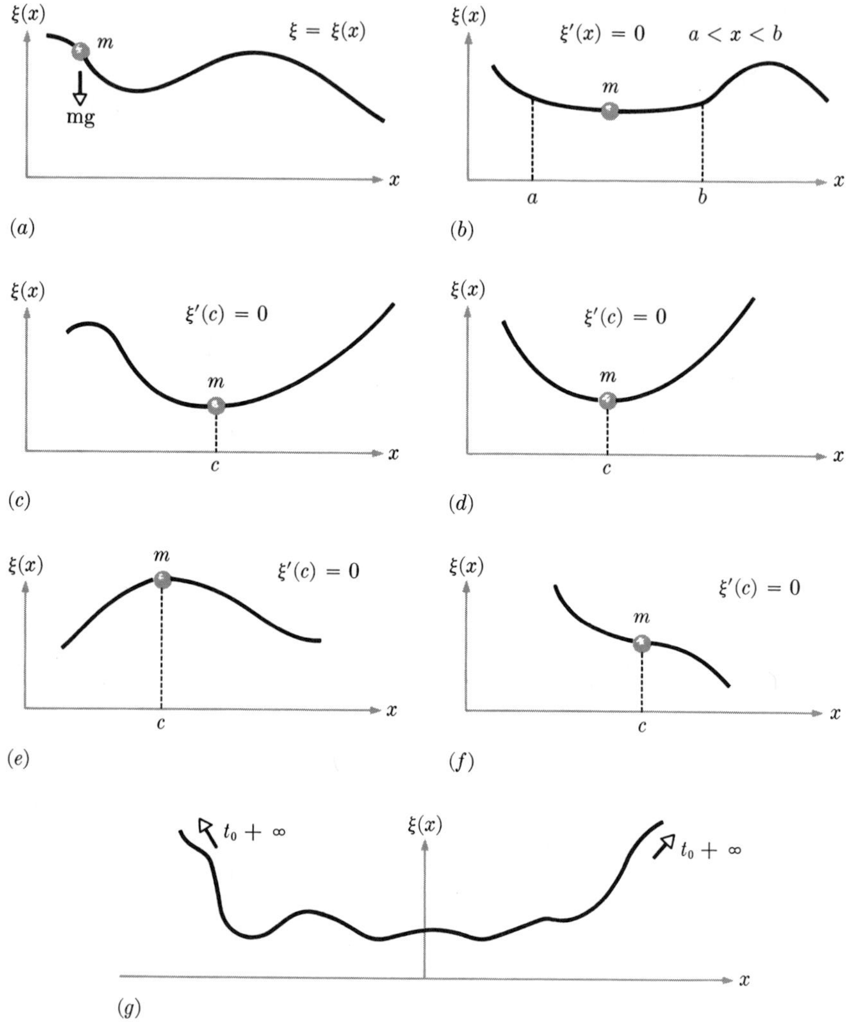

FIG. 6.6 (*a*) Bead on a wire used to illustrate stability situations: (*b*) stable equilibrium, (*c*) asymptotically stable equilibrium, (*d*) asymptotically stable in the large equilibrium, (*e*) and (*f*) unstable equilibrium, (*g*) bounded motion.

[that is, $\xi'(x) < 0$, $c - \epsilon < x < c$; $\xi'(c) = 0$; $\xi'(x) > 0$, $c < x < c + \epsilon$], then for a small displacement (less than ϵ in magnitude) of the bead from such a point, it will ultimately return to the point. This, the *asymptotically stable* situation, is illustrated in Fig. 6.6*c*.

If the wire curves up strictly monotonically on either side of the only possible equilibrium point [that is, $\xi'(x) < 0$, $x < c$; $\xi'(c) = 0$; $\xi'(x) > 0$, $x > c$], then for an arbitrarily large displacement of the bead from such a point, it will ultimately return to the point. This, the *asymptotically stable in the large* situation, is illustrated in Fig. 6.6*d*.

If the wire curves down on *either* side of a possible equilibrium point, then for a small displacement of the bead from such a point, it can leave the neighborhood entirely. This, the *unstable* situation, is illustrated in Fig. 6.6*e* and *f*.

If the wire has arbitrary shape, but ultimately curves up as $x \to \pm\infty$, then the motion of the bead with *any finite* initial displacement and momentum remains bounded. This, the *bounded* (or *Lagrange stable*) situation, is illustrated in Fig. 6.6*g*.

Hopefully the simple example discussed above may be employed to bolster intuition in the following formal definitions of stability. We need consider only a free system

$$\dot{\boldsymbol{\xi}}(t) = \mathbf{h}(\boldsymbol{\xi}(t),t)$$

with the equilibrium state

$$\boldsymbol{\xi} \equiv \mathbf{0}$$

that is,

$$\mathbf{h}(\mathbf{0},t) \equiv \mathbf{0}$$

The discussion of the stability of an equilibrium state of any free system can be undertaken in these terms after a simple constant transformation of the origin of coordinates to the equilibrium state in question. Similarly, the discussion of the stability of the solution for a forced system with a specified input function can be undertaken after a nonconstant transformation of the origin of coordinates to the solution in question. Hence, if the state-transition function for the free system

$$\dot{\boldsymbol{\xi}}(t) = \mathbf{h}(\boldsymbol{\xi}(t),t) \qquad \boldsymbol{\xi}(t_0) = \boldsymbol{\xi}_0$$

is $\boldsymbol{\phi}(t;\boldsymbol{\xi}_0,t_0)$, such that

$$\dot{\boldsymbol{\phi}}(t;\boldsymbol{\xi}_0,t_0) = \mathbf{h}(\boldsymbol{\phi}(t;\boldsymbol{\xi}_0,t_0),t)$$

and

$$\boldsymbol{\phi}(t_0;\mathbf{0},t_0) = \boldsymbol{\xi}_0$$

the original solution is always

$$\boldsymbol{\phi}(t;\mathbf{0},t_0) = \mathbf{0}$$

We first define stability (in the sense of Liapunov).

(6.6) Liapunov stability
The equilibrium state **0** of a *free* system is said to be *stable* if for every real number $\epsilon > 0$ there exists a real number $\delta(\epsilon,t_0) > 0$ such that

$$\|\xi_0\| \leq \delta$$

implies

$$\|\phi(t;\xi_0,t)\| \leq \epsilon$$

for all $t \geq t_0$ (and $\epsilon \geq \delta$, obviously). ▮

In other words, if the equilibrium state is stable, we can make the norm of the solution, $\|\phi(t;\delta_0,t_0)\|$, as small as we desire simply by restricting the size of the initial condition $\|\delta_0\|$. Figure 6.7 illustrates (in two dimensions) the concept of Liapunov stability. A more stringent type of stability is one that demands the attainment of the equilibrium state in the limit.

(6.7) Asymptotic stability
The equilibrium **0** of a *free* system is said to be *asymptotically stable* if

(1) It is *stable*,
(2) Every motion starting sufficiently near **0** converges to **0** as $t \to \infty$. ▮

In other words, the equilibrium state **0** is asymptotically stable if it is stable and there exists a real constant $r(t_0) > 0$ such that to every real number $\mu > 0$, there corresponds a real number $T(\mu;\xi_0,t_0) > 0$ such that

$$\|\xi_0\| \leq r(t_0)$$

implies

$$\|\phi(t;\xi_0,t_0)\| \leq \mu$$

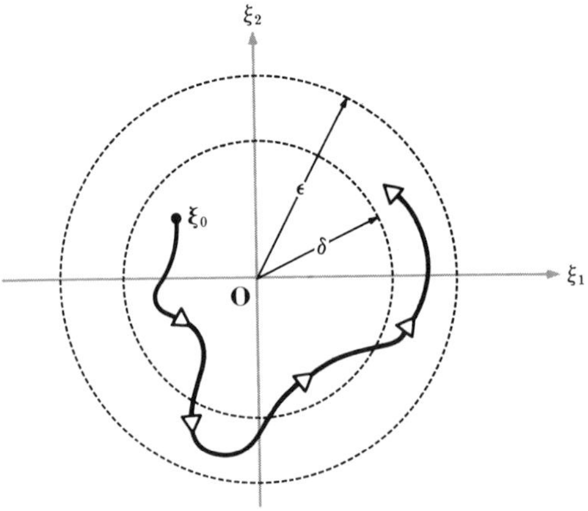

FIG. 6.7 A phase-plane plot of a system with a Liapunov stable equilibrium state at the origin.

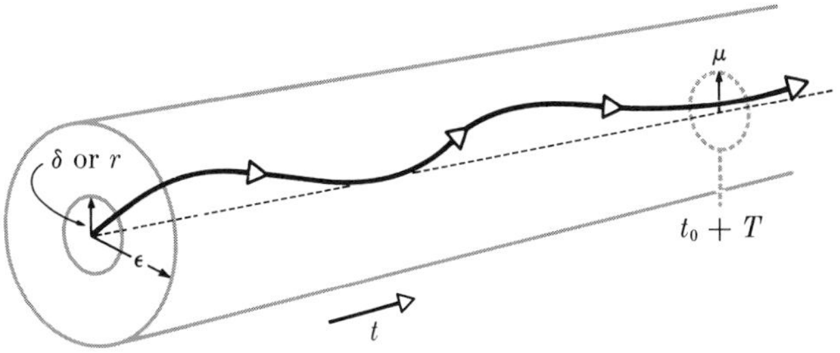

FIG. 6.8 Illustration of an asymptotically stable equilibrium state.

for all $t \geq t_0 + T$. Figure 6.8 illustrates (in two dimensions) the concept of asymptotic stability. We may next be concerned with the number of equilibrium states; in particular, if there is one equilibrium state and all free motion converges to it, it is the *ground state.*

(6.8) Asymptotic stability in the large

The equilibrium state **0** of a *free* system is said to be *asymptotically stable* in the large (or globally *asymptotically stable*) if

(1) It is *stable,*
(2) Every motion starting at ξ_0 such that $\|\xi_0\| < r < \infty$ converges to **0** as $t \to \infty$. ▮

In other words, the equilibrium state **0** is asymptotically stable in the large if it is stable and all free motion which evolves from any initially bounded state converges to it. In general we may be concerned with an opposite type of problem; that is, under what circumstances does the motion evolving from a specific state remain bounded?

(6.9) Bounded motion (Lagrange stability)

The state ξ_0 of a free system is said to be *bounded* (more precisely, to be associated with bounded motion) or Lagrange stable if for every t_0, there exists a real finite constant $B(\xi_0,t_0) < \infty$ such that

$$\|\phi(t;\xi_0,t)\| \leq B$$

for $t \geq t_0$. ▮

We note that a bounded (or Lagrange stable) state need not be an equilibrium state.

Each of the above concepts is easily translated to apply to nonzero equilibrium states or to discussion of the stability of motion of forced systems (see the problems).

There are, moreover, a myriad of prefixes and adjectives which may accompany any of these concepts, thus rendering them more stringent: *equi*—corresponds to uniform convergence or independence from the direction of ξ_0 with dependence merely on $\|\xi_0\|$ [for example, $T[\mu;\|\xi_0\|,t_0)$ or $B(\|\xi_0\|,t_0)$]; *uniformly*—corresponds to independence from t_0 [for example, $\delta(\epsilon)$, $T(\mu;\xi_0)$, r, $B(\xi_0)$]; finally, there may be the combination, *uniformly equi*.

6.5 STABILITY OF FREE LINEAR SYSTEMS—LIAPUNOV'S FIRST METHOD

We consider first a free (lumped) system described by

$$\dot{\mathbf{x}}(t) = \mathbf{A}(t)\mathbf{x}(t)$$

The origin

$$\mathbf{x} = \mathbf{0}$$

is an equilibrium state; moreover, it is the only equilibrium state if

$$\det(\mathbf{A}(t)) \neq 0 \qquad t \geq t_0$$

Note that in the case of a free linear system, the associated free system to be discussed in the study of the stability of its equilibrium states is identical to it:

$$\dot{\boldsymbol{\xi}}(t) = \mathbf{A}(t)\boldsymbol{\xi}(t) \tag{6.10}$$

or

$$\mathbf{h}(\boldsymbol{\xi}(t),t) = \mathbf{A}(t)\boldsymbol{\xi}(t)$$

The general solution of this homogeneous equation is of the form

$$\boldsymbol{\xi}(t) = \boldsymbol{\Phi}(t,t_0)\boldsymbol{\xi}_0$$

for

$$\boldsymbol{\xi}(t_0) = \boldsymbol{\xi}_0$$

where $\boldsymbol{\Phi}(t,t_0)$ is the state-transition matrix.

It is possible and desirable to translate the stability criteria of definitions (6.6) to (6.9) into conditions on the state-transition matrix $\boldsymbol{\Phi}(t,t_0)$. Consider Liapunov stability first. The origin of the system described by (6.10) is stable if for every real $\epsilon > 0$, we can find a real $\delta > 0$ such that

$$\|\boldsymbol{\xi}_0\| \leq \delta \tag{6.11}$$

implies

$$\|\boldsymbol{\Phi}(t,t_0)\boldsymbol{\xi}_0\| \leq \epsilon$$

But, from the properties of norms (see Sec. 3.10)

$$\|\boldsymbol{\Phi}(t,t_0)\boldsymbol{\xi}_0\| \le \|\boldsymbol{\Phi}(t,t_0)\| \, \|\boldsymbol{\xi}_0\|$$

and because of (6.11)

$$\|\boldsymbol{\Phi}(t,t_0)\boldsymbol{\xi}_0\| \le \|\boldsymbol{\Phi}(t,t_0)\|\delta$$

Now if we assume that $\|\boldsymbol{\Phi}(t,t_0)\|$ is bounded for all time by some finite number M, that is,

$$\|\boldsymbol{\Phi}(t,t_0)\| \le M < \infty \qquad \text{for all } t \ge t_0$$

then by choosing

$$\delta = \frac{\varepsilon}{M}$$

the stability definition is satisfied. Thus we are led to state the following theorem.

(6.12) Theorem
The equilibrium state **0** of the free, linear, time-variable system

$$\dot{\boldsymbol{\xi}}(t) = \mathbf{A}(t)\boldsymbol{\xi}(t)$$

is stable if and only if the norm of the associated state-transition matrix is uniformly bounded in t, that is,

$$\|\boldsymbol{\Phi}(t,t_0)\| \le M < \infty \qquad \text{for all } t \ge t_0$$

Proof
We have already shown sufficiency.

Necessity: Suppose $\|\boldsymbol{\Phi}(t,t_0)\|$ is not uniformly bounded in $t \ge t_0$, then

$$\lim_{t\to\infty} \|\boldsymbol{\Phi}(t,t_0)\| = \infty$$

(Note: $\|\boldsymbol{\Phi}(t,t_0)\| \ne \infty$ for finite t and t_0, because there may be no finite escape time.) By the definition of matrix norm,

$$\|\boldsymbol{\Phi}(t,t_0)\| = \sup_{\|\boldsymbol{\xi}_{0t}\|=1} \|\boldsymbol{\Phi}(t,t_0)\boldsymbol{\xi}_{0t}\|$$

for any $t \ge t_0$ there exists a vector $\hat{\boldsymbol{\xi}}_{0t}$ of unit norm,

$$\|\hat{\boldsymbol{\xi}}_{0t}\| = 1$$

such that

$$\|\boldsymbol{\Phi}(t,t_0)\| = \|\boldsymbol{\Phi}(t,t_0)\hat{\boldsymbol{\xi}}_{0t}\|$$

For this choice of initial condition we have

$$\|\boldsymbol{\xi}(t)\| = \|\boldsymbol{\Phi}(t,t_0)\hat{\boldsymbol{\xi}}_{0t}\| = \|\boldsymbol{\Phi}(t,t_0)\|$$

In the limit we have

$$\lim_{t\to\infty} \|\boldsymbol{\xi}_{0t}\| = 1$$

and

$$\lim_{t\to\infty} \|\boldsymbol{\xi}(t)\| = \lim_{t\to\infty} \|\boldsymbol{\Phi}(t,t_0)\| = \infty$$

The initial choice $\boldsymbol{\xi}_{0t} = \delta\boldsymbol{\xi}_{0t}$ $(\delta > 0)$ so that

$$\|\boldsymbol{\xi}_{0t}\| = \delta$$

and

$$\lim_{t\to\infty} \|\hat{\boldsymbol{\xi}}_{0t}\| = \delta$$

does not alter the situation since

$$\lim_{t\to\infty} \|\boldsymbol{\xi}(t)\| = \delta \lim_{t\to\infty} \|\boldsymbol{\Phi}(t,t_0)\| = \infty$$

again. This result is a contradiction of the stability hypothesis; i.e., given any $\epsilon > 0$, there exists no $\delta > 0$ such that $\|\boldsymbol{\xi}_0\| < \delta$ implies $\|\boldsymbol{\xi}(t)\| \leq \epsilon$ for all $t \geq t_0$. ▮

We notice immediately that for a free linear system the criterion for stability of the origin is identical to that for the boundedness of all initially finite states.

(6.13) Theorem

Any initially finite state $\boldsymbol{\xi}_0$, $\|\boldsymbol{\xi}_0\| < \infty$ of a free linear system is bounded if and only if the norm of the associated state-transition matrix is uniformly bounded in t:

$$\|\boldsymbol{\Phi}(t,t_0)\| \leq M < \infty \qquad \text{for all } t \geq t_0$$ ▮

The proof of this theorem parallels that of the immediately preceding theorem, and, hence, may be omitted. Because the conditions are identical, we have the immediate corollary.

(6.14) Corollary

The equilibrium state **0** of a free linear system is stable (in the sense of Liapunov) if and only if every initially finite state is bounded (i.e., it is stable in the sense of Lagrange). ▮

The additional condition on the norm of the state-transition matrix which ensures asymptotic stability is that it converges to zero as t approaches infinity.

(6.15) Theorem
The equilibrium state **0** of the free linear system

$$\dot{\boldsymbol{\xi}}(t) = \mathbf{A}(t)\boldsymbol{\xi}(t)$$

is asymptotically stable if and only if the norm of the associated state-transition matrix is uniformly bounded in t and approaches zero as t approaches infinity:

$$\|\boldsymbol{\Phi}(t,t_0)\| \leq M < \infty \qquad \text{for all } t > t_0$$

and

$$\lim_{t\to\infty} \|\boldsymbol{\Phi}(t,t_0)\| = 0 \qquad \text{for all } -\infty < t < \infty$$ ∎

The proof of this theorem is left as an exercise. Because the conditions for asymptotic stability for a free linear system are stated solely in terms of the norm of the state-transition matrix, they coincide with the conditions for asymptotic stability in the large. Since

$$\|\boldsymbol{\xi}(t)\| \leq \|\boldsymbol{\Phi}(t,t_0)\| \; \|\boldsymbol{\xi}_0\|$$

and

$$\lim_{t\to\infty} \|\boldsymbol{\Phi}(t,t_0)\| = 0$$

implies

$$\lim \|\boldsymbol{\xi}(t)\| = 0$$

for all

$$\|\boldsymbol{\xi}_0\| < \infty$$

In other words, if the origin is an asymptotically stable equilibrium state for a free linear system, it is asymptotically stable in the large and there may be no other equilibrium state. We state this result normally as the following theorem.

(6.16) Theorem
The equilibrium state **0** of a free linear system

$$\dot{\boldsymbol{\xi}}(t) = \mathbf{A}(t)\boldsymbol{\xi}(t)$$

is asymptotically stable if and only if it is asymptotically stable in the large. ∎

We recognize immediately that the origin may be taken to be the ground state for any linear system so long as it is asymptotically stable.

It is interesting to apply the above stability conditions to the state-transition matrix

$$\boldsymbol{\Phi}(t,t_0) = e^{\mathbf{A}(t-t_0)}$$

which is associated with the free, linear, time-invariant system

$$\dot{\xi}(t) = \mathbf{A}\xi(t)$$

It will emerge that we may state the conditions for the various types of stability directly in terms of properties of the matrix **A**.

First we must be more explicit about the meaning of $\|\mathbf{\Phi}(t,t_0)\|$. Consider first the l_1^n norm of an n vector $\mathbf{w} = (w_1,w_2, \ldots ,w_n)'$ taken with respect to its natural basis:

$$\|\mathbf{w}\|_1 \equiv \sum_{k=1}^{n} |w_k|$$

Now, if we are given an $n \times n$ matrix **F**,

$$\mathbf{F} = [f_{kl}]$$

we have

$$\|\mathbf{Fw}\|_1 = \sum_{k=1}^{n} \left| \sum_{l=1}^{n} f_{kl}w_l \right|$$

and we recognize that

$$\|\mathbf{F}\|_1 = \sup_{l} \left(\sum_{k=1}^{n} |f_{kl}| \right)$$

is the appropriate matrix norm. For the l_2^n norm of an n vector $\mathbf{w} = (w_1,w_2, \ldots ,w_n)'$ taken with respect to its natural basis, we have

$$\|\mathbf{w}\|_2 \equiv |\sqrt{\mathbf{w}^*\mathbf{w}}|$$

where * denotes conjugate transpose. Now, if we are given an $n \times n$ matrix **F**,

$$\mathbf{F} = [f_{kl}]$$

we have

$$\|\mathbf{Fw}\|_2 = |\sqrt{\mathbf{w}^*\mathbf{F}^*\mathbf{Fw}}|$$

Hence, to find the l_2^n norm of **F**, we must solve the following problem:

$$\max\ (\mathbf{w}^*\mathbf{F}^*\mathbf{Fw}) \text{ subject to } \mathbf{w}^*\mathbf{w} = 1$$

This problem is equivalent to the maximization in the free problem

$$\mathbf{w}^*\mathbf{F}^*\mathbf{Fw} - \lambda\mathbf{w}^*\mathbf{w}$$

where the Lagrange multiplier λ is ultimately to be determined from the constraint $\mathbf{w}^*\mathbf{w} = 1$. Differentiation with respect to (the real and imaginary parts of each component of) **w** yields the following two conditions:

$$\mathbf{F}^*\mathbf{F}\mathbf{w} = \lambda\mathbf{w}$$

and

$$\mathbf{v}^*\mathbf{F}^*\mathbf{F}\mathbf{v} - \lambda\mathbf{v} \qquad \mathbf{v} < 0$$
$$\mathbf{v} \neq \lambda\mathbf{w}$$

That is, **w** is a unit eigenvector of the $n \times n$ matrix $\mathbf{F}^*\mathbf{F}$ corresponding to the maximum eigenvalue

$$\|\mathbf{F}\|_2 = |\sqrt{\lambda_M(\mathbf{F}^*\mathbf{F})}|$$

the l_2^n norm of the $n \times n$ matrix **F** is the absolute value of the square root of the maximum eigenvalue of $\mathbf{F}^*\mathbf{F}$. For the l_∞^n norm of an n vector $\mathbf{w} = (\mathbf{w}_1, \ldots, \mathbf{w}_n)'$ taken with respect to its natural basis, we have

$$\|\mathbf{w}\|_\infty \equiv \sup_k |w_k|$$

Now, if we are given an $n \times n$ matrix F,

$$\mathbf{F} = [f_{kl}]$$

we have

$$\|\mathbf{F}\mathbf{w}\|_\infty = \sup_k \left|\sum_{l=1}^{n} f_{kl}w_l\right|$$

we recognize that

$$\|\mathbf{F}\|_\infty \equiv \sup_k \left(\sum_{l=1}^{n} |f_{kl}|\right)$$

is the appropriate matrix norm. The result is that although the l_2^n norm is the more natural and intuitive in the vector case, when we are dealing with matrices, the l_1^n norm and the l_∞^n norm are to be preferred for their simplicity. The difference is of little consequence; in stability studies we may always work with the most convenient matrix norm, since if one is zero, all are zero, and if one is bounded, all are bounded (see Prob. 6.1).

For a linear, time-invariant free system of order n,

$$\dot{\xi}(t) = \mathbf{A}\xi(t)$$

for which the $n \times n$ constant matrix **A** has $k (k \leq n)$ distinct eigenvalues $\lambda_1, \lambda_2, \ldots, \lambda_k$ of multiplicity $m_1, m_2, \ldots, m_k$, respectively; a typical term in the state-transition matrix has the following form:

$$\phi_{kl}(t,t_0) = \sum_{q=1}^{k} \left[\sum_{r=1}^{m_q} c_{qr}(t - t_0)^{r-1}\right] e^{\lambda_q(t-t_0)}$$

Hence, we may state immediately the necessary and sufficient conditions for stability of the origin or boundedness of the finite states of a free, linear, time-invariant system

$$\dot{\xi}(t) = \mathbf{A}\xi(t)$$

(1) All eigenvalues of the $n \times n$ constant matrix $\mathbf{A}$ have nonpositive real parts;
(2) Those eigenvalues of the $n \times n$ constant matrix $\mathbf{A}$ with zero real parts (if any) be associated only with the constant term ($t^0 = 1$) in the modal expansion of $e^{\mathbf{A}t}$.

The second condition is critical; it exhibits the difference between

$$|e^{j\omega t}| = |\cos \omega t + j \; sin \; \omega t| = 1$$

which is uniformly bounded for $t \geq 0$, and

$$|t^r e^{j\omega t}| = t^r |e^{j\omega t}| = t^r |\cos \omega t + j \sin \omega t| = t^r$$

which is not uniformly bounded for $t \geq 0$ and for $r = 1, 2, \ldots$. Of course,

$$|t^r e^{(\sigma + j\omega t)}| = t^r e^{\sigma t}$$

is bounded for $t \geq 0$ and $\sigma < 0$ for $r = 0, 1, 2, \ldots$. The second condition above is awkwardly stated, although compatible with the level of the preceding material on matrices.

Fortunately, the necessary and sufficient conditions for the asymptotic stability (in the large) of the origin for a free, linear, time-invariant system

$$\dot{\xi}(t) = \mathbf{A}\xi(t)$$

are more easily stated than the above:

> *All eigenvalues of the $n \times n$ constant matrix $\mathbf{A}$ must have negative real parts.*

Since asymptotic stability (in the large) is usually the desired behavior, rather than merely stability, the test becomes quite simple.

(6.17) Example
The RLC network of Fig. 6.9 is described by the state equations

$$\begin{bmatrix} \dot{x}_1(t) \\ \dot{x}_2(t) \end{bmatrix} = \begin{bmatrix} 0 & -1 \\ 1 & R \end{bmatrix} \begin{bmatrix} x_1(t) \\ x_2(t) \end{bmatrix}$$

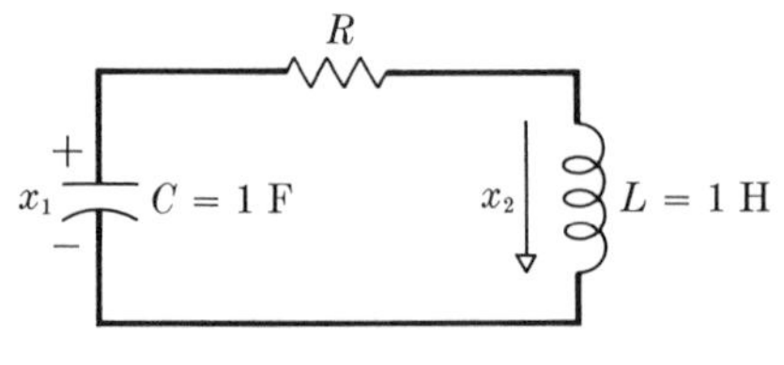

FIG. 6.9 An RLC network used to study stability.

The eigenvalues of the **A** matrix are

$$\lambda_1 = -\frac{R}{2} + \sqrt{\left(\frac{R}{2}\right)^2 - 1}$$

and

$$\lambda_2 = -\frac{R}{2} - \sqrt{\left(\frac{R}{2}\right)^2 - 1}$$

If $R \leq 0$, at least one of the eigenvalues has a positive real part and the system is known to be unstable. If $R > 0$, both eigenvalues have negative real parts and the system is asymptotically stable. If $R = 0$, the eigenvalues have zero real parts and the system is stable in the sense of Liapunov, but not asymptotically stable. ∎

For linear time-invariant systems, stability is an inherent property and not dependent on the system's characterization. The reason for this fact is that the eigenvalues of the **A** matrix are independent of time-invariant transformations, and we have shown that stability is directly related to the system's **A** matrix.

Thus far, the stability definitions and criteria introduced have required explicit knowledge of the solution of the associated free differential-state equation—with the exception of the linear time-invariant case, where stability criteria may be stated in terms of properties (of the eigenvalues) of the $n \times n$ constant matrix **A**. We may again resort to linearization about an equilibrium point (about a solution in general) for a free nonlinear system to obtain an associated free linear system so that (local) stability may be discussed in terms of a known situation. Hence, given

$$\dot{\boldsymbol{\xi}}(t) = \mathbf{h}(\boldsymbol{\xi}(t),t)$$

and

$$\mathbf{h}(\mathbf{0},t) \equiv \mathbf{0}$$

suppose that **h** may be expanded in a Taylor series about the origin as follows:

$$\mathbf{h}(\boldsymbol{\xi}(t),t) = \left.\frac{\partial \mathbf{h}}{\partial \boldsymbol{\xi}}\right|_{\mathbf{0}} \boldsymbol{\xi}(t) + \mathbf{O}\|\boldsymbol{\xi}(t)\|^2$$

where, as indicated each component of the n-vector remainder term is of order $\|\boldsymbol{\xi}(t)\|^2$ for all t. We may define the $n \times n$ matrix

$$\mathbf{A}(t) \equiv \left.\frac{\partial \mathbf{h}(\boldsymbol{\xi}(t),t)}{\partial \boldsymbol{\xi}(t)}\right|_{\boldsymbol{\xi}(t)=\mathbf{0}}$$

and we should suspect that the stability of the origin of the associated free linear system

$$\dot{\mathbf{n}}(t) = \mathbf{A}(t)\mathbf{n}(t)$$

may have some bearing upon that of the original. That is, since we are interested in the stability of the equilibrium state **0**, we expect $\|\boldsymbol{\xi}(t)\|^2$ to remain small (if it does not, stability is not indicated). The conditions under which the relation can be made are difficult to enunciate in general; however, they are quite easy to come by when the $n \times n$ matrix **A** turns out to be constant. The following theorems are referred to as *Liapunov's first method.*

(6.18) Theorem

Given the *autonomous* differential-state equations

$$\dot{\mathbf{x}}(t) = \mathbf{f}(\mathbf{x}(t))$$

the equilibrium state $\mathbf{x}_e$,

$$\mathbf{f}(\mathbf{x}_e) = \mathbf{0}$$

is asymptotically stable if the equilibrium state **0** of the associated free, linear, time-invariant system

$$\dot{\boldsymbol{\xi}}(t) = \mathbf{A}\boldsymbol{\xi}(t)$$

is asymptotically stable, where

$$\mathbf{A} \equiv \left.\frac{\partial \mathbf{f}(\mathbf{x}(t))}{\partial \mathbf{x}(t)}\right|_{\mathbf{x}_e}$$

Proof

The Taylor series expansion of **f** about the origin yields

$$\dot{\boldsymbol{\xi}}(t) = \mathbf{A}\boldsymbol{\xi}(t) + \mathbf{0}(\|\boldsymbol{\xi}(t)\|^2)$$

where each component of **0** is of order $\|\boldsymbol{\xi}(t)\|^2$. The complete solution of this differential equation in implicit form is

$$\boldsymbol{\xi}(t) = e^{\mathbf{A}(t-t_0)}\boldsymbol{\xi}_0 + \int_{t_0}^{t} e^{\mathbf{A}(t-\tau)}\mathbf{0}(\|\boldsymbol{\xi}(\tau)\|^2)\,d\tau$$

Moreover,

$$\|\boldsymbol{\xi}(t)\| \leq \|e^{\mathbf{A}(t-t_0)}\|\,\|\boldsymbol{\xi}_0\| + \int_{t_0}^{t} \|e^{\mathbf{A}(t-\tau)}\|\,\|\mathbf{0}(\|\boldsymbol{\xi}(\tau)\|^2)\|\,d\tau$$

and for asymptotic stability of the free, linear, time-invariant system characterized by the $n \times n$ constant matrix **A**, it must be true that there exist positive constants K and σ such that

$$\|e^{\mathbf{A}t}\| \leq Ke^{-\sigma t} \qquad \text{for all } t$$

Hence,

$$\|\boldsymbol{\xi}(t)\| \leq Ke^{-\sigma(t-t_0)}\|\boldsymbol{\xi}_0\| + K\int_{t_0}^{t} e^{-\sigma(t-\tau)}\|\mathbf{O}\|\,d\tau$$

Now, given $\varepsilon > 0$ there exists a $\delta > 0$ such that

$$\|\mathbf{O}(\|\boldsymbol{\xi}(t)\|^2)\| \leq \frac{\varepsilon}{K}\|\boldsymbol{\xi}(t)\| \qquad \text{for } \|\boldsymbol{\xi}(t)\| \leq \delta$$

thus, so long as $\|\boldsymbol{\xi}(t)\| \leq \delta$, it follows that

$$e^{\sigma(t-t_0)}\|\boldsymbol{\xi}(t)\| \leq K\|\boldsymbol{\xi}_0\| + \epsilon\int_{t_0}^{t} e^{\sigma(t-t_0)}\|\boldsymbol{\xi}(\tau)\|\,d\tau$$

From the Bellman-Gronwall inequality (see Chap. 4), it follows that

$$e^{\sigma(t-t_0)}\|\boldsymbol{\xi}(t)\| \leq Ke^{\varepsilon(t-t_0)}\|\boldsymbol{\xi}_0\|$$

or

$$\|\boldsymbol{\xi}(t)\| \leq Ke^{-(\sigma-\varepsilon)(t-t_0)}\|\boldsymbol{\xi}_0\|$$

If ε is chosen so that $\varepsilon < \sigma$, then

$$\|\boldsymbol{\xi}(t)\| \leq K\|\boldsymbol{\xi}_0\|$$

so long as $\|\boldsymbol{\xi}(t)\| \leq \delta$. Thus, if

$$\|\boldsymbol{\xi}_0\| < \frac{\delta}{K}$$

if follows that

$$\|\boldsymbol{\xi}(t)\| \leq \delta e^{-(\sigma-\varepsilon)(t-t_0)} \qquad \text{for all } t \geq t_0$$ ∎

There is, moreover, an equally valuable instability theorem for autonomous systems.

(6.19) Theorem

Given the *autonomous* differential-state equations

$$\dot{\mathbf{x}}(t) = \mathbf{f}(\mathbf{x}(t))$$

the equilibrium state $\mathbf{x}_e$,

$$\mathbf{f}(\mathbf{x}_e) = \mathbf{0}$$

is unstable if the equilibrium state $\mathbf{0}$ of the associated free, linear, time-invariant system

$$\dot{\boldsymbol{\xi}}(t) = \mathbf{A}\boldsymbol{\xi}(t)$$

is unstable, where

$$\mathbf{A} = \left.\frac{\partial \mathbf{f}(\mathbf{x}(t))}{\partial \mathbf{x}(t)}\right|_{\mathbf{x}_e}$$ ∎

The proof of this theorem may be affected in a manner similar to that of the above upon choosing the initial state to be an eigenvector of norm δ which is associated with an eigenvalue with a positive real part.

(6.20) Example
Consider a free system described by the state equations

$$\dot{x}_1 = x_2$$

and

$$\dot{x}_2 = (x_1^2 + x_2^2 - 1)(x_1^2 + x_2^2 - 2)(x_1^2 + x_2^2 - 3)x_2 - x_1$$

An equilibrium state associated with this system is

$$\mathbf{x}_{e1} = \begin{bmatrix} 0 \\ 0 \end{bmatrix}$$

We may employ Liapunov's first method to determine stability. The linearized system about the equilibrium state is described by

$$\begin{bmatrix} \dot{\xi}_1 \\ \dot{\xi}_2 \end{bmatrix} = \begin{bmatrix} 0 & 1 \\ -1 & 6 \end{bmatrix} \begin{bmatrix} \xi_1 \\ \xi_2 \end{bmatrix}$$

The eigenvalues of the **A** matrix are $\lambda_1 = 3 + 2\sqrt{2}$ and $\lambda_2 = 3 - 2\sqrt{2}$. Since at least one eigenvalue has a positive real part, the equilibrium state **0** is unstable for the linearized system, and therefore, for the original nonlinear system. ∎

(6.21) Example
Consider the free system described by

$$\dot{x}_1 = x_2$$

and

$$\dot{x}_2 = -x_1 - kx_2 + x_2^3$$

This system has an equilibrium state at the origin. The linearized system is described by

$$\begin{bmatrix} \dot{\xi}_1 \\ \dot{\xi}_2 \end{bmatrix} = \begin{bmatrix} 0 & 1 \\ -1 & -k \end{bmatrix} \begin{bmatrix} \xi_1 \\ \xi_2 \end{bmatrix}$$

and the eigenvalues of the **A** matrix are

$$\lambda_1 = -\frac{k}{2} + \sqrt{\left(\frac{k}{2}\right)^2 - 1}$$

and

$$\lambda_2 = -\frac{k}{2} - \sqrt{\left(\frac{k}{2}\right)^2 - 1}$$

If $k > 0$, the original system has an asymptotically stable equilibrium state since the origin of the linearized system is asymptotically stable. If $k < 0$, the original system has an unstable equilibrium state. If $k = 0$, we cannot make any definite statement about the stability of the equilibrium state, since the conditions of either Theorem (6.18) or (6.19) are not satisfied. ▮

(6.22) Example

In Example (2.16) of Chap. 2, we found that a simple undamped pendulum could be characterized by the second-order differential equation

$$\ddot{\theta} + k \sin \theta = 0$$

or by the state equations

$$\dot{x}_1 = x_2$$

and

$$\dot{x}_2 = -k \sin x_1$$

where k is a constant dependent on gravity and pendulum length. The origin is an equilibrium state. The associated linear system is described by

$$\dot{\xi} = \begin{bmatrix} 0 & 1 \\ -k & 0 \end{bmatrix} \xi$$

Since the eigenvalues of the **A** matrix, $\lambda_1 = j\sqrt{k}$, $\lambda_2 = -j\sqrt{k}$, are purely imaginary, Liapunov's first method yields no information about the stability of the origin of the original nonlinear system. (Observe the origin is stable, but not asymptotically stable.)

Assume now that viscous damping is present. The second-order differential equation then becomes

$$\ddot{\theta} + c\dot{\theta} + k \sin \theta = 0$$

where c is the coefficient of viscous damping. A suitable set of state equations are

$$\dot{x}_1 = x_2$$

and

$$\dot{x}_2 = -k \sin x_1 - cx_2$$

Again the origin is an equilibrium state and the associated linear system is described by

$$\dot{\boldsymbol{\xi}} = \begin{bmatrix} 0 & 1 \\ -k & -c \end{bmatrix} \boldsymbol{\xi}$$

The eigenvalues are

$$\lambda_1 = -\frac{c}{2} + \sqrt{\left(\frac{c}{2}\right)^2 - k}$$

and

$$\lambda_2 = -\frac{c}{2} - \sqrt{\left(\frac{c}{2}\right)^2 - k}$$

which have negative real parts. Thus the origin is an asymptotically stable equilibrium state for the associated linear system, and therefore, the original nonlinear system. ∎

When Liapunov's first method fails to yield information concerning the stability of an equilibrium state, more sophisticated methods must be employed.

6.6 LIAPUNOV'S SECOND METHOD

The method for determining stability presented in the previous section will not always yield the desired information. In this section, we present a more sophisticated method.

By way of introduction, consider a bead rolling in a cup as illustrated in Fig. 6.10. This situation is the two-dimensional equivalent of the bead sliding on a wire discussed previously. The system is describable by the pair of differential-state equations

$$\dot{x}_1 = f_1(x_1,x_2,t)$$

and

$$\dot{x}_2 = f_2(x_1,x_2,t)$$

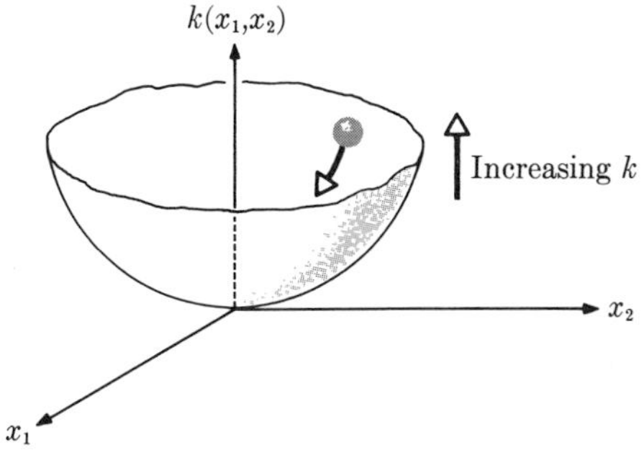

FIG. 6.10 A bead sliding in a cup defined by $k(x_1,x_2)$.

Clearly, if the bead starts at the bottom of the cup, it will stay there. Thus, the origin is an equilibrium state, i.e.,

$$f_1(0,0,t) = f_2(0,0,t) = 0 \qquad \text{for } t \geq t_0$$

Suppose that the cup can be defined by $k(x_1,x_2,t)$ such that

$$k(0,0,t) = 0 \qquad \text{for } t \geq t_0$$

and

$$k(x_{1a},x_{2a},t) \geq k(x_{1b},x_{2b},t)$$

whenever

$$x_{1a}^2 + x_{2a}^2 > x_{1b}^2 + x_{2b}^2$$

Then, if

$$\frac{dk}{dt} \leq 0$$

for any possible state along the solution, the quantity $[x_1(t)]^2 + [x_2(t)]^2$ cannot increase and the equilibrium state $x_1 = x_2 = 0$ is stable. Moreover, if

$$\frac{dk}{dt} < 0$$

for any possible state along the solution (except, of course, $x_1 = x_2 = 0$), the quantity $[x_1(t)]^2 + [x_2(t)]^2$ must decrease to zero and the equilibrium state $x_1 = x_2 = 0$ is asymptotically stable. The equation k = constant defines a closed surface in the state space; moreover, the surface defined for any positive value of k encloses all those defined for smaller positive values of k. If at any point on any of these closed surfaces, the motion is inward, the equilibrium state at the origin is attained. Thus stability may be determined in terms of the properties of the cup and not by solving the state equations. For a third-order system, we could attempt to use a series of two-dimensional surfaces (e.g., nested spheres or ellipsoids) in the state space; the extension to n-dimensional spaces is not conceptually difficult. To facilitate our discussion, several concepts must be introduced.

(6.23) Positive definite

A scalar function $V(\mathbf{x})$ of n variables $x_1(t), x_2(t), \ldots, x_n(t)$ is said to be *positive definite* in some region R of the origin if

(1) $V(\mathbf{x})$ is continuously differentiable in R
(2) $V(\mathbf{0}) = 0$
(3) $V(\mathbf{x}) > 0$ for all $\mathbf{x} \neq \mathbf{0}$ contained in R ∎

If condition (3) of definition (6.23) were to read

$$V(\mathbf{x}) \geq 0 \qquad \text{for all } \mathbf{x} \text{ contained in } R$$

then $V(\mathbf{x})$ would be called *positive semidefinite;* if

$$V(\mathbf{x}) < 0 \qquad \text{for all } \mathbf{x} \text{ contained in } R$$

then $V(\mathbf{x})$ is *negative definite;* and if

$$V(\mathbf{x}) \leq 0 \qquad \text{for all } \mathbf{x} \neq 0 \text{ contained in } R$$

then $V(\mathbf{x})$ is *negative semidefinite.*

(6.24) Example

$$V(\mathbf{x}) = x_1^2 + x_2^2 + \cdots + x_n^2 \qquad \mathbf{x} = (x_1, x_2, \ldots, x_n)'$$

is positive definite for all values of x.

$$V(\mathbf{x}) = x_1^2 + x_2^2 + x_2^3 \qquad \mathbf{x} = (x_1, x_2)'$$

is positive definite for all values of x_1 and for all $|x_2| < 1$.

$$V(\mathbf{x}) = (x_1 + x_2)^2 + x_3^2 \qquad \mathbf{x} = (x_1, x_2, x_3)'$$

is positive semidefinite. ∎

We have already shown that stability studies may, without loss of generality, always be carried out in terms of a free system

$$\dot{\mathbf{x}}(t) = \mathbf{f}(\mathbf{x}(t), t)$$

with an equilibrium state at the origin

$$\mathbf{f}(\mathbf{0}, t) = \mathbf{0} \qquad \text{for } t \geq t_0$$

Our object is to find a test for stability that does not require the explicit solution of the differential-state equations. We state, without proof, the following theorem concerning stability.

(6.25) Theorem (Liapunov)
The equilibrium state $\mathbf{x} = \mathbf{0}$ of a free system is stable if there exists a positive-definite function $V(\mathbf{x}(t))$ in some region R such that its total time derivative $\dot{V}(\mathbf{x}(t))$ along the solution of the differential-state equation

$$\dot{\mathbf{x}}(t) = \mathbf{f}(\mathbf{x}(t),t)$$

is negative semidefinite. ∎

Any function $V(\mathbf{x})$ such that the conditions of Theorem (6.25) are met is called a *Liapunov* function. To see how the existence of a Liapunov function guarantees stability, consider the two-dimensional state space shown in Fig. 6.11. For stability we must show that given any $\epsilon > 0$, there exists a $\delta > 0$ such that if $\|\mathbf{x}_0\| < \delta$, then $\|\phi(t;x_0,t_0)\| < \epsilon$ for all $t > t_0$. Let ϵ be as shown in Fig. 6.11. We know that a $V(\mathbf{x})$ exists such that $V(\mathbf{x}) > 0$ for all $x \neq 0$. Consider that contour (projection) of $V(\mathbf{x}) = k \leq \epsilon$ for all $\mathbf{x}$. δ is then chosen to be the shortest distance between the equilibrium state $\mathbf{0}$ and the curve $V(\mathbf{x}) = k$. Now consider any $\mathbf{x}_0$ lying in the circle defined by radius δ. Certainly $V(\mathbf{x}_0) < k$ and, moreover, since $V(\mathbf{x}) > 0$ and $\dot{V}(\mathbf{x}) \leq 0$, that is, $V(\mathbf{x})$ is *nonincreasing*, the trajectory starting from $\mathbf{x}_0$ cannot ever exit from the area enclosed by $V(\mathbf{x}) = k$. Thus stability is ensured.

The modification of Theorem (6.25) to test for asymptotic stability should be apparent.

(6.26) Theorem
The equilibrium state $\mathbf{x} = \mathbf{0}$ is asymptotically stable if there exists a positive-definite function $V(\mathbf{x})$ in some region R such that its total time derivative $\dot{V}(\mathbf{x})$ along the solution of the differential-state equation is negative definite. ∎

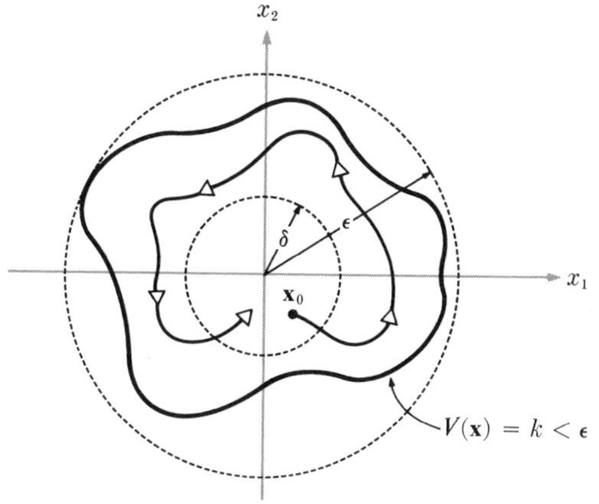

FIG. 6.11 Demonstration of Liapunov's second method.

To see how these conditions guarantee asymptotic stability, refer again to Fig. 6.11. The requirement that $\dot{V}(\mathbf{x}) < 0$ means that the $V(\mathbf{x})$ curve shrinks as time increases and therefore any trajectory starting from $\mathbf{x}_0$ must eventually return to the origin.

The reader should bear in mind that even if a function $V(\mathbf{x})$ is chosen and it does not satisfy the conditions of either of the theorems, the system may still be stable because another $V(\mathbf{x})$ might satisfy the conditions. In other words, a Liapunov function $V(\mathbf{x}(t))$ which works is sufficient in stability studies; a "guess" which does not work merely indicates that we must continue in our quest for one which does.

The consequences of these two theorems are quite far reaching. We may, with luck, ascertain local stability properties of equilibriums without knowing the solution of the differential-state equations.

(6.27) Example

Consider a system described by

$$\dot{x}_1 = x_2$$

and

$$\dot{x}_2 = q(x_1,x_2)$$

with $q(0,0) = 0$. As a trial Liapunov function, take

$$V(x_1,x_2) = \tfrac{1}{2}x_1^2 + \tfrac{1}{2}x_2^2$$

which is certainly positive definite. Then

$$\dot{V}(x_1,x_2) = x_1\dot{x}_1 + x_2\dot{x}_2 = x_1x_2 + x_2q(x_1,x_2)$$

A sufficient condition for asymptotic stability is that

$$x_1x_2 + x_2q(x_1,x_2)$$

be negative definite in some region of the origin. Observe that if

$$q(x_1,x_2) = -\frac{x_1^2}{x_2} - 3x_1 - x_2$$

then

$$\dot{V}(x_1,x_2) = -(x_1 + x_2)^2$$

and we would have stability. Recognize that failure of the test for a trial Liapunov function does not imply instability; it may merely indicate a bad original choice. For example, if

$$q(x_1,x_2) = -3x_2 - 2x_1$$

then

$$\dot{V}(x_1,x_2) = -3x_2^2 - x_1x_2$$

which is not negative definite even though the given linear time-invariant system does have an asymptotically stable equilibrium state at the origin. In the latter case, there must be a Liapunov function (according to Theorem 6.26), but the trial one we have chosen is not it. ▮

It is interesting to investigate what consequences Liapunov's second method has on linear time-invariant systems. To facilitate the discussion, we digress briefly to define a positive-definite matrix.

(6.28) Positive-definite matrix

A matrix $\mathbf{A}$ is *positive definite* if the *quadratic form* $\mathbf{x}'\mathbf{A}\mathbf{x}$ is positive definite, i.e.,

$$V(\mathbf{x}) \equiv \mathbf{x}'\mathbf{A}\mathbf{x} > 0$$

for all $\mathbf{x} \neq 0$. ▮

If $\mathbf{x}'\mathbf{A}\mathbf{x} \geq 0$, then $\mathbf{A}$ is said to be *positive semidefinite;* if $\mathbf{x}'\mathbf{A}\mathbf{x} < 0$, then $\mathbf{A}$ is *negative definite;* if $\mathbf{x}'\mathbf{A}\mathbf{x} \leq 0$, then $\mathbf{A}$ is *negative semidefinite.* We can now state the following theorem.

(6.29) Theorem

Given the autonomous linear system

$$\dot{\mathbf{x}}(t) = \mathbf{A}\mathbf{x}(t)$$

the origin is an asymptotically stable (in the large) equilibrium state if and only if given any symmetric positive-definite matrix $\mathbf{Q}$, the symmetric matrix $\mathbf{P}$ which is the solution of the linear-matrix equation

$$\mathbf{A}'\mathbf{P} + \mathbf{P}\mathbf{A} = -\mathbf{Q}$$

is also positive definite. (Note: A symmetric matrix $\mathbf{Q}$ is one in which $q_{ij} = q_{ji}$.)

Proof

Sufficiency: Assume

$$\mathbf{A}'\mathbf{P} + \mathbf{P}\mathbf{A} = -\mathbf{Q}$$

with $\mathbf{P}$ and $\mathbf{Q}$ both symmetric and positive definite. Then a Liapunov function is

$$V(\mathbf{x}(t)) = \mathbf{x}'(t)\mathbf{P}\mathbf{x}(t) > 0$$

because

$$\begin{aligned} \dot{V}(\mathbf{x}(t)) &= \dot{\mathbf{x}}'(t)\mathbf{P}\mathbf{x}(t) + \mathbf{x}'(t)\mathbf{P}\dot{\mathbf{x}}(t) \\ &= \mathbf{x}'(t)\mathbf{A}'\mathbf{P}\mathbf{x}(t) + \mathbf{x}'(t)\mathbf{P}\mathbf{A}\mathbf{x}(t) \\ &= -\mathbf{x}'(t)\mathbf{Q}\mathbf{x}(t) < 0 \end{aligned}$$

Necessity: The necessity proof is not so easy; we show here that it is plausible. We must show that if **A** possesses only eigenvalues with negative real parts, then **P** is positive definite for an arbitrary positive-definite **Q**. Consider

$$\mathbf{A}'\mathbf{P} + \mathbf{P}\mathbf{A} = -\mathbf{Q}$$

and suppose that **S** is a modal matrix for **A**, then

$$\mathbf{S}'\mathbf{A}'(\mathbf{S}')^{-1}\mathbf{S}'\mathbf{P}\mathbf{S} + \mathbf{S}'\mathbf{P}\mathbf{S}\mathbf{S}^{-1}\mathbf{A}\mathbf{S} = -\mathbf{S}'\mathbf{Q}\mathbf{S}$$

or

$$\mathbf{J}'\hat{\mathbf{P}} + \mathbf{P}\mathbf{J} = -\hat{\mathbf{Q}}$$

where

$$\mathbf{S}^{-1}\mathbf{A}\mathbf{S} = \mathbf{J} \qquad \text{the Jordan form associated with } \mathbf{A},$$
$$\mathbf{S}'\mathbf{Q}\mathbf{S} = \hat{\mathbf{Q}} \qquad \text{a symmetric positive-definite matrix,}$$

and

$$\mathbf{S}'\mathbf{P}\mathbf{S} = \hat{\mathbf{P}} \qquad \text{a symmetric matrix,}$$

which must be shown to be positive definite. ∎

The following relation to stability studies is also useful.

(6.30) Corollary

Given the autonomous linear system

$$\dot{\mathbf{x}}(t) = \mathbf{A}\mathbf{x}(t)$$

the origin is a stable equilibrium state if and only if there exists a symmetric nonnegative-definite matrix **Q** such that the symmetric-matrix solution **P** of the equation.

$$\mathbf{A}'\mathbf{P} + \mathbf{P}\mathbf{A} = -\mathbf{Q}$$

is positive definite. ∎

We shall not prove this corollary.

We must employ caution in the application of these theorems to stability investigations: **Q** is given, **P** must be found. If **P** were given and **Q** to be found, the problem would be too easy. We may nonetheless attempt to pick **P** and find **Q**, but a negative answer is of no use.

(6.31) Example

The second-order differential equation

$$\ddot{x} + a\dot{x} + bx = 0$$

has the asymptotically stable equilibrium state $x = \dot{x} = 0$ if $a > 0$ and $b > 0$. Consider the state description

$$\dot{x}_1 = x_2$$

and

$$\dot{x}_2 = -bx_1 - ax_2$$

or

$$\mathbf{A} = \begin{bmatrix} 0 & 1 \\ -b & -a \end{bmatrix}$$

Try picking $\mathbf{P} = \mathbf{1}$:

$$\mathbf{A}'\mathbf{P} + \mathbf{P}\mathbf{A} = \mathbf{A}' + \mathbf{A} = \begin{bmatrix} 0 & 1 - b \\ 1 - b & -2a \end{bmatrix}$$

$$\mathbf{Q} = \begin{bmatrix} 0 & b - 1 \\ b - 1 & 2a \end{bmatrix}$$

a matrix which is positive definite only if

$$2a > 0 \qquad \text{and} \qquad -(b - 1)^2 > 0$$

which is impossible. That is, we can draw no conclusions about the stability of the system since $\mathbf{x}'(t)\mathbf{P}\mathbf{x}(t)$ is *not* a Liapunov function for $\mathbf{P} = \mathbf{1}$. ▮

6.7 THE MACROSCOPIC VIEW OF STABILITY

Let us now turn our attention away from the study of stability of equilibrium states and consider the input-output behavior of systems, i.e., the macroscopic behavior. We will introduce a new form of stability and discuss its relation to what has preceded.

We have shown that the Laplace transform of any nth-order, linear, time-invariant differential equation may be written as [see (5.77)]

$$(6.32) \qquad Y(s) = H(s)U(s) + E(s)$$

From (5.116) we have

$$E(s) = \mathbf{c}'(s\mathbf{1} - \mathbf{A})^{-1}\mathbf{x}_0$$

and

$$H(s) = \mathbf{c}'(s\mathbf{1} - \mathbf{A})^{-1}\mathbf{b} + d$$

The system's transfer function $H(s)$ is the Laplace transform of the impulse response $h(t)$ which is a function of the system matrix $\mathbf{A}$. In Sec. 6.5 we have seen that stability studies for linear time-invariant systems may be carried out in terms of the eigenvalues of $\mathbf{A}$, hence we may be motivated to investigate the properties of the transfer function $H(s)$ as a means to determine stability in the sense of these definitions. Since we are now concerned with the input-output behavior of a system, it is convenient to define input-output stability.

(6.33) Stability bounded input-bounded output (*BIBO*)
A system is said to be a *stable bounded input-bounded output* if every bounded input

$$|u(t)| \leq M_u < \infty \qquad \text{for all } t$$

is associated only with bounded outputs,

$$|y(t)| \leq M_y < \infty \qquad \text{for all } t$$ ∎

An assumption which usually accompanies this definition, but need not, is that the initial state is a zero state at $t = -\infty$. We note that the system in question may be multiple valued (i.e., more than one output function y may be associated with a given input function u); hence, the definition may apply to the most general nonlinear system. We first discuss stability *BIBO* and its implications for linear time-invariant systems, and then we relate it to the other types of stability. Stability *BIBO* may be determined in terms of the impulse response.

(6.34) Theorem
A linear time-invariant system with impulse response $h(t)$ is stable *BIBO* if and only if

$$\int_0^\infty |h(\tau)|\, d\tau = M < \infty$$

(Recall that $h(t) = 0$ for $t < 0$ for physical systems.)

Proof
Sufficiency: Assume that

$$\int_0^\infty |h(\tau)|\, d\tau = M < \infty$$

and let $u(t)$ be a bounded input, i.e.,

$$|u(t)| \leq M_u \qquad \text{for all } t$$

The system's zero-state response can be obtained from the convolution integral. Therefore

$$\begin{aligned}|y(t)| &= \left| \int_0^{\infty} h(\tau)u(t-\tau)\,d\tau \right| \\ &\leq \int_0^{\infty} |h(\tau)|\,|u(t-\tau)|\,d\tau \\ &\leq M_u \int_0^{\infty} |h(\tau)|\,d\tau \\ &\leq M_u M < \infty \qquad \text{for all } t\end{aligned}$$

Hence the system is stable *BIBO*.

Necessity: Assume that the system is stable *BIBO*, but that

$$\int_{-\infty}^{\infty} |h(\tau)|\,d\tau = \infty$$

The systems zero-state response at any time t_1 is given by the convolution integral

$$y(t_1) = \int_{-\infty}^{t_1} h(t_1-\tau)u(\tau)\,d\tau$$

Consider the unity (bounded) input

$$u(\tau) = \frac{h(t_1-\tau)}{|h(t_1-\tau)|}$$

Then

$$\begin{aligned}|y(t_1)| &= \left| \int_{-\infty}^{t_1} \frac{(h(t_1-\tau))^2}{|h(t_1-\tau)|}\,d\tau \right| = \left| \int_{-\infty}^{t_1} |h(t_1-\tau)|\,d\tau \right| \\ &= \int_{\infty}^{t_1} |h(t_1-\tau)|\,d\tau = \infty\end{aligned}$$

which contradicts the original assumption. ∎

As a consequence of this theorem, the impulse response $h(t)$ associated with a *BIBO* stable system has a Fourier transform, and hence a Laplace transform $H(s)$. Moreover, the region of convergence associated with this Laplace transform or transfer function includes the $j\omega$ axis. Since we are concerned with causal systems, for which $h(t) = 0$ for $t < 0$, the region of convergence includes the entire right half plane. Thus we have the following theorem.

(6.35) Theorem
A linear time-invariant system is stable *BIBO* if and only if its transfer function $H(s)$ has no singularities in the closed right half plane. ∎

(6.36) Example
Let us investigate *BIBO* stability of the second-order system characterized by

$$\ddot{y}(t) - \dot{y}(t) - 6y(t) = \dot{u}(t) - 3u(t)$$

The transfer function of this system is found to be

$$H(s) = \frac{s-3}{s^2-s-6} = \frac{1}{s+2}$$

$H(s)$ has a single pole $s = -2$ in the left half plane, and therefore, the system is stable *BIBO*. ∎

6.8 CONTROLLABILITY AND OBSERVABILITY

We now proceed to ascertain what (if any) is the correlation between input-output stability and the stability of state-space equilibriums as previously defined. We again restrict our study to the lumped, linear, time-invariant case for which concrete results are explicitly available. Beginning with the state equations for a single input—single output system

$$\dot{\mathbf{x}}(t) = \mathbf{A}\mathbf{x}(t) + \mathbf{b}u(t)$$

and

$$y(t) = \mathbf{c}'\mathbf{x}(t) + du(t)$$

we recognize that the causal solution is

$$y(t) = \mathbf{c}' \int_{-\infty}^{t} e^{\mathbf{A}(t-\tau)}\mathbf{b}u(\tau)\,d\tau + du(t)$$

(where the initial state at $t = -\infty$ is taken to be a zero state).

The impulse response can be taken as

$$h(t) = \mathbf{c}'e^{\mathbf{A}t}\mathbf{b} + d\delta(t)$$

and the *BIBO* stability requirement

$$\int_0^\infty |h(t)|\,dt < \infty$$

becomes

$$\int_0^\infty |\mathbf{c}'e^{\mathbf{A}t}\mathbf{b} + d\delta(t)|\,dt < \infty$$

or

$$\int_0^\infty |\mathbf{c}'e^{\mathbf{A}t}\mathbf{b}|\,dt < \infty$$

since it is assumed that $d < \infty$. We recognize that typically $\mathbf{c}'e^{\mathbf{A}t}\mathbf{b}$ will be a sum of terms of the form

$$t^r e^{\lambda_q t}$$

where λ_q is an eigenvalue of the $n \times n$ constant matrix $\mathbf{A}$ of multiplicity $r + 1$ (at least). A necessary and sufficient condition that

$$\int_0^\infty |\mathbf{c}'e^{\mathbf{A}t}\mathbf{b}|\, dt < \infty$$

is that each eigenvalue that appears in the sum $\mathbf{c}'e^{\mathbf{A}t}\mathbf{b}$ have a negative real part. However, not all eigenvalues of $\mathbf{A}$ need appear in the sum $\mathbf{c}'e^{\mathbf{A}t}\mathbf{b}$, as is illustrated by the following examples.

(6.37) Example

Consider the system characterized by the state equations

$$\dot{\mathbf{x}}(t) = \begin{bmatrix} \lambda_1 & 0 \\ 0 & \lambda_2 \end{bmatrix} \mathbf{x}(t) + \begin{bmatrix} 1 \\ 1 \end{bmatrix} u(t)$$

and

$$y(t) = (1 \quad 0)\mathbf{x}(t)$$

Observe that

$$\mathbf{c}'e^{\mathbf{A}t}\mathbf{b} = e^{\lambda_1 t}$$

and λ_2 does not appear. ▮

(6.38) Example

Consider the system characterized by

$$\ddot{y}(t) - \dot{y}(t) - 6y(t) = \dot{u}(t) - 3u(t)$$

If we choose as states

$$x_1 = y$$

and

$$x_2 = \dot{y} - y - u$$

then the system may be described by the state equations

$$\dot{\mathbf{x}}(t) = \begin{bmatrix} 1 & 1 \\ 6 & 0 \end{bmatrix} \mathbf{x}(t) + \begin{bmatrix} 1 \\ -3 \end{bmatrix} u(t)$$

and

$$y(t) = (1 \quad 0)\mathbf{x}(t)$$

It is easy to show that

$$e^{\mathbf{A}t} = \frac{1}{5} \begin{bmatrix} 3e^{3t} + 2e^{-2t} & e^{3t} - e^{-2t} \\ 6e^{3t} - 6e^{-2t} & 2e^{3t} + 3e^{-2t} \end{bmatrix}$$

so that

$$\mathbf{c}'e^{\mathbf{A}t}\mathbf{b} = e^{-2t}$$

and the eigenvalue (mode, natural frequency) $\lambda = 3$ does not appear. ▮

In Sec. 6.5 we have shown that a necessary and sufficient condition for the equilibrium state (the origin) of a lumped, linear, time-invariant system to be asymptotically stable (in the large) is that *all* the eigenvalues of **A** have negative real parts. Thus we may conclude that a *sufficient* (but by no means necessary) condition for stability bounded input-bounded output of a lumped, linear, time-invariant system is that the equilibrium state of the associated free system be asymptotically stable (in the large). The following example shows that mere stability of an equilibrium state does not suffice to guarantee stability *BIBO*.

(6.39) Example
Consider the simple lumped, linear, time-invariant system characterized by the state equations

$$\dot{\mathbf{x}}(t) = \begin{bmatrix} 0 & 1 \\ -1 & 0 \end{bmatrix} \mathbf{x}(t) + \begin{bmatrix} 0 \\ 1 \end{bmatrix} u(t)$$

and

$$\mathbf{y}(t) = (1 \quad 0)\mathbf{x}(t)$$

The equilibrium state

$$\mathbf{x} = \mathbf{0}$$

for the associated free system

$$\dot{\mathbf{x}}(t) = \begin{bmatrix} 0 & 1 \\ -1 & 0 \end{bmatrix} \mathbf{x}(t)$$

is stable, but the bounded input

$$u(t) = \sin t \qquad t > 0$$

yields the unbounded zero-state response

$$y(t) = -\tfrac{1}{2}t \cos t \qquad t > 0$$

▮

With stability it is possible to have a resonance condition which asymptotic stability disallows. The following example illustrates that *BIBO* stability does not imply asymptotic stability.

(6.40) Example
Once again consider the system discussed in Example (6.38) characterized by the state equations

$$\dot{\mathbf{x}}(t) = \begin{bmatrix} 1 & 1 \\ 6 & 0 \end{bmatrix} \mathbf{x}(t) + \begin{bmatrix} 1 \\ -3 \end{bmatrix} u(t)$$

and

$$\mathbf{y}(t) = (1 \quad 0)\mathbf{x}(t)$$

The equilibrium state $\mathbf{x} = \mathbf{0}$ for the associated free system

$$\dot{\mathbf{x}}(t) = \begin{bmatrix} 1 & 1 \\ 6 & 0 \end{bmatrix} \mathbf{x}(t)$$

is unstable since $\mathbf{A}$ has a positive real eigenvalue. The system is stable *BIBO* since the only eigenvalue that appears in the term $\mathbf{c}'e^{\mathbf{A}t}\mathbf{b}$ is negative. ∎

It should now become clear why *BIBO* stability does not imply asymptotic stability. The impulse response or transfer function, on which *BIBO* stability is based, does not necessarily display all the modes (eigenvalues of the $\mathbf{A}$ matrix) of the system, while asymptotic stability is based on all the modes of the system. Basically there are four possibilities:

(1) The input (or inputs) excites all the system's modes and all these modes are present at the output (or outputs).
(2) The input (or inputs) excites all the system's modes, but one or more of these modes cannot be observed at the output (or outputs).
(3) All the modes of the system may be observed at the output (or outputs), but not all the modes can be excited by the input (or inputs).
(4) Not all the modes of the system can be observed at the output (or outputs), and not all the modes can be excited by the input (or inputs).

Roughly speaking, systems which fall into the first and second categories are said to be completely controllable; and systems in the first and third categories are said to be completely observable. We are being rather loose at this point in describing a "system" as being completely controllable or completely observable. In fact, what we mean is that a particular system realization is completely controllable or completely observable. Problem (6.10) shows that it is possible that a given system may be represented by several different sets of state equations. Some of these sets may be completely controllable, others may be completely observable, and still others may be neither completely controllable nor completely observable. Therefore, the reader should bear in mind that it is a particular realization (or characterization) itself that is completely controllable or observable and not the system, although in the sequel we will continue to refer to the system as having or not having these attributes.

In general, systems are not completely controllable or completely observable, but can be thought of as being composed of four subsystems which are

(1) Completely controllable and observable
(2) Completely controllable, but not completely observable
(3) Completely observable, but not completely controllable
(4) Not completely controllable and not completely observable.

The transfer function only characterizes that *part* of the system which is completely controllable *and* completely observable. Thus if an entire system is completely controllable and completely observable, all the modes can be excited (controlled) and observed, so that then stability *BIBO* implies asymptotic stability.

Although a detailed study of controllability and observability is beyond the scope of this text, it is instructive to determine under what conditions all the natural modes of a system can be excited and observed. Note that from a design standpoint such conditions are important if we wish to design with the transfer function—i.e., the system may be stable *BIBO*, but the designer may be unaware of unstable equilibrium states. (This problem is particularly true in active RC circuits, for example.)

Consider a single input—single output system characterized by

$$\dot{\mathbf{x}}(t) = \mathbf{A}\mathbf{x}(t) + \mathbf{b}u(t) \tag{6.41a}$$

and

$$y(t) = \mathbf{c}'\mathbf{x}(t) + du(t) \tag{6.41b}$$

We first assume that $\mathbf{A}$ has the distinct eigenvalues $\lambda_1, \lambda_2, \ldots, \lambda_n$. Let $\mathbf{S}$ be a modal matrix associated with $\mathbf{A}$. Transformation of the system to its natural basis is accomplished if we let

$$\boldsymbol{\xi} = \mathbf{S}^{-1}\mathbf{x}$$

Then (6.41) becomes

$$\dot{\boldsymbol{\xi}}(t) = \mathbf{S}^{-1}\mathbf{A}\mathbf{S}\boldsymbol{\xi}(t) + \mathbf{S}^{-1}\mathbf{b}u(t)$$

and

$$y(t) = \mathbf{c}'\mathbf{S}\boldsymbol{\xi}(t) + du(t)$$

But

$$\mathbf{S}^{-1}\mathbf{A}\mathbf{S} = \boldsymbol{\Lambda} = \text{diag}\,(\lambda_1,\lambda_2, \ldots ,\lambda_n)$$

so that the state equations of the transformed system are

$$\dot{\boldsymbol{\xi}} = \boldsymbol{\Lambda}\boldsymbol{\xi} + \hat{\mathbf{b}}u \tag{6.42a}$$

and

$$y = \hat{\mathbf{c}}'\boldsymbol{\xi} + du \tag{6.42b}$$

where

$$\hat{\mathbf{b}} = \mathbf{S}^{-1}\mathbf{b} \qquad \text{and} \qquad \hat{\mathbf{c}}' = \mathbf{c}'\mathbf{S}$$

The matrix equation (6.42*a*) represents n uncoupled, first-order differential equations of the form

$$\dot{\xi}_k = \lambda_k\xi_k + \hat{b}_k u \qquad (k = 1, 2, \ldots, n)$$

the zero-state solution of each of which is

$$\xi_k(t) = \int_0^t e^{\lambda_k(t-\tau)}\hat{b}_k u(\tau)\,d\tau$$

We conclude therefore that the only way each of the modes can be excited is for

$$\hat{b}_k \neq 0 \qquad \text{for } k = 1, 2, \ldots, n$$

We wish to translate this condition to one on the original system. To this end observe that the matrix

$$\hat{\mathbf{Q}}_c \simeq = [\hat{\mathbf{b}} \mid \boldsymbol{\Lambda}\hat{\mathbf{b}} \mid \cdots \mid \boldsymbol{\Lambda}^{n-1}\hat{\mathbf{b}}] = \begin{bmatrix} \hat{b}_1 & \lambda_1\hat{b}_1 & \cdots & \lambda_1^{n-1}\hat{b}_1 \\ \hat{b}_2 & \lambda_2\hat{b}_2 & \cdots & \lambda_2^{n-1}\hat{b}_2 \\ \cdots & \cdots & \cdots & \cdots \\ \hat{b}_n & \lambda_n\hat{b}_n & \cdots & \lambda_n^{n-1}\hat{b}_n \end{bmatrix}$$

is nonsingular if $\hat{b}_k \neq 0$ for $k = 1, 2, \ldots, n$.

But since

$$\boldsymbol{\Lambda} = \mathbf{S}^{-1}\mathbf{A}\mathbf{S}$$

and

$$\hat{\mathbf{b}} = \mathbf{S}^{-1}\mathbf{b},$$

then

$$\hat{\mathbf{Q}}_c = \mathbf{S}^{-1}\mathbf{Q}_c$$

where

(6.43) $$\mathbf{Q}_c = [\mathbf{b} \mid \mathbf{A}\mathbf{b} \mid \cdots \mid \mathbf{A}^{n-1}\mathbf{b}]$$

Since $\mathbf{S}^{-1}$ is nonsingular, we finally have that if the *controllability matrix* $\mathbf{Q}_c$ is nonsingular, then all the modes of the system can be excited, i.e., the system is completely controllable.

The above result is valid even if the matrix $\mathbf{A}$ does not have distinct eigenvalues. For this case, the system is transformed to

$$\dot{\boldsymbol{\xi}}(t) = \mathbf{J}\boldsymbol{\xi}(t) + \hat{\mathbf{b}}u(t)$$

and

$$y(t) = \hat{\mathbf{c}}'\boldsymbol{\xi}(t) + du(t)$$

where $\mathbf{J}$ is the Jordan canonical form of $\mathbf{A}$. The "natural modes" corresponding to the eigenvalue λ_k of multiplicity m_k may be considered to be $e^{\lambda_k t}$, $te^{\lambda_k t}$, . . . , $(t^{m_k})/(m_k!)e^{\lambda_k t}$, and the zero-state solution is of the form

$$\xi_k(t) = \int_0^t e^{\lambda_k(t-\tau)} \sum_{n=0}^{m_k} \frac{(t-\tau)^{m_k}}{m_k!}\hat{b}_k u(\tau)\,d\tau$$

Although considerably more difficult, reasoning roughly akin to that given above for the case of distinct eigenvalues yields the same condition on the controllability matrix $\mathbf{Q}_c$.†

(6.44) Example

The system of Example (6.38) has

$$\mathbf{A} = \begin{bmatrix} 1 & 1 \\ 6 & 0 \end{bmatrix}$$

and

$$\mathbf{b} = \begin{bmatrix} 1 \\ -3 \end{bmatrix}$$

Thus

$$\mathbf{Q}_c = \begin{bmatrix} 1 & -2 \\ -3 & 6 \end{bmatrix}$$

which is singular. Thus the system is not controllable. This result is more easily visualized in the eigenvector basis. A modal matrix associated with $\mathbf{A}$ is

$$\mathbf{S} = \begin{bmatrix} 1 & 1 \\ -3 & 2 \end{bmatrix}$$

so that the transformed system is characterized by

$$\dot{\boldsymbol{\xi}}(t) = \begin{bmatrix} -2 & 0 \\ 0 & 3 \end{bmatrix} \boldsymbol{\xi}(t) + \begin{bmatrix} 1 \\ 0 \end{bmatrix} u(t)$$

Observe that the mode associated with the eigenvalue $\lambda = -2$ cannot be excited by the input. ∎

Assuming that all the modes are excitable, we now wish to determine under what conditions they can be observed. We see from Equation (6.42*b*) that all modes can be observed if

$$\hat{c}_k \neq 0 \qquad k = 1, 2, \ldots, n$$

Again we desire a condition based on the original system. Consider the matrix

$$\hat{\mathbf{Q}}_0 = \begin{bmatrix} \hat{\mathbf{c}}' \\ \hat{\mathbf{c}}\mathbf{\Lambda} \\ \cdot \\ \cdot \\ \cdot \\ \hat{\mathbf{c}}'\mathbf{\Lambda}^{n-1} \end{bmatrix} = \begin{bmatrix} \hat{c}_1 & \hat{c}_2 & \hat{c}_n \\ \hat{c}_1\lambda_1 & \hat{c}_2\lambda_2 & \hat{c}_n\lambda_n \\ \cdots & \cdots & \cdots \\ \hat{c}_1\lambda_1{}^{n-1} & \hat{c}_2\lambda_2{}^{n-1} & \hat{c}_n\lambda_n{}^{n-1} \end{bmatrix}$$

† L. A. Zadeh and C. A. Desoer, "Linear System Theory," McGraw-Hill, New York, 1963.

which is nonsingular if $\hat{c}_k \neq 0$ for $k = 1, 2, \ldots, n$. But since

$$\hat{\mathbf{Q}}_0 = \mathbf{\Lambda} = \mathbf{S}^{-1}\mathbf{AS}$$

and

$$\hat{\mathbf{c}}' = \mathbf{c}'\mathbf{S}$$

then

$$\hat{\mathbf{Q}}_0 = \mathbf{Q}_0\mathbf{S}$$

where

$$\mathbf{Q}_0 = \begin{bmatrix} \mathbf{c}' \\ \hdashline \mathbf{c}'\mathbf{A} \\ \hdashline \cdot \\ \cdot \\ \cdot \\ \hdashline \mathbf{c}'\mathbf{A}^{n-1} \end{bmatrix} \tag{6.45}$$

Since **S** is nonsingular, we have that the system is completely observable if the *observability matrix* $\mathbf{Q}_0$ is nonsingular. Again the above result holds even if the eigenvalues of **A** are not distinct; instead of the diagonal matrix $\mathbf{\Lambda}$, we use the Jordan canonical form **J**.

(6.46) Example

Consider the system described by

$$\dot{\mathbf{x}}(t) = \begin{bmatrix} -3 & 5 \\ 2 & 0 \end{bmatrix} \mathbf{x}(t) + \begin{bmatrix} 1 \\ 2 \end{bmatrix} u(t)$$

and

$$y(t) = (1 \quad -1)\mathbf{x}(t)$$

Since

$$\mathbf{Q}_0 = \begin{bmatrix} 1 & -1 \\ -5 & 5 \end{bmatrix}$$

is of rank 1, the system is not observable. This result is more readily seen in terms of the transformed system. A modal matrix associated with **A** is

$$\mathbf{S} = \begin{bmatrix} 5 & 1 \\ -2 & 1 \end{bmatrix}$$

and the transformed system is characterized by

$$\dot{\boldsymbol{\xi}}(t) = \begin{bmatrix} -5 & 0 \\ 0 & 2 \end{bmatrix} \boldsymbol{\xi}(t) + \begin{bmatrix} -\frac{1}{7} \\ \frac{12}{7} \end{bmatrix} u(t)$$

and

$$y(t) = (8 \quad 0)\boldsymbol{\xi}(t)$$

Observe that the output involves only the mode that corresponds to the eigenvalue $\lambda = -5$. ∎

The following two examples emphasize the relationship between asymptotic stability, stability *BIBO*, controllability, and observability.

(6.47) Example

The network shown in Fig. 6.12 is characterized by the following state equations:

$$\dot{\mathbf{x}}(t) = \begin{bmatrix} -1 & 0 \\ 0 & -1 \end{bmatrix} \mathbf{x}(t) + \begin{bmatrix} 1 \\ 1 \end{bmatrix} v(t)$$

and

$$i(t) = (1 \quad -1)\mathbf{x}(t) + v(t)$$

We observe that the equilibrium state at the origin of the associated free system is asymptotically stable, while the zero-state input-output relation

$$i(t) = v(t)$$

indicates stability bounded input-bounded output. The pertinent matrices are

$$\mathbf{A} = \begin{bmatrix} -1 & 0 \\ 0 & -1 \end{bmatrix} \qquad \mathbf{B} = \begin{bmatrix} 1 \\ 1 \end{bmatrix} \qquad \mathbf{C} = [1 \quad -1]$$

so

$$\mathbf{Q}_0 = \begin{bmatrix} 1 & -1 \\ -1 & 1 \end{bmatrix}$$

and

$$\mathbf{Q}_c = \begin{bmatrix} 1 & -1 \\ 1 & -1 \end{bmatrix}$$

both of which are of rank 1. In this example, we have both asymptotic stability and stability bounded input-bounded output even though neither $\mathbf{Q}_0$ nor $\mathbf{Q}_c$ is of rank 2.

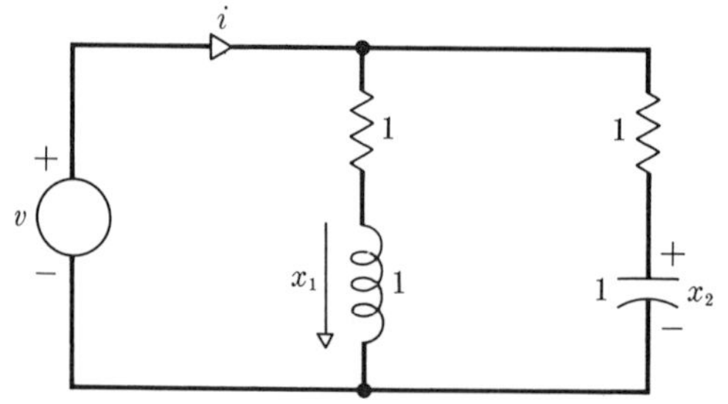

FIG. 6.12 Example (6.47).

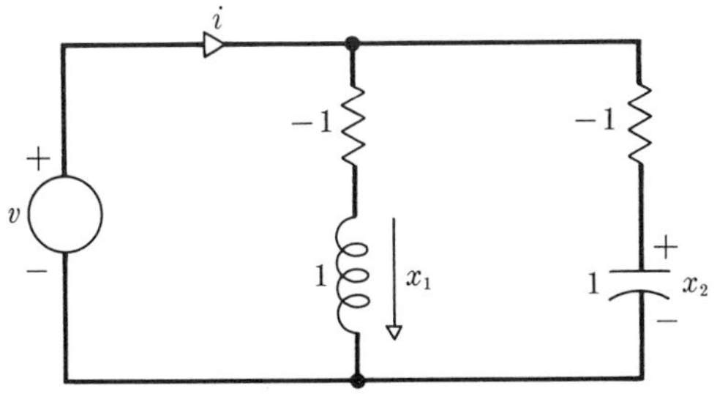

FIG. 6.13 Example (6.48).

(6.48) Example

Consider the network shown in Fig. 6.13. The state equations are

$$\dot{\mathbf{x}}(t) = \begin{bmatrix} 1 & 0 \\ 0 & 1 \end{bmatrix} \mathbf{x}(t) + \begin{bmatrix} 1 \\ 1 \end{bmatrix} v(t)$$

and

$$i(t) = [1 \quad 1]\mathbf{x}(t) - v(t)$$

The equilibrium state at the origin of the associated free system is unstable, but the zero-state input-output relation

$$i(t) = -v(t)$$

indicates stability bounded input-bounded output. The pertinent matrices are

$$\mathbf{A} = \begin{bmatrix} 1 & 0 \\ 0 & 1 \end{bmatrix} \qquad \mathbf{B} = \begin{bmatrix} 1 \\ 1 \end{bmatrix} \qquad \text{and } \mathbf{c} = [1 \quad 1]$$

so

$$\mathbf{Q}_0 = \begin{bmatrix} 1 & 1 \\ 1 & 1 \end{bmatrix}$$

and

$$\mathbf{Q} = \begin{bmatrix} 1 & 1 \\ 1 & 1 \end{bmatrix}$$

both of which are of rank 1. The similarity of the network here and the one of Example (6.47), and the attendant discrepancy of the stability results, indicates the importance of the rank of the matrices $\mathbf{Q}_c$ and $\mathbf{Q}_0$. In other words, we must proceed with caution in cases where either of these matrices drops below full rank.

6.9 SUMMARY

In this chapter we discussed various forms of stability. Formal definitions of *stability* and *asymptotic stability* were presented, and we linked these properties to the properties of state-transition matrices for linear systems, and the **A** matrix for linear time-invariant systems. The macroscopic concept of *stability BIBO* was defined. The ideas of *controllability* and *observability* were used to relate macroscopic and microscopic stability.

6.10 PROBLEMS

(6.1) Prove the following statements about n-vector norms:

(*a*) $\|\mathbf{x}\|_1 = 0 \Leftrightarrow \|\mathbf{x}\|_2 = 0 \Leftrightarrow \|\mathbf{x}\|_\infty = 0$;
(*b*) $\|\mathbf{x}\|_1$ bounded $\Leftrightarrow$ $\|\mathbf{x}\|_2$ bounded $\Leftrightarrow$ $\|\mathbf{x}\|_\infty$ bounded

Note that the first statement is trivial (why?); these facts allow us to study stability in any convenient space (why?).

(6.2) Define (1) stability, (2) instability, (3) asymptotic stability, (4) asymptotic stability in the large, and (5) boundedness relative to each of the following situations:

(*a*) Nonzero equilibrium states for free systems;
(*b*) Solutions for forced systems.

(6.3) Given the linear system described by

$$\dot{\mathbf{x}}(t) = \mathbf{A}(t)\mathbf{x}(t) + \mathbf{B}(t)\mathbf{u}(t) \qquad \mathbf{x}(t_0) = \mathbf{x}_0$$

state the necessary and sufficient conditions for stability, asymptotic stability, asymptotic stability in the large, and boundedness for the solution which accompanies a given input function. The statement is to be in terms of the matrices

$$\mathbf{A}(t),\ \mathbf{B}(t), \text{ and } \mathbf{\Phi}(t,t_0)$$

Repeat for the case when **A** and **B** are constant. The statement is to be in terms of properties of the matrices **A** and **B**.

(6.4) Consider the problem of a particle in a central force field; the equations of motion are:

$$\frac{d}{dt}(m\dot{r}) - mr\dot{\theta}^2 = -\frac{k}{r^2}$$

and

$$\frac{d}{dt}(mr^2\dot{\theta}) = 0$$

Discuss the stability of the solution associated with a circular orbit. How is the period of revolution affected? Compare with the linear oscillator.

(6.5) Recall Prob. 4.6. What can you say about the stability of the equilibrium state at the origin for self-adjoint systems?

(6.6) Consider two point masses of equal size supported on a pivot of equal lever arms as shown in Fig. 6.14. The point masses are attracted

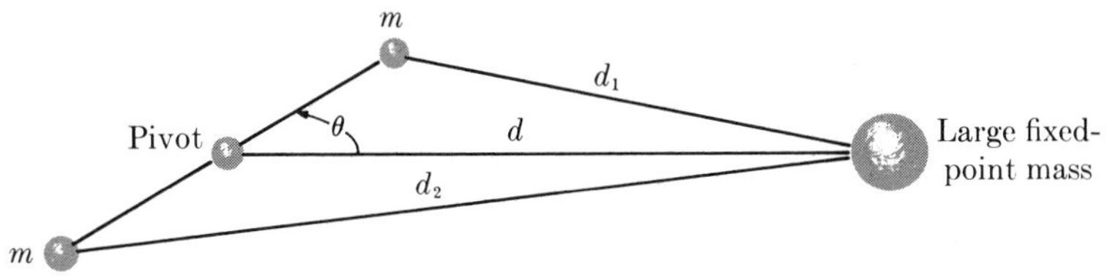

FIG. 6.14 Prob. (6.6).

to a large fixed mass according to the inverse-square law

$$f = \frac{k}{d^2}$$

(*a*) For what values of θ is the system in equilibrium?
(*b*) Which of the equilibriums are stable?
(*c*) Are any of the equilibriums asymptotically stable?
(*d*) Find a Liapunov function which establishes the (local) stability of the stable equilibriums.

Note: Useful information is that the potential energy of each point mass is proportional to $1/r(1/d_1$ or $1/d_2)$ while the kinetic energy is proportional to $\dot{\theta}^2$

(6.7) Find a Liapunov function for the system described by

$$\dot{x}_1 = x_2$$

and

$$\dot{x}_2 = -2x_1 - 3x_2$$

(see Example 6.27).

(6.8) Determine if the system whose block-diagram representation is shown in Fig. 6.15 is completely controllable or completely observable. Is this system stable *BIBO*?

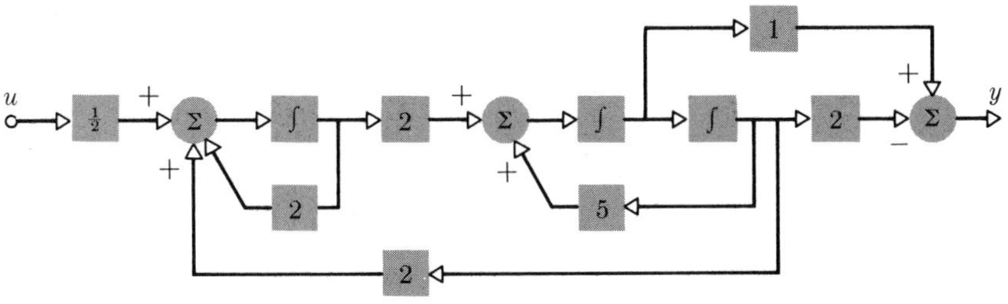

FIG. 6.15 Prob. (6.8).

(6.9) Given a lumped, linear, time-invariant system characterized by the state equations

$$\dot{\mathbf{x}}(t) = \mathbf{A}\mathbf{x}(t) + b\mathbf{u}(t)$$

and

$$y(t) = \mathbf{c}'\mathbf{x}(t)$$

where

$$\mathbf{A} = \begin{bmatrix} -3 & -3 & 0 & 1 \\ 26 & 36 & -3 & -25 \\ 30 & 39 & -2 & -27 \\ 30 & 43 & -3 & -32 \end{bmatrix}$$

$$\mathbf{b} = \begin{bmatrix} 3 \\ -1 \\ 0 \\ 1 \end{bmatrix}$$

and

$$\mathbf{c} = [-5, -8, 1, 5]'$$

(*a*) Find $\mathbf{Q}_c$, $\mathbf{Q}_0$.

(*b*) Is the above system completely controllable or completely observable?

(*c*) Find the transfer function matrix for the system.

(6.10) Consider the transfer function

$$H(s) = \frac{s^2 + 3s + 2}{s^3 + 6s^2 + 11s + 6}$$

(*a*) Verify that each of the following three "systems" is a realization of $H(s)$:

$$(1) \quad \mathbf{A} = \begin{bmatrix} 0 & 1 & 0 \\ 0 & 0 & 1 \\ -6 & -11 & -6 \end{bmatrix} \quad \mathbf{B} = \begin{bmatrix} 1 \\ -3 \\ 9 \end{bmatrix} \quad \mathbf{C} = [1 \ 0 \ 0];$$

$$(2) \quad \mathbf{A} = \begin{bmatrix} 0 & 0 & -6 \\ 1 & 0 & -11 \\ 0 & 1 & -6 \end{bmatrix} \quad \mathbf{B} = \begin{bmatrix} 1 \\ 0 \\ 0 \end{bmatrix} \quad \mathbf{C} = [1 \ -3 \ 9];$$

$$(3) \quad \mathbf{A} = \begin{bmatrix} -3 & 0 & 0 \\ 0 & -8 & 0 \\ 0 & 0 & -7 \end{bmatrix} \quad \mathbf{B} = \begin{bmatrix} 1 \\ 2 \\ 0 \end{bmatrix} \quad \mathbf{C} = [1 \ 0 \ 3].$$

(*b*) Discuss the controllability and observability of the three realizations.

(*c*) Which, if any, of the realizations is equivalent to the differential equation

$$(D^3 + 6D^2 + 11D + 6)y(t) = (D^2 + 3D + 2)u(t)$$

For those realizations which are not equivalent to this differential equation, exhibit an input-output pair which demonstrates nonequivalence.

(*d*) Discuss stability *BIBO* of this system.

(6.11) The rotational motion of a rigid body may be described by the equation

$$\frac{d}{dt}(\mathcal{J}\boldsymbol{\omega}) = \boldsymbol{\tau}$$

where $\mathcal{J}$ is the 3×3 moment of inertia tensor (matrix for our purposes), $\boldsymbol{\omega}$ is the three-vector representing the angular velocity about an orthogonal set of three axes, and $\boldsymbol{\tau}$ is the three-vector representing the torque about each of these three axes. The moment of inertia tensor is symmetric (why?) so it may be diagonalized; the three eigenvalues of $\mathcal{J}$ are called the principle moments of inertia, and the corresponding eigenvectors define an orthogonal (why?) set of principle axes. Hence, we may assume that the problem is formulated in terms of principle moments and principle axes at the outset. The equations of motion at their simplest are

$$\mathcal{J}_1\dot{\omega}_1(t) - \omega_2(t)\omega_3(t)(\mathcal{J}_2 - \mathcal{J}_3) = \tau_1(t)$$
$$\mathcal{J}_2\dot{\omega}_2(t) - \omega_3(t)\omega_1(t)(\mathcal{J}_3 - \mathcal{J}_1) = \tau_2(t)$$

and

$$\mathcal{J}_3\dot{\omega}_3(t) - \omega_1(t)\omega_2(t)(\mathcal{J}_1 - \mathcal{J}_2) = \tau_3(t)$$

where $\mathcal{J}_1$, $\mathcal{J}_2$, and $\mathcal{J}_3$ are the principle moments of inertia. In the absence of torque, these equations become

$$\dot{\omega}_1 = \frac{\mathcal{J}_2 - \mathcal{J}_3}{\mathcal{J}_1}\omega_2\omega_3$$

$$\dot{\omega}_2 = \frac{\mathcal{J}_3 - \mathcal{J}_1}{\mathcal{J}_2}\omega_3\omega_1$$

and

$$\dot{\omega}_3 = \frac{\mathcal{J}_1 - \mathcal{J}_2}{\mathcal{J}_3}\omega_1\omega_2$$

Consider the case

$$0 < \mathcal{J}_1 < \mathcal{J}_2 < \mathcal{J}_3$$

and discuss the stability of motion in the following situations:

(a) ω_1 is a nonzero constant, $\omega_2 = \omega_3 = 0$;
(b) ω_2 is a nonzero constant, $\omega_3 = \omega_1 = 0$;
(c) ω_3 is a nonzero constant, $\omega_1 = \omega_2 = 0$.

Note: Each of the above is an obvious solution of the equations of motion. Discuss the implications of these results on satellite design.

COMPUTATIONAL ASPECTS OF SYSTEM THEORY

7

Effective use of general purpose digital computers allows us the only reasonable route to large-scale system studies. Most computer centers now have "system simulation packages" which enable even a relatively unsophisticated user to perform difficult analyses efficiently. Our purpose in this chapter is not to discuss the use of these packages, which differ from computer to computer anyway, but rather their underlying theory. With what we have from the preceding six chapters, we are in a reasonable position to study the approaches and limitations of system-theoretic computational algorithms.

7.1 LINEAR-STATE EQUATIONS

Any lumped linear system is describable in terms of the standard-form state equations

$$\dot{\mathbf{x}}(t) = \mathbf{A}(t)\mathbf{x}(t) + \mathbf{B}(t)\mathbf{u}(t) \tag{7.1}$$

and

$$\mathbf{y}(t) = \mathbf{c}(t)\mathbf{x}(t) + \mathbf{D}(t)\mathbf{u}(t) \tag{7.2}$$

The solution of the linear differential-state equation (7.1) is crucial; once it is solved for $\mathbf{x}$, the output $\mathbf{y}$ follows simply from the input-state-output equation (7.2) by matrix multiplication and addition. In Chap. 5 we discovered that the solution of (7.1) may be written as

$$\mathbf{x}(t) = \mathbf{\Phi}(t,t_0)\mathbf{x}(t_0) + \int_{t_0}^{t} \mathbf{\Phi}(t,\tau)\mathbf{B}(\tau)u(\tau)\,d\tau \tag{7.3}$$

where the state-transition matrix $\mathbf{\Phi}(t,\tau)$ has the following properties:

$$\frac{\partial \mathbf{\Phi}(t,\tau)}{\partial t} = \mathbf{A}(t)\mathbf{\Phi}(t,\tau)$$

and

$$\mathbf{\Phi}(t,\tau) = \mathbf{1} \qquad \text{for } t = \tau$$

If the lumped system in question is time invariant as well as linear, the associated differential-state equation is

$$\dot{\mathbf{x}}(t) = \mathbf{A}\mathbf{x}(t) + \mathbf{B}\mathbf{u}(t) \tag{7.4}$$

and its solution is

$$\mathbf{x}(t) = e^{\mathbf{A}(t-t_0)}\mathbf{x}(t_0) + \int_{t_0}^{t} e^{\mathbf{A}(t-\tau)}\mathbf{B}\mathbf{u}(\tau)\,d\tau \tag{7.5}$$

We first focus our attention on linear *time-invariant* systems, both because they are simpler, and because they admit a vast number of alternative numerical approaches.

One method for solution of (7.4) is by means of the one-sided Laplace transform

$$\mathbf{X}(s) = (s\mathbf{1} - \mathbf{A})^{-1}[\mathbf{B}\mathbf{U}(s) + \mathbf{x}_0] \tag{7.6}$$

where $\mathbf{x}_0$ is the initial state at the initial time $t_0 = 0$. If we are interested in the complex-frequency behavior of the system, as is often the case with electrical-network studies, for example, then we might choose to evaluate (7.6) at several values of the complex variable s. For each fixed value of s the solution of (7.6) entails a complex-matrix inversion and some subsequent matrix multiplications. Another approach to the solution of (7.6) is to consider it rather to be a set of simultaneous linear algebraic equations where

$$\mathbf{MX} = \mathbf{Z}$$
$$\mathbf{M} \equiv (s\mathbf{1} - \mathbf{A})$$

and

$$\mathbf{Z} = [\mathbf{BU}(s) + \mathbf{x}_0]$$

Sometimes it is more efficient computationally to solve such specific simultaneous linear equations than to invert the corresponding matrix. In a subsequent section, we consider algorithms for the solution of simultaneous linear algebraic equations; at this point, we wish merely to motivate the introduction of such algorithms. If we wish to find the time response $\mathbf{x}(t)$ from the inverse Laplace transform of $\mathbf{X}(s)$, we must obtain the poles of $(s\mathbf{1} - \mathbf{A})^{-1}$, that is, the eigenvalues of $\mathbf{A}$. Francis' QR algorithm[1] yields the poles, and then it is a relatively simple matter to obtain a partial fraction expansion of (7.6). The *fast Fourier transform* is also useful for the computational translation of frequency-domain response into the time domain, as well as the converse.

An alternative approach to the solution of (7.4) is the integration of both sides, which first yields the *implicit* formula

$$\mathbf{x}(t) = \mathbf{x}(t_0) + \int_{t_0}^{t} [\mathbf{Ax}(\tau) + \mathbf{Bu}(\tau)]\, d\tau \qquad (7.7)$$

There are a myriad of methods for approximating the integration with a summation so that the solution of (7.7) may be reduced effectively to that of simultaneous linear algebraic equations. The z transform of Chap. 5 becomes extremely useful in determining the stability of such algorithms.

Finally, we can consider the direct discretization of (7.5). For time $t_k = kT$, we have

$$\mathbf{x}(kT) = e^{\mathbf{A}t}\mathbf{x}((k-1)T) + \int_0^T e^{\mathbf{A}\tau}\, d\tau\, \mathbf{B} \qquad (7.8)$$

Once we have $e^{\mathbf{A}T}$ and $\int_0^T e^{\mathbf{A}\tau}\, d\tau\, \mathbf{B}$ to the desired accuracy, in theory we may obtain any $\mathbf{x}(kT)$ by iterating from the initial $\mathbf{x}(0) = \mathbf{x}_0$.

In succeeding sections, we are to investigate in some detail the various numerical techniques to which we have merely alluded above. This is not to be a thorough and rigorous study of numerical-analysis algorithms, but rather an introduction to those useful in system studies.

[1] B. N. Parlett, The LU and QR Algorithms, in A. Ralston and H. S. Wiff (eds.), "Mathematical Methods for Digital Computers," vol. 2, pp. 116–130, Wiley, New York, 1967.

7.2 SOLUTIONS OF SIMULTANEOUS LINEAR ALGEBRAIC EQUATIONS

Central to many system-analysis problems is the solution of a set of simultaneous linear algebraic equations of the form

$$
\begin{aligned}
a_{11}x_1 + a_{12}x_2 + \cdots + a_{1n}x_n &= b_1 \\
a_{21}x_1 + a_{22}x_2 + \cdots + a_{2n}x_n &= b_2 \\
\cdots\cdots\cdots\cdots\cdots\cdots\cdots& \\
a_{n1}x_1 + a_{n2}x_2 + \cdots + a_{nn}x_n &= b_n
\end{aligned} \tag{7.9}
$$

where the a_{ij} and the b_i are known and the x_j are unknown ($i, j = 1, 2, \ldots n$). For example, as indicated in the last section, the Laplace transform of the differential-state equation

$$\dot{\mathbf{x}}(t) = \mathbf{Ax}(t) + \mathbf{Bu}(t) \qquad \mathbf{x}(0) = \mathbf{x}_0$$

yields

$$(s\mathbf{1} - \mathbf{A})\mathbf{X}(s) = [\mathbf{Bu}(s) + \mathbf{x}_0]$$

in general a set of complex simultaneous linear algebraic equations for each value of the complex-frequency variable s.

For convenience we consider the matrix form of (7.9)

$$\mathbf{Ax} = \mathbf{b} \tag{7.10}$$

where

$$\mathbf{A} = \begin{bmatrix} a_{11} & a_{12} & \cdots & a_{1n} \\ a_{21} & a_{22} & \cdots & a_{2n} \\ \cdots & \cdots & \cdots & \cdots \\ a_{n1} & a_{n2} & \cdots & a_{nn} \end{bmatrix}$$

$$\mathbf{b} = (b_1, b_2, \ldots, b_n)'$$

and

$$\mathbf{x} = (x_1, x_2, \ldots, x_n)'$$

The reader should not confuse the **A**, **x**, and **b** of expression (7.10) with the state-equation notation. Most of the literature uses this notation as a standard. An often-encountered method for solution of (7.10) is Cramer's rule. The unknown x_j is obtained by replacing the jth column of the matrix **A** by the vector **b**; the ratio of the determinant of this modified matrix to that of the original matrix **A** is the solution x_j. Hence $n + 1$ $(n \times n)$-matrix determinants must be evaluated in order that the entire solution vector **x** be obtained. Fortunately, there are far more efficient means for solution of simultaneous linear algebraic equations by digital computer than Cramer's rule. Because of its explicit nature, Cramer's rule does find a great deal of use in theoretical proofs of general properties of classes of simultaneous linear algebraic equations, however. Before proceeding to better means, we illustrate the use of Cramer's rule with a simple second-order example.

(7.11) Example
To solve

$$3x_1 + 2x_2 = 5$$

and

$$x_1 - 4x_2 = 2$$

by Cramer's rule we first find

$$\Delta = \det \begin{bmatrix} 3 & 2 \\ 1 & -4 \end{bmatrix} = -14$$

and then

$$x_1 = \frac{1}{\Delta} \det \begin{bmatrix} 5 & 2 \\ 2 & -4 \end{bmatrix} = \frac{-24}{-14} = \frac{12}{7}$$

and

$$x_2 = \frac{1}{\Delta} \det \begin{bmatrix} 3 & 5 \\ 1 & 2 \end{bmatrix} = \frac{1}{-14} = -\frac{1}{14}$$

We may verify the validity of these results by substituting them into the original pair of equations. ∎

For more than two simultaneous linear algebraic equations, gaussian elimination is more efficient (and more accurate, when employed properly) than Cramer's rule. Gaussian elimination is but the formal name for the familiar means of solving simultaneous linear algebraic equations by successive elimination of unknowns. Before formalizing gaussian elimination, we can illustrate it with a simple example.

(7.12) Example
To find the solution of the set of three simultaneous linear algebraic equations

(7.13*a*) $2x_1 + x_2 + 3x_3 = 2$
(7.13*b*) $3x_1 - 2x_2 - x_3 = 1$

and

(7.13*c*) $x_1 - x_2 + x_3 = -1$

we first express x_1 in terms of the other variables in (7.13*a*)

(7.13*a'*) $x_1 = 1 - \frac{1}{2}x_2 - \frac{3}{2}x_3$

and then substitute this result into (7.13*b*) and (7.13*c*),

(7.13*b'*) $-\frac{7}{2}x_2 - \frac{11}{2}x_3 = -2$
(7.13*c'*) $-\frac{3}{2}x_2 - \frac{1}{2}x_3 = -2$

We next express x_2 in terms of the other variable x_3 in (7.13b′)

(7.13b″) $x_2 = \frac{4}{7} - \frac{11}{7}x_3$

and substitute this result into (7.13c′)

(7.13c″) $\frac{26}{14}x_3 = -\frac{16}{14}$

or

(7.13c‴) $x_3 = -\frac{8}{13}$

We may now obtain the value of x_2 from (7.13b″)

$$x_2 = \frac{20}{13}$$

and successively x_1 from (7.13a′):

$$x_1 = \frac{15}{13}$$

Once x_3 has been found, the remainder of the process is called *back substitution.* The matrix approach to the solution of this same problem better illustrates the bookkeeping involved. In matrix terms (7.13) becomes

$$\begin{bmatrix} 2 & 1 & 3 \\ 3 & -2 & -1 \\ 1 & -1 & 1 \end{bmatrix} \begin{bmatrix} x_1 \\ x_2 \\ x_3 \end{bmatrix} = \begin{bmatrix} 2 \\ 1 \\ 1 \end{bmatrix} \tag{7.14}$$

Proceeding as before, we obtain the equivalent of (7.13a′) by dividing the first row of both the 3×3 matrix on the left and the 3×1 matrix on the right-hand side of the equation by the coefficient 2 of x_1 in the first row,

$$\begin{bmatrix} 1 & \frac{1}{2} & \frac{3}{2} \\ 3 & -2 & -1 \\ 1 & -1 & 1 \end{bmatrix} \begin{bmatrix} x_1 \\ x_2 \\ x_3 \end{bmatrix} = \begin{bmatrix} 1 \\ 1 \\ -1 \end{bmatrix} \tag{7.14a}$$

We obtain the equivalents of (7.13b′) and (7.13c′) by first multiplying the first rows by the respective coefficients 3 and 1 of x_1 in the second and third rows, and subtracting the results from each of these rows, respectively,

$$\begin{bmatrix} 1 & \frac{1}{2} & \frac{3}{2} \\ 0 & -\frac{7}{2} & -\frac{11}{2} \\ 0 & -\frac{3}{2} & -\frac{1}{2} \end{bmatrix} \begin{bmatrix} x_1 \\ x_2 \\ x_3 \end{bmatrix} = \begin{bmatrix} 1 \\ -2 \\ -2 \end{bmatrix} \tag{7.14b}$$

Next we proceed to normalize the second rows in (7.14b) by dividing through by $-\frac{7}{2}$, the coefficient of x_2, to obtain

$$\begin{bmatrix} 1 & \frac{1}{2} & \frac{3}{2} \\ 0 & 1 & \frac{11}{7} \\ 0 & -\frac{3}{2} & -\frac{1}{2} \end{bmatrix} \begin{bmatrix} x_1 \\ x_2 \\ x_3 \end{bmatrix} = \begin{bmatrix} 1 \\ \frac{4}{7} \\ -2 \end{bmatrix} \tag{7.14a′}$$

Upon multiplication of the second row by $-\frac{3}{2}$, the coefficient of x_2 in the third equation, and subtraction of the result from the third row, we obtain

$$(7.14b') \quad \begin{bmatrix} 1 & \frac{1}{2} & \frac{3}{2} \\ 0 & 1 & \frac{11}{7} \\ 0 & 0 & \frac{26}{14} \end{bmatrix} \begin{bmatrix} x_1 \\ x_2 \\ x_3 \end{bmatrix} = \begin{bmatrix} 1 \\ \frac{4}{7} \\ -\frac{16}{14} \end{bmatrix}$$

Finally, we may normalize the third row in (7.14b') to obtain

$$(7.14c) \quad \begin{bmatrix} 1 & \frac{1}{2} & \frac{3}{2} \\ 0 & 1 & \frac{11}{7} \\ 0 & 0 & 1 \end{bmatrix} \begin{bmatrix} x_1 \\ x_2 \\ x_3 \end{bmatrix} = \begin{bmatrix} 1 \\ \frac{4}{7} \\ -\frac{8}{13} \end{bmatrix}$$

a matrix expression which is equivalent to the equations (7.13c'''), (7.13b''), and (7.13a'), and is now easily solved for x_3, x_2, and x_1 by back substitution. ∎

We now proceed to discuss, in general, gaussian elimination in the solution of a set of n simultaneous linear algebraic equations written in matrix form,

$$(7.15) \quad \begin{bmatrix} a_{11} & a_{12} & \cdots & a_{1n} \\ a_{21} & a_{22} & \cdots & a_{2n} \\ \cdots & \cdots & \cdots & \cdots \\ a_{n1} & a_{n2} & \cdots & a_{nn} \end{bmatrix} \begin{bmatrix} x_1 \\ x_2 \\ \vdots \\ x_n \end{bmatrix} = \begin{bmatrix} a_{1,n+1} \\ a_{2,n+1} \\ \vdots \\ a_{n,n+1} \end{bmatrix}$$

where we have employed

$$a_{i,n+1} \equiv b_i \qquad (i = 1, 2, \ldots, n)$$

for notational convenience. So that we may proceed smoothly to a solution, we assume that the matrix of coefficients $[a_{ij}]$ on the left-hand side of Eq. (7.15) is nonsingular. Initially, suppose that a_{11} is nonzero and divide the first row $(a_{11},a_{12}, \ldots, a_{in},a_{1,n+1})$ by a_{11}. Next subtract the product of a_{i1} and this new first row from each of the succeeding rows, respectively, $(i = 2, 3, \ldots, n)$. The result of these operations is

$$(7.16) \quad \begin{bmatrix} 1 & a_{12}^{(1)} & \cdots & a_{1n}^{(1)} \\ 0 & a_{22}^{(1)} & \cdots & a_{2n}^{(1)} \\ \cdots & \cdots & \cdots & \cdots \\ 0 & a_{n2}^{(1)} & \cdots & a_{nn}^{(1)} \end{bmatrix} \begin{bmatrix} x_1 \\ x_2 \\ \vdots \\ x_n \end{bmatrix} = \begin{bmatrix} a_{1,n+1}^{(1)} \\ a_{2,n+1}^{(1)} \\ \vdots \\ a_{n,n+1}^{(1)} \end{bmatrix}$$

where the coefficients $a_{i,j}^{(1)}$ are given explicitly by

$$a_{ij}^{(1)} = \frac{a_{ij}}{a_{11}} \qquad (j = 1, 2, \ldots, n, n + 1)$$

and

$$a_{ij}^{(1)} = a_{ij} - \frac{a_{i1}}{a_{11}} a_{1j} \qquad \begin{array}{l} i = 2, 3, \ldots, n \\ j = 1, 2, \ldots, n, n + 1 \end{array}$$

where the superscript in parentheses indicates the number of the operation. If a_{11} were zero, we could always interchange the first row with another so as to obtain a new and nonzero a_{11}. If all a_{i1} $(i = 1, 2, \ldots, n)$ were zero, the original matrix $\mathbf{A}$ would be singular and the equations would have no unique solution. We could even proceed to the solution of such a set of singular equations by making x_1 an "independent" variable, but we omit discussion of this case here, because it becomes too complicated in detail.

Upon the assumption that the coefficient $a_{22}^{(1)}$, which resulted from the above operations, is nonzero, we divide it through the second row and then subtract $a_{i2}^{(1)}$ times the result from each succeeding row $(i = 3, 4, \ldots, n)$ to obtain

$$\begin{bmatrix} 1 & a_{12}^{(1)} & a_{13}^{(1)} & \cdots & a_{1n}^{(1)} \\ 0 & 1 & a_{23}^{(2)} & \cdots & a_{2n}^{(2)} \\ 0 & 0 & a_{33}^{(2)} & \cdots & a_{3n}^{(2)} \\ \cdots & \cdots & \cdots & \cdots & \cdots \\ 0 & 0 & a_{n3}^{(2)} & \cdots & a_{nn}^{(2)} \end{bmatrix} \begin{bmatrix} x_1 \\ x_2 \\ x_3 \\ \cdot \\ \cdot \\ \cdot \\ x_n \end{bmatrix} = \begin{bmatrix} a_{1,n+1}^{(1)} \\ a_{2,n+1}^{(2)} \\ a_{3,n+1}^{(2)} \\ \cdot \\ \cdot \\ \cdot \\ a_{n,n+1}^{(2)} \end{bmatrix} \tag{7.17}$$

Again, if $a_{22}^{(1)}$ were zero, we could effect a row interchange so as to place a nonzero element in the (2,2) position, provided that the matrix were nonsingular. Column interchanges, as well as row interchanges, are possible, and sometimes desirable; however these entail a renumbering of the variables x_j.

The above procedure is to be repeated for a total of n steps, each time on a matrix of one order lower. The final set of equations which results is

$$\begin{bmatrix} 1 & a_{12}^{(1)} & a_{13}^{(1)} & a_{14}^{(1)} & \cdots & a_{1,n-1}^{(1)} & a_{1n}^{(1)} \\ 0 & 1 & a_{23}^{(2)} & a_{24}^{(2)} & \cdots & a_{2,n-1}^{(2)} & a_{2n}^{(2)} \\ 0 & 0 & 1 & a_{34}^{(3)} & \cdots & a_{3,n-1}^{(3)} & a_{3n}^{(3)} \\ \cdots & \cdots & \cdots & \cdots & \cdots & \cdots & \cdots \\ 0 & 0 & 0 & 0 & \cdots & 0 & 1 \end{bmatrix} \begin{bmatrix} x_1 \\ x_2 \\ x_3 \\ \cdot \\ \cdot \\ \cdot \\ x_n \end{bmatrix} = \begin{bmatrix} a_{1,n+1}^{(1)} \\ a_{2,n+1}^{(2)} \\ a_{3,n+1}^{(3)} \\ \cdot \\ \cdot \\ \cdot \\ a_{n,n+1}^{(n)} \end{bmatrix} \tag{7.18}$$

where all elements below the main diagonal are zero and those on the main diagonal are unity. We observe that the superscripts in parentheses on the elements $a_{ij}^{(i)}$ indicate the number of times the (i,j)th element has been modified.

The matrix of coefficients (7.18) is said to be in *upper-triangular form*. It is easy to obtain the solution from (7.18) by *back substitution*,

$$\text{(7.19)}\quad x_i = a_{i,n+1}^{(i)} - \sum_{j=i+1}^{n} a_{ij}^{(i)} x_j \qquad (i = n, n-1, \ldots, 2, 1)$$

Gaussian elimination is easily programmed for a digital computer; a flow diagram for such a program is given in Fig. 7.1. It is possible that numerical errors may arise if gaussian elimination is used directly as indicated above. The following example illustrates how roundoff errors may cause incorrect answers.

(7.20) Example

Given the two simultaneous linear algebraic equations

$$0.0034x_1 + 5.6231x_2 = 0.0647$$

and

$$1.0112x_1 + 3.1334x_2 = -0.7259$$

Suppose that we are working with fixed-point arithmetic and that we may carry, at most, only five significant digits, as indicated by the coefficients above. The pair of equations which results from the first round of gaussian elimination is

$$1.0000x_1 + 1653.9x_2 = 19.029$$

and

$$-1669.3x_2 = -0.7913$$

from which we obtain the ostensible solution

$$x_2 = 0.0005 \qquad \text{and} \qquad x_1 = 18.202$$

But the substitution of these values into the second of the original equations yields

$$(1.0112)(18.202) + (3.1334)(0.0005) = 18.407 \neq -0.7259$$

indicating gross error. ∎

In general, roundoff errors may occur if any of the divisors $a_{ii}^{(i)}$ is very small in magnitude relative to the elements $a_{ki}^{(i)}$, $k > i$. We may attempt to avoid such division by comparatively small numbers by rearranging the elements according to magnitude, a procedure called *pivoting*. In particular, at the ith round of gaussian elimination, we must locate the element $a_{i-1ik-1}^{(i-1)}$, $k \geq i - 1$ with the greatest magnitude and

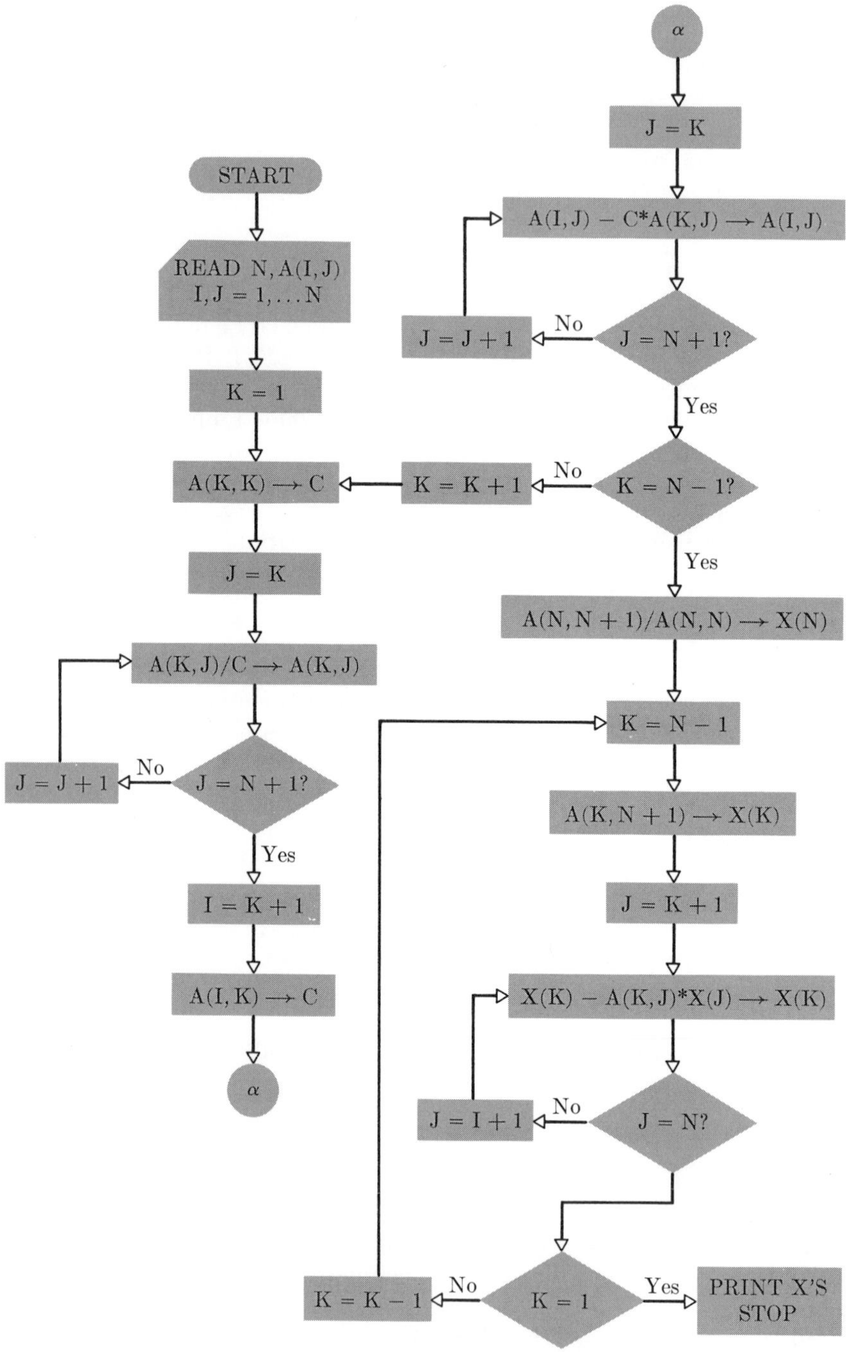

FIG. 7.1 Flow diagram for the gaussian elimination solution of $\mathbf{Ax} = \mathbf{b}$.

then interchange rows $i - 1$ and k. The resulting modified-coefficient matrix is then operated on as before. Matrices for which such problems arise are termed *ill conditioned*, and in bad cases, even this pivoting scheme may fail to alleviate such problems.

Often it is necessary to solve the set of simultaneous linear algebraic equations (7.9) for several different values of the "forcing" vector $\mathbf{b} = (b_1, b_2, \ldots, b_n)'$. More specifically, we may desire solutions for the following set of m simultaneous linear algebraic equations:

(7.21*a*) $\mathbf{A}\mathbf{x}_1 = \mathbf{b}_1$
(7.21*b*) $\mathbf{A}\mathbf{x}_2 = \mathbf{b}_2$
$$\vdots$$
(7.21*m*) $\mathbf{A}\mathbf{x}_m = \mathbf{b}_m$

This situation could arise, for example, were we to desire the response of an electrical circuit to various combinations of excitations. The nodal-admittance matrix would remain fixed, but the equivalent current-source forcing vector would change with each situation.

Additional motivation for the study of the solution of sets of simultaneous linear algebraic equations is provided by the frequent problem of matrix inversion. If $\mathbf{A} = [a_{ij}]$ denotes a given $n \times n$ nonsingular matrix, we let $\mathbf{\Phi} \equiv [\phi_{ij}]$ denote its inverse (we use $\mathbf{\Phi}$ instead of $\mathbf{A}^{-1}$ for notational convenience), then

(7.22) $$\mathbf{A}\mathbf{\Phi} = \mathbf{1}$$

Consider the columns of the inverse matrix $\mathbf{\Phi}$ to be a set of n vectors $\boldsymbol{\phi}_k$ ($k = 1, 2, \ldots, n$), that is,

$$\mathbf{\Phi} \equiv \begin{bmatrix} \boldsymbol{\phi}_1 & \boldsymbol{\phi}_2 & \cdots & \boldsymbol{\phi}_n \\ \downarrow & \downarrow & & \downarrow \end{bmatrix}$$

Then from (7.22) it follows that

(7.23) $$\mathbf{A}\boldsymbol{\phi}_k = \mathbf{e}_k \qquad (k = 1, 2, \ldots, n)$$

where the unit vectors $\mathbf{e}_k$ are defined as follows:

$$\mathbf{e}_1 \equiv \begin{bmatrix} 1 \\ 0 \\ 0 \\ \cdot \\ \cdot \\ \cdot \\ 0 \\ 0 \end{bmatrix}, \mathbf{e}_2 \equiv \begin{bmatrix} 0 \\ 1 \\ 0 \\ \cdot \\ \cdot \\ \cdot \\ 0 \\ 0 \end{bmatrix}, \ldots, \mathbf{e}_n \equiv \begin{bmatrix} 0 \\ 0 \\ 0 \\ \cdot \\ \cdot \\ \cdot \\ 0 \\ 1 \end{bmatrix}$$

Hence, we may determine the inverse of **A** from the solutions of the set of n simultaneous linear algebraic equations (7.23).

One approach to the solution of a set of m simultaneous linear algebraic equations might be to employ gaussian elimination on each of the m constituents. However, there would be a great deal of redundancy in such a procedure, because the same operations would be made each time on **A**. It would be better to operate simultaneously on all the $\mathbf{b}_k$ ($k = 1, 2, \ldots, m$) or to store from the manipulations on **A** that information necessary to appropriately process any **b** vector. In practice, the latter approach is usually taken, because the requisite information is easily obtained and conveniently stored in the course of transforming **A**.

Let the $n \times n$ matrix **U** denote the upper-triangular matrix in (7.18):

$$(7.24)\quad \mathbf{U} \equiv \begin{bmatrix} 1 & a_{12}{}^{(1)} & a_{13}{}^{(1)} & \cdots & a_{1n}{}^{(1)} \\ 0 & 1 & a_{23}{}^{(2)} & \cdots & a_{2n}{}^{(2)} \\ 0 & 0 & 1 & \cdots & a_{3n}{}^{(3)} \\ \cdots & \cdots & \cdots & \cdots & \cdots \\ 0 & 0 & 0 & \cdots & 1 \end{bmatrix}$$

Then (7.18) may be written as

$$(7.25)\quad \mathbf{Ux} = \hat{\mathbf{b}}$$

which is easily solved by back substitution. The information we need to transform the vector **b** into $\hat{\mathbf{b}}$ is contained in those values of the matrix **A**, which ultimately are transformed into the below the diagonal-zero or the diagonal-unity elements of **U**. Specifically, we need only save those values of the modified matrix **A** which arise just prior to the stage at which they become 0 or 1. We may verify this result upon consideration of the $\hat{\mathbf{b}}$ vector. The first element of $\hat{\mathbf{b}}$ is

$$(7.26a)\quad a_{1,n+1}^{(1)} = \frac{a_{1,n+1}}{a_{11}}$$

and in addition to $a_{1,n+1}$ (or b_1), we must know the value of a_{11}; that is, the element which occupies the (1,1) position of **A** just prior to that position being occupied by unity. The second element of $\hat{\mathbf{b}}$ is

$$(7.26b)\quad a_{2,n+1}^{(2)} = \frac{[a_{2,n+1} - a_{21}a_{1,n+1}^{(1)}]}{a_{22}{}^{(1)}}$$

so that in addition to $a_{2,n+1}$ (the second element of **b**) and $a_{1,n+1}^{(1)}$ (the first element of $\hat{\mathbf{b}}$, which was obtained above), we must know a_{21} and $a_{22}{}^{(1)}$, the elements which occupy the respective positions (2,1) and (2,2) of the modified matrix **A** just prior to being transformed into 0 and 1, respectively. In general, the kth element of $\hat{\mathbf{b}}$ is

$$(7.26k)\quad a_{k,n+1}^{(k)} = \frac{\left[a_{k,n+1} - \sum_{j=1}^{k-1} a_{kj}a_{j,n+1}^{(j)}\right]}{a_{kk}^{(k-1)}}$$

which depends on the kth value of $\mathbf{b}$, the preceding $k - 1$ values of $\hat{\mathbf{b}}$ (which have already been calculated), and those elements which occupy the $(k,1)$, $(k,2)$, . . . , (k,k) positions of the modified matrix $\mathbf{A}$ before being transformed into the 0's and 1 of the kth row of $\mathbf{U}$.

Consider the lower-triangular matrix $\mathbf{L}$ defined by

$$(7.27)\quad \mathbf{L} \equiv \begin{bmatrix} a_{11} & 0 & 0 & \cdots & 0 \\ a_{21} & a_{22}^{(1)} & 0 & \cdots & 0 \\ a_{31} & a_{32}^{(1)} & a_{33}^{(2)} & \cdots & 0 \\ \cdots & \cdots & \cdots & \cdots & \cdots \\ a_{n1} & a_{n2}^{(1)} & a_{n3}^{(2)} & \cdots & a_{nn}^{(n-1)} \end{bmatrix}$$

Observe that each of the main diagonal terms is nonzero. The coefficients of $\hat{\mathbf{b}}$ are obtained from the easily solved matrix equation

$$(7.28)\quad \mathbf{L}\hat{\mathbf{b}} = \mathbf{b}$$

which is equivalent to the set of equations (7.26). Determination of $\hat{\mathbf{b}}$ is called *forward substitution*, because $\hat{b}_1$ is first found, then $\hat{b}_2$ from knowledge of $\hat{b}_1$, etc.

Hence, the lower-triangular matrix $\mathbf{L}$ (7.27) contains the information necessary to transform $\mathbf{b}$ into $\hat{\mathbf{b}}$. Moreover, $\mathbf{L}$ is obtained with no additional work as a by-product of the transformation of $\mathbf{A}$ into the upper-triangular matrix $\mathbf{U}$. In fact, since we need not explicitly store the information that $\mathbf{U}$ has only 0's below the main diagonal and 1's on the main diagonal or that $\mathbf{L}$ has only 0's above the main diagonal, we may write a computer program which stores the requisite information on $\mathbf{L}$ and $\mathbf{U}$ in the same storage space originally occupied by $\mathbf{A}$.

The relation between $\mathbf{L}$ and $\mathbf{U}$ and $\mathbf{A}$ is even more explicit than we may infer from the above discussion. Because

$$\mathbf{L}\hat{\mathbf{b}} = \mathbf{b}$$

and

$$\mathbf{Ux} = \hat{\mathbf{b}}$$

then

$$\mathbf{LUx} = \mathbf{b}$$

for any $\mathbf{b}$. But

$$\mathbf{Ax} = \mathbf{b}$$

so we see that

$$\mathbf{A} = \mathbf{LU}$$

We can recover the original matrix **A** by multiplying **L** and **U**. Hence, what we have done in the above solution procedure is to factor or decompose **A** into the product of a lower-triangular matrix **L** and an upper-triangular matrix **U** (with 1's on the main diagonal). The main result is, of course, that the difficult task of solving the matrix equation

$$\mathbf{Ax} = \mathbf{b}$$

for arbitrary **b** is reduced to the relatively simpler task of finding the vector $\hat{\mathbf{b}}$ by forward substitution from

$$\mathbf{L}\hat{\mathbf{b}} = \mathbf{b}$$

and then finding the solution vector **x** by *back substitution* from

$$\mathbf{Ux} = \hat{\mathbf{b}}$$

This process is called the *LU factorization* of **A**. A flow diagram for the *LU* factorization is given in Fig. 7.2.

There remains one property of the *LU* factorization which is worthy of consideration. Since **A**, **L**, and **U** are all $n \times n$ matrices and

$$\mathbf{A} = \mathbf{LU}$$

then

$$\det(\mathbf{A}) = \det(\mathbf{L})\det(\mathbf{U})$$

But

$$\det(\mathbf{U}) = 1$$

and

$$\det(\mathbf{L}) = \prod_{i=1}^{n} a_{ii}^{(i-1)}$$

which is the product of the terms on the main diagonal. Consequently, the determinant of **A** is also easily obtained from the *LU* factorization. Moreover, we may monitor the value of the determinant as the factorization procedure evolves; if the *pivot element* $\mathbf{a}_{ii}^{(i-1)}$ is small in magnitude relative to those preceding it, we have a strong indication of ill conditioning.

7.3 EIGENVALUES OF A MATRIX

We have seen repeatedly that knowledge of the natural frequencies of a lumped, linear, time-invariant system, or the eigenvalues of its characterizing matrix **A**, is crucial to its complete analysis. Rather than survey the myriad techniques which have been evolved for eigenvalue determi-

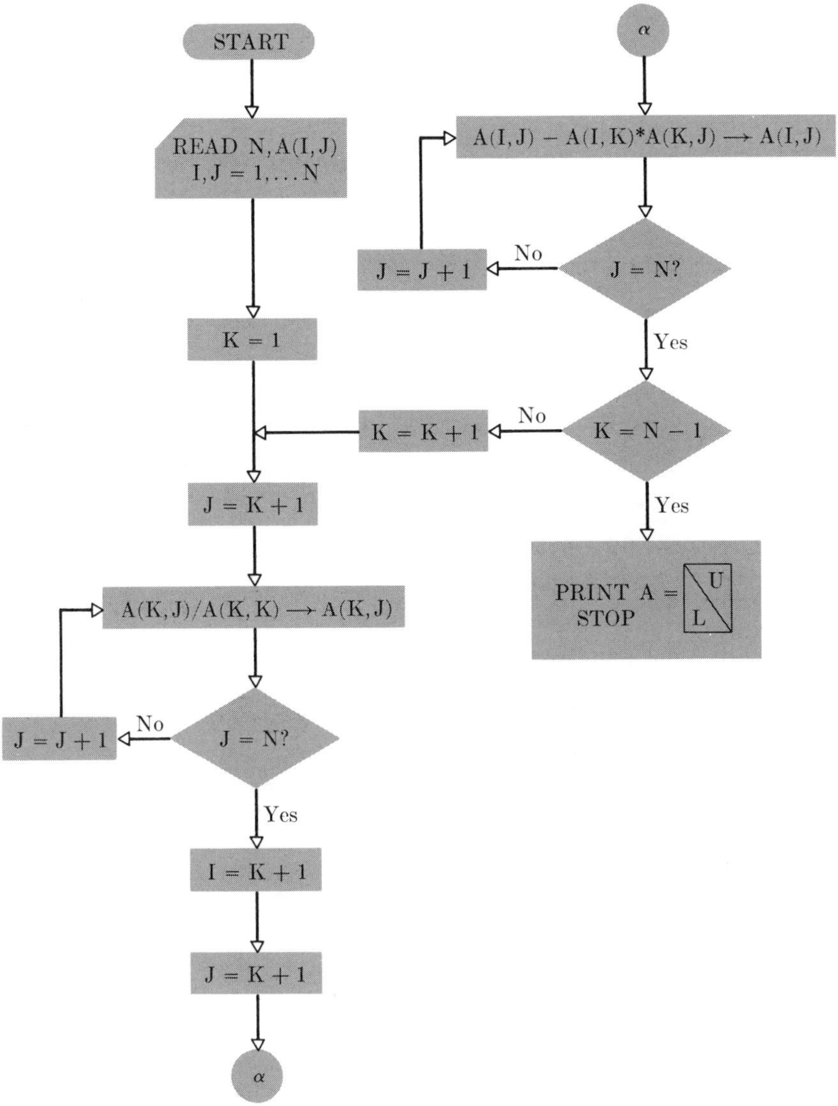

FIG. 7.2 *LU* factorization of **A**.

nation, we present two powerful methods which have attained the most prominence. The first of these is the *LR transformation*, and the second, and more generally useful, is the *QR transformation*.

In the original development,[1] "**L**" and "**R**" were employed as

[1] H. Rutishauser, "Solution of Eigenvalue Problems with the LR-transformation," Nat. Bur. Standards App. Math. Ser., No. 49, p. 47, 1958.

mnemonics for left- and right-triangular matrices, respectively, in the factorization of **A**. Since we have already called these same matrices **L** and **U**, respectively, in the foregoing discussion of simultaneous equation solution and matrix inversion, we will continue to do so here as well. Given an $n \times n$ nonsingular matrix **A**, we may employ gaussian elimination to decompose it into the product of a lower-triangular matrix **L** and an upper-triangular matrix **U** (which has all 1's on the main diagonal) so that

$$\mathbf{A} = \mathbf{L}\mathbf{U}$$

For convenience we employ the subscript "1" to denote the original situation, so that

$$\mathbf{A} \equiv \mathbf{A}_1 = \mathbf{L}_1\mathbf{U}_1$$

Both $\mathbf{U}_1$ and $\mathbf{L}_1$ must be nonsingular, since $\mathbf{A}_1$ must be for us to be able to effect this factorization in the first place, so

$$\mathbf{L}_1 = \mathbf{A}_1\mathbf{U}_1^{-1}$$

and

$$\mathbf{U}_1 = \mathbf{L}_1^{-1}\mathbf{A}_1$$

Next we define the matrix

$$\mathbf{A}_2 \equiv \mathbf{U}_1\mathbf{L}_1 = \mathbf{L}_1^{-1}\mathbf{A}_1\mathbf{L}_1 = \mathbf{U}_1\mathbf{A}_1\mathbf{U}_1^{-1}$$

and observe that it has the same eigenvalues as $\mathbf{A}_1$, since it has been obtained by a similarity transformation on the original. In turn we may similarly factor

$$\mathbf{A}_2 = \mathbf{L}_2\mathbf{U}_2$$

and define

$$\mathbf{A}_3 \equiv \mathbf{U}_2\mathbf{L}_2 = \mathbf{L}_2^{-1}\mathbf{A}_2\mathbf{L}_2 = \mathbf{U}_2\mathbf{A}_2\mathbf{U}_2^{-1}$$

which also must have the same eigenvalues as $\mathbf{A}_1$. Continuing, we can construct the sequence

$$\mathbf{A}_k = \mathbf{L}_k\mathbf{U}_k = \mathbf{U}_{k-1}\mathbf{L}_{k-1} \qquad (k = 2, 3, 4, \ldots)$$

where $\mathbf{A}_k$, $\mathbf{L}_k$, and $\mathbf{U}_k$ have the following properties:

(1) Because each $\mathbf{A}_k$ is derived from its successor by means of a similarity transformation, all the $\mathbf{A}_k$ have the same eigenvalues.
(2) If we define

$$\hat{\mathbf{U}}_k = \mathbf{U}_k\mathbf{U}_{k-1} \cdots \mathbf{U}_2\mathbf{U}_1$$

and

$$\hat{\mathbf{L}}_k = \mathbf{L}_1\mathbf{L}_2 \cdots \mathbf{L}_{k-1}\mathbf{L}_k$$

then $\hat{\mathbf{U}}_k$ and $\hat{\mathbf{L}}_k$ are also upper- and lower-triangular matrices, respectively. Moreover

$$\begin{aligned}\mathbf{A}_{k+1} &= \mathbf{L}_k^{-1}\mathbf{A}_k\mathbf{L}_k = \mathbf{U}_k\mathbf{A}_k\mathbf{U}_k^{-1} \\ &= \mathbf{L}_k^{-1}\mathbf{L}_{k-1}\mathbf{A}_{k-1}\mathbf{L}_{k-1}\mathbf{L}_k = \mathbf{U}_k\mathbf{U}_{k-1}\mathbf{A}_{k-1}\mathbf{U}_{k-1}^{-1}\mathbf{U}_k^{-1} \\ &= \hat{\mathbf{L}}_k^{-1}\mathbf{A}_1\hat{\mathbf{L}}_k = \hat{\mathbf{U}}_k\mathbf{A}_1\hat{\mathbf{U}}_k^{-1}\end{aligned}$$

(3) Because

$$\mathbf{L}_k\mathbf{U}_k = \mathbf{U}_{k-1}\mathbf{L}_{k-1}$$

it follows that

$$\begin{aligned}\hat{\mathbf{L}}_k\hat{\mathbf{U}}_k &= \mathbf{L}_1\mathbf{L}_2 \cdots \mathbf{L}_{k-1}\mathbf{L}_k\mathbf{U}_k\mathbf{U}_{k-1} \cdots \mathbf{U}_2\mathbf{U}_1 \\ &= \mathbf{L}_1\mathbf{L}_2 \cdots \mathbf{L}_{k-1}\mathbf{U}_{k-1}\mathbf{L}_{k-1}\mathbf{U}_{k-1} \cdots \mathbf{U}_2\mathbf{U}_1 \\ &= (\mathbf{L}_1\mathbf{U}_1)^k = \mathbf{A}_1^k\end{aligned}$$

In order to establish the utility of the *LR* transformation, we need the following theorem.

(7.29) Theorem

If

$$\hat{\mathbf{U}}_\infty \equiv \lim_{k\to\infty} \hat{\mathbf{U}}_k$$

exists and is nonsingular, then

$$\mathbf{A}_\infty \equiv \lim_{k\to\infty} \mathbf{A}_k$$

exists and is in lower-triangular form.

Proof

The sequence $\{\mathbf{U}_k\}$ is assumed to converge, hence

$$\lim_{k\to\infty} \mathbf{U}_k = \lim_{k\to\infty} (\hat{\mathbf{U}}_k^{-1}\hat{\mathbf{U}}_{k-1}) = \mathbf{1}$$

and

$$\begin{aligned}\mathbf{L}_\infty &= \lim_{k\to\infty} \mathbf{L}_k = \lim_{k\to\infty} (\mathbf{U}_k^{-1}\mathbf{A}_{k+1}) \\ &= \lim_{k\to\infty} (\hat{\mathbf{U}}_{k-1}\mathbf{A}_1\hat{\mathbf{U}}_k^{-1}) \\ &= \hat{\mathbf{U}}_\infty\mathbf{A}_1\hat{\mathbf{U}}_\infty^{-1}\end{aligned}$$

Hence,

$$\begin{aligned}\mathbf{A}_\infty &= \lim_{k\to\infty} \mathbf{A}_k \\ &= \lim_{k\to\infty} = \mathbf{L}_k\mathbf{U}_k \\ &= \mathbf{L}_\infty\end{aligned}$$

which exists and is in lower-triangular form. ∎

The result of this theorem is that ultimately we may transform the matrix **A** into a lower-triangular matrix $\mathbf{L}_\infty$, which has the same eigenvalues as **A**, but for which the eigenvalues are easily obtained, since they are merely the diagonal entries of $\mathbf{L}_\infty$. An investigation of the convergence of the sequence $\{\hat{\mathbf{U}}_k\}$ is beyond our scope. The *LR* transformation will converge for any symmetric positive-definite matrix **A**, which is not the usual case, and many other matrices as well. The *LR* transformation fails, however, when the original matrix **A** is singular (has at least one eigenvalue of value zero) because it relies on the *LU* factorization, which may only be obtained for nonsingular matrices. Since we are interested in the practical use of the *LR* transformation, we cannot allow $k \to \infty$. In general we can continue the *LU* factorization procedure until the above diagonal terms of $\mathbf{A}_k$ change by less than some prescribed tolerance. The eigenvalues of **A** are then approximately equal to the diagonal elements of $\mathbf{A}_k$.

(7.30) Example

In order to see how the *LR* transformation works, let us find the eigenvalues of the matrix

$$\mathbf{A} = \mathbf{A}_1 = \begin{bmatrix} 2 & 1 \\ 2 & 3 \end{bmatrix}$$

Then

$$\mathbf{L}_1 = \begin{bmatrix} 2 & 0 \\ 2 & 2 \end{bmatrix} \quad \text{and} \quad \mathbf{U}_1 = \begin{bmatrix} 1 & \frac{1}{2} \\ 0 & 1 \end{bmatrix}$$

so that

$$\mathbf{A}_2 = \mathbf{U}_1\mathbf{L}_1 = \begin{bmatrix} 3 & 1 \\ 2 & 2 \end{bmatrix}$$

The *LU* factorization of $\mathbf{A}_2$ yields

$$\mathbf{L}_2 = \begin{bmatrix} 3 & 0 \\ 2 & \frac{4}{3} \end{bmatrix} \quad \text{and} \quad \mathbf{U}_2 = \begin{bmatrix} 1 & \frac{1}{3} \\ 0 & 1 \end{bmatrix}$$

from which we obtain

$$\mathbf{A}_3 = \mathbf{U}_2\mathbf{L}_2 = \begin{bmatrix} \frac{11}{3} & \frac{4}{9} \\ 2 & \frac{4}{3} \end{bmatrix}$$

Proceeding, we have

$$\mathbf{L}_3 = \begin{bmatrix} \frac{11}{3} & 0 \\ 2 & \frac{32}{33} \end{bmatrix} \quad \text{and} \quad \mathbf{U}_3 = \begin{bmatrix} 1 & \frac{4}{33} \\ 0 & 1 \end{bmatrix}$$

and

$$\mathbf{A}_4 = \begin{bmatrix} \frac{128}{33} & \frac{138}{1089} \\ 2 & \frac{32}{33} \end{bmatrix}$$

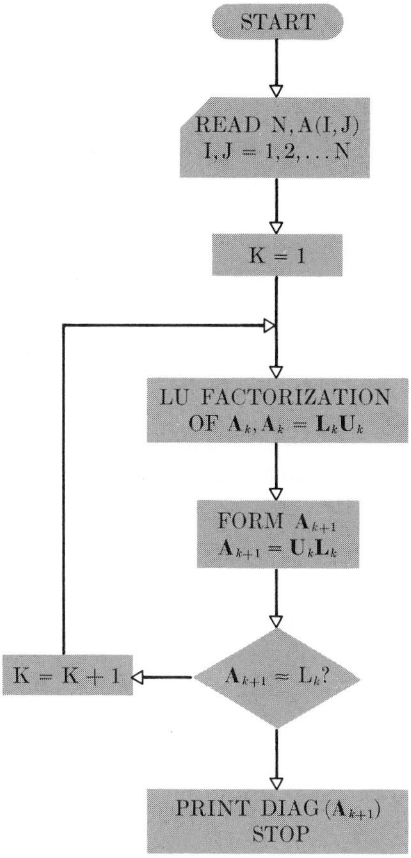

FIG. 7.3 A flow diagram of the *LR* transformation for determination of eigenvalues.

Observe that the diagonal elements of $\mathbf{A}_4$ are approximately 4 and 1, respectively, which are the eigenvalues of $\mathbf{A}$. Moreover, the above diagonal term of the sequence $\mathbf{A}_2$, $\mathbf{A}_3$, $\mathbf{A}_4$ is approaching zero.

A block diagram of the *LR* transformation procedure is given in Fig. 7.3.

For the purpose of numerical stability, it is more desirable to decompose the matrix $\mathbf{A}$ into the product of an orthogonal matrix $\mathbf{Q}$ and an upper-triangular matrix $\mathbf{U}$. An orthogonal matrix $\mathbf{Q}$ is one for which

$$\mathbf{QQ}' = \mathbf{1}$$

or

$$\mathbf{Q}' = \mathbf{Q}^{-1}$$

The *QR* transformation was originally called so because

$$\mathbf{A} = \mathbf{QU}$$

is factored into the product of an orthogonal matrix $\mathbf{Q}$ and a right-hand upper-triangular matrix $\mathbf{U}$. It is always possible to find such matrices $\mathbf{Q}$ and $\mathbf{U}$ for any given real-valued matrix $\mathbf{A}$†. In analogy to the *LR* transformation discussed above, we define

$$\mathbf{A}_k = \mathbf{Q}_k\mathbf{U}_k = \mathbf{U}_{k-1}\mathbf{Q}_{k-1}$$

Observe that all the matrices $\mathbf{A}_k$ are similar and, therefore, have the same eigenvalues. As before, if the sequence $\{\mathbf{Q}_k\}$ converges, then $\mathbf{A}_k$ converges to an upper-triangular matrix which has its eigenvalues on the main diagonal. Most computation centers have available subroutines for finding the eigenvalues of a given real-valued square matrix by means of the *QR* transformation.

Before leaving this topic, we should observe that eigenvalue computation must be extremely time consuming, entailing what amounts to repeated matrix inversion, itself a time-consuming task.

7.4 FAST FOURIER TRANSFORM

In Chap. 5 we have seen the Fourier transform to be a useful tool in the determination of the zero-state response of linear time-invariant systems. The *fast Fourier transform* (FFT) is a highly efficient means for the practical implementation of Fourier transforms on digital computers.

Let $g(t)$ be any Fourier transformable function of time. Then the Fourier transform of $g(t)$ is given by

$$(7.31a)\quad G(\omega) \equiv \int_{-\infty}^{\infty} g(t)e^{-j\omega t}\,dt$$

And the original time function may be recovered from its Fourier transform by means of the inverse transform

$$(7.31b)\quad g(t) = \frac{1}{2\pi}\int_{-\infty}^{\infty} G(\omega)e^{j\omega t}\,d\omega$$

In general we are interested in $g(t)$ only over some finite time interval, say $0 \leq t \leq T$. Since we are to use a digital computer, we may deal only in a finite number of discrete samples of both the time domain function $g(t)$ and the frequency domain function $G(\omega)$. Recall from the *sampling theorem* (5.68) of Chap. 5 that if $G(\omega)$ is bandlimited, that is,

$$G(\omega) = 0 \qquad \text{for } |\omega| \geq \omega_c$$

† The proof of this statement and the means for finding $\mathbf{Q}$ and $\mathbf{U}$ is beyond our scope, but detailed treatments are given in a number of references; see, for example, J. G. F. Francis, The QR Transformation, *The Computer Journal,* vol. 4, pp. 265–271, 1961.

then $g(t)$ can be determined completely from samples spaced, at most, π/ω_c seconds apart. Henceforth we assume $G(\omega)$ to be so bandlimited.

We first must investigate the properties of the Fourier transform of the sampled time signal. We consider the sampling of $g(t)$ to be performed by its multiplication by an infinite sequence of impulse functions which occur every $\Delta t = \pi/\omega_c$ seconds. More specifically, if we define this sequence by

$$(7.32)\quad s_{\Delta t}(t) \equiv \sum_{n=-\infty}^{\infty} \delta(t - n\,\Delta t)$$

then the sampled version of $g(t)$ is given by

$$(7.33)\quad \hat{g}(t) = s_{\Delta t}(t)g(t) = \sum_{n=-\infty}^{\infty} \delta(t - n\,\Delta t)g(t)$$

(Of course, this relation must be strictly interpreted in the sense of distributions.) Let $S_{\Delta t}(\omega)$, $G(\omega)$, and $\hat{G}(\omega)$ be the Fourier transforms of $s_{\Delta t}(t)$, $g(t)$, and $\hat{g}(t)$, respectively; then, since the Fourier transform of the product of two time functions corresponds to the convolution of their frequency-domain counterparts, we have

$$(7.34)\quad \hat{G}(\omega) = \frac{1}{2\pi}\int_{-\infty}^{\infty} S_{\Delta t}(\omega - \lambda)G(\lambda)\,d\lambda$$

In order to continue the above development, we must digress to show that

$$(7.35)\quad S_{\Delta t}(\omega) \equiv \mathfrak{F}[s_{\Delta t}(t)] = \omega_0 \sum_{n=-\infty}^{\infty} \delta(\omega - n\omega_0)$$

where $\omega_0 \equiv 2\pi/\Delta t = 2\omega_c$. To do so, we consider the inverse Fourier transformation

$$(7.36)\quad \frac{1}{2\pi}\int_{-\infty}^{\infty} \omega_0 \sum_{n=-\infty}^{\infty} \delta(\omega - n\omega_0)e^{j\omega t}\,d\omega$$

$$= \frac{1}{\Delta t}\sum_{n=-\infty}^{\infty}\int_{-\infty}^{\infty} e^{j\omega t}\,\delta(\omega - n\omega_0)\,d\omega$$

$$= \frac{1}{\Delta t}\sum_{n=-\infty}^{\infty} e^{jn\omega_0 t}$$

where we have assumed the infinite integration and summation interchangeable, an operation which may be justified in this instance only in the sense of distributions. Now consider the function

$$k_N(t) = \frac{1}{\Delta t}\sum_{n=-N}^{N} e^{jn\omega_0 t}$$

which reduces to the inverse Fourier transform (7.36) in the limit as $N \to \infty$, and define

$$l \equiv n + N$$

so that, more conveniently,

$$k_N(t) = \frac{1}{\Delta t} e^{-jN\omega_0 t} \sum_{l=0}^{2N} e^{jl\omega_0 t}$$

Suppose we define

$$\sigma_{2N} \equiv \sum_{l=0}^{2N} e^{jl\omega_0 t}$$

then

$$\sigma_{2N+1} = \sigma_{2N} + e^{j(2N+1)\omega_0 t} = e^{j\omega_0 t}\sigma_{2N+1}$$

so that

$$\sigma_{2N} = \frac{1 - e^{j(2N+1)\omega_0 t}}{1 - e^{j\omega_0 t}}$$

Hence,

$$\begin{aligned} k_N(t) &= \frac{1}{\Delta t} e^{-jN\omega_0 t} \frac{1 - e^{j(2N+1)\omega_0 t}}{1 - e^{j\omega_0 t}} \\ &= \frac{1}{\Delta t} \frac{e^{-jN\omega_0 t} - e^{j(N+1)\omega_0 t}}{1 - e^{j\omega_0 t}} \\ &= \frac{1}{\Delta t} \frac{e^{j(N+1)\omega_0 t} - e^{-jN\omega_0 t}}{e^{j\omega_0 t} - 1} \\ &= \frac{1}{\Delta t} \frac{2je^{j1/2\omega_0 t}(e^{j(N+1/2)\omega_0 t} - e^{-j(N+1/2)\omega_0 t})}{2je^{j1/2\omega_0 t}(e^{j1/2\omega_0 t} - e^{-j1/2\omega_0 t})} \\ &= \frac{1}{\Delta t} \frac{\sin [(N + 1/2)\omega_0 t]}{\sin [1/2\omega_0 t]} \end{aligned}$$

The *Fourier series kernal* $k_N(t)$ is periodic with period $\Delta t = 2\pi/\omega_0$:

$$\begin{aligned} k_N(t + \Delta t) &= \frac{1}{\Delta t} \frac{\sin [(N + 1/2)\omega_0(t + \Delta t)]}{\sin [1/2\omega_0(t + \Delta t)]} \\ &= \frac{1}{\Delta t} \frac{\sin [(N + 1/2)\omega_0 t] \cos [(N + 1/2)\omega_0 \Delta t] + \cos [(N + 1/2)\omega_0 t] \sin [(N + 1/2)\omega_0 \Delta t]}{\sin [1/2\omega_0 t] \cos [1/2\omega_0 \Delta t] + \cos [1/2\omega_0 t] \sin [1/2\omega_0 \Delta t]} \end{aligned}$$

but $\omega_0 \Delta t = 2\pi$ so that

$$k_N(t + \Delta t) = \frac{1}{\Delta t} \frac{\sin [(N + 1/2)\omega_0 t]}{\sin [1/2\omega_0 t]}$$

What remains is to show that

$$\lim_{N\to\infty} k_N(t) = \delta(t) \qquad \text{for } -\frac{\Delta t}{2} \leq t \leq \frac{\Delta t}{2}$$

To do so, we consider

$$k_N(t) = \frac{\sin\,[(N + 1/2)\omega_0 t]}{\pi t} \cdot \frac{\pi t}{\Delta t \sin\,[1/2\omega_0 t]}$$

Since $\pi t/\sin\,[1/2\omega_0 t]$ remains bounded in the interval $-\Delta t/2 \leq t \leq \Delta t/2$ and is independent of N, we need only show that

$$\delta(t) = \lim_{N\to\infty} \frac{\sin \omega t}{\pi t} \qquad \omega = (N + 1/2)\omega_0$$

But we know that this expression is valid (in the sense of distributions) from the discussion of the Riemann-Lebesgue lemma and Eq. (5.45) in Chap. 5. Hence we have

$$\begin{aligned} k_N(t) &= \frac{\pi t}{\Delta t \sin\,[1/2\omega_0 t]}\,\delta(t) \\ &= \delta(t)\left[\lim_{t\to 0} \frac{\pi t}{\Delta t \sin\,[1/2\omega_0 t]}\right] \\ &= \delta(t)\left[\frac{\pi}{\Delta t\, 1/2\omega_0}\right] \\ &= \delta(t) \end{aligned}$$

Finally, returning to (7.34), we substitute (7.35) to obtain

$$\text{(7.37)} \qquad \begin{aligned} \hat{G}(\omega) &= \frac{1}{\Delta t} \sum_{n=-\infty}^{\infty} G(\omega - n\omega_0) \\ &= \frac{1}{\Delta t} \sum_{n=-\infty}^{\infty} G\left(f - \frac{n}{\Delta t}\right) \end{aligned}$$

where $f \equiv \omega/2\pi$. We observe that because $G(\omega)$ is bandlimited as shown in Fig. 7.4*a*, $\hat{G}(\omega)$ is periodic as shown in Fig. 7.4*b*; that is, $\hat{G}(\omega)$ is the periodic repetition of $G(\omega)$, and complete information on $G(\omega)$ is contained in each period of $\hat{G}(\omega)$ *since no overlapping occurs*. The Fourier transform of a sampled function with samples every Δt seconds is periodic in frequency with period $2\pi/\Delta t$. Because $G(\omega)$ can be obtained exactly from (any complete period of) $\hat{G}(\omega)$, we can obtain $G(\omega)$ and, therefore, $g(t)$ completely from the sampled function $\hat{g}(t)$. Having established these results, we may proceed with confidence to the *fast Fourier transform*, which relies on such sampling schemes.

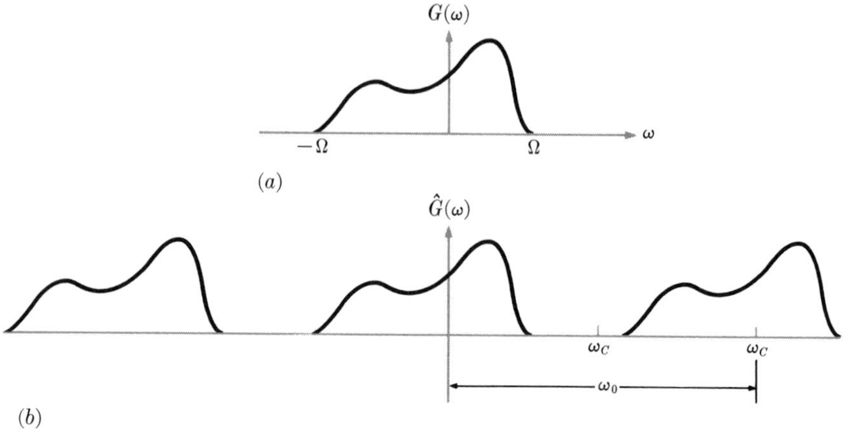

FIG. 7.4 The discrete Fourier transform of a bandlimited function represented in (*a*) is periodic as shown in (*b*).

Assume that we have N samples of $g(t)$, where each sample is Δt seconds apart, and define $t_k \equiv k\,\Delta t$, where $k = 0, 1, 2, \ldots, N-1$. For convenience of exposition, we also assume that $N = 2^\gamma$, where γ is an integer. Similarly assume that we are to have N samples of $G(\omega)$, where each sample is $\Delta\omega$ rads/sec apart, and define $\omega_n \equiv n\,\Delta\omega$, where

$$n = (-N/2 + 1, N/2 + 2, \ldots, -1, 0, 1, 2, \ldots, N/2 - 1, N/2)$$

Expressions (7.31*a*) and (7.31*b*) in this instance become

$$\text{(7.38)}\quad G(\omega_n) = \Delta t \sum_{k=0}^{n-1} g(t_k)e^{-j\omega_n t_k} \qquad (n = 0, 1, \ldots, N-1)$$

and

$$\text{(7.39)}\quad g(t_k) = \frac{\Delta\omega}{2\pi} \sum_{n=0}^{N-1} G(\omega_n)e^{j\omega_n t_k} \qquad (k = 0, 1, \ldots, N-1)$$

respectively. Here we have changed the limits from $[-N/2, N/2]$ to $[0, N-1]$ for computational convenience, with no loss of generality. The only change which results from this substitution is that the "fold-over" frequency is shifted from 0 to $N/2$. We now take $\Delta\omega = 2\pi/T$ and since $t = T/N$, it follows that

$$\omega_n = n\,\Delta\omega = \frac{2\pi n}{T}$$

and

$$t_k = k\,\Delta t = \frac{kT}{N}$$

so that

$$\omega_n t_k = \frac{2\pi n^k}{N}$$

For notational convenience, we redefine

$$G(n) \equiv G(\omega_n)$$

and

$$g(k) \equiv g(t_k)$$

recognizing that we need only know $\Delta\omega$ and Δt to recover the actual arguments from their integer substitutes. Expressions (7.38) and (7.39), with this new notation, become

$$(7.40)\quad G(n) = \Delta t \sum_{k=0}^{N-1} g(k)e^{-j2\pi nk/N} \qquad (n = 0, 1, \ldots, N-1)$$

and

$$(7.41)\quad g(k) = \frac{\Delta\omega}{2} \sum_{n=0}^{N-1} G(n)e^{j2\pi nk/N} \qquad (k = 0, 1, \ldots, N-1)$$

respectively. These two expressions define the forward and inverse *discrete Fourier transform*.

Observe that N complex multiplications are required to find each coefficient $G(n)$ from (7.40). Thus a complete set of N coefficients requires N^2 complex multiplications. Now suppose that we consider N to be a product of two factors:

$$N = N_1 N_2$$

Let us express the indexes n and k in (7.40) in terms of N_1 and N_2 as follows:

$$n = n_1 N_2 + n_0 \qquad \begin{aligned} n_0 &= 0, 1, \ldots, N_2 - 1 \\ n_1 &= 0, 1, \ldots, N_1 - 1 \end{aligned}$$

and

$$k = k_1 N_1 + k_0 \qquad \begin{aligned} k_0 &= 0, 1, \ldots, N_1 - 1 \\ k_1 &= 0, 1, \ldots, N_2 - 1 \end{aligned}$$

then (7.40) can be rewritten as

$$(7.42)\quad G(n) = \Delta t \sum_{k_0=0}^{N_1-1} \sum_{k_1=0}^{N_2-1} g(k_0,k_{10})e^{-j2\pi n(k_1N+k_0)/N}$$

where we have allowed the abuse of notation

$$g(k_0,k_1) \equiv g(k) = g(k_1 N_1 + k_0)$$

We can expand the exponential in (7.42) as

$$\begin{aligned} e^{-j2\pi n(k_1N+k_0)/N} &= e^{-j2\pi nk_0/N}e^{-j2\pi nk_1N_1/N} \\ &= e^{-j2\pi nk_0/N}e^{-j2\pi k_1N_1(nN_2+n_0)/N} \\ &= e^{-j2\pi nk_0/N}e^{-j2\pi k_1n_1}e^{-j2\pi k_1N_1n_0/N} \end{aligned}$$

but

$$e^{-j2\pi k_1n_1} = \cos\,(2k_1n_1\pi) - j\,\sin\,(2k_1n_1\pi) = 1$$

since k_1 and n_1 are integers, so that

$$e^{-j2\pi n(k_1N+k_0)/N} = e^{-j2\pi nk_0/N}e^{-j2\pi k_1n_0N_1/N}$$

Substitution of this relationship in (7.42) yields

$$(7.43)\quad G(n) = G(n_1,n_0) \equiv \Delta t \sum_{k_0=0}^{N_1-1} g_1(k_0,n_0)e^{-j2\pi k_0(n_1N_2+n_0)/N}$$

where

$$(7.44)\quad g_1(k_0,n_0) \equiv \sum_{k_1=0}^{N_2-1} g(k_0,k_1)e^{-j2\pi k_1n_0N_1/N}$$

To count the number of complex multiplications required for the computation of $G(n)$ from (7.43) and (7.44), we observe that there are N elements represented by the data set $g(k_0,k_1)$, and Eq. (7.44) implies N_2 multiplications for each $g(k_0,k_1)$ for a total of NN_2 multiplications. Equation (7.43) implies N_1 multiplications for each of the N values of $g_1(k_0,n_0)$, thus the N coefficients $G(n)$, $n = 0, 1, 2, \ldots, N-1$ require $N(N_1+N_2)$ complex multiplications.

For instance, if $N = 10{,}000$, $N_1 = 100$, $N_2 = 100$, then

$$N(N_1+N_2) = 2 \times 10^6$$

whereas the number of multiplications originally required was

$$N^2 = 10^8$$

thus a reduction of multiplications by a factor of 50 is realized.

Now consider the possibility of decomposing N into a product of m factors:

$$N = N_1N_2 \cdots N_m$$

It is possible to show that the total number of complex multiplications required is

$$N(N_1+N_2+\cdots+N_m)$$

If we let $N_1 = N_2 = \cdot \cdot \cdot = N_m = 2$

$$N = 2^m$$

then

$$m = \log_2 N$$

and the total number of complex multiplications required is

$$m2N = 2N \log_2 N$$

which for large N is considerably less than the N^2 multiplications we originally thought we needed.

The above ideas form the basis of the FFT. Let

$$W = e^{-j2\pi/N}$$

and define $N \times N$ matrix

$$\mathbf{W} = [W_{n+1,k+1}] \equiv [W^{nk}] \qquad (n, k = 0, 1, \ldots, N-1)$$

so $n + 1$ denotes row and $k + 1$ denotes column. For example, in the case $N = 4$, we have

$$[W^{nk}] = \begin{bmatrix} W^0 & W^0 & W^0 & W^0 \\ W^0 & W^1 & W^2 & W^3 \\ W^0 & W^2 & W^4 & W^6 \\ W^0 & W^3 & W^6 & W^9 \end{bmatrix}$$

Moreover, we define the two N vectors

$$\mathbf{G} \equiv [G(n)] \qquad (n = 0, 1, \ldots, N-1)$$

and

$$\mathbf{g} \equiv [g(k)] \qquad (k = 0, 1, \ldots, N-1)$$

For example, in the case again of $N = 4$, we have

$$[G(n)] \equiv \begin{bmatrix} G(0) \\ G(1) \\ G(2) \\ G(3) \end{bmatrix} \qquad \text{and} \qquad [g(k)] \equiv \begin{bmatrix} g(0) \\ g(1) \\ g(2) \\ g(3) \end{bmatrix}$$

In terms of these definitions the forward discrete Fourier transform (7.40) may be written in matrix form as

$$(7.45a) \quad [G(n)] = \Delta t[W^{nk}][g(k)]$$

but the Δt multiplier is merely a scale factor and may be dropped to obtain the more convenient

$$(7.45b) \quad [G(n)] = [W^{nk}][g(k)]$$

For example, in the case $N = 4$, we have

$$(7.46)\quad \begin{bmatrix} G(0) \\ G(1) \\ G(2) \\ G(3) \end{bmatrix} = \begin{bmatrix} W^0 & W^0 & W^0 & W^0 \\ W^0 & W^1 & W^2 & W^3 \\ W^0 & W^2 & W^4 & W^6 \\ W^0 & W^3 & W^6 & W^9 \end{bmatrix} \begin{bmatrix} g(0) \\ g(1) \\ g(2) \\ g(3) \end{bmatrix}$$

Similarly, we can write the inverse discrete Fourier transform (7.41) in matrix form as

$$(7.47a)\quad [g(k)] = \frac{\Delta\omega}{2\pi}[W^{-nk}][G(n)]$$

or, ignoring the scale factor $\Delta\omega/2\pi$,

$$(7.47b)\quad [g(k)] = [W^{-nk}][G(n)]$$

But we may further simplify these expressions because

$$\begin{aligned} W^{nk} &= e^{-j2\pi nk/N} \\ &= \cos(2\pi nk/N) - j\sin(2\pi nk/N) \\ &= \cos[2\pi(nk, \bmod N)] - j\sin[2\pi(nk, \bmod N)] \end{aligned}$$

where $(nk, \bmod N)$ is the integer remainder which results in the division nk/N. For instance $(6, \bmod 4) = 2$, $(8, \bmod 4) = 0$, and $(9, \bmod 4) = 1$. Hence

$$W^{nk} = W^{(nk, \bmod N)}$$

with $W^0 = 1$, of course. Therefore, (7.46) becomes

$$(7.48)\quad \begin{bmatrix} G(0) \\ G(1) \\ G(2) \\ G(3) \end{bmatrix} = \begin{bmatrix} 1 & 1 & 1 & 1 \\ 1 & W^1 & W^2 & W^3 \\ 1 & W^2 & 1 & W^2 \\ 1 & W^3 & W^2 & W^1 \end{bmatrix} \begin{bmatrix} g(0) \\ g(1) \\ g(2) \\ g(3) \end{bmatrix}$$

In general the evaluation of either equation (7.45) or (7.47) requires N^2 complex multiplications and additions. For reasonably large values of N, excessive amounts of computer time are entailed. The *fast Fourier transform*[1] is an extremely efficient means for computing (7.45) or (7.47), which takes full advantage of the special structure of the $[W^{nk}]$ matrix. The fast Fourier transform reduces the necessary computations by a factor of $(\log_2 N)/N$. For example, if $N = 2^{10} = 1,024$, then the fast Fourier transform requires

$$N \log_2 N = 10{,}240$$

complex multiplications and additions, whereas the conventional approach would require $N^2 = 1,048{,}576$, or more than 50 times as many.

[1] J. W. Cooley and J. W. Tukey, An Algorithm for the Machine Calculation of Complex Fourier Series, *Math. Comput.*, vol. 19, pp. 297–301, April, 1965.

Because the forms of equations (7.45) and (7.47) are similar, an algorithm which enhances the evaluation of either one is easily extendible to the other upon the mere interchange of the roles of $g(k)$ and $G(n)$ and appropriate sign- and scale-factor changes. Hence, we will discuss the fast Fourier transform algorithm only in terms of (7.45) and the reader should be able to extend it to (7.47).

The Cooley-Tukey algorithm, which is the crux of the fast Fourier transform, provides a method for factoring the $N \times N$ matrix $[W^{nk}]$ into the product of $\gamma(N \times N)$ matrices (recall $N = 2^\gamma$) in such a way that the overall number of complex multiplications and additions required to evaluate (7.45) is minimized. Although the algorithm is easy to implement, it is difficult to motivate all the steps entailed, so we leave their complete explanation to the references.[1] We will first give the algorithm and then illustrate it by means of a simple example. Symbolically we rewrite (7.45*b*)

$$(7.49) \quad [G(n)] = [W^{nk}]_\gamma [W^{nk}]_{\gamma-1} \cdots [W^{nk}]_1 [g(k)]$$

and define

$$(7.50) \quad [g_p(n)] = [W^{nk}]_p [W^{nk}]_{p-1} \cdots [W^{nk}]_1 [g(k)] \qquad (p = 0, 1)$$

Then

$$[g_p(n)] = [W^{nk}]_p [g_{p-1}(n)] \qquad p = 1, 2, \ldots, \gamma$$

with

$$[g_0(n)] = [g(n)]$$

and

$$[G(n)] = [W^{nk}]_\gamma [g_\gamma(n)]$$

The matrices $[W^{nk}]p$ are found from a *tree graph* such as that shown in Fig. 7.5. Rules for construction of tree graphs are as follows. Refer to Fig. 7.5 as a guide.

(1) Draw a vertical array of N nodes to represent the components of the vector $[g_0(k)]$ where $k = 0, 1, \ldots, N - 1$. (These are the sample points of the time function $g(t)$.) The argument k is expressed as a biasing number of γ bits. (For $N = 16$, $\gamma = \log_2 N = 4$.)
(2) Draw γ more vertical arrays of nodes to the right. Each array represents $[g_p(n)]$, $p = 1, 2, \ldots, \gamma$. Address each node as a binary number. Nodes on the same horizontal level have the same binary address.
(3) At each node, a circle is drawn and a number is placed inside. This

[1] See, for example, E. O. Brigham and R. E. Morrow, The Fast Fourier Transform, *IEEE Spectrum*, pp. 63–70, Dec., 1967. The reader might also be interested in the Special Issue on Fast Fourier Transform, *IEEE Trans. on Audio Electroacoustics*, vol. AU-15, no. 2, pp. 113–117, June, 1967.

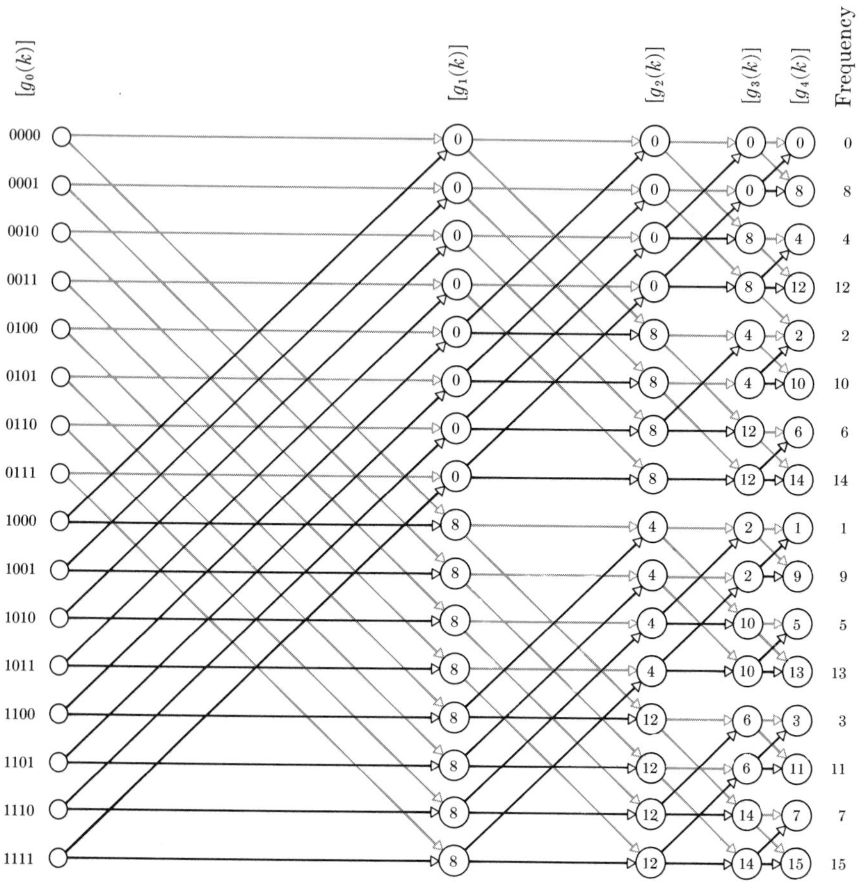

FIG. 7.5 The tree graph for $N = 16$.

number is computed as follows. The number in the circle of the kth node ($k = 0, 1, \ldots, N-1$) in the lth array ($l = 0, 1, \ldots, \gamma$) is found by (*a*) writing the binary number k, (*b*) scaling or sliding this number $(\gamma - l)$ places to the right and filling in the newly opened bit positions on the left by zeros, (*c*) reversing the order of the bits, and (*d*) using the decimal representation.

As an example, consider the case of $\gamma = 4$, $k = 13$, and $l = 1$. In binary representation, $k = 1101$. After scaling $\gamma - l = 3$ bits to the right and filling with zeros, the number is 0001; reversing the order, we have 1000, the decimal equivalent of which is 8.

(4) Let the binary representation of k be $k_{\gamma-1} \cdots k, k_0$. For instance, if $k = 1001$, then $k_3 = 1$, $k_2 = 1$, $k_1 = 0$, and $k_0 = 1$. The tree graph

can now be completed. Draw a solid line to the kth node in the lth column from the pth node in the $(l-1)$st column, where other than that it must have a 1 in the $(\gamma - l)$th bit position, p has the same binary representation as k. Similarly, draw a dashed line to the kth node in the lth column from the qth node in the $(l-1)$st column, where other than the fact that it must have a 0 in the $(\gamma - l)$th bit position, q has the same binary representation as k.

In the tree graph as constructed above the solid lines indicate multiplication, the dashed lines indicate addition, and the number in each node indicates the power nk of W^{nk}.

We are now ready to use the tree graph to find the matrices $[W^{nk}]_p$, $p = 1, 2, \ldots, \gamma$. First consider $[W^{nk}]_1$, which transforms the vector $[g_0(k)]$ into $[g_1(k)]$. Using the tree graph of Fig. 7.6 as an example, we see that $g_1(00)$ is obtained by multiplying $g_0(10)$ by $W^0 = e^{-j2(0)/N}$ (where the power $nk = 0$ is the number in the 00th node of the first column) and adding $g_0(00)$:

$$g_1(00) = g_0(00) + W^0 g_0(10)$$

Similarly, we find that

$$g_1(01) = g_0(01) + W^0 g_0(11)$$
$$g_1(10) = g_0(00) + W^2 g_0(10)$$

and

$$g_1(11) = g_0(01) + W^2 g_0(11)$$

These equations may be written in matrix form as

$$(7.51a)\quad [g_1(k)] = \begin{bmatrix} 1 & 0 & W^0 & 0 \\ 0 & 1 & 0 & W^0 \\ 1 & 0 & W^2 & 0 \\ 0 & 1 & 0 & W^2 \end{bmatrix} [g_0(k)]$$

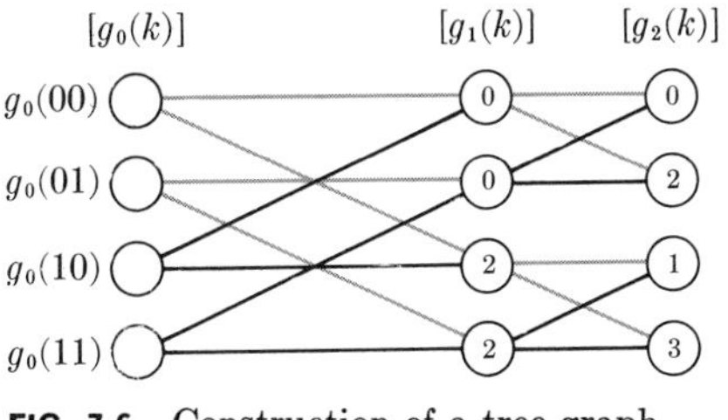

FIG. 7.6 Construction of a tree graph.

so that

$$[W^{nk}]_1 = \begin{bmatrix} 1 & 0 & W^0 & 0 \\ 0 & 1 & 0 & W^0 \\ 1 & 0 & W^2 & 0 \\ 0 & 1 & 0 & W^2 \end{bmatrix}$$

The matrix form is misleading, because from the equations that preceded it, we can see that only four complex multiplications and additions are indicated, even if we should include in our count multiplication by $W^0 = 1$.

Using the tree graph of Fig. 7.6, we also find that

$$(7.51b)\quad [g_2(k)] = \begin{bmatrix} 1 & W^0 & 0 & 0 \\ 1 & W^2 & 0 & 0 \\ 0 & 0 & 1 & W^1 \\ 0 & 0 & 1 & W^3 \end{bmatrix} [g_1(k)]$$

Again, note that only four complex multiplications and additions are necessary and

$$[W^{nk}]_2 = \begin{bmatrix} 1 & W^0 & 0 & 0 \\ 1 & W^2 & 0 & 0 \\ 0 & 0 & 1 & W^1 \\ 0 & 0 & 1 & W^3 \end{bmatrix}$$

The vector $[G(n)]$ is obtained from $[g_\gamma(k)]$ by reversing the order of the bits representing k, that is, for this example

$$\begin{bmatrix} G(0) \\ G(1) \\ G(2) \\ G(3) \end{bmatrix} = \begin{bmatrix} g_2(00) \\ g_2(10) \\ g_2(01) \\ g_2(11) \end{bmatrix} = \begin{bmatrix} g_2(0) \\ g_2(2) \\ g_2(1) \\ g_2(3) \end{bmatrix}$$

To see that the proper results have been obtained, we combine (7.51a) and (7.51b) to obtain

$$[g_2(k)] = [W^{nk}]_2[W^{nk}]_1[g_0(k)]$$

$$= \begin{bmatrix} 1 & W^0 & 0 & 0 \\ 1 & W^2 & 0 & 0 \\ 0 & 0 & 1 & W^1 \\ 0 & 0 & 1 & W^3 \end{bmatrix} \begin{bmatrix} 1 & 0 & W^0 & 0 \\ 0 & 1 & 0 & W^0 \\ 1 & 0 & W^2 & 0 \\ 0 & 1 & 0 & W^2 \end{bmatrix} [g_0(k)]$$

or

$$\begin{bmatrix} g_2(0) \\ g_2(1) \\ g_2(2) \\ g_2(3) \end{bmatrix} = \begin{bmatrix} 1 & 1 & 1 & 1 \\ 1 & W^2 & 1 & W^2 \\ 1 & W^1 & W^2 & W^3 \\ 1 & W^3 & W^2 & W^1 \end{bmatrix} \begin{bmatrix} g(0) \\ g(1) \\ g(2) \\ g(3) \end{bmatrix}$$

$$(7.52) \quad \begin{bmatrix} G(0) \\ G(1) \\ G(2) \\ G(3) \end{bmatrix} = \begin{bmatrix} 1 & 1 & 1 & 1 \\ 1 & W^1 & W^2 & W^3 \\ 1 & W^2 & 1 & W^2 \\ 1 & W^3 & W^2 & W^1 \end{bmatrix} \begin{bmatrix} g(0) \\ g(1) \\ g(2) \\ g(3) \end{bmatrix}$$

where in addition to interchanging the second and third rows of the square matrix, we have used the relations $W^0 = 1$ and $W^5 = W^2$. Observe that (7.52) and (7.48) agree, but that it was only necessary to perform $N \log_2 N = N\gamma = 8$ complex multiplications and additions with the Cooley-Tukey algorithm, whereas the original equation (7.48) indicated $N^2 = 16$ such operations. The computational saving is

$$\frac{\log_2 N}{N} = \frac{\gamma}{N} = \frac{1}{2}$$

in this instance; for large values of N it becomes significantly greater.

7.5 NUMERICAL INTEGRATION

In system analysis, we frequently encounter the standard-form differential-state equation

$$(7.53) \quad \dot{\mathbf{x}}(t) = \mathbf{f}(\mathbf{x}(t),\mathbf{u}(t),t)$$

For the particular case of linear systems, this state equation takes the linear form

$$(7.54) \quad \dot{\mathbf{x}}(t) = \mathbf{A}(t)\mathbf{x}(t) + \mathbf{B}(t)\mathbf{u}(t)$$

In general we may only obtain an explicit solution to this equation for a specified input function u. To solve the differential-state equation numerically, we first integrate both sides to obtain the implicit formula

$$(7.55) \quad \mathbf{x}(t) - \mathbf{x}(t_0) = \int_{t_0}^{t} \mathbf{f}(\mathbf{x}(\tau),\mathbf{u}(\tau),\tau)\, d\tau$$

or

$$(7.56) \quad \mathbf{x}(t) - \mathbf{x}(t_0) = \int_{t_0} [\mathbf{A}(\tau)\mathbf{x}(\tau) + \mathbf{B}(\tau)\mathbf{u}(\tau)]\, d\tau$$

for the linear case. These expressions are termed *implicit,* because the solution for $\mathbf{x}(t)$ is in terms of itself. We introduce the topic of numerical integration in terms of the notationally convenient scalar expression

$$(7.57) \quad h(t) = \int_0^\tau g(\tau)\, d\tau$$

since the vector case is essentially no different. In this section, we will study various techniques for numerical evaluation of (7.57). We will find the z-transform methods of Chap. 6 useful in this study. (Whereas we have taken the initial time t_0 in (7.57) to be zero, the results are easily modified to accommodate arbitrary starting times.)

We first rewrite (7.57) as

$$(7.58) \quad h(t) = \sum_{k=0}^{N-1} \int_{k\Delta t}^{(k+1)\,\Delta t} g(\tau)\, d\tau$$

where Δt is chosen so that $N = t/\Delta t$ is an integer. In other words, we consider the integral of $g(\tau)$ over the interval $0 \le \tau \le t$ to be a sum of integrals over the small intervals $k\,\Delta t \le \tau \le (k+1)\,\Delta t$ for $k = 0, 1, 2, \ldots,$ $N - 1$. The continuous-time function $g(\tau)$ is representable in a digital computer only at a finite set of sample points, which we naturally assume to be taken at the times $0, \Delta t, 2\Delta t, \ldots, N\,\Delta t$, that is, we only have available the values $g(k\,\Delta t)$, $k = 0, 1, 2, \ldots, N$.

Now, let $f(\tau)$ be a function equal to $g(\tau)$ at the sample points,

$$f(k\,\Delta t) = g(k\,\Delta t) \qquad (k = 0, 1, 2, \ldots, N)$$

but has some other specified form between the sample points. For example, if $g(\tau)$ is the function shown in Fig. 7.7*a*, and if $f(\tau)$ is assumed to be constant between sample points, then $f(\tau)$ may be the piecewise-constant function shown in Fig. 7.7*c*.

The integral of the curve $g(\tau)$ of Fig. 7.7*a* over the interval $0 \le \tau \le t$ is the area under the curve. This area is approximated by the area of the rectangles shown in Fig. 7.7*b*, but this area is equal to that under the piecewise-constant curve of Fig. 7.7*c*. Hence, we approximate the integral of $g(\tau)$ by the easily evaluated integral of the approximating function $f(\tau)$. The approximation improves, of course, as the sampling interval Δt is decreased in size. From (7.58) we have

$$(7.59) \quad h(t) = \sum_{k=0}^{N-1} \int_{k\,\Delta t}^{(k+1)\,\Delta t} g(\tau)\, d\tau = \sum_{0=k}^{N-1} \int_{k\,\Delta t}^{(k+1)\,\Delta t} f(\tau)\, d\tau$$
$$= \sum_{k=0}^{N-1} f(k\,\Delta t)\,\Delta t$$

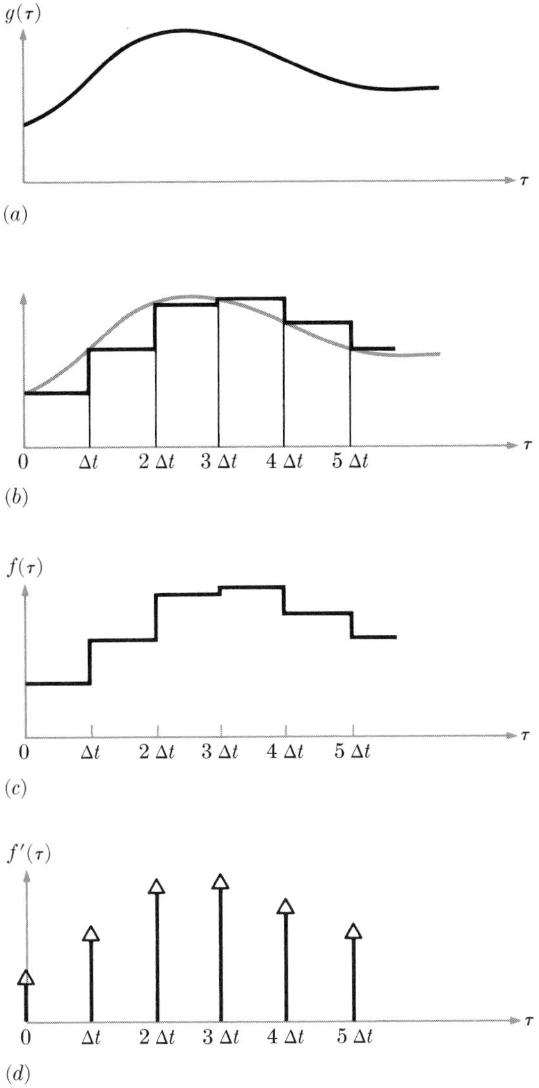

FIG. 7.7 (*a*) The area under a curve $g(\tau)$ is approximated by (*b*) the area under rectangles. (*c*) $f(\tau)$ is a piecewise constant approximation to $g(\tau)$. (*d*) The derivative of $f(\tau)$.

since $f(\tau) = f(k\ \Delta t)$ for $k\ \Delta t \leq \tau \leq (k+1)\ \Delta t$. Now, since $t = N\ \Delta t$

$$\begin{aligned} h(N\ \Delta t) &\simeq \sum_{k=0}^{N-1} f(k\ \Delta t)\ \Delta t \\ &= \sum_{k=0}^{N-2} f(k\ \Delta t)\ \Delta t + f((N-1)\ \Delta t)\ \Delta t \\ &= h((N-1)\ \Delta t) + f((N-1)\ \Delta t)\ \Delta t \end{aligned}$$

which may also be written as

(7.60) $h(N\ \Delta t) = h((N-1)\ \Delta t) + g((N-1)\ \Delta t)\ \Delta t$

because $f(\tau)$ and $g(\tau)$ are equal at the sample points. The *recursion* relation (7.60) is a simple scheme for numerical integration; it is often referred to as rectangular integration or the *forward Euler* method.

(7.61) Example
Consider the integral

$$h(t) = \int_0^t \tau\, d\tau = \frac{t^2}{2}$$

With the integration scheme (7.60) we have

(7.62) $\hat{h}(N\ \Delta t) = \hat{h}((N-1)\ \Delta t) + (N-1)(\Delta t)^2$

where we have employed $\hat{h}$ to distinguish the numerical-integration approximation from the exact solution $h(t) = t^2/2$. Upon the evaluation of (7.62) for $\Delta t = 0.1$ and $\hat{h}(0) = 0$, we have the results of Table 7.1. For the time interval under consideration, the results are reasonable. ▮

TABLE 7.1

N	$N\ \Delta t$	$\hat{h}(N\ \Delta t)$	$\frac{t^2}{2}$	*Error (magnitude)*
0	0.0	0.0	0.0	0.0
1	0.1	0.0	0.005	0.005
2	0.2	0.01	0.020	0.010
3	0.3	0.03	0.045	0.015
4	0.4	0.07	0.080	0.010
5	0.5	0.11	0.125	0.015
6	0.6	0.17	0.180	0.010
7	0.7	0.24	0.245	0.005
8	0.8	0.32	0.320	0.000
9	0.9	0.41	0.405	0.005
10	1.0	0.51	0.500	0.010

The following notational scheme is now introduced for convenience

$$k \equiv k\ \Delta t$$

and

$$h_k \equiv h(k\ \Delta t)$$

If an initial time t_0 other than 0 is assumed then

$$k \equiv t_0 + k\,\Delta t$$

and

$$h_k \equiv h(t_0 + k\,\Delta t)$$

Rewriting (7.60) in terms of this notation yields

$$h_N = h_{N-1} + g_{N-1}\,\Delta t \qquad (N = 1, 2, \ldots)$$

or, more conventionally as

$$h_{k+1} = h_k + g_k\,\Delta t \qquad (k = 0, 1, \ldots) \tag{7.63}$$

A physical interpretation of the forward Euler method can be made if we first rewrite (7.57) as a differential equation:

$$\dot{h}(t) = g(t)$$

From (7.63) we have

$$g_k = \frac{1}{\Delta t}\,[h_{k+1} - h_k]$$

In other words, we are using the following approximation for the derivative:

$$\dot{h}(t) \simeq \frac{1}{\Delta t}\,[h_{k+1} - h_k]$$

Therefore, essentially the forward Euler method approximates the slope of the computed solution with that of the actual solution at each time point as illustrated in Fig. 7.8.

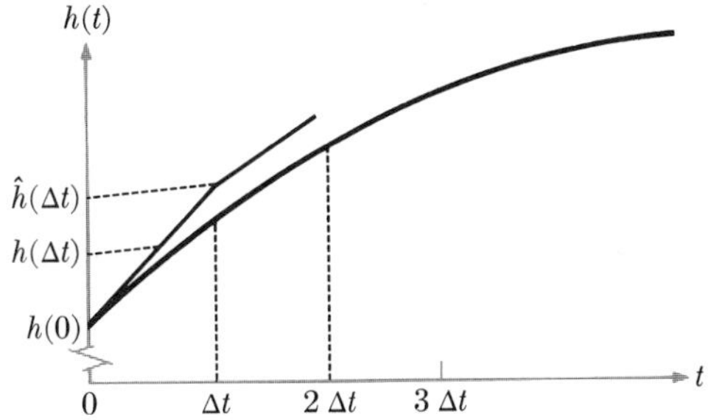

FIG. 7.8 Physical interpretation of the forward Euler method; at each approximate solution point, the extrapolation to the next point is linearly based on an approximation to the slope of the actual solution at that point.

We are really interested in the solution of differential-state equation (7.53) or its integrated version (7.55). Application of the forward Euler method (7.63) to this vector equation yields the numerical solution

$$(7.64)\quad \mathbf{x}_{k+1} = \mathbf{x}_k + \mathbf{f}(\mathbf{x}_k,\mathbf{u}_k,k)\,\Delta t$$

or for the linear case

$$(7.65)\quad \mathbf{x}_{k+1} = (\mathbf{1} + \Delta t\,\mathbf{A}_k)\mathbf{x}_k + \mathbf{B}_k\mathbf{u}_k$$

Due to the approximations involved, there will be an inherent error in any numerical integration scheme. Let us investigate the error which arises when the forward Euler method is used to solve the linear, time-invariant, homogeneous-state equation

$$\dot{\mathbf{x}}(t) = \mathbf{A}\mathbf{x}(t)$$

The exact solution for initial time $t = 0$ and initial condition $\mathbf{x}_0$ is

$$\mathbf{x}(t) = e^{\mathbf{A}t}\mathbf{x}_0$$

whereas the computed solution from (7.63) is

$$\hat{\mathbf{x}}_{N+1} = (\mathbf{1} + \Delta t\,\mathbf{A})\hat{\mathbf{x}}_N \qquad (N = 0, 1, \ldots)$$

but

$$\hat{\mathbf{x}}_N = (\mathbf{1} + \Delta t\,\mathbf{A})\mathbf{x}_{N-1} = (\mathbf{1} + \Delta t\,\mathbf{A})^2\mathbf{x}_{N-2}$$

and so forth, so that

$$\hat{\mathbf{x}}_N = (\mathbf{1} + \Delta t\,\mathbf{A})^N\mathbf{x}_0 \qquad (N = 0, 1, 2, \ldots)$$

The error between the exact and computed solutions is

$$\begin{aligned}\boldsymbol{\varepsilon}(N) &\equiv \mathbf{x}_N - \hat{\mathbf{x}}_N \\ &= e^{N\,\Delta t\,\mathbf{A}} - (\mathbf{1} + \Delta t\,\mathbf{A})^N\end{aligned}$$

In order to proceed with as little mathematical complication as possible, assume that the $n \times n$ matrix $\mathbf{A}$ has the n distinct eigenvalues $\lambda_1, \lambda_2, \ldots, \lambda_n$, and $\mathbf{S}$ is a modal matrix for $\mathbf{A}$ so that

$$\boldsymbol{\Lambda} = \operatorname{diag}(\lambda_1,\lambda_2, \ldots ,\lambda_n) = \mathbf{S}^{-1}\mathbf{A}\mathbf{S}$$

Then the error can be written as

$$\boldsymbol{\varepsilon}(N) = \mathbf{S}[e^{N\,\Delta t\,\boldsymbol{\Lambda}} - (\mathbf{1} + \Delta t\,\boldsymbol{\Lambda})^N]\mathbf{S}^{-1}$$

The matrix

$$\hat{\boldsymbol{\varepsilon}}(N) = e^{N\,\Delta t\,\boldsymbol{\Lambda}} - (\mathbf{1} + \Delta t\,\boldsymbol{\Lambda})^N$$

is diagonal and it is convenient to study the behavior of the error as $N \rightarrow \infty$ in terms of the n scalar expressions

$$\epsilon_p(N) = e^{N\,\Delta t\,\lambda_p} - (1 + \Delta t\,\lambda_p)^N \qquad (p = 1, 2, \ldots, n)$$

Certainly, what we would like is

$$\lim_{N \to \infty} \epsilon_p(N) = 0 \qquad (p = 1, 2, \ldots, n)$$

i.e., zero asymptotic error. Either we must have

$$e^{\Delta t \lambda_p} = (1 + \Delta t \, \lambda_p)$$

which is unlikely (particularly for complex eigenvalues, and certainly not simultaneously for all n distinct λ_p), or

$$\lim_{N \to \infty} [e^{N \Delta t \lambda_p}] = 0$$

$$\lim_{N \to \infty} [(1 + \Delta t \, \lambda_p)^N] = 0 \qquad (p = 1, 2, \ldots, n)$$

The first condition imposes the convergence criterion

$$|e^{\Delta t \lambda_p}| < 1$$

or

$$\operatorname{Re} \{\lambda_p\} < 0 \qquad (p = 1, 2, \ldots, n)$$

on the eigenvalues; that is, the equilibrium state $\mathbf{x} = 0$ must be asymptotically stable. The second condition imposes the convergence criterion

$$|1 + \Delta t \, \lambda_p| < 1$$

or

$$0 < \Delta t < -\frac{2 \operatorname{Re} \{\lambda_p\}}{|\lambda_p|^2} \qquad (p = 1, 2, \ldots, n)$$

that is, we must restrict the step size to

$$\Delta t < \min_{p = 1, 2, \ldots, n} \left[\frac{-2 \operatorname{Re} \{\lambda_p\}}{|\lambda_p|^2} \right]$$

Observe that although the error may approach zero as $N \to \infty$, there may be substantial error for finite N. A natural question to ask is whether or not better results will be obtained if the approximation curve $f(\tau)$ is taken to be other than a piecewise-constant function. For example, instead of the zeroth-order piecewise-constant approximation, we may entertain the possibility of using an mth-order approximation polynomial, $m = 1, 2, \ldots$. A general investigation into this question is most conveniently discussed in terms of z transforms.

Given the samples of the function $f(\tau)$, $f(k \, \Delta t)$, $k = 0, 1, 2, \ldots$, we can consider the sequence $\{f(k \, \Delta t)\}$ to be a discrete-time function which possesses a one-sided z transform. Normally we would write

$$\mathcal{Z}\{f(k \, \Delta t)\} = \sum_{k=0}^{\infty} f(k \, \Delta t) z^{-k}$$

but for the sake of convenience, we abuse notation and write

$$(7.66)\quad \mathcal{Z}[f(t)] = F(z) = \sum_{k=0}^{\infty} f(k\,\Delta t)z^{-k}$$

realizing that by $[f(t)]$ we actually mean the sampled sequence

$$\{f(k\,\Delta t)\} = \{f(0),f(\Delta t),f(2t), \ . \ . \ .\}$$

In Chap. 6 we dropped Δt, assuming it to be equal to 1, but for present purposes, it is necessary to preserve this scale factor. Finally, if $f(t)$ is discontinuous at a sample point, we will choose

$$f(k\,\Delta t) = f(k\,\Delta t^{+}) = \lim_{\varepsilon\to 0} f(k\,\Delta t + \varepsilon)$$

for positive ε.

To begin we wish to find the z transform which corresponds to the rectangular integration scheme (7.63). If

$$H(z) = \mathcal{Z}[h(t)]$$

and

$$G(z) = \mathcal{Z}[g(t)]$$

then from (7.63)

$$H(z) = z^{-1}H(z) + z^{-1}G(z)\,\Delta t$$

since in general if $F(z) = \{f(k\,\Delta t)\}$, then

$$\begin{aligned} z^{-1}F(z) &= \sum_{k=0}^{\infty} z^{-(k+1)}f(k\,\Delta t) \\ &= \sum_{k=0}^{\infty} z^{-k}f((k-1)\,\Delta t) \\ &= \mathcal{Z}\{f((k-1)\,\Delta t)\} \end{aligned}$$

hence

$$(7.67)\quad H(z) = \frac{\Delta t}{z-1}\,G(z)$$

We may think of this relation as describing a discrete-time system with input $G(z)$, output $H(z)$, and transfer function

$$(7.68)\quad T(z) = \frac{\Delta t}{z-1}$$

We observe that the original recursion relation (7.63) is easily recovered from (7.67) by first rewriting (7.68) in terms of powers of z^{-1},

$$T(z) = \frac{z^{-1}\,\Delta t}{1 - z^{-1}}$$

and then multiplying through (7.68) by the denominator,

$$(1 - z^{-1})H(z) = z^{-1}\,\Delta t\, G(z)$$

We note that

$$Z^{-1}[z^{-m}F(z)] = \{f((k - m)\,\Delta t)\} = \{f_{k-m}\}$$

so that we obtain

$$h_k - h_{k-1} = \Delta t\, g_{k-1}$$

which is equivalent to (7.63).

To consider the question posed above—what happens if a higher-order polynomial approximation is used for $f(\tau)$ between sample points—we must first introduce some preliminaries. Consider again the curves shown in Fig. 7.7. Since $f(\tau)$ is a piecewise-constant function with discontinuities only at the sample points $k\,\Delta t$, its derivative is a sequence of impulse functions:

$$\text{(7.69)} \quad \frac{df(\tau)}{d\tau} = \sum_{k=0}^{\infty} a_k \delta(\tau - k\,\Delta t)$$

as shown in Fig. 7.7*d*. The weight of each impulse is given by

$$\text{(7.70)} \quad a_k = f(k\,\Delta t) - f((k - 1)\,\Delta t)$$

i.e., it is the backward difference of $f(\tau)$ at $\tau = k\,\Delta t$. But because $f(\tau)$ and $g(\tau)$ are equal at the sample points, we may write

$$a_k = g(k\,\Delta t) - g((k - 1)\,\Delta t)$$

as well. The sequence of impulses (7.70) does not possess a z transform in the ordinary sense, hence we define the *z form* of $df(\tau)/d\tau$ as

$$\text{(7.71)} \quad Z^*\left[\frac{df(\tau)}{d\tau}\right] = \sum_{k=0}^{\infty} a_k z^{-k}$$

Now, suppose that instead of using a piecewise-constant approximation to $g(\tau)$ between sample points, we choose to use an $(n - 1)$st-order polynomial of the form $\tau^{n-1}/n!$. We let $f_n(\tau)$ denote such an approximation to $g(\tau)$, and we observe that the nth derivative of $f_n(\tau)$ is a piecewise-constant function with discontinuities at the sample points. (Note: The subscript n here is *not* used to denote $n\ \Delta t$.) Designating $f(\tau)$ to be this piecewise-constant function, we can write

$$f(\tau) = \frac{d^n}{d\tau^n}[f_n(\tau)]$$

so that $f_n(\tau)$ is the nth integral of $f(\tau)$. Consequently, the $(n+1)$st derivative of $f_n(\tau)$ is a sequence of delta functions which occur at the sample points $k\ \Delta t$; that is,

$$\frac{d^{n+1}}{d\tau^{n+1}}[f_n(\tau)] = \sum_{k=0}^{\infty} a_k\delta(\tau - k\ \Delta t)$$

or we can think of $f_n(\tau)$ as being the $(n+1)$st integral of the sequence of delta functions:

$$f_n(\tau) = \underbrace{\int^{\tau}\int^{\tau}\cdots\int^{\tau}}_{n+1}\left[\sum_{k=0}^{\infty} a_k\delta(\sigma - k\ \Delta t)\right](d\sigma)^{n+1}$$

The z transform of $f_n(\tau)$ can be found by superposition:

$$\text{(7.72)}\quad \mathcal{Z}[f_n(\tau)] = \sum_{k=0}^{\infty} a_k\mathcal{Z}\left[\int_0^{\tau}\cdots\int_0^{\tau}\delta(\sigma - k\ \Delta t)(d\sigma)^{n+1}\right]$$

$$= \sum_{k=0}^{\infty} a_k\mathcal{Z}\left[\frac{(\tau - k\ \Delta\tau)^n}{n!}\right]$$

$$= \left[\sum_{k=0}^{\infty} a_k z^{-k}\right]\mathcal{Z}\left[\frac{\tau^n}{n!}\right] = \mathcal{Z}^*\left[\frac{df(\tau)}{d\tau}\right]\mathcal{Z}\left[\frac{\tau^n}{n!}\right]$$

Since a_k is the backward difference of $f(\tau)$,

$$\text{(7.73)}\quad \mathcal{Z}^*\left[\frac{df(\tau)}{d\tau}\right] = \sum_{k=0}^{\infty} a_k z^{-k}$$

$$= \sum_{k=0}^{\infty}[f(k\ \Delta t) - f((k-1)\ \Delta t)]z^{-k}$$

$$= F(z)(1 - z^{-1})$$

where $F(z)$ is as defined in (7.66). Hence,

$$\text{(7.74)}\quad \mathcal{Z}[f_n(t)] = \mathcal{Z}\{f_n(k\ \Delta t)\}$$

$$= (1 - z^{-1})\mathcal{Z}\left[\frac{\tau^n}{n!}\right]F(z)$$

Upon again considering (7.58) we have

$$(7.75)\quad h(t) \simeq \sum_{k=0}^{N-1} \int_{k\,\Delta t}^{(k+1)\,\Delta t} f_n(\tau)\,d\tau = \sum_{k=0}^{N-1} [f_{n+1}((k+1)\,\Delta t) - f_{n+1}(k\,\Delta t)]$$

so that

$$h(N\,\Delta t) \simeq h((N-1)\,\Delta t) + f_{n+1}(N\,\Delta t) - f_{n+1}((N-1)\,\Delta t)$$

since $t = N\,\Delta t$. The z transform of this relation is

$$(7.76)\quad H(z) = \mathcal{Z}\left[\frac{\tau^{n+1}}{(n+1)!}\right] F(z)(1 - z^{-1})$$

which follows from (7.74). But $g(\tau)$ and $f_n(\tau)$ must be equal at the sample points,

$$g(k\,\Delta t) = f_n(k\,\Delta t)$$

so that

$$G(z) = \mathcal{Z}\{f_n(k\,\Delta t)\} = \mathcal{Z}\left[\frac{\tau^n}{n!}\right] F(z)$$

and therefore

$$(7.77)\quad F(z) = \frac{G(z)}{\mathcal{Z}[n/n!]}$$

Finally, upon combination of (7.76) and (7.77) we obtain

$$(7.78)\quad H(z) = \frac{\mathcal{Z}\,[\tau^{n+1}/(n+1)!]}{\mathcal{Z}\,[\tau^n/n!]}\,G(z)$$

which we may consider as being descriptive of a discrete-time system with the transfer function

$$(7.79)\quad T(z) = \frac{\mathcal{Z}\,[\tau^{n+1}/(n+1)!]}{\mathcal{Z}\,[\tau^n/n!]}$$

More appropriately, we should term $T(z)$ an *integration operator*.[1] It can

[1] This method for the generation of z-transform integration operators is presented in detail in M. Cuénod and A. E. Durling, "A Discrete Time Approach for System Analysis," Academic, New York, 1969, with specific application to system analysis, and A. E. Durling, "Analog, Digital and Hybrid Computation," Holt, New York (in preparation), with application to simulation and computation.

be shown that

$$\text{(7.80)}\quad \mathcal{Z}\left[\frac{\tau^n}{n!}\right] = \lim_{a\to 0}\left\{\frac{(-1)^n}{n!}\left[\frac{\partial}{\partial a^n}\left(\frac{z}{z - e^{-a\,\Delta t}}\right)\right]\right\} \qquad (n = 0, 1, 2, \ldots)$$

Hence, for $n = 0$ we have

$$\mathcal{Z}[1] = \mathcal{Z}\{1\} = \frac{z}{z-1}$$

and for $n = 1$

$$\mathcal{Z}[\tau] = \mathcal{Z}\{k\,\Delta t\} = \frac{z\,\Delta t}{(z-1)^2}$$

etc. These results coincide with those of Table 5.5 of Chap. 5 when $\Delta t = 1$, as should be expected.

Finally, we are in a position to discuss the integration schemes that result from (7.78) for the various values of n. If $n = 0$, that is, we are approximating $g(\tau)$ with a zeroth-order, or piecewise-constant, curve between the sample points, then

$$\begin{aligned} H(z) &= \frac{\mathcal{Z}[\tau]}{\mathcal{Z}[1]}\,G(z) \\ &= \frac{\Delta t\, z/(z-1)^2}{z/(z-1)}\,G(z) = \frac{\Delta t}{z-1}\,G(z) \end{aligned}$$

which gives the rectangular integration scheme (forward Euler method) we have already discussed, as expected. For $n = 1$, that is, the assumption that there is a first-order curve approximating $g(\tau)$ between sample points, (7.78) becomes

$$\begin{aligned} H(z) &= \frac{\mathcal{Z}[\tau^2/2]}{\mathcal{Z}[\tau]} = \frac{[(\Delta t)^2 z(z+1)]/[2(z-1)^3]}{\Delta t z/(z-1)^2}\,G(z) \\ &= \frac{\Delta t}{2}\,\frac{z+1}{z-1}\,G(z) \end{aligned}$$

To obtain the related recursion relation, we rewrite this expression as

$$H(z) = \frac{\Delta t}{2}\,\frac{1+z^{-1}}{1-z^{-1}}\,G(z)$$

or

$$(1 - z^{-1})H(z) = \frac{\Delta t}{2}\,(1 + z^{-1})G(z)$$

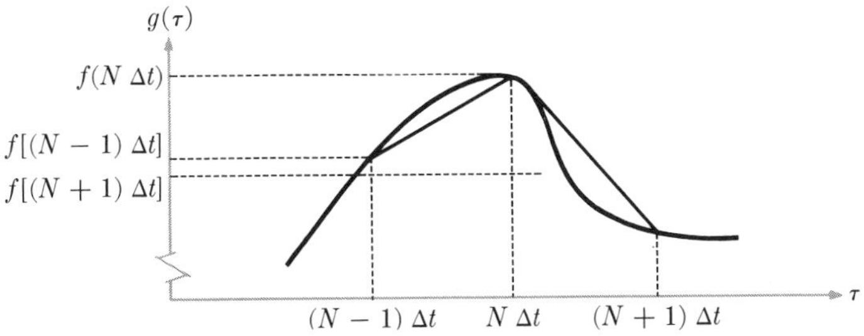

FIG. 7.9 Graphical illustration of trapezoidal rule.

Upon inverse z transformation, we obtain

$$(7.81)\quad h(k\,\Delta t) - h((k-1)\,\Delta t) = \frac{\Delta t}{2}\,[g(k\,\Delta t) + g((k-1)\,\Delta t)]$$

or reverting back to the subscript notation

$$(7.82)\quad h_k - h_{k-1} = \frac{\Delta t}{2}\,[g_k + g_{k-1}]$$

This integration scheme is called the *trapezoidal rule*, because the area under the curve $g(\tau)$ is approximated by the areas under a related set of trapezoids as shown in Fig. 7.9.

(7.83) Example

Consider the integral

$$h(t) = \int_0^t \cos(\tau)\,d\tau = \sin(t)$$

The trapezoidal integration scheme (7.82) approximates $h(t)$ with $\hat{h}(t)$ where

$$\hat{h}_k = \hat{h}_{k-1} + \frac{\Delta t}{2}\,[\cos(k\,\Delta t) + \cos((k-1)\,\Delta t)]$$

In Table 7.2 a comparison of the actual and approximate values of $h(t)$ is made for different values of the step size Δt. Observe that as the step size Δt decreases, the approximation improves. Moreover there is a point beyond which further decreases in Δt produce no significant improvement in the approximation. For example, essentially the same results are obtained for $\Delta t = 0.05$ and $\Delta t = 0.1$. Thus it appears that one method for choosing an appropriate step size is to first choose an arbitrary step size and run through the integration. Then reduce the step size and perform the integration again. If the results re-

TABLE 7.2

t	$h(t)$	$\hat{h}(t)$ $\Delta t = 0.05$	$\Delta t = 0.1$	$\Delta t = 0.5$	$\Delta t = 1$	$\Delta t = 2$
0.5	0.479	0.479	0.479	0.469		
1.0	0.841	0.841	0.840	0.823	0.770	
1.5	0.997	0.997	0.997	0.977		
2.0	0.909	0.909	0.908	0.890	0.832	0.584
2.5	0.598	0.598	0.598	0.586		
3.0	0.141	0.141	0.141	0.138	0.129	
3.5	−0.351	−0.351	−0.350	−0.343		
4.0	−0.757	−0.757	−0.756	−0.741	−0.693	−0.486
4.5	−0.978	−0.977	−0.977	−0.957		
5.0	−0.959	−0.959	−0.958	−0.939	−0.878	
5.5	−0.706	−0.705	−0.705	−0.691		
6.0	−0.279	−0.279	−0.279	−0.274	−0.256	−0.179
6.5	0.215	0.215	0.215	0.210		

main about the same, the step size is adequate, otherwise a further decrease is indicated. ∎

In terms of the differential-state equation (7.53), trapezoidal rule becomes

$$\mathbf{x}_{k+1} = \mathbf{x}_k + \frac{\Delta t}{2}\left[\mathbf{f}(\mathbf{x}_k,\mathbf{u}_k,k) + \mathbf{f}(\mathbf{x}_{k+1}, \mathbf{u}_{k+1}, k+1)\right] \tag{7.84}$$

or for the linear case

$$\mathbf{x}_{k+1} = \left(1 + \mathbf{A}_k\frac{\Delta t}{2}\right)\mathbf{x}_k + \frac{\Delta t}{2}\mathbf{A}_{k+1}\mathbf{x}_{k+1} + \frac{\Delta t}{2}\left[\mathbf{B}_k\mathbf{x}_k + \mathbf{B}_{k+1}\mathbf{x}_{k+1}\right] \tag{7.85}$$

For $n = 2$, that is, with a second-order approximation to $g(t)$ between the sample points, (7.78) becomes

$$\begin{aligned} H(z) &= \frac{\mathcal{Z}[\tau^3/6]}{\mathcal{Z}[\tau^2/2]}G(z) \\ &= \frac{(\Delta t)^4/6[z(z^2+4z+1)]/(z-1)^4}{(\Delta t)^3/2[z(z+1)]/(z-1)^3}G(z) \\ &= \frac{\Delta t}{3}\left(\frac{z^2+4z+1}{z^2-1}\right)G(z) \end{aligned}$$

We can rewrite this expression as

$$H(z) = \frac{\Delta t}{3}\,\frac{1+4z^{-1}+z^{-2}}{1-z^{-2}}\,G(z)$$

so that

$$(1 - z^{-2})H(z) = \frac{\Delta t}{3}(1 + 4z^{-1} + z^{-2})G(z)$$

which indicates the recursion formula

$$h(k\,\Delta t) - h((k-2)\,\Delta t) = \frac{\Delta t}{3}[g(k\,\Delta t) + 4g((k-1)\,\Delta t) + g((k-2)\,\Delta t)]$$

or

$$(7.86)\quad h_k - h_{k-2} = \frac{\Delta t}{3}[g_k + 4g_{k-1} + g_{k-2}]$$

This integration scheme is often called *Simpson's rule,* which simultaneously involves three sample points.

(7.87) Example

Consider the integral

$$h(t) = \int_0^t e^{2\tau}\,d\tau = \tfrac{1}{2}(e^{2t} - 1)$$

Using Simpson's rule (7.86) to approximate $h(t)$ yields

$$\hat{h}_k = \hat{h}_{k-2} + \frac{\Delta t}{3}[e^{2(k\,\Delta t)} + 4e^{2((k-1)\,\Delta t)} + e^{2((k-2)\,\Delta t)}]$$

In Table 7.3 we compare the values of $h(t)$ with $\hat{h}(t)$ for various values of the step size Δt. ▮

We can continue indefinitely considering approximating curves and corresponding integration schemes of arbitrarily high order. The z-transform approach is an excellent means for generating such integration formulas.

An alternative method for generating integration schemes results from consideration of Taylor series expansions. For motivational pur-

TABLE 7.3

t	$h(t)$	$\Delta t = 0.1$	$\Delta t = 0.2$	$\Delta t = 0.5$	$\Delta t = 1$
1.0	3.195	3.195	3.381	3.210	4.130
2.0	26.80	26.80	26.80	26.93	28.39
3.0	201.20	201.20	201.40	202.20	213.90
4.0	1490.00	1490.00	1490.00	1497.00	1578.00

poses consider the homogeneous differential-state equation

$$(7.88)\quad \dot{\mathbf{x}}(t) = \mathbf{A}\mathbf{x}(t) \qquad \mathbf{x}(0) = \mathbf{x}_0$$

the exact solution of which is

$$\mathbf{x}(t) = e^{\mathbf{A}t}\mathbf{x}_0$$

for the initial time $t_0 = 0$. We also know from our earlier studies that for the two times $k\,\Delta t$ and $(k-1)\,\Delta t$

$$\mathbf{x}_k = e^{\mathbf{A}\,\Delta t}\mathbf{x}_{k-1}$$

Moreover, the Taylor series expansion of $e^{\mathbf{A}\,\Delta t}$ is

$$e^{\mathbf{A}\,\Delta t} = \mathbf{1} + \Delta t\,\mathbf{A} + \frac{1}{2}(\Delta t)^2\mathbf{A} + \frac{1}{3!}(\Delta t)^3\mathbf{A}^3 + \cdots$$

so that

$$(7.89)\quad \begin{aligned} \mathbf{x}_k &= (\mathbf{1} + \Delta t\,\mathbf{A} + \tfrac{1}{2}(\Delta t)^2\mathbf{A}^2 + \cdots)\mathbf{x}_{k-1} \\ &= (\mathbf{1} + \Delta t\,\mathbf{A} + \tfrac{1}{2}(\Delta t)^2\mathbf{A}^2 + \cdots)^k\mathbf{x}_0 \end{aligned}$$

Recall that application of the forward Euler method of integration to (7.88) resulted in the equation

$$\hat{\mathbf{x}}_k = (\mathbf{1} + \mathbf{A}\,\Delta t)^k\mathbf{x}_0$$

where the circumflex over $\mathbf{x}_k$ emphasizes that it is an approximate solution. Essentially this method approximates $e^{\mathbf{A}t}$ with the first two terms of its Taylor series. Application of trapezoidal rule to (7.88) yields

$$\hat{\mathbf{x}}_k - \hat{\mathbf{x}}_{k-1} = \frac{\Delta t}{2}\mathbf{A}(\hat{\mathbf{x}}_k + \hat{\mathbf{x}}_{k-1})$$

but $\hat{\mathbf{x}}_k$, an unknown, appears on both sides of this equation. We revert to forward Euler and employ

$$\mathbf{x}_k = (\mathbf{1} + \Delta t\,\mathbf{A})\mathbf{x}_{k-1}$$

so that we finally have

$$\hat{\mathbf{x}}_k = (\mathbf{1} + \Delta t\,\mathbf{A} + \tfrac{1}{2}(\Delta t)^2\mathbf{A}^2)\hat{\mathbf{x}}_{k-1}$$

or

$$\hat{\mathbf{x}}_k = (\mathbf{1} + \Delta t\,\mathbf{A} + \tfrac{1}{2}(\Delta t)^2\mathbf{A}^2)^k\mathbf{x}_0$$

Comparing this equation with (7.89), we see that trapezoidal rule agrees with the exact solution to order $(\Delta t)^2$.

The fact that the forward Euler method and trapezoidal rule have led to numerical-integration formulas which agree with the leading terms of the Taylor series expansion for $e^{\mathbf{A}t}$ for the special case of the homogeneous, linear, time-invariant, differential-state equation (7.88) may lead us to infer a Taylor series approach to the numerical integration of the more general differential-state equation

$$\dot{\mathbf{x}}(t) = \mathbf{f}(\mathbf{x}(t),\mathbf{u}(t),t) \qquad \mathbf{x}(t_0) = \mathbf{x}_0$$

In particular, we recognize that from a Taylor series expansion

$$\mathbf{x}_{k+1} = \mathbf{x}_k + \Delta t\, \dot{\mathbf{x}}_k + \frac{1}{2}(\Delta t)^2\, \ddot{\mathbf{x}}_k + \frac{1}{3!}(\Delta t)^3\, \dddot{\mathbf{x}}_k + \cdots$$

provided that the derivatives exist. Reverting to the given equation we find that

$$\dot{\mathbf{x}}_k = \mathbf{f}(\mathbf{x}_k,\mathbf{u}_k,k)$$

$$\ddot{\mathbf{x}}_k = \frac{\partial \mathbf{f}}{\partial \mathbf{x}_k}\bigg|\, \dot{\mathbf{x}}_k + \frac{\partial \mathbf{f}}{\partial \mathbf{u}_k}\bigg|\, \dot{\mathbf{u}}_k + \frac{\partial \mathbf{f}}{\partial t_k}\bigg|$$

and so forth, where $\partial\mathbf{f}/\partial\mathbf{x}$ and $\partial\mathbf{f}/\partial\mathbf{u}$ are the appropriate jacobian matrices as described in Chap. 4. Thus we have the following formulas for the Taylor series method of order p:

$$\mathbf{x}_0 \equiv \mathbf{x}(t_0)$$

$$\mathbf{x}_k^{(l)} \equiv \frac{d^{l-1}}{dt^{l-1}} f(\mathbf{x}(t),\mathbf{u}(t),t)\bigg|_{t_0+k\,\Delta t} \qquad (l = 1, 2, \ldots, p)$$

and

$$\mathbf{x}_{k+1} = \mathbf{x}_k + \Delta t\, \mathbf{x}_k^{(1)} + \frac{1}{2}(\Delta t)^2\mathbf{x}_k^{(2)} + \cdots \frac{1}{p!}(\Delta t)^p\mathbf{x}_k^{(p)}$$

provided that the appropriate derivatives exist. In application of this method, successive substitutions eliminate the necessity of finding time derivatives of $\mathbf{x}(t)$, and we may assume $\mathbf{u}(t)$ to be given a priori so that reasonably accurate numerical-differentiation techniques are applicable. Given the homogeneous, linear, time-invariant, differential-state equation (7.78), the Taylor series integration method of order p results in the expected algorithm:

$$\mathbf{x}_k = \left(\mathbf{1} + \Delta t\, \mathbf{A} + \frac{1}{2}(\Delta t)^2\mathbf{A}^2 + \frac{1}{3!}(\Delta t)^3\mathbf{A}^3 + \cdots \frac{1}{p}(\Delta t)^p\mathbf{A}^p\right)^k \mathbf{x}_0$$

Obviously, accuracy increases with order. Let us now attempt to consider the application of the Taylor series of order 2 to the linear, time-invariant, differential-state equation

$$\dot{\mathbf{x}}(t) = \mathbf{A}\mathbf{x}(t) + \mathbf{B}\mathbf{u}(t) \qquad \mathbf{x}(t_0) = \mathbf{x}_0$$

We have

$$\mathbf{x}_k^{(1)} = \mathbf{A}\mathbf{x}_k + \mathbf{B}\mathbf{u}_k$$

and

$$\mathbf{x}_k^{(2)} = \mathbf{A}\mathbf{x}_k^{(1)} + \mathbf{B}\dot{\mathbf{u}}(t_0 + k\,\Delta t) = \mathbf{A}^2\mathbf{x}_k + \mathbf{A}\mathbf{B}\mathbf{u}_k + \mathbf{B}\dot{\mathbf{u}}(t_0 + k\,\Delta t)$$

and the major impediment becomes that of approximating $\dot{\mathbf{u}}$. If $\mathbf{u}$ is sufficiently smooth and the step size is sufficiently small, we may take

$$\dot{\mathbf{u}}(t_0 + k\,\Delta t) \simeq \frac{1}{\Delta t}\,[\mathbf{u}(t_0 + (k+1)\,\Delta t) - \mathbf{u}(t_0 - k\,\Delta t)]$$

Hence the explicit integration formula

$$\begin{aligned}\mathbf{x}_{k+1} &= \mathbf{x}_k + \Delta t\,(\mathbf{A}\mathbf{x}_k + \mathbf{B}\mathbf{u}_k) \\ &\qquad + \frac{1}{2}(\Delta t)^2\left[\mathbf{A}^2\mathbf{x}_k + \mathbf{A}\mathbf{B}\mathbf{u}_k + \frac{1}{\Delta t}\mathbf{B}(\mathbf{u}_{k+1} - \mathbf{u}_k)\right] \\ &= \mathbf{x}_k + \Delta t\,[\mathbf{A}\mathbf{x}_k + \tfrac{1}{2}\mathbf{B}(\mathbf{u}_k + \mathbf{u}_{k+1})] + \tfrac{1}{2}(\Delta t)^2(\mathbf{A}^2\mathbf{x}_k + \mathbf{A}\mathbf{B}\mathbf{u}_k)\end{aligned}$$

For the nonhomogeneous case, there are better methods than those based on Taylor series for the integration of linear, time-invariant, differential-state equations of the form

$$\dot{\mathbf{x}}(t) = \mathbf{A}\mathbf{x}(t) + \mathbf{B}\mathbf{u}(t) \qquad \mathbf{x}(t_0) = \mathbf{x}_0$$

The exact solution is given by

$$\mathbf{x}(t) = e^{\mathbf{A}(t-t_0)}\mathbf{x}_0 + e^{\mathbf{A}t}\int_{t_0}^{t} e^{-\mathbf{A}\tau}\mathbf{B}\mathbf{u}(\tau)\,d\tau$$

or for one time increment by

$$\mathbf{x}_{k+1} = e^{\mathbf{A}\,\Delta t}\mathbf{x}_k + e^{\mathbf{A}(t_0+(k+1)\,\Delta t)}\int_{t_0+k\,\Delta t}^{t_0+(k+1)\,\Delta t} e^{-\mathbf{A}\tau}\mathbf{B}\mathbf{u}(\tau)\,d\tau$$

Applying Simpson's rule, to the integral on the right-hand side, we obtain the explicit integration formula

$$\mathbf{x}_{k+1} = e^{\mathbf{A}\,\Delta t}\left(\mathbf{x}_k + \frac{\Delta t}{6}\mathbf{B}\mathbf{u}_k\right) + \frac{2\Delta t}{3}e^{\mathbf{A}\frac{\Delta t}{2}}\mathbf{B}\mathbf{u}_{k+\frac{1}{2}} + \frac{\Delta t}{2}\mathbf{B}\mathbf{u}_{k+1}$$

where we have introduced the convenient notation

$$\mathbf{u}_{k+\frac{1}{2}} \equiv \mathbf{u}(t_0 + (k + \tfrac{1}{2})\,\Delta t)$$

This formula together with its error properties and limitations was introduced by Liou and discussed extensively by Liou and Whitney in a series of papers.[1] Liou has advocated the evaluation of $\exp \mathbf{A}(\Delta t/2)$ by power

[1] M. L. Liou, A Numerical Solution of Linear, Time-invariant Systems, *Proc. Third Ann. Allerton Conf. Circuit and System Theory*, pp. 669–676, University of Illinois, Urbana, Ill., October, 1965; M. L. Liou, A Novel Method for Evaluating Transient Response, *Proc. IEEE*, vol. 54, no. 1, pp. 20–23, 1966; D. E. Whitney and M. L. Liou, Propagated Error Bounds for Numerical Solution of Transient Response, *Proc. IEEE*, vol. 54, no. 8, pp. 1084–1085, 1966; D. E. Whitney, Propagation and Control of Roundoff Error in the Matrix Exponential Method, *Proc. IEEE*, vol. 54, no. 10, pp. 1483–1484, 1966; and W. Everling and M. L. Liou, On the Evaluation of e^{At} by Power Series, *Proc. IEEE*, vol. 55, no. 3, p. 413, 1967.

series (that is, by the Taylor series method);

$$e^{\mathbf{A}\frac{\Delta t}{2}} \simeq \mathbf{1} + \frac{\Delta t}{2}\mathbf{A} + \frac{1}{2}\left(\frac{\Delta t}{2}\right)^2 \mathbf{A}^2 + \cdots$$

and he gives an error bound for this approach as well. We discuss an improvement on this technique in the next section.

Runge-Kutta methods may be said to be based on Taylor series in the following sense. Suppose that we have an explicit integration formula of the form

$$\mathbf{x}_{k+1} = \mathbf{x}_k + \Delta t\, \boldsymbol{\phi}(\mathbf{x}_k, t_k; \Delta t)$$

where we have indicated implicitly the dependence on $\mathbf{u}$ in terms of t_k, k, and Δt. A Runge-Kutta method of order p is one for which $\boldsymbol{\phi}$ does not involve derivatives of $\mathbf{x}$, but differs from the Taylor series expansion formula only by terms of order $(\Delta t)^{p+1}$ (and higher). It is easy to show that the forward Euler method is a Runge-Kutta method of order 1 and that the trapezoidal method is a Runge-Kutta method of order 2 (the verification of this statement is left to the reader). Usually the designation *Runge-Kutta* indicates the most commonly employed fourth-order Runge-Kutta algorithm:

$$\mathbf{x}_0 = \mathbf{x}(t_0)$$

and

$$\mathbf{x}_{k+1} = \mathbf{x}_k + \Delta t\, \boldsymbol{\phi}(\mathbf{x}_k, t_k; \Delta t)$$

where

$$\boldsymbol{\phi}(\mathbf{x}_k, t_k, \Delta t) \equiv \tfrac{1}{6}(\boldsymbol{\alpha}_k + 2\boldsymbol{\beta}_k + 2\boldsymbol{\gamma}_k + \boldsymbol{\delta}_k)$$

and

$$\boldsymbol{\alpha}_k \equiv \mathbf{f}(\mathbf{x}_k, \mathbf{u}_k, t_k)$$

$$\boldsymbol{\beta}_k \equiv \mathbf{f}\left(\mathbf{x}_k + \frac{\Delta t}{2}\alpha_k,\ \mathbf{u}_{k+1/2} t_{k+\frac{1}{2}}\right)$$

$$\boldsymbol{\gamma}_k \equiv \mathbf{f}\left(\mathbf{x}_k + \frac{\Delta t}{2}\boldsymbol{\beta}_k,\ \mathbf{u}_{k+1/2},\ t_{k+\frac{1}{2}}\right)$$

and

$$\boldsymbol{\delta}_k \equiv \mathbf{f}(\mathbf{x}_k + \Delta t\, \boldsymbol{\gamma}_k,\ \mathbf{u}_{k+1},\ t_{k+1})$$

where we have again employed the convenient notation

$$t_{k+1/2} \equiv t_0(k + \tfrac{1}{2})\, \Delta t$$

and

$$u_{k+1/2} \equiv u(t_{k+\frac{1}{2}})$$

The derivation of these formulas is too complicated to be presented here;[1]

[1] See, for example, P. Henrici, "Discrete Variable Methods 'n Ordinary Differential Equations," Wiley, New York, 1962.

it suffices to say that this fourth-order Runge-Kutta method is relatively accurate, but also relatively slow. We may, of course, obtain a more detailed integration formula upon application of the above fourth-order Runge-Kutta formulas to linear, time-invariant, differential-state equations of the form

$$\dot{\mathbf{x}}(t) = \mathbf{A}\mathbf{x}(t) + \mathbf{B}\mathbf{u}(t) \qquad \mathbf{x}(t_0) = \mathbf{x}_0$$

First we have

$$\begin{aligned}
\boldsymbol{\alpha}_k &= \mathbf{A}\mathbf{x}_k + \mathbf{B}\mathbf{u}_k \\
\boldsymbol{\beta}_k &= \mathbf{A}\left[\mathbf{x}_k + \frac{\Delta t}{2}(\mathbf{A}\mathbf{x}_k + \mathbf{B}\mathbf{u}_k)\right] + \mathbf{B}\mathbf{u}_{k+\frac{1}{2}} \\
&= \left(\mathbf{A} + \frac{\Delta t}{2}\mathbf{A}^2\right)\mathbf{x}_k + \frac{\Delta t}{2}\mathbf{A}\mathbf{B}\mathbf{u}_k + \mathbf{B}\mathbf{u}_{k+\frac{1}{2}} \\
\boldsymbol{\gamma}_k &= \mathbf{A}\left\{\mathbf{x}_k + \frac{\Delta t}{2}\left[\left(\mathbf{A} + \frac{\Delta t}{2}\mathbf{A}^2\right)\mathbf{x}_k + \frac{\Delta t}{2}\mathbf{A}\mathbf{B}\mathbf{u}_k + \mathbf{B}\mathbf{u}_{k+\frac{1}{2}}\right]\right\} + \mathbf{B}\mathbf{u}_{k+\frac{1}{2}} \\
&= \left(\mathbf{A} + \frac{\Delta t}{2}\mathbf{A}^2 + \frac{(\Delta t)^2}{4}\mathbf{A}^3\right)\mathbf{x}_k + \frac{(\Delta t)^2}{4}\mathbf{A}^2\mathbf{B}\mathbf{u}_k \\
&\qquad + \left(\frac{\Delta t}{2}\mathbf{A}\mathbf{B} + \mathbf{B}\right)\mathbf{u}_{k+\frac{1}{2}}
\end{aligned}$$

and

$$\begin{aligned}
\boldsymbol{\delta}_k &= \mathbf{A}\left\{\mathbf{x}_k + \Delta t\left[\left(\mathbf{A} + \frac{\Delta t}{2}\mathbf{A}^2 + \frac{(\Delta t)^2}{4}\mathbf{A}^3\right)\mathbf{x}_k + \frac{\Delta t}{4}\mathbf{A}^2\mathbf{B}\mathbf{u}_k \right.\right. \\
&\qquad \left.\left. + \left(\frac{\Delta t}{2}\mathbf{A}\mathbf{B} + \mathbf{B}\right)\mathbf{u}_{k+1}\right]\right\} + \mathbf{B}\mathbf{u}_{k+1} \\
&= \left(\mathbf{A} + \Delta t\,\mathbf{A}^2 + \frac{(\Delta t)^2}{2}\mathbf{A}^3 + \frac{(\Delta t)^4}{4}\mathbf{A}^4\right)\mathbf{x}_k + \frac{\Delta t}{4}\mathbf{A}^3\mathbf{B}\mathbf{u}_k \\
&\qquad + \left(\frac{(\Delta t)^2}{2}\mathbf{A}^2\mathbf{B} + \Delta t\,\mathbf{A}\mathbf{B})\right)\mathbf{u}_{k+\frac{1}{2}} + \mathbf{B}\mathbf{u}_{k+1}
\end{aligned}$$

hence,

$$\begin{aligned}
\mathbf{x}_{k+1} &= \mathbf{x}_k + \frac{\Delta t}{6}(\boldsymbol{\alpha}_k + 2\boldsymbol{\beta}_k + 2\boldsymbol{\gamma}_k + \boldsymbol{\delta}_k) \\
&= (1 + \Delta t\,\mathbf{A} + \tfrac{1}{2}(\Delta t)^2\mathbf{A}^2 + \tfrac{1}{6}(\Delta t)^3\mathbf{A}^3 + \tfrac{1}{24}(\Delta t)^4\mathbf{A}^4)x_k \\
&\qquad + \tfrac{1}{6}(1 + \Delta t\,\mathbf{A} + \tfrac{1}{2}(\Delta t)^2\mathbf{A}^2 + \tfrac{1}{4}(\Delta t)^3\mathbf{A}^3)\mathbf{B}\mathbf{u}_k \\
&\qquad\qquad + \tfrac{2}{3}(1 + \tfrac{1}{2}(t)\mathbf{A} + \tfrac{1}{8}(t)^2\mathbf{A}^2)\mathbf{B}\mathbf{u}_{k+\frac{1}{2}} + \mathbf{B}\mathbf{u}_{k+1}
\end{aligned}$$

We recognize that the first term on the right-hand side of this expression agrees to the fourth-order with the Taylor series for exp $(\mathbf{A}\,\Delta t)$. We leave to the exercises at the end of this chapter the verification that the remaining terms agree also to the fourth-order with the Taylor series for

$$e^{\mathbf{A}\,\Delta t}\int_0^{\Delta t} e^{-\mathbf{A}\xi}\,\mathbf{B}\mathbf{u}(t_k+\xi)\,d\xi$$

Consider again the trapezoidal-integration formula applied to the general differential-state equation (7.53)

$$\mathbf{x}_{k+1} = \mathbf{x}_k + \frac{\Delta t}{2}\,[\mathbf{f}(\mathbf{x}_k,\mathbf{u}_k,t_k) + \mathbf{f}(\mathbf{x}_{k+1},\mathbf{u}_{k+1},t_{k+1})]$$

and recognize the following alternative to replacing $\mathbf{x}_{k+1}$ on the right-hand side by means of the forward Euler integration formula

$$\mathbf{x}_{k+1} = \mathbf{x}_k + \Delta t\,\mathbf{f}(\mathbf{x}_k,\mathbf{u}_k,t_k)$$

We may compute $\mathbf{x}_{k+1}$ by successive approximations $\mathbf{x}_{k+1}^0$, $\mathbf{x}_{k+1}^1$, $\mathbf{x}_{k+1}^2$, . . . by employing the integration formula

$$\mathbf{x}_{k+1}^{l+1} = \mathbf{x}_k + \frac{\Delta t}{2}\,[\mathbf{f}(\mathbf{x}_k,\mathbf{u}_k,t_k) + \mathbf{f}(\mathbf{x}_{k+1}^l,\mathbf{u}_{k+1},t_{k+1})] \qquad (l = 0, 1, \ldots)$$

where we may obtain the starting value $\mathbf{x}_{k+1}$ from the forward Euler integration formula

$$\mathbf{x}_{k+1}^0 = \mathbf{x}_k + \Delta t\,\mathbf{f}(\mathbf{x}_k,\mathbf{u}_k,t_k)$$

It is fortunately simple to ascertain circumstances under which the above successive approximation scheme converges.

A *sufficient* condition for the successive approximation scheme

$$\mathbf{x}_{k+1}^{l+1} = \mathbf{x}_k + \frac{\Delta t}{2}\,[\mathbf{f}(\mathbf{x}_k,\mathbf{u}_k,t_k) + \mathbf{f}(\mathbf{x}_{k+1}^l,\mathbf{u}_{k+1},t_{k+1})] \qquad (l = 0, 1, 2, \ldots)$$

to converge to the desired solution

$$\mathbf{x}_{k+1} = \mathbf{x}_k + \frac{\Delta t}{2}\,[\mathbf{f}(\mathbf{x}_k,\mathbf{u}_k,t_k) + \mathbf{f}(\mathbf{x}_{k+1},\mathbf{u}_{k+1},t_{k+1})] \tag{7.90}$$

is that $\Delta t/2[\mathbf{f}(\mathbf{x}_{k+1},\mathbf{u}_{k+1},t_{k+1})]$ be a contraction:

$$\frac{\Delta t}{2}\,\|f(\mathbf{x}_{k+1}^a,\mathbf{u}_{k+1},t_{k+1}) - \mathbf{f}(\mathbf{x}_{k+1}^b,\mathbf{u}_{k+1},t_{k+1})\| \le C\|\mathbf{x}_{k+1}^a - \mathbf{x}_{k+1}^b\|$$

where $\mathbf{x}_{k+1}^a$ and $\mathbf{x}_{k+1}^b$ are arbitrary vectors in the solution space X and $0 \le C < 1$.

We must now digress to discuss the following theorems.

(7.91) Fixed-point theorem
Given an n-vector set of (coupled) simultaneous nonlinear algebraic equations

$$\mathbf{x} = \boldsymbol{\psi}(\mathbf{x})$$

in the n-vector unknown $\mathbf{x}$, a *sufficient* condition that these equations possess a unique solution $\hat{\mathbf{x}} \in X$,

$$\hat{\mathbf{x}} = \boldsymbol{\psi}(\hat{\mathbf{x}})$$

is that $\boldsymbol{\psi}$ be a contraction,

$$\|\boldsymbol{\psi}(x_a) - \boldsymbol{\psi}(x_b)\| \leq C\|\mathbf{x}_a - \mathbf{x}_b\|$$

where

$$0 \leq C < 1$$

for all $\mathbf{x}_a, \mathbf{x}_b \in x$. ▮

More important for our purpose is the following.

(7.92) Contraction-mapping principle
Given an n-vector set of (coupled) simultaneous nonlinear algebraic equations

$$\mathbf{x} = \boldsymbol{\psi}(\mathbf{x})$$

a *sufficient* condition that the sequence of successive approximations generated by the *algorithm*

$$\mathbf{x}^{l+1} = \boldsymbol{\psi}(\mathbf{x}^l) \qquad (l = 0, 1, 2, \ldots)$$

converges to the *unique* solution $\hat{\mathbf{x}} \in X$,

$$\hat{\mathbf{x}} = \boldsymbol{\psi}(\hat{\mathbf{x}})$$

for any initial guess $\mathbf{x}^0$, is that $\boldsymbol{\psi}$ be a *contraction,*

$$\|\boldsymbol{\psi}(\mathbf{x}_a) - \boldsymbol{\psi}(\mathbf{x}_b)\| \leq C\|\mathbf{x}_a - \mathbf{x}_b\|$$

where

$$0 \leq C < 1$$

for all $\mathbf{x}_a, \mathbf{x}_b \in X$. ▮

(The proofs of these two results are relegated to the problems at the end of this chapter.)

Hence we recognize the *sufficient* condition that Δt be chosen sufficiently small that $(\Delta t/2)\mathbf{f}(\mathbf{x}_{k+1},\mathbf{u}_{k+1},t_{k+1})$ be a contraction in application of the successive approximation scheme

$$\mathbf{x}_{k+1}^{l+1} = \mathbf{x}_k + \frac{\Delta t}{2}[\mathbf{f}(\mathbf{x}_k,\mathbf{u}_k,t_k) + \mathbf{f}(\mathbf{x}_{k+1}^l,\mathbf{u}_{k+1},t_{k+1})]$$

Such a choice of step size Δt is always possible for "well-behaved" functions $\mathbf{f}$. In fact a *sufficient* condition that the n-vector set of (coupled), simultaneous, nonlinear, ordinary, differential-state equations

$$\dot{\mathbf{x}}(t) = \mathbf{f}(\mathbf{x}(t),\mathbf{u}(t),t) \qquad \mathbf{x}(t_0) = \mathbf{x}_0$$

possess a unique solution in X for $t_0 \leq t \leq \infty$, and a given excitation $\mathbf{u}$, is that $\mathbf{f}$ satisfy a Lipshitz condition in $\mathbf{x}$:

(7.93) Definition (Lipshitz)
The n-vector function $\mathbf{f}(\mathbf{x}(t),\mathbf{u}(t),t)$ is said to be Lipshitz in $\mathbf{x} \in X$ if

$$\|f(\mathbf{x}_a,\mathbf{u}(t),t) - \mathbf{f}(\mathbf{x}_b,\mathbf{u}(t),t)\| \leq K\|\mathbf{x}_a - \mathbf{x}_b\|$$

where

$$0 \leq K < \infty$$

for all $\mathbf{x}_a$, $\mathbf{x}_b \in X$ and for any given excitation $\mathbf{u}$ and for all t, $t_0 \leq t < \infty$. ▮
Hence if $\mathbf{f}$ is Lipshitz in $\mathbf{x}$ with the constant K, we need only ensure that

$$\Delta t < \frac{2}{K}$$

(In some nonlinear time-variable problems, we may employ such criteria to alter the maximal step size from time point to time point.)

The origin of the terminology *predictor-corrector* should by now be apparent. In the scheme introduced in the first paragraph above, we have employed the forward Euler integration formula

$$\mathbf{x}_{k+1}^0 = \mathbf{x}_k + \Delta t\, \mathbf{f}(\mathbf{x}_k,\mathbf{u}_k,t)$$

to *predict* the value of $\mathbf{x}_{k+1}$ and the trapezoidal-integration formula

$$\mathbf{x}_{k+1}^{l+1} = \mathbf{x}_k + \frac{\Delta t}{2}[\mathbf{f}(\mathbf{x}_k,\mathbf{u}_k,t) + \mathbf{f}(\mathbf{x}_{k+1}^l,\mathbf{u}_{k+1},t_{k+1})]$$

to successively *correct* the predicted value. [*Note:* If we terminate the corrections in one step with $\mathbf{x}_{k+1}^l$, we revert to the trapezoidal-integration formula (7.82).] The results of predictor-corrector integration schemes based on relatively simple formulas (such as Euler and trapezoidal) may not be particularly impressive, however. Obviously what is required is a more sophisticated approximation to the integral which appears in

$$\mathbf{x}(t_{k+1}) = \mathbf{x}(t_k) + \int_{t_k}^{t_{k+1}} \mathbf{f}(\mathbf{x}(t),\mathbf{u}(t),t)\, dt$$

A popular integration formula is given by the (*Adam's*) *predictor-corrector* algorithm:

$$\mathbf{x}_{k+1}^0 = \mathbf{x}_k + \frac{\Delta t}{24}[-9\mathbf{f}(\mathbf{x}_{k-3},\mathbf{u}_{k-3},t_{k-2}) + 37\mathbf{f}(\mathbf{x}_{k-2},\mathbf{u}_{k-2},t_{k-2})$$
$$- 59\mathbf{f}(\mathbf{x}_{k-1},\mathbf{u}_{k-1},t_{k-1}) + 55f(\mathbf{x}_k,\mathbf{u}_k,t_k)] \qquad (k = 3, 4, \ldots)$$

is the predictor, and

$$\mathbf{x}_{k+1}^{l+1} = \mathbf{x}_k + \frac{h}{24}\,[\mathbf{f}(\mathbf{x}_{k-2},\mathbf{u}_{k-2},t_{k-2}) - 5\mathbf{f}(\mathbf{x}_{k-1},\mathbf{u}_{k-1},t_{k-1})$$
$$+ 19\mathbf{f}(\mathbf{x}_k,\mathbf{u}_k,t_k) + 9\mathbf{f}(\mathbf{x}_{k+1}^{l},\mathbf{u}_{k+1},t_{k+1})] \qquad \begin{array}{l}(k = 3, 4, \ldots)\\ (l = 0, 1, 2, \ldots)\end{array}$$

is the corrector. This integration method is not "self-starting"; we must obtain values for x_1 and x_2, in addition to the given x_0, in order to begin to apply the algorithm. Since the subsequent accuracy depends on that for x_1 and x_2, usually a very accurate integration method (such as fourth-order Runge-Kutta or high-order Taylor series) is employed to "start" the above predictor-corrector algorithm. There are obvious advantages to predictor-corrector integration methods: They are easily derived, and therefore easily adapted to special circumstances; and they are efficient, introducing few new computations per step (provided that not too many correction iterations are undertaken). In practice, the step size Δt is adjusted so that no more than two correction iterations are entailed per step (thus rendering the above algorithm more efficient, although not necessarily more accurate, than the fourth-order Runge-Kutta method presented).

A desirable property of any numerical integration scheme is that it be stable; in other words, qualitatively that the approximate solution remain close to the actual solution. It is relatively easy to investigate stability of integration schemes which are generated from (7.78) in terms of the following theorem.

(7.94) Theorem

A linear, time-invariant, discrete-time system is stable *BIBO* if the system transfer function $H(z)$ has no poles outside the unit circle, i.e., all the poles of $H(z)$ have magnitude less than 1. ▮

This theorem is easily proved and left as an exercise for the reader.

Now consider the state equation for a linear, time-invariant system

$$\mathbf{x}(t) = \mathbf{A}\mathbf{x}(t) + \mathbf{B}\mathbf{u}(t) \qquad \mathbf{x}(0) = \mathbf{x}_0$$

or upon integration over the interval $(k - 1)\,\Delta t \leq t \leq k\,\Delta t$:

$$\mathbf{x}_k = \mathbf{x}_{k-1} + \int_{(k-1)\,\Delta t}^{k\,\Delta t} [\mathbf{A}\mathbf{x}(\tau) + \mathbf{B}\mathbf{u}(\tau)]\,d\tau$$

Using the forward Euler method, we have

$$\mathbf{x}_k = [\mathbf{1} + \Delta t\,\mathbf{A}]\mathbf{x}_{k-1} + \Delta t\,\mathbf{B}\mathbf{u}_{k-1}$$

The z-transformed equation is

$$[\mathbf{1} - (\mathbf{1} + \Delta t\,\mathbf{A})z^{-1}]\mathbf{X}(z) = \Delta t\,\mathbf{BU}(z)z^{-1}$$

or

$$\mathbf{X}(z) = \Delta t\,[z\mathbf{1} - (\mathbf{1} + \Delta t\,\mathbf{A})]^{-1}\mathbf{BU}(z)$$

The associated discrete-time system transfer-function matrix, or integration-operator matrix, is

$$\mathbf{H}(z) = \Delta t\,[z\mathbf{1} - (\mathbf{1} + \Delta t\,\mathbf{A})]^{-1}$$

and stability which depends on the poles of $\mathbf{H}(z)$ is also dependent on the eigenvalues of $(\mathbf{H}(z))^{-1}$.

(7.95) Example

Consider a system which is characterized by

$$\dot{\mathbf{x}}(t) = \begin{bmatrix} -1 & 1 \\ 0 & -2 \end{bmatrix}\mathbf{x}(t) + \begin{bmatrix} 0 \\ 1 \end{bmatrix}\mathbf{u}(t)$$

The natural frequencies of this system are -2 and -3. The inverse of the integration-operator matrix for rectangular integration associated with this system is

$$\mathbf{H}^{-1}(z) = \Delta t \begin{bmatrix} z - (1 - \Delta t) & -\Delta t \\ 0 & z - (1 - 2\,\Delta t) \end{bmatrix}$$

The eigenvalues of $\mathbf{H}^{-1}(z)$ are

$$\lambda_1 = 1 - \Delta t$$

and

$$\lambda_2 = 1 - 2\,\Delta t$$

Observe that this integration scheme will be stable if $\Delta t < 1$, that is, if the step size is smaller than the magnitude of the smallest natural frequency (fastest time constant) of the original system.

7.6 CALCULATION OF $e^{\mathbf{A}t}$—NUMERICAL EVALUATION OF THE EXACT SOLUTION

The linear, time-invariant, differential-state equation

$$\dot{\mathbf{x}}(t) = \mathbf{Ax}(t) + \mathbf{Bu}(t) \qquad \mathbf{x}(t_0) = \mathbf{x}_0$$

has the exact solution

$$\mathbf{x}(t) = e^{\mathbf{A}(t-t_0)}\mathbf{x}_0 + \int_{t_0}^{t} e^{\mathbf{A}(t-\tau)}\mathbf{Bu}(\tau)\,d\tau$$

In Chap. 4 we obtained from this the discrete relation

$$\mathbf{x}(k\,\Delta t) = e^{\mathbf{A}\,\Delta t}\mathbf{x}((k-1)\,\Delta t) + \mathbf{u}((k-1)\,\Delta t)\int_0^{\Delta t} e^{\mathbf{A}\sigma}\,d\sigma\,\mathbf{B} \tag{7.96}$$

where the input $\mathbf{u}$ is assumed to be a piecewise-constant function for computational purposes. For (7.96) to be useful, we must have some means to evaluate $e^{\mathbf{A}t}$ and $\int_0^t e^{\mathbf{A}\sigma}\,d\sigma$. Since

$$(7.97) \quad e^{\mathbf{A}\,\Delta t} = \sum_{k=0}^{\infty} \frac{1}{k!} (\mathbf{A}\,\Delta t)^k$$

and this series is uniformly convergent for any finite Δt, we have

$$(7.98) \quad \int_0^{\Delta t} e^{\mathbf{A}\sigma}\,d\sigma = \sum_{k=0}^{\infty} \frac{1}{k!} \mathbf{A}^k \int_0^{\Delta t} \sigma^k\,d\sigma$$

$$= \sum_{k=0}^{\infty} \frac{1}{(k+1)!} \mathbf{A}^k (\Delta t)^{k+1}$$

$$= \Delta t \sum_{k=0}^{\infty} \frac{1}{(k+1)!} (\mathbf{A}\,\Delta t)^k$$

We focus our attention on the computation of $e^{\mathbf{A}\,\Delta t}$ since the other is essentially similar. Ganapathy and Subba Rao[1] and Mastascusa[2] have derived a technique for calculation of $e^{\mathbf{A}\,\Delta t}$ which is based on the Cayley-Hamilton theorem.

Recall from the Cayley-Hamilton theorem (3.85) that every $n \times n$ matrix $\mathbf{A}$ satisfies its characteristic equation. From this result we reason that it should be possible to find $e^{\mathbf{A}\,\Delta t}$ in terms of the first $n-1$ powers of $\mathbf{A}$. The following scheme accomplishes this.

Step 1: Compute the first $n-1$ powers of $\mathbf{A}$:

$$\mathbf{A}^2, \mathbf{A}^3, \ldots, \mathbf{A}^{n-1}$$

Step 2: Calculate the coefficients of the characteristic equation

$$q_0 + q_1\lambda + q_2\lambda^2 + \cdots q_{n-1}\lambda^{n-1} + \lambda^2 = 0$$

by Bôcher's[3] formula

$$\begin{aligned} q_{n-1} &= -T_1 \\ q_{n-2} &= -\tfrac{1}{2}(q_{n-1}T_1 + T_2) \\ q_{n-3} &= -\tfrac{1}{3}(q_{n-2}T_1 + q_{n-1}T_2 + T_3) \\ &\cdots\cdots\cdots\cdots \\ q_0 &= -\frac{1}{n}(q_1T_1 + q_2T_2 + \cdots + q_{n-1}T_{n-1} + T_n) \end{aligned}$$

[1] S. Ganapathy and A. Subba Rao, Transient Response Evaluation from the State Transition Matrix, *Proc. IEEE*, vol. 57, no. 3, pp. 347–348, March, 1969.

[2] E. J. Mastascusa, A Method for Calculating $e^{\mathbf{A}t}$ Based on the Cayley-Hamilton Theorem, *Proc. IEEE*, vol. 57, no. 7, pp. 1328–1329, July, 1969.

[3] M. Bôcher, "Introduction to Higher Algebra," p. 296, Macmillan, New York.

where

$$T_k = \text{trace}(\mathbf{A}^k)$$

Step 3: From the Cayley-Hamilton theorem

$$\mathbf{A}^n = -q_{n-1}\mathbf{A}^{n-1} - q_{n-2}\mathbf{A}^{n-2} - \cdots - q_0\mathbf{1}$$

Higher powers of **A** are found by successive multiplications of this expression by **A**. We have

$$\mathbf{A}^{n+m} = \alpha_{0m}\mathbf{1} + \alpha_{1m}\mathbf{A} + \alpha_{2m}\mathbf{A}^2 + \cdots \alpha_{n-1,m}\mathbf{A}^{n-1}$$

for $m = 0, 1, 2, \ldots$ where

$$\begin{aligned} \alpha_{00} &= -q_0 \\ \alpha_{10} &= -q_1 \\ &\cdots\cdots \\ \alpha_{n-1,0} &= -q_{n-1} \end{aligned}$$

and the remaining α's are determined from the recursion relations

$$\begin{aligned} \alpha_{0m} &= -q_0\alpha_{0,m-1} \\ \alpha_{1m} &= \alpha_{0,m-1} - q_1\alpha_{1,m-1} \\ \alpha_{2m} &= \alpha_{1,m-1} - q_2\alpha_{2,m-1} \\ &\cdots\cdots\cdots\cdots \\ \alpha_{n-1,m} &= \alpha_{n-2,m-1} - q_{n-1}\alpha_{n-1,m-1} \end{aligned}$$

Step 4: For any given choice of Δt, $e^{\mathbf{A}\,\Delta t}$ can be written as

$$\begin{aligned} e^{\mathbf{A}\,\Delta t} &= \sum_{k=0}^{\infty} \frac{1}{k!}(\mathbf{A}\,\Delta t)^k \\ &= \sum_{k=0}^{n-1} \frac{1}{k!}(\mathbf{A}\,\Delta t)^k + \sum_{k=0}^{\infty} \frac{(\Delta t)^{n+k}}{(n+k)!}\left[\sum_{j=0}^{n-1} \alpha_{jk}\mathbf{A}^j\right] \\ &= \sum_{j=0}^{n-1} \mathbf{A}^j \left[\frac{(\Delta t)^{j-1}}{(j-1)!} + \sum_{k=0}^{\infty} \frac{\alpha_{jk}(\Delta t)^{n+k}}{k!}\right] \end{aligned}$$

Thus from the already computed matrices $\mathbf{A}^2, \mathbf{A}^3, \ldots, \mathbf{A}^{n-1}$ and the α's, $e^{\mathbf{A}\,\Delta t}$ is quite easily calculated to any desired accuracy without actual series summation of powers of **A** higher than $n - 1$.

7.7 PROBLEMS

(7.1) Use gaussian elimination to find the solution of the following sets of simultaneous algebraic equations

$$(a) \quad \begin{aligned} x_1 + 2x_2 &= 6 \\ 4x_1 + 3x_2 &= 0, \end{aligned}$$

(b) $$\begin{aligned} 2x_1 + 6x_2 &= 1 \\ x_1 + 3x_2 + 6x_3 &= 2 \\ -5x_1 + 2x_2 - x_3 &= 3, \end{aligned}$$

(c) $$\begin{aligned} 7x_1 + 4x_2 + 8x_3 &= 1 \\ 3x_1 + 2x_2 + 4x_3 &= 6 \\ 9x_1 + 6x_2 + 7x_3 &= 3. \end{aligned}$$

(7.2) Decompose the following matrices into the products of a lower-triangular matrix **L** and an upper-triangular matrix **U** with 1's on the main diagonal:

(a) $$\begin{bmatrix} 12 & 20 & 15 \\ 3 & 6 & 4 \\ 2 & 3 & 6 \end{bmatrix}$$

(b) $$\begin{bmatrix} 1 & 5 & 0 & 1 \\ 1 & 2 & 1 & 0 \\ 4 & 1 & 3 & 2 \\ 5 & 0 & 5 & 1 \end{bmatrix}$$

(c) $$\begin{bmatrix} 6 & 7 & 5 & 4 \\ 1 & 0 & 0 & 1 \\ 1 & 2 & 3 & 4 \\ 2 & 1 & 1 & 0 \end{bmatrix}$$

(7.3) Consider the following sets of simultaneous equations:

$$\begin{aligned} x_1 - x_2 \qquad\qquad\qquad &= 1 \\ -x_1 + 5x_2 - 2x_3 - x_4 &= 0 \\ - 2x_2 + 3x_3 - \tfrac{1}{2}x_4 &= 0 \\ - x_2 - \tfrac{1}{2}x_3 + \tfrac{9}{4}x_4 &= 2 \end{aligned}$$

Solve these equations for x_1, x_2, x_3, and x_4 using *LU* factorization and forward and backward substitution.

If we define an operation as one multiplication and addition or one division, determine the number of nontrivial operations performed to find the solution above. (A nontrivial operation is one that does not involve multiplication or addition by zero.)

If the above set of equations is rearranged as follows

$$\begin{aligned} -x_1 + 5x_2 - 2x_3 - x_4 &= 0 \\ - 2x_2 + 3x_3 - \tfrac{1}{2}x_4 &= 0 \\ - x_2 - \tfrac{1}{2}x_3 + \tfrac{9}{4}x_4 &= 0 \\ x_1 - x_2 \qquad\qquad\qquad &= 1 \end{aligned}$$

how many nontrivial operations are needed to solve for x_1, x_2, x_3, and x_4 using *LU* factorization? Can you draw any conclusions concerning the ordering of equations and the number of nontrivial operations involved in their solution?

(7.4) Draw the tree graph used in the fast Fourier transform algorithm for $N = 8$, and describe its use.

(7.5) Find an explicit integration formula based on the so-called *backward Euler formula:*

$$\mathbf{x}_{k+1} = \mathbf{x}_k + \Delta t\,\mathbf{f}(\mathbf{x}_{k+1}, \mathbf{u}_{k+1}, t_0 + (k+1)\,\Delta t)$$

(Hint: As with the trapezoidal method, employ the forward Euler method to approximate $\mathbf{x}_{k+1}$ on the right-hand side.) Compare the result with the forward Euler and trapezoidal-integration formulas.

(7.6) Find an explicit-integration formula which is based on the approximation

$$\mathbf{x}(t_{k+1}) \simeq \mathbf{x}(t_k) + \Delta t\,\mathbf{f}\left(\mathbf{x}\left(t_k + \frac{\Delta t}{2}\right), \mathbf{u}\left(t_k + \frac{\Delta t}{2}\right), t_k + \frac{\Delta t}{2}\right)$$

i.e., the slope of the solution is approximated by that at the midpoint between the two end points for any step.

(7.7) Verify that the forward Euler method and the trapezoidal method are Runge-Kutta methods of orders 1 and 2, respectively.

(7.8) Derive general formulas for first- and second-order Runge-Kutta methods for the nonlinear, time-variable, differential-state equations

$$\dot{\mathbf{x}}(t) = \mathbf{f}(\mathbf{x}(t),\mathbf{u}(t),t) \qquad \mathbf{x}(t_0) = \mathbf{x}_0$$

(7.9) Show that the fourth-order Runge-Kutta method given in the text agrees with the Taylor series to the fourth order for the special class of linear, time-invariant, differential-state equations of the form

$$\dot{\mathbf{x}}(t) = \mathbf{A}\mathbf{x}(t) + \mathbf{B}\mathbf{u}(t) \qquad \mathbf{x}(t_0) = \mathbf{x}_0$$

(7.10) Use the z transform to determine if the trapezoidal-rule algorithm for any time step is stable when applied to the state equations

$$\dot{\mathbf{x}}(t) = \begin{bmatrix} -1 & -1 \\ 0 & -2 \end{bmatrix} \mathbf{x}(t) + \begin{bmatrix} 0 \\ 1 \end{bmatrix} \mathbf{u}(t)$$

(7.11) Discuss the stability of the implicit *backward Euler* method of numerical integration:

$$h_{k+1} = h_k + \Delta t g_{k+1}$$

How does this scheme compare with the explicit forward Euler method? What conclusions can be drawn?

(7.12) Prove the *fixed-point theorem:* Given an n-vector set of (coupled) simultaneous nonlinear algebraic equations

$$\mathbf{x} = \boldsymbol{\psi}(\mathbf{x})$$

in the n-vector unknown $\mathbf{x}$, a *sufficient* condition that these equations possess a unique solution of $\hat{\mathbf{x}} \in X$,

$$\hat{\mathbf{x}} = \boldsymbol{\psi}(\hat{\mathbf{x}})$$

is that $\boldsymbol{\psi}$ be a contraction,

$$\|\boldsymbol{\psi}(\mathbf{x}_a) - \boldsymbol{\psi}(\mathbf{x}_b)\| \leq C\|\mathbf{x}_a - \mathbf{x}_b\|$$

where

$$0 \leq C < 1$$

for all $\mathbf{x}_a, \mathbf{x}_b \in X$.

(7.13) Prove the *contraction-mapping principle:* Given an n-vector set of (coupled) simultaneous nonlinear algebraic equations

$$\mathbf{x} = \boldsymbol{\psi}(\mathbf{x})$$

a *sufficient* condition that the sequence of successive approximations generated by the *algorithm*

$$\mathbf{x}^{l+1} = \boldsymbol{\psi}(\mathbf{x}^l)$$

converges to the unique solution $\hat{\mathbf{x}} \in X$,

$$\hat{\mathbf{x}} = \boldsymbol{\psi}(\hat{\mathbf{x}})$$

for any initial guess $\mathbf{x}^0$, is that $\boldsymbol{\psi}$ be a contraction,

$$\|\boldsymbol{\psi}(\mathbf{x}_a) - \boldsymbol{\psi}(\mathbf{x}_b)\| \leq C\|\mathbf{x}_a - \mathbf{x}_b\|$$

where

$$0 \leq C < 1$$

for all $\mathbf{x}_a, \mathbf{x}_b \in X$.

(7.14) Prove that the Lipshitz condition is *sufficient* for the differential-state equation

$$\dot{\mathbf{x}}(t) = \mathbf{f}(\mathbf{x}(t),\mathbf{u}(t),t) \qquad \mathbf{x}(t_0) = \mathbf{x}_0$$

to possess a *unique* solution for a given $\mathbf{u}$ on $t_0 \leq t < \infty$.

(7.15) Discuss the possibility of obtaining $\exp \mathbf{A}(\Delta t)$ by means of a predictor-corrector approach.

INDEX